90025

South County –
12721 St. Wats
63127

Addison-Wesley
Informal
Geometry

Mervin L. Keedy
Marvin L. Bittinger
Stanley A. Smith
Charles W. Nelson

Addison-Wesley Publishing Company

Menlo Park, California • Reading, Massachusetts
Don Mills, Ontario • Wokingham, England • Amsterdam
Sydney • Singapore • Tokyo • Madrid • Bogotá
Santiago • San Juan

Authors

Mervin L. Keedy
Purdue University

Marvin L. Bittinger
Indiana University—Purdue University

Stanley A. Smith
Baltimore County Public Schools

Charles W. Nelson
University of Florida

ISBN 0-201-20448-7

IJKL-VH- 910

Contents

Symbols

Symbol	Meaning
$\overleftrightarrow{RS}, \ell$	line containing R and S, line ℓ (p. 1)
cm	centimeter(s) (p. 2)
$\overline{BC}$	line segment with endpoints B and C (pp. 1, 41)
$\triangle ABC$	triangle with vertices A, B, and C (p. 7)
Q'	Q prime (pp. 7, 98)
ℓ_1	line number one (ℓ sub 1) (p. 20)
$\mathcal{K}$	plane (p. 21)
AB	distance between A and B, length of $\overline{AB}$ (p. 31)
$|x|$	absolute value of x (p. 32)
$A\text{-}B\text{-}C$	B is between A and C (p. 40)
$\overrightarrow{AB}$	ray with endpoint A and containing B (p. 41)
$\angle ABC, \angle B$	angle with sides $\overrightarrow{BA}$ and $\overrightarrow{BC}$, angle with vertex B (p. 45)
$\circ$	degrees(s) (p. 48)
$m\angle ABC$	measure of $\angle ABC$ (p. 48)
$\cong$	is congruent to (pp. 73, 74)
$\not\cong$	is not congruent to (p. 73)
$\perp$	is perpendicular to (p. 83)
$\not\perp$	is not perpendicular to (p. 83)
⌐	shows a right angle (p. 83)
⊀ ✕	shows congruence (p. 96)
$\longleftrightarrow$	corresponds to (p. 98)
△	triangles (p. 130)
$<, >$	is less than, is greater than (p. 159)
$\parallel$	is parallel to (p. 189)
$\not\parallel$	is not parallel to (p. 189)
mm	millimeter(s) (p. 213)
m	meter(s) (p. 213)
km	kilometer(s) (p. 213)
mL	milliliter(s) (p. 213)
L	liter(s) (p. 213)
kL	kiloliter(s) (p. 213)
mg	milligram(s) (p. 213)
g	gram(s) (p. 213)
kg	kilogram(s) (p. 213)
t	metric ton(s) (p. 213)
in.	inch(es) (p. 255)
ft	foot (feet) (p. 255)
yd	yard(s) (p. 255)
mi	mile(s) (p. 255)
fl oz	fluid ounce(s) (p. 255)
c	cup(s) (p. 255)
pt	pint(s) (p. 255)
qt	quart(s) (p. 255)
gal	gallon(s) (p. 255)
oz	ounce(s) p. 255)
lb	pound(s) (p. 255)
T	customary ton(s) (p. 255)
$\square$	parallelogram (p. 220)
$\sim$	is similar to (p. 265)
$\sqrt{\ }$	square root of (p. 276)
n-gon	polygon with n sides (p. 312)
p	perimeter (p. 317)
cm^2	square centimeter(s) (p. 344)
s	length of side of square; perimeter of triangle; length of side of regular polygon (pp. 345, 351, 362)
A	area (p. 343)
ℓ, w	length; width (p. 345)
mm^2	square millimeter(s) (p. 367)
m^2	square meter(s) (p. 345)
km^2	square kilometer(s) (p. 346)
b	base length (p. 349)
h	height (p. 349)
$\approx$	is approximately equal to (p. 399)
a	apothem (p. 362)
dm	decimeter(s) (p. 367)
$\odot$	circle (p. 375)
r	radius (p. 375)
d	diameter; distance (pp. 376, 452)
$\overparen{AB}$	arc with endpoints A and B (p. 388)
$\overparen{ACB}$	arc with endpoints A and B and containing C (p. 388)
$m\overparen{AB}$	measure of AB (p. 389)
π	"pi" approximately 3.14 (p. 400)
c	circumference (p. 400)
A_n	A sub n, area of an n-sided regular polygon (p. 403)
$A_\odot$	area of a circle (p. 403)
$A\square$	area of a parallelogram (p. 405)
(a,b)	ordered pair consisting of x-coordinate a and y-coordinate b (p. 447)
$P(a,b)$	point P located by coordinates a and b (p. 447)
m	slope (p. 455)
cm^3	cubic centimeters(s) (p. 512)
dm^3	cubic decimeters(s) (p. 512)
B	base area (p. 513)
V	volume (p. 513)
k	slant height (p. 524)
$\sin A$	sine of $\angle A$ (p. 543)
$\cos A$	cosine of $\angle A$ (p. 546)
$\tan A$	tangent of $\angle A$ (p. 547)
$'$	minutes (p. 552)

1 The Organization of Geometry

1   Drawings in Geometry

After finishing Section 1, you should be able to
▲   *copy line segments using a straightedge and compass.*
▲▲   *bisect a segment using a compass and straightedge.*

In geometry, drawings help us picture shapes and make discoveries.
Here are the drawing tools we will use.

Compass Straightedge   Protractor   Drawing Triangles

▲   Drawing and Copying Segments

A **line** is straight and extends indefinitely in
both directions. The arrows in the figure
show this.

$\overleftrightarrow{RS}$ is read "line RS."

A **segment** consists of two points of a line
and all the points between them.

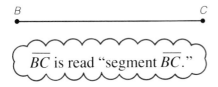

$\overline{BC}$ is read "segment $\overline{BC}$."

Find some segments in this spider's web.

Examples   1. Draw a segment, $\overline{AB}$, 3 cm long.

A   B

Make a straight mark with a straightedge or ruler. A ruler is a straightedge with marks on it. Then with the ruler make two marks 3 cm apart. Label the points A and B. A and B are the endpoints of the segment $\overline{AB}$.

2. Copy $\overline{AB}$.

A   B

Step 1

Draw a straight mark with a straightedge. Mark a point C.

C

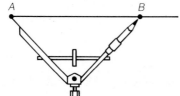   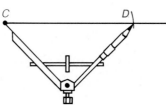

Step 2   **Step 3**

Open your compass so that it fits $\overline{AB}$.

Keep the same setting. Place the compass point on C and make a mark at D.

$\overline{CD}$ is a copy of $\overline{AB}$.

Try This...   1. Draw a segment, $\overline{MN}$, about 6 cm long. Copy $\overline{MN}$ using a compass and straightedge.

▲▲ Bisecting Segments

The **midpoint** of a segment is a point halfway between its endpoints. To **bisect** a segment, we find its midpoint.

What midpoints of segments can you find in this window?

We can bisect a segment with a compass and a straightedge.

Example   3. Bisect $\overline{AB}$ using a compass
and straightedge.

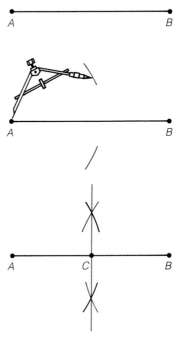

Step 1

Open the compass to more than
half the length of $\overline{AB}$. Place the
point at A and draw two arcs as
shown in the picture.

Step 2

Keep the same setting. Place the
compass point at B and make two
arcs that intersect the other two.

Step 3

Join the points of intersection
using a straightedge. Point C
is the midpoint of $\overline{AB}$.

Try This...   2. Draw a segment about 7 cm long. Bisect it using a compass and
straightedge.

Segments can be bisected by trial and error, using a compass
or a divider. (A **divider** is like a compass, but it has metal points
on both ends.)

Example   4. Bisect segment $\overline{CD}$ by trial
and error. Use a compass.

Step 1

Open your compass to about half
the length of $\overline{CD}$. Place the point
at C and the pencil on the segment.

Step 2

Lift the point and twirl the compass about
the pencil. If the point just reaches D,
the pencil is on the midpoint.

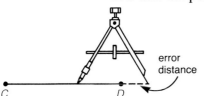

error
distance

Step 3

In this case our first estimate was
too large. Close the compass about
half the **error distance.**
Then try again.

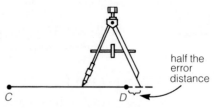

half the
error
distance

Step 4

On each try, close the compass setting
by about half the error distance.
Keep trying until the compass is open
to half the length of $\overline{CD}$. Then use
it to mark the midpoint P.

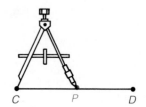

Try This...   3. Draw a segment about 8 cm long. Bisect it by trial and error.
Use a compass.

▶◀ Activity

A   B   C

How many different segments can you
create in the figure shown at right?
Use graph paper and colored pencils
to help you find each segment.
(Think of $\overline{AB}$ and $\overline{BA}$ as naming
the same segment.) Name each of the
segments you find.

D   E   F

G   H   I

Now try this game with a classmate.
First, create a figure by labeling points
on graph paper. Then, taking turns
with your classmate, name one
segment. The winner is the player to
find the last segment.

Exercises

▲ **Use a ruler to draw each segment. Copy the segments using a straightedge and compass.**

1. $\overline{RS}$, 6 cm long   2. $\overline{PQ}$, 8 cm long   3. $\overline{TV}$, 3 cm long
4. $\overline{QT}$, 9 cm long   5. $\overline{GK}$, about 4 cm long   6. $\overline{CL}$, about 8 cm long

▲▲ **Use a compass and straightedge.**

7. Draw a segment about 8 cm long. Bisect it.
8. Draw a segment about 5 cm long. Bisect it.
9. Draw a segment about 12 cm long. Bisect it by trial and error.

▶ Extension Exercises

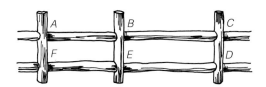

10. Name all the segments formed by these fence rails and posts.

11. Find three other examples of segments from the physical world.

12. Find three other examples of midpoints of segments from the physical world.

▶◀ Activity

Fold an 8 1/2-inch by 11-inch piece of paper in half crosswise. Unfold the paper. What does the fold represent?

Label one endpoint of the fold A and the other B. Now fold the paper in half the other way. What does this fold represent?

Label the endpoints C and D.

Look at both folds. What is the measure of $\overline{AB}$? What is the measure of $\overline{CD}$?

Label the point where $\overline{AB}$ intersects $\overline{CD}$, 0.

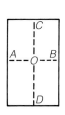

Measure $\overline{AO}$ and $\overline{OB}$. What are their lengths?
Measure $\overline{CO}$ and $\overline{OD}$. What are their lengths?

What can you conclude about $\overline{AB}$ and $\overline{CD}$?
What is another name for O?

2   More About Drawings

After finishing Section 2, you should be able to
▲   *use a straightedge and drawing triangle to draw perpendiculars.*
▲▲ *copy a triangle using a compass and straightedge.*

▲   The Drawing Triangle

Perpendicular lines or segments, if they intersect, form square corners. Find some perpendiculars in this picture.

A drawing triangle can be used to draw perpendiculars. If you do not have a drawing triangle, you can make one from stiff cardboard.

Example   1. Use a straightedge and drawing triangle to draw a line perpendicular to $\overleftrightarrow{RS}$ at Q.

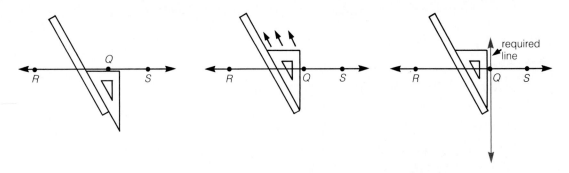

Step 1

Use the straightedge and triangle together. Line up the triangle along $\overleftrightarrow{RS}$.

Step 2

Slide the triangle along the straightedge until its edge crosses Q.

Step 3

Draw a line containing Q. The line is perpendicular to $\overleftrightarrow{RS}$.

Try This...   1. Draw a segment, $\overline{PQ}$, about 4 cm long. Choose any point T on $\overline{PQ}$. Use a drawing triangle and straightedge to draw a line perpendicular to $\overline{PQ}$ at T.

Example   2. Use a straightedge and drawing triangle to draw a line perpendicular to a line, $\overleftrightarrow{AB}$, and containing point C.

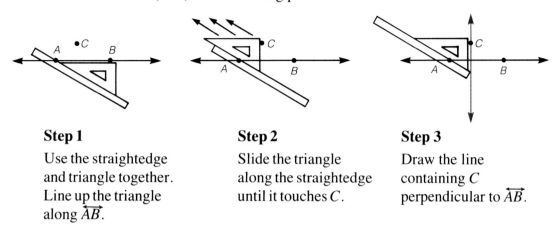

Step 1

Use the straightedge and triangle together. Line up the triangle along $\overleftrightarrow{AB}$.

Step 2

Slide the triangle along the straightedge until it touches C.

Step 3

Draw the line containing C perpendicular to $\overleftrightarrow{AB}$.

Try This...   2. Draw a line, $\overleftrightarrow{FT}$. Choose a point G not on $\overleftrightarrow{FT}$. Use the drawing triangle and straightedge to draw a line perpendicular to $\overleftrightarrow{FT}$ and containing G.

▲▲ Copying Triangles

A **triangle** consists of three segments joined at their endpoints. Each corner of the triangle is a **vertex.**

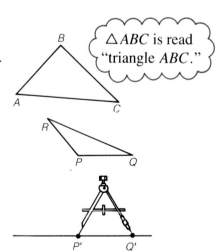

$\triangle ABC$ is read "triangle ABC."

Example   3. Use a compass and straightedge to copy $\triangle PQR$.

Step 1

P' is read "P prime."

Copy $\overline{PQ}$ using a straightedge and compass. Label the endpoints P' and Q'.

Step 2

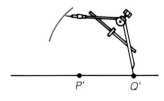

Copy $\overline{QR}$. To do this, open the compass to the distance QR. Then place the point on Q' and draw an arc as shown.

Step 3

Now copy $\overline{PR}$. To do this, open the compass to the distance PR. Place the point on P' and make a second arc that crosses the first. The two arcs cross at point R'. Point R' is the other vertex of the copy.

Step 4

Finally, using a straightedge, draw $\overline{Q'R'}$ and $\overline{P'R'}$.

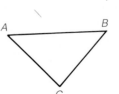

Try This...   3. Using compass and straightedge, copy $\triangle ABC$.

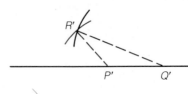

4. Using compass and straightedge, draw a triangle with sides the same lengths as these segments.

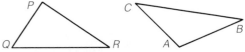

Exercises

▲   **Use a straightedge and drawing triangle.**

1. Draw a segment, $\overline{RF}$, about 6 cm long. Choose any point S on $\overline{RF}$. Draw a line perpendicular to $\overline{RF}$ at S.

2. Draw a line, $\overleftrightarrow{CH}$. Choose a point P not on $\overleftrightarrow{CH}$. Draw a line perpendicular to $\overleftrightarrow{CH}$ containing P.

3. Draw a segment, $\overline{DE}$, about 8 cm long. Choose any point Q on $\overline{DE}$. Draw a line perpendicular to $\overline{DE}$ at Q.

4. Draw a line, $\overleftrightarrow{MN}$. Choose a point R not on $\overleftrightarrow{MN}$. Draw a line perpendicular to $\overleftrightarrow{MN}$ containing R.

▲▲   **Use a compass and straightedge.**

5. Copy $\triangle PQR$.   6. Copy $\triangle ABC$.

Draw a triangle with sides having these lengths.

7. 3 cm, 5 cm, 4.5 cm

8. 2.5 cm, 3.5 cm, 5 cm

▶▶ Challenge Exercise

9. Use a straightedge and drawing triangle. Draw $\overleftrightarrow{RS}$. Draw lines perpendicular to $\overleftrightarrow{RS}$ at R and S. Compare the lines.

3 | Geometric Conclusions from Drawings

After finishing Section 3, you should be able to
▲   *make drawings of geometric figures and look for patterns in them.*
▲▲   *provide counterexamples to disprove statements.*

▲   Drawing Geometric Figures

In geometry we can find out many things by making drawings and
studying them.

Example   1. Draw a triangle, cut it out, and tear off the corners. Arrange
the corners as shown and see what happens.

Step 1

Draw a large triangle
using a straightedge.

Step 2

Cut out the triangle.
Then tear off the corners.

Step 3

Place the corners together.
They seem to form a straight line.

Thus it looks as if the angles of a triangle combine to form a
straight line. (They have measures that add up to 180°.)

Try This...   1. Draw a four-sided figure (quadrilateral).
Tear off the corners and place them
together. See what happens.

A **median** of a triangle is a segment from a vertex
to the midpoint of the opposite side.

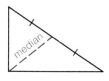

How many medians of triangles can
you find in the picture?

Example   2. Draw a large triangle.
Draw its medians and see
what happens.

Step 1

Use a whole sheet of paper
to draw a large triangle.

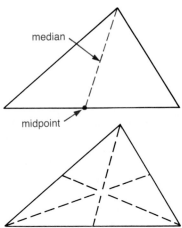

Step 2

Bisect one of the sides. Then join the
midpoint with the opposite vertex. This
segment is a median.

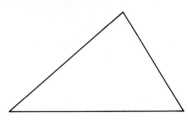

median

midpoint

Step 3

Draw the other two medians in
the same way. What do you
notice about the medians?

Try This...   2. Draw two more triangles and their medians. What do you
observe?

In examples 1 and 2, you reached some conclusions by observing
geometric figures. This is called *inductive reasoning*.

Inductive reasoning is reaching a conclusion on the basis of
examples.

▲▲ Counterexamples

The problem with inductive reasoning is that you can rarely check
all examples. Thus, you cannot be sure that a conclusion reached by
inductive reasoning is correct. An example that disproves a statement
is called a *counterexample*.

Examples   Suggest a possible counterexample for each conclusion.

3. All swans are white.
    Possible counterexample: a swan that is not white.

4. For all triangles, the medians intersect in a point.
    Possible counterexample: a triangle whose medians do not
    intersect in a point.

Try This...   Suggest a possible counterexample for each conclusion.

3. Beets are red.   4. Any number divided by itself is 1.

Exercises

▲ **Use a drawing triangle and ruler. Draw the figures
described. Study the angles formed and look for patterns.
What do you observe?**

1. Three triangles, each with all sides the same length.

2. Three triangles, each with two sides the same length.

3. Three triangles, each with no sides the same length.

4. Draw a square. Find the midpoints of the sides of the square
    and label them P, Q, R, S. Draw $\overline{PQ}$, $\overline{QR}$, $\overline{RS}$, and $\overline{SP}$.
    What do you observe?

▲▲ **Suggest a possible counterexample for each statement.**

5. All roses are red.   6. All rectangles are squares.

7. All squash are green.   8. All triangles are equiangular.

9. All corn is yellow.   10. All triangles are isosceles.

11. Every even number greater than 4 is the sum of two odd primes.

12. 3, 5, and 7 form the only prime triple.

13. If a triangle has two angles of the same size, the sides
     opposite them are the same length.

14. In a triangle, the longest side is always opposite the largest angle.

4	Deductive Reasoning

After finishing Section 4, you should be able to
▲   *use deductive reasoning to reach conclusions in simple cases.*

Deductive reasoning is often used in mathematics.

> **Deductive reasoning** allows us to reach a
> conclusion on the basis of some assumption.

Examples   Use the following assumptions. What can you conclude?

1.   *Assumptions:*   (a)   All Texans are Americans.
                     (b)   All citizens of Dallas are Texans.

     Conclusion: All citizens of Dallas are Americans.

2.   *Assumptions:*   (a)   All Californians are skiers.
                     (b)   Zach is a Californian.

     Conclusion: Zach is a skier.

3.   *Assumptions:*   (a)   If you shop at "Crazy Harry's," you will
                           save money.
                     (b)   You shopped at "Crazy Harry's."

     Conclusion: You saved money.

Try This...   Use the following assumptions. What can you conclude?

1.   (a)   All rectangles are polygons.
     (b)   All squares are rectangles.

2.   (a)   If a number is prime, then it has exactly two factors.
     (b)   The number 11 is prime.

In Section 3 you found that the angle measures of a triangle add
up to 180°. You then found that angle measures of a quadrilateral
add up to 360°. You used inductive reasoning both times.

Deductive reasoning could have saved you some effort.

Example 4. Start with the assumption that angle measures of a triangle add up to 180°. Use this to show that angle measures of a quadrilateral add up to 360°.

Draw a quadrilateral and one of its diagonals.

Notice that two triangles are formed. Their angles combine to form the angles of the quadrilateral. So the total for the quadrilateral is 180° + 180°, or 360°.

By using deductive reasoning, you were able to reach the conclusion without experimenting.

Try This... 3. Start with the assumption that the measures of the angles of a triangle add up to 180°. Use this to show what the total angle measure must be for a five-sided figure (pentagon).

Exercises

▲ **Use the following assumptions. What can you conclude?
Refer to the Glossary for terms that are unfamiliar.**

1. (a) All mammals have hair.
    (b) All elephants are mammals.

2. (a) All jumbos are mumbos.
    (b) All mumbos are gumbos.

3. (a) If $a = b$, then $b = a$.
    (b) $a = b$.

4. (a) If it rains, then the grass will grow.
    (b) It rains.

5. (a) The angle measures of a triangle add up to 180°.
    (b) One angle of the triangle measures 90°.

6. (a) The angle measures of a triangle add up to 180°.
    (b) A hexagon can be divided into four triangles.

7. (a) All squares are rectangles.
    (b) The diagonals of a rectangle bisect each other.

8. (a) $\triangle ABC$ has one obtuse angle.
    (b) An obtuse triangle has one obtuse angle.

9. (a) The angle measures of a triangle add up to 180°.
    (b) An octagon can be divided into six triangles.

10. (a) The angle measures of a triangle add up to 180°.
    (b) One angle of the triangle measures 90°.
    (c) The other two angles have the same measure.

5 Informal and Formal Geometry

After finishing Section 5, you should be able to
▲ *identify words that are undefined in our informal development of geometry.*
▲▲ *tell which postulate is suggested by a situation.*
▲▲ *apply the ideas of points, lines, and planes.*

Facts in geometry can be obtained in several ways.

Through Experimenting

Earlier in the chapter, you found geometric facts by experimenting with drawings.

Through Reasoning

In the previous section, you obtained geometric facts by reasoning them out. Here are two approaches used in reasoning out geometric facts.

1. *Formal Reasoning*

   Mathematicians often reason things out and write down proofs of their conclusions. This way of obtaining facts in geometry is called *formal*.

2. *Informal Reasoning*

   When we do not write proofs of geometric facts, our approach to geometry is called *informal*.

Our approach to geometry will be informal. We shall experiment and reason things out, but we shall not write proofs of geometric facts.

▲ Definitions

Definitions are important in geometry. We need to understand terms that we will use in reasoning out geometric facts. We shall not define every term, but we will start with a few terms whose meanings we will accept. Here are our undefined terms.

Undefined Term	Intuitive Understanding
Point	The smallest thing in geometry. It has no size. We represent it with a dot.
Line	A set of points that is continuous (without gaps). It is straight and continues forever in both directions.
Plane	A flat surface that extends indefinitely in all directions.

We can use these undefined terms to define other terms.

DEFINITIONS

Space is the set of all points.

Collinear points are points that are on the same line.

Think of these windows as points. If it is possible for a straight line to touch all of them, then they are collinear.

1, 2, and 5 are collinear.

DEFINITION

Noncollinear points are points that are not on the same line.

1, 2, and 3 are noncollinear.
Name another example of noncollinear points.

Example   1. Identify the undefined terms in the definition of **space**.
"Point" is undefined.

Try This...   1. In the definition of collinear points, identify the undefined terms.

<u>DEFINITION</u>

Coplanar points are points that are in the same plane.

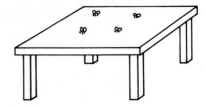

Think of the bees as points and the table as a plane. The bees on the table are coplanar.

<u>DEFINITION</u>

Noncoplanar points are not all in the same plane.

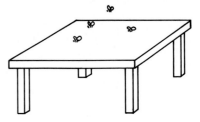

In this picture, the bees are noncoplanar.

▲▲ Postulates

Even in formal geometry, mathematicians do not try to prove everything. They start with a few facts that they assume are true. Then they use these facts to prove others. The facts that mathematicians assume are true are called *postulates*.

In our informal study of geometry, we will assume that the postulates are true, just as we would in a formal study of geometry.

POSTULATE
1

Given any two points, there is exactly one line containing the two points.

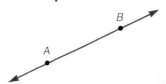

POSTULATE
2

Given any three points, there is at least one plane containing them. Given any three noncollinear points, there is exactly one plane containing them.

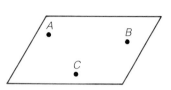 

Postulates 1 and 2 tell us that two points determine a line and three noncollinear points determine a plane. Postulate 3 assures us that there is a difference between lines, planes, and space.

POSTULATE
3

Any line contains at least two points. Any plane contains at least three noncollinear points. Space contains at least four noncoplanar points.

Examples   Which postulate is suggested by each statement?

2. The camera tripod does not wobble.   Postulate 2
3. A taut clothesline forms a straight line.   Postulate 1
4. A door is different from the edge of a door.   Postulate 3

Try This...   Which postulate is suggested by each statement?

2. Space is not flat like a plane.

3. A bracing wire forms a straight line.

4. A three-runner ice boat rests on the ice without wobbling.

 Points, Lines, and Planes

We can apply the postulates to problems involving points, lines, and planes.

Example   5.   Consider a T.V. antenna tower.
Name a set of three collinear points.
Name a set of four coplanar points.

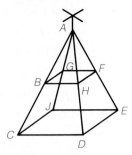

A, H, and *D* are collinear.
C, D, E, and *J* are coplanar.

Try This...   5.   Consider the drawing in Example 5. Name three other sets,
each containing three collinear points. Name three other sets,
each containing four coplanar points.

Example   6.   How many lines are determined by three noncollinear points,
A, B, and *C*? Draw a picture to explain your answer.

Each pair of points determines a line.
Thus, three lines are determined.

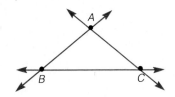

Try This...   6.   How many lines are determined by four points, no three of
which are collinear? Draw a picture to explain your answer.

Exercises

▲   **In each definition, identify the words that are undefined.**

1.   Noncollinear points   2. Coplanar points   3.   Noncoplanar points

▲▲   **Which postulate is suggested by each statement?**

4.   A three-legged stool sits level
on a floor.

5.   A rope stretched tight at a
building site forms a straight line.

6.   A line is not like a point.

7.   A surveyor's transit tripod does
not wobble.

8. A gardener uses a stretched cord to make straight rows.

9. Space consists of more than one point.

10. A desk top is different from the edge of the desk.

11. A box is different from the corner of the box.

12. A groundskeeper uses two stakes and a string to mark a straight line for a baseline.

13. The head and hands of a gymnast doing a headstand form the vertices of a triangle.

▲▲▲ Solve the following.

14. How many lines are determined by five points, no three of which are collinear? Draw a picture to explain your answer.

15. How many lines are determined by six points, no three of which are collinear? Draw a picture to explain your answer.

16. Consider the drawing of a tent. Name three sets of three collinear points. Name three sets of four coplanar points.

17. Points R and S are contained in $\overleftrightarrow{GK}$. Points R and S are also contained in $\overleftrightarrow{FH}$. What is true of $\overleftrightarrow{GK}$ and $\overleftrightarrow{FH}$?

18. Explain how a football field can be marked off by using stakes in the ground.

19. Three noncollinear points G, H, and K, are in plane $\mathcal{M}$. Points G, H, and K are also in plane $\mathcal{P}$. What is true of planes $\mathcal{M}$ and $\mathcal{P}$?

▶ Extension Exercises

Find two examples of each of these in the real world.

20. Collinear points

21. Noncollinear points

22. Coplanar points

23. Noncoplanar points

▶▶ Challenge Exercises

24. Consider $\overleftrightarrow{RS}$. Explain how you know that there is a point not on $\overleftrightarrow{RS}$.

25. How many lines are determined by n points, no three of which are collinear?

26. What is the greatest number of connections needed for 15 computers if each computer is to be connected to every other computer?

6 | Theorems

After finishing Section 6, you should be able to
▲ *tell which postulate or theorem explains the conclusion.*

When definitions and postulates are used to prove a fact, that fact is
called a *theorem*. In this book, we shall list many theorems.
Sometimes we will show you how theorems are proved, but you will
not be expected to write formal proofs. The proof for Theorem 1.1 is
shown below. The proof explains how we arrived at this fact about
intersecting lines.

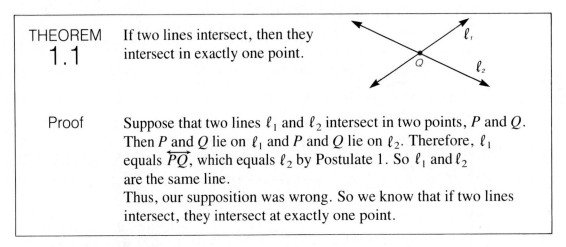

| THEOREM 1.1 | If two lines intersect, then they intersect in exactly one point. |

Proof   Suppose that two lines ℓ_1 and ℓ_2 intersect in two points, P and Q.
Then P and Q lie on ℓ_1 and P and Q lie on ℓ_2. Therefore, ℓ_1
equals $\overleftrightarrow{PQ}$, which equals ℓ_2 by Postulate 1. So ℓ_1 and ℓ_2
are the same line.
Thus, our supposition was wrong. So we know that if two lines
intersect, they intersect at exactly one point.

We will use geometric facts, whether they are definitions, postulates,
or theorems, to reach conclusions. Here are additional postulates
and theorems.

POSTULATE
4   If two points lie in a plane, then the line containing them is in
the plane.

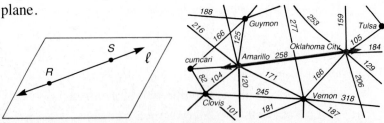

POSTULATE
5
If two planes intersect, then their intersection is a line.

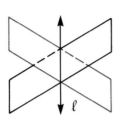

Postulates 4 and 5 lead to the following theorems.

THEOREM
1.2
If a line and a plane intersect and the line is not in the plane, then they intersect in a point.

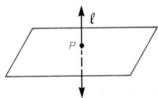

THEOREM
1.3
If ℓ is a line and P is a point not on the line, then ℓ and P are contained in exactly one plane.

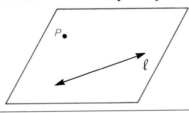

Examples   Tell which postulate or theorem explains the conclusion.

1. Two planes cannot intersect in a point   Postulate 5

2. $\overleftrightarrow{AB}$ is not in plane $\mathcal{K}$, but it intersects plane $\mathcal{K}$.   Theorem 1.2
   Therefore, $\overleftrightarrow{AB}$ cannot intersect plane $\mathcal{K}$
   in two points.

3. A line not in a plane cannot contain more than   Theorem 1.3
   one point of the plane.

4. A line and a point on the line cannot be   Postulate 4
   contained in more than one plane.

Try This...   Tell which postulate or theorem explains the conclusion.

1. Plane $\mathcal{K}$ and plane $\mathcal{M}$ intersect in $\overleftrightarrow{AB}$.

2. Points A and B are in plane $\mathcal{M}$. So $\overleftrightarrow{AB}$ is in plane $\mathcal{M}$.

3. Two lines cannot intersect in two different points.

Exercises

▲   **Tell which theorem or postulate explains each conclusion.**

1. Two points cannot determine more than one line.
2. Three noncollinear points cannot be contained in two planes.
3. A line and a point not on the line are in only one plane.
4. It is impossible for two lines to have two points in common.
5. Plane $\mathcal{K}$ and Plane $\mathcal{L}$ cannot intersect in only one point.
6. If points P and Q are in a plane, then $\overleftrightarrow{PQ}$ is in the plane.
7. Two lines cannot look like this: 8.   A line and a plane cannot look like this:

9. All the points of space cannot be contained in only one plane.

▲▲ **Tell which postulate or theorem each picture suggests.**

10. A folded sheet of paper.   11.   A carpenter's chalkline.

12. A tetherball pole.   13.   The line-crossing pattern in a tile floor.   14.   A three-legged stool.

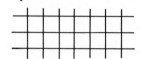

7	Conditional Sentences

After finishing Section 7, you should be able to

▲   *identify the hypothesis and conclusion of a conditional sentence.*

▲▲   *write the converse of a conditional sentence.*

▲   If–Then Sentences

Many theorems are stated in "if–then" form. "If–then" sentences are called *conditional sentences*. The "if" part of the sentence is the *hypothesis*. The "then" part of the sentence is the *conclusion*.

$$\text{If } P\text{, then } Q.$$
$$\uparrow \qquad \uparrow$$
hypothesis   conclusion

Examples   Identify each hypothesis and conclusion.

1. If the snow is deep, then school is closed.
   hypothesis   conclusion

2. If a figure has four sides, then it is a quadrilateral.
   hypothesis   conclusion

3. If two lines intersect, then they intersect in exactly one point.
   hypothesis   conclusion

Try This...   Identify each hypothesis and conclusion.

1. If it rains, then you will get wet.

2. If a number is odd, then it is not even.

3. If two points are in a plane, then the line containing them is in the plane.

4. Theorem 1.4, which follows, is stated in a conditional sentence. Identify the hypothesis and the conclusion.

<table>
<tr><td>THEOREM
1.4</td><td>If two lines ℓ_1 and ℓ_2 intersect, then the two lines are contained in exactly one plane.</td><td>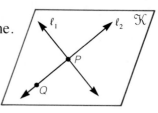</td></tr>
</table>

▲▲ Converses

If we interchange the hypothesis and conclusion of a conditional sentence, we obtain a new conditional sentence called its *converse*.

Conditional: If P, then Q.
Converse: If Q, then P.

Examples Write the converse of each of the following sentences.

4. If a figure is a triangle, then it has three sides.
   Converse: If a figure has three sides, then it is a triangle.

5. If my name is Joe, then I am a boy.
   Converse: If I am a boy, then my name is Joe.

Example 5 illustrates the fact that true conditional sentences may or may not have true converses.

Try This... Write the converse of each sentence.

5. If a figure is a square, then it has four sides.

6. If school is closed, then students are happy.

Exercises

▲ **Identify the hypothesis and conclusion in each statement.**

1. If a number has three factors, then it is a composite number.

2. If a number is odd, then it is not divisible by 2.

3. If the grass is green, then there are no weeds.

4. If water freezes, then the temperature is low.

5. If $2x = 10$, then $x = 5$.

6. If $3y + 2 = 17$, then $y = 5$.

7. If Mary is wary, then Tim is slim.

8. If Joe is slow, then Terry is merry.

9. If it rains, then it pours.

10. If the butter is hard, then the bread tears.

▲▲ **11-20. Write the converse of each conditional sentence in Exercises 1-10.**

▶▶ Challenge Exercises

Rewrite each statement in "if–then" form.

21. Spare the rod and spoil the child.

22. $x = 3$ when $3x = 9$.

23. Too much pepper ruins the sauce.

24. All squares are rectangles.

25. Write the converse of Theorem 1.4.
     Is the converse true or false?

▶◀ Activity

Three friends named Lena, Oscar, and Britt went to a costume party. One was dressed as a baseball player, another as a doctor, and the third as an astronaut. If Britt is the doctor, then Oscar is the astronaut. If Britt is the astronaut, then Oscar is the baseball player. If Oscar is not the baseball player, then Lena is the astronaut. If Lena is the baseball player, then Britt is the astronaut. What is each person's costume?

To help you solve this problem, cut out shapes to represent Lena, Oscar, Britt, and each costume. Juggle around the people and costumes until all the conditions are satisfied. (Another way to find the solution is to make a table. Which method is easier?)

Consumer Application   Reading Advertisements

Influenced by the wording of advertisements, consumers may shop
in a new store or try a new product. Many advertisements
in magazines and newspapers contain examples of
conditional sentences.

**Do your teeth
look dull?
Have they lost
their sparkle?
Then read on!!!**

If you've always
wanted a beautiful smile,
then brush with
BRIGHTWHITE.
BRIGHTWHITE will
bring back the sparkle
in your smile.

Example Identify the conditional sentence
in this advertisement. Find the
hypothesis and the conclusion.
Then write its converse.

If you've always wanted a beautiful smile, then
brush with BRIGHTWHITE.

Write down the
conditional
sentence.

If you've always wanted a beautiful smile,
<small>hypothesis</small>

then brush with BRIGHTWHITE.
<small>conclusion</small>

Identify the
hypothesis
and the conclusion.

If you brush with BRIGHTWHITE, then you've
always wanted a beautiful smile.

Write the converse.

**Identify the conditional sentence in each advertisement. Find the
hypothesis and conclusion for each sentence. Then write its converse.**

1.

If you're out running a
couple of miles a day,
then you're on your way
to building a better body.
And what better way to
show off all your hard
work than in **RUNTEX**
shorts and tops?

For the look and comfort
that all runners want, buy
the **RUNTEX** label.

2.

**Rub-A-
Tub-Tub.**

That's our motto.

If you're tired of scrubbing
tubs clean, then use
SCRUBEASE. Gently rub
SCRUBEASE on your tub
and then rinse off with
water. There's no scrub-
bing with ***SCRUBEASE***.

Soon Rub-A-Tub-Tub will
be your motto, too.

3.

I bet you haven't tasted
a green bean this fresh
since you were a kid
on your grandfather's
farm. If freshness is
what counts, then shop
at the FARM MART.
All our produce arrives
daily, fresh from local
farmers.

Chapter Review

 Use a ruler and compass.

1. Draw a segment, 7 cm long.

2. Draw a segment about 6 cm long. Bisect it.

 Use a ruler, drawing triangle, and compass.

3. Draw a segment, $\overline{GK}$, about 8 cm long. Choose any point X on $\overline{GK}$ and use the drawing triangle to draw a line perpendicular to $\overline{GK}$ at X.

4. Copy $\triangle RFK$.

3 **Suggest a possible counterexample for each statement.**

5. All triangles are equilateral.

6. All leaves turn red in autumn.

4 **Use the following assumptions. What can you conclude?**

7. (a) All fish have gills.
   (b) All trout are fish.

8. (a) All squares are rhombuses.
   (b) The diagonals of a rhombus are perpendicular.

5 **Which postulate is suggested by each statement?**

9. A three-legged podium does not wobble.
10. A bricklayer uses a cord stretched between two nails to make straight rows.

6 **Tell which theorem or postulate justifies each conclusion.**

11. Two different lines cannot contain the same two points.
12. A line not in a plane cannot intersect the plane in two points.

7 **Identify the hypothesis and conclusion. Then write the converse.**

13. If the rain falls, then the weeds grow.
14. If $x^2 = 16$, then $x = 4$.

Chapter Test

Use a ruler and compass.

1. Draw a segment, 9 cm long.

2. Draw a segment about 8 cm long. Bisect it.

Use a ruler, drawing triangle, and compass.

3. Draw a segment, $\overline{PL}$, about 9 cm long. Choose any point T on $\overline{PL}$ and use the drawing triangle to draw a line perpendicular to $\overline{PL}$ at T.

4. Copy $\triangle RST$.

Suggest a possible counterexample for each statement.

5. All intersecting lines are perpendicular.

6. All cars have six cylinders.

Use the following assumptions. What can you conclude?

7. (a) All birds have feathers.
   (b) All ostriches are birds.

8. (a) The angle measures of a hexagon add up to 720°.
   (b) A regular hexagon has all angles the same size.

Which postulate is suggested by each statement?

9. A table top is different from the edge of the table.

10. A three-legged chair sits level on a tile floor.

Tell which theorem or postulate justifies each conclusion.

11. Two different planes cannot intersect in two different lines.

12. A line and a point not on the line cannot be in two different planes.

Identify the hypothesis and conclusion. Then write the converse.

13. If the sky is blue, then the sun will shine.

14. If $2x = 14$, then $x = 7$.

Skills Review   Absolute Value

> number of units
> an integer is from 0
> on a number line

$|-2| = 2$ |←2 units→|

$-2 \quad -1 \quad 0 \quad 1 \quad 2$

Find the absolute value.

1. The absolute value of -3 is ▓ .

2. The absolute value of 5 is ▓ .

3. The absolute value of 0 is ▓ .

4. The absolute value of -6 is ▓ .

Simplify.

5. $|2|$

6. $|-3|$

7. $|1|$

8. $|10|$

9. $|-16|$

10. $|-4|$

11. $|8|$

12. $|11|$

13. $|-5|$

14. $|-8|$

15. $|22|$

16. $|-25|$

17. $|30|$

18. $|-17|$

19. $|32|$

20. $|-42|$

21. $|44|$

22. $|-48|$

23. $|-50|$

24. $|19|$

25. $|66|$

26. $|-75|$

27. $|-99|$

28. $|100|$

29. $|101|$

30. $|1 + 1|$

31. $|0 + 3|$

32. $|5 - 3|$

33. $|6 + 2|$

34. $|9 - 5|$

35. $|20 - 17|$

36. $|14 + 6|$

37. $|3 + 15|$

38. $|25 - 5|$

39. $|8 + 8|$

40. $|50 - 25|$

41. $|50 + 25|$

42. $|0 + 0|$

43. $|0 - 0|$

44. $|50 + 1|$

45. $|88 - 33|$

46. $|90 + 11|$

47. $|75 + 25|$

48. $|100 - 1|$

49. $|98 + 27|$

50. $|2 - 3|$

51. $|1 - 4|$

52. $|0 - 2|$

53. $|5 - 4|$

54. $|6 - 7|$

55. $|10 - 15|$

56. $|20 - 30|$

57. $|25 - 45|$

58. $|15 - 30|$

59. $|30 - 15|$

60. $|32 - 11|$

61. $|24 - 44|$

62. $|52 - 57|$

63. $|100 - 150|$

64. $|25 - 75|$

65. $|0 - 100|$

66. $|0 - 1,000|$

67. $|4,000 - 0|$

68. $|2,000 + 0|$

69. $|0 + 3,300|$

2
Points and Angles

Coordinates and Distance

1

After finishing Section 1, you should be able to
▲ *name coordinates of points on a line.*
▲▲ *use coordinates to find distances.*
▲▲ *use distances to find coordinates.*

▲ Coordinates

The paper clip is 5 cm long, regardless of how we place the ruler.

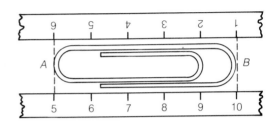

POSTULATE
6

The Distance Postulate

To every pair of distinct points *A* and *B*, there corresponds a positive number, *AB*, called the *distance* between them.

If we apply the idea of a ruler to a line, we can make a number line.

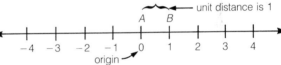

The number corresponding to a point on the line is called the *coordinate* of that point. The point *A*, with coordinate zero, is called the *origin*. *AB* is called the *unit distance*.

Example   1. Find the coordinates of *A*, *B*, and *C*.

The coordinates are −5, 3, and 1, respectively.

Try This...   1. For the number line above find the coordinates of
D, *E*, *F*, and *G*.

Examples   Name the points on the line having these coordinates.

2. −3   3. 2   4. −2.5

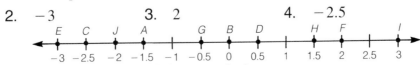

The points are *E*, *F*, and *C*, respectively.

Try This... Name the points on the line having these coordinates.

2. 0

3. −2

4. 0.5

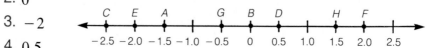

▲▲ Finding Distances

We can find distances on a number line by subtracting coordinates.

Examples Find these distances on the line.

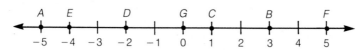

5. *BC*   *BC* = 3 − 1 = 2
6. *AC*   *AC* = 1 − (−5) = 6
7. *AB*   *AB* = 3 − (−5) = 8

Try This... Find these distances on the line above.

5. *EF*   6. *DB*   7. *GF*

When subtracting coordinates, order makes a difference.
For example,

$$AB = 3 - (-5) = 8,$$

but changing the order gives us

$$AB = -5 - 3 = -8$$

Because we want distance to be positive, we take the **absolute value** of the difference. Then the order doesn't matter.

Examples Find these distances on the line above.

8. *AF* $AF = |5 - (-5)| = |10| = 10$
                 or, $AF = |-5 - 5| = |-10| = 10$

9. *BE* · $BE = |3 - (-4)| = |7| = 7$
                 or, $BE = |-4 - 3| = |-7| = 7$

10. *FB* $FB = |5 - 3| = |2| = 2$
                 or, $FB = |3 - 5| = |-2| = 2$

Try This...   Find these distances on the line in Example 5.

        8. *CD*   9. *EG*   10. *DF*

 Finding Coordinates

We can use distances to find coordinates.

Example   11. Let the coordinates of *A* and *B* be *a* and *b*, respectively. If
$AB = 7$ and $a = -1$, find the coordinate *b*.
There are two possibilities:

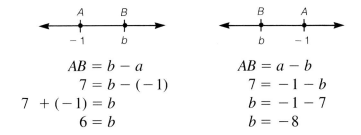

$$AB = b - a \qquad\qquad AB = a - b$$
$$7 = b - (-1) \qquad\quad 7 = -1 - b$$
$$7 + (-1) = b \qquad\qquad b = -1 - 7$$
$$6 = b \qquad\qquad\qquad b = -8$$

Try This...   11. Let the coordinates of *A* and *B* be *a* and *b*, respectively. If
$AB = 9$ and $a = 3$, find the coordinate *b*.

The matching of real numbers and points on a line is called a
coordinate system.

POSTULATE   *The Ruler Postulate*

    7   Every line has at least one coordinate system.

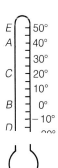

▲   **Name the coordinate of each point on the thermometer.**

     1. *A*   2. *B*   3. *C*   4. *D*   5. *E*

Use the number line for Exercises 6-21.

Name the coordinate of each point on the number line.

6. *F*   7. *G*   8. *H*   9. *J*   10. *K*

Name the points that have these coordinates.

11. -4 12. 8   13. -9 14. -7 15. -3

16. Solve the coded message. Give the letter of the point named by each
     coordinate on the line.

___ ___ ___ ___ ___ ___ ___ ___ ___ ___ ___ ___ ___
8   -4 8 -8 -7 4 -7 2 10 -7 0 -10 -3

▲▲ **Find these distances on the line.**

17. *AB*   18. *BC*   19. *CD*   20. *DE*   21. *EF*

Find the daily range in temperature.

22. High: 23°C   23. High: 9°C   24. High: -13°C   25. High: 15°C
     Low: 10°C   Low: -5°C   Low: -27°C   Low: -12°C

▲
▲▲ **Let the coordinates of *P* and *Q* be *p* and *q*, respectively. Find the
coordinate *q* from the given information.**

26. *PQ* = 15 and *p* = -3.   27. *PQ* = 7 and *p* = 7.
28. *PQ* = 2 and *p* = 1.   29. *PQ* = 5 and *p* = -6.

▶ Extension Exercises

Suppose that points *A*, *B*, *C*, and *D* are
evenly spaced on a number line as shown.
From the given information,
find the other coordinates.

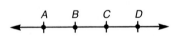

30. *A* = 1 and *B* = 4.   31. *B* = 1 and *D* = 2.

32. *C* = 0 and *D* = 5.   33. *A* = -2 and *C* = 2.

34. *A* = -4 and *D* = -1.   35. *A* = -2 and *D* = 1.

2	Coordinate Systems

After finishing Section 2, you should be able to
▲ *form new coordinate systems from a given coordinate system on a line.*

We can form other systems from one coordinate system on a line by adding to it.

1. Mark a coordinate system on a line.
   Add 2 to each coordinate.

2. Mark another coordinate system on a line.
   Add − 3 to each coordinate. What do you observe?

Adding a number to each coordinate corresponds to sliding a ruler along a line.

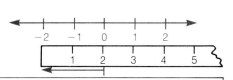

THEOREM 2.1	If the same number is added to each coordinate of a coordinate system, then a new coordinate system is obtained.

Example   1. Add 3 to each coordinate on the line to find a new coordinate system. Compare the distances in the two systems between the points *A*, *B*, and *C*.

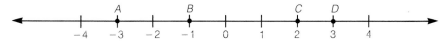

Adding 3 to each coordinate, we get

First system: $AB = |-1 - (-3)|$
$AB = |-1 + 3| = 2.$
Also, $AC = |2 - (-3)| = 5$
and $BC = |2 - (-1)| = 3.$

Second system: $AB = |2 - 0| = 2,$
$AC = |5 - 0| = 5,$
and $BC = |5 - 2| = 3.$

Try This...   1. Use the first system in Example 1. Add -2 to each coordinate and name the new coordinates of A, B, C, and D. Compare the distances in the two systems between points A, B, and D.

Example   2. The degrees on the Celsius and Kelvin scales are the same size. Absolute zero is $0°$ on the Kelvin scale and $-273°$ on the Celsius scale. That is, $0°K = -273°C$.

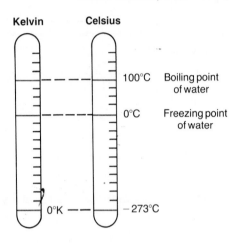

We can make a Kelvin scale by adding 273 to each number on the Celsius scale.

What are the freezing and the boiling points of water on the Kelvin scale?

The freezing point of water is
$$0 + 273 = 273°K$$

The boiling point of water is
$$100 + 273 = 373°K$$

Try This...   2. Change 52°C to degrees Kelvin.

3. Change 350°K to degrees Celsius.

Another way to form a new coordinate system is to multiply each coordinate by -1.

1. Mark a coordinate system on a line. Multiply each coordinate by -1.

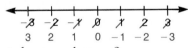

What do you observe?

Multiplying each coordinate by -1 corresponds to flipping the number line about the origin.

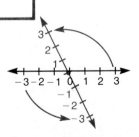

THEOREM
2.2

If each coordinate of a coordinate system is multiplied by -1, then a new coordinate system is obtained.

Example

3. Multiply each coordinate on the line by -1 to obtain a new coordinate system. Compare distances in the two coordinate systems.

Multiplying by -1, we get

First system: $AB = |0 - (-3)| = |0 + 3| = 3$
Also, $AC = 5, AD = 7, BC = 2, BD = 4,$ and
                 $CD = 2.$

Second system: $AB = |0 - 3| = |-3| = 3$
Similarly, the other distances are the same as in the first system.

Try This...

4. Multiply each coordinate on the line by -1 to form a new coordinate system. Compare distances as in Example 3.

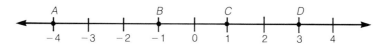

In measuring a segment, we usually place the ruler so that one endpoint corresponds to 0 and the other endpoint corresponds to some positive number. The following theorem corresponds to this.

THEOREM
2.3

The Ruler Placement Theorem

If A and B are any points on a line, then there is a coordinate system in which the coordinate of A is the origin and the coordinate of B is a positive number.

Example   4. Find a new coordinate system on the line in which the coordinate of A is 0 and the coordinate of B is a positive number.

Add −2 to each coordinate (so the coordinate of A becomes 0).

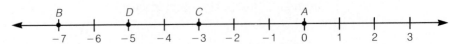

Multiply each coordinate by −1 (so the coordinate of B is positive).

Try This...   5. Use the original coordinate system in Example 4. Find a new system in which the coordinate of C is 0 and the coordinate of D is a positive number.

Exercises

▲   **Change these temperatures to Kelvin or Celsius.**

1.   − 50°C   2.   38°C   3.   360°K   4.   200°K

Find a new coordinate system by adding the number to each coordinate in the system pictured.

5.   4   6.   5
7.   − 1   8.   − 6

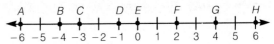

9–12.   Begin with the coordinate systems you found in Exercises 5–8. Find new coordinate systems by multiplying by − 1.

For each pair of points, find a new system in which the coordinate of the first point is 0 and the coordinate of the second point is positive.

13.   F and B   14.   G and A
15.   H and D   16.   D and B

▶ Extension Exercises

17. Points A, B, and C are collinear, and $AB = CB = 4$. If the coordinate of B is 3, and the coordinate of A is greater than the coordinate of C, find the coordinates of both A and C.

18. Points A, B, and C are collinear, and $AB = BC = 3$. If the coordinate of B is 1, and the coordinate of C is negative, find the coordinates of A and C.

19. The pictures below are physical examples of coordinate systems. Name two other examples.

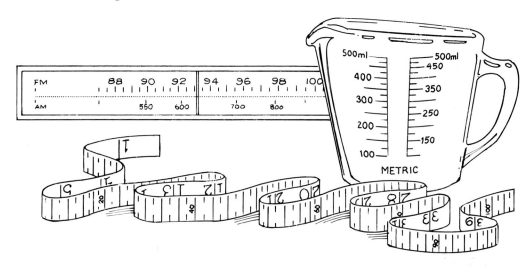

▶◀ Activity

Choose the best customary unit for measuring the following objects:

• the length of a pencil
• the height of the classroom door
• the width of your classroom
• the distance between the center of town and the edge of town

Now estimate the lengths of various objects in your classroom. Find the sum of the differences between your estimate and the actual length. Compare your sum with your classmates'. Who was the best estimator?

3 | Betweenness of Points

After finishing Section 3, you should be able to
▲ *apply the definition of betweenness.*
▲▲ *recognize subsets of lines such as segments, rays, and opposite rays.*
▲▲▲ *solve problems involving the concept of betweenness.*

▲ Betweenness

Which points are between *A* and *D*?

1. Trace these points on a sheet of paper.

$$B$$
$$A \qquad \qquad C \qquad \qquad D \quad E$$

2. Draw a line through points *A* and *E*.
3. Which distance is greater, *AB* + *BE* or *AE*?
4. Which distance is greater, *AC* + *CE* or *AE*?
5. Which distance is greater, *AD* + *DE* or *AE*?

___
DEFINITION
___

B is **between** *A* and *C* whenever *A*, *B*, and *C* are collinear and *AB* + *BC* = *AC*.

$$A \qquad B \quad C$$

We write "*A-B-C*" for "*B* is between *A* and *C*."

Examples   1. *D*, *E*, and *F* are collinear. *DE* = 5, *EF* = 18, and *DF* = 13. Which point is between the other two?

E-D-F because *ED* + *DF* = *EF*. That is, 5 + 13 = 18.

2. If *PQ* = 12, and *QR* = 10, what is *PR*?

Because *P-Q-R*, *PR* = *PQ* + *QR*.
Thus, *PR* = 12 + 10 = 22.

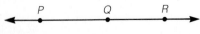
$$P \qquad \qquad Q \qquad \qquad R$$

Try This... 1. A, B, and C are collinear. $AB = 11$, $BC = 3.5$, and $AC = 7.5$. Which point is between the other two?

2. If $DE = 12$, and $FE = 3$, what is DF?

▲▲ Subsets of Lines

Betweenness can be used to define certain sets of points contained in lines. Some of these subsets are defined in the chart.

Term	Symbol	Definition	Picture
Segment	$\overline{AB}$	The set of points containing A, B, and all points between A and B. A and B are called *endpoints* of the segment.	A •———• B
Ray	$\overrightarrow{AB}$	The segment, $\overline{AB}$, together with the set of all points X such that A-B-X. Point A is called the *endpoint* of the ray.	A •——•—→ B
Opposite rays		$\overrightarrow{AB}$ and $\overrightarrow{CD}$ are opposite rays whenever $A = C$ and B-A-D or B-C-D.	B ←•——•——•→ D, C A

Examples   Lines $\overleftrightarrow{AC}$ and $\overleftrightarrow{DE}$ intersect at B.

3. Name all the segments shown.
$\overline{AB}$, $\overline{BC}$, $\overline{AC}$, $\overline{DB}$, $\overline{BE}$, and $\overline{DE}$.

4. Name all the rays shown.
$\overrightarrow{BA}$, $\overrightarrow{BC}$, $\overrightarrow{AB}$ (or $\overrightarrow{AC}$), $\overrightarrow{CB}$ (or $\overrightarrow{CA}$),
$\overrightarrow{BD}$, $\overrightarrow{BE}$, $\overrightarrow{DB}$ (or $\overrightarrow{DE}$), $\overrightarrow{EB}$ (or $\overrightarrow{ED}$)
When naming a ray, the endpoint and *any* other point may be used.

5. Name all the pairs of opposite rays shown.
$\overrightarrow{BA}$ and $\overrightarrow{BC}$, and $\overrightarrow{BD}$ and $\overrightarrow{BE}$.

Try This... $\overleftrightarrow{AE}$ and $\overleftrightarrow{DB}$ intersect at C.

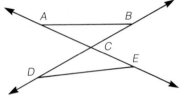

       3. Name all the segments shown.

       4. Name all the pairs of opposite
         rays shown.

Example   6. On $\overleftrightarrow{AD}$, what points do $\overline{AC}$ and $\overline{BD}$ have in common?

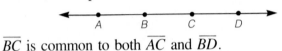

      $\overline{BC}$ is common to both $\overline{AC}$ and $\overline{BD}$.

Try This...   5. Refer to $\overleftrightarrow{AD}$ above. What points do $\overrightarrow{BD}$ and $\overrightarrow{DA}$ have in
       common?

 Using Betweenness

Betweenness and distance can be used to
define the midpoint of a segment.

<u>DEFINITION</u>

M is the **midpoint** of a segment,
$\overline{AB}$, whenever A-M-B and
$AM = MB$ (or, $AM = MB = \frac{1}{2}AB$).
The midpoint M is said to **bisect** $\overline{AB}$.

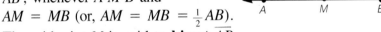

Every segment has exactly one midpoint. The definition of midpoint
does not say this, but it can be proven.

THEOREM
2.4   Every segment has exactly one midpoint.

Examples   For each segment, find the coordinate of the midpoint.

     7. $\underset{0}{\overset{A}{\bullet}} \quad \overset{M}{\bullet} \quad \underset{5}{\overset{B}{\bullet}}$ $AB = 5$. Thus, $AM = \dfrac{5}{2}$.

                 Coordinate of $M = 0 + \dfrac{5}{2} = \dfrac{5}{2}$.

8.

AB = 8 − 2 = 6. Thus, $AM = \dfrac{6}{2}$.

Coordinate of $M = 2 + \dfrac{6}{2} = 5$.

9.

AB = 1 − (−5) = 6. Thus, $AM = \dfrac{6}{2}$.

Coordinate of $M = -5 + \dfrac{6}{2} = -2$.

Try This..   For each segment, find the coordinate of the midpoint.

6.

7.

Exercises

▲ **Points *P*, *Q*, and *R* are collinear. Which point is between the
other two?**

  1. $PR = 63, QP = 17,$ and $QR = 46$.   2. $PR = 43, RQ = 35,$ and $QP = 8$.
  3. $RQ = 12, RP = 17,$ and $QP = 5$.   4. $PR = 3PQ$ and $RQ = 4PQ$.
  5. $QR = 0.6, RP = 1.7,$ and   6. $QP = 19.7, QR = 11.3,$ and
      $QP = 2.3$. $PR = 31$.

Suppose *B* is between *A* and *C*.

  7. If $AB = 16.3$ and $BC = 7.5$, what is AC?
  8. If $AC = 23$, and $BC = 14\frac{1}{2}$, what is AB?
  9. If $BC = 0.034$ and $AC = 1.248$, what is AB?
  10. If $AB = 129$ and $BC = 23$, what is CA?
  11. If $AC = 2\frac{1}{4}$ and $AB = 1\frac{1}{2}$, what is BC?
  12. If $AB = 2BC$ and $AC = 27$, what are AB and BC?

▲▲ **Name all the segments, rays, and pairs of opposite rays shown.**

  13. *A-B-C*   14. *A-B-C* and *D-C-E*

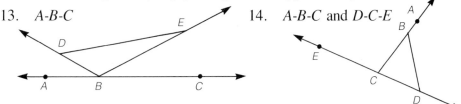

15. What set of points do $\overrightarrow{RS}$ and $\overrightarrow{SR}$ have in common?

16. If *L-M-N*, what set of points do $\overrightarrow{NL}$ and $\overrightarrow{MN}$ have in common?

For each segment, find the coordinate of the midpoint.

17.
```
 A      M       B
 •──────•───────•
 0              26
```

18.
```
 A      M      B
 •──────•──────•
 -4            0
```

19.
```
 A      M      B
 •──────•──────•
 5             18
```

20.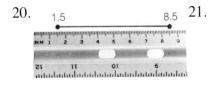

21.

▶ Extension Exercises

22. Draw a line, select four points on it, and name them *A, B, C,* and D from left to right. Name all the betweenness relationships.

23. *A, B, C,* and *D* are four points on a line, and *A-B-C.* How many positions are possible for *D* with respect to *A, B,* and *C*?

24. *AB* = 13 and the coordinate of *B* is 6. What is the coordinate of *A*?

25. *PQ* = 26 and the coordinate of *P* is 12. What is the coordinate of *Q*?

26. *AB* = 13, the coordinate of *B* is 6, and *B* is between *A* and the origin. What is the coordinate of *A*?

27. *PQ* = 26, the coordinate of *P* is −3, and *P* is between *Q* and the origin. What is the coordinate of *Q*?

▶▶ Challenge Exercises

28. Describe the set of all points *X* such that *A-X-B*.

29. Write a formula (different from the method used in Examples 7–9) for finding the coordinate of the midpoint of a segment, given only the coordinates of the endpoints.

▶◀ Activity

Cut out a square, triangle, circle, rectangle, and star from paper. Arrange the shapes in order following these statements.
- The square is between the rectangle and the star.
- The rectangle is between the circle and the square.
- The triangle is between the circle and the square.
- The rectangle is between the circle and the triangle.
- The star is to the left of the circle.

4	Angles

After finishing Section 4, you should be able to
▲   *identify angles and parts of angles, and*
   name angles in different ways.

An angle is a familiar figure.

DEFINITION

An **angle** is a figure consisting of two rays with a
common endpoint. If the rays are opposite rays, the
angle is called a *straight angle*.

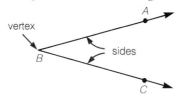 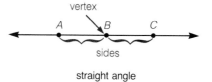

straight angle

The angles above may be named $\angle ABC$ or $\angle CBA$.
The middle letter *always* names the vertex. If there
are no other angles with vertex B, we may write $\angle B$.

We sometimes use numerals to name angles.

$\angle 1$ is $\angle ABE$ (or $\angle ABD$)
$\angle 2$ is $\angle EDF$
$\angle 3$ is $\angle EBC$ (or $\angle DBC$)

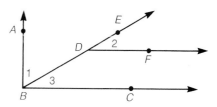

Examples   Identify all the angles and name them in as many ways as possible.

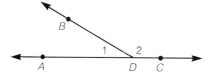

1. There are three angles: $\angle ADB$ or $\angle BDA$ or $\angle 1$,
                              $\angle BDC$ or $\angle CDB$ or $\angle 2$,
                 and $\angle ADC$ or $\angle CDA$.

(We do not use $\angle D$ because it could name
any of the three angles.)

2. There is one angle that may be named ∠PQR, ∠RQP, or ∠Q.

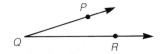

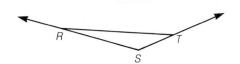

3. There is one angle shown: ∠RST or ∠TSR or ∠S. (Remember, the sides of an angle are rays, not segments.)

Remark   Later we will look at drawings such as the one in Example 3. We will refer to ∠TRS (or ∠RTS) because $\overline{RT}$ and $\overline{RS}$ determine $\overrightarrow{RT}$ and $\overrightarrow{RS}$ (or $\overline{TR}$ and $\overline{TS}$ determine $\overrightarrow{TR}$ and $\overrightarrow{TS}$).

Try This...   Identify all the angles and list all the names for them.

1.   2.   3.

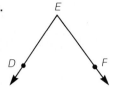   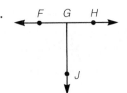   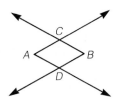

Examples   Identify the vertex and the sides of each angle.

4.

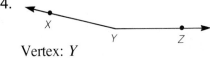

Vertex: *Y*
Sides: $\overrightarrow{YX}$ and $\overrightarrow{YZ}$

5. All three angles in the bicycle have vertex *E*.
Sides of ∠DEG: $\overrightarrow{ED}$ and $\overrightarrow{EG}$
Sides of ∠FEG: $\overrightarrow{EF}$ and $\overrightarrow{EG}$
Sides of ∠DEF: $\overrightarrow{ED}$ and $\overrightarrow{EF}$

Try This...   Identify the vertex and the sides of each angle.

4.   5.

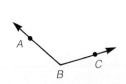   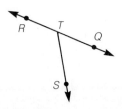

Sometimes we refer to the **interior** of an angle.

Points *P*, *Q*, and *R* are in the interior of ∠*ABC*. Points *X*, *Y*, and *Z* are *not* in the interior of ∠*ABC*. No points *on* the angle itself are in the interior. Straight angles have no interior.

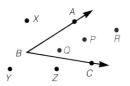

Exercises

▲ **Name each angle in as many different ways as possible. Identify the vertex and sides.**

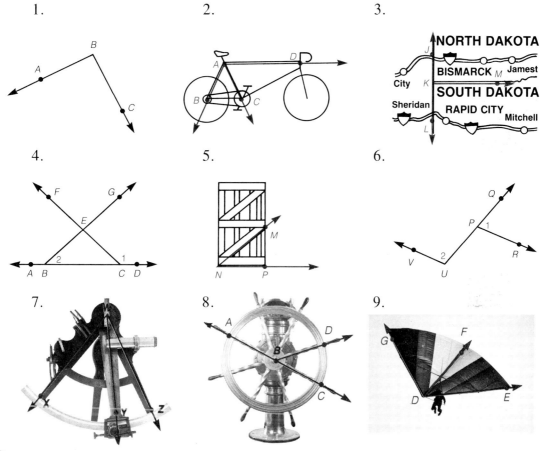

1.

2.

3.

4.

5.

6.

7.

8.

9.

▶ Extension Exercises

10. How many angles are formed by two intersecting lines?

11. How many angles are formed by three lines that intersect in one point?

5	Angle Measurement

After finishing Section 5, you should be able to
▲ *measure angles with a protractor.*
▲▲ *draw angles with a given measure.*
▲▲ *classify angles according to their measures.*

▲ Measuring Angles

We can use a protractor to find the measure of an angle. The usual unit of angle measure is called a *degree*.

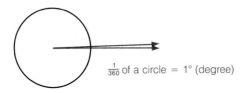

$\frac{1}{360}$ of a circle = 1° (degree)

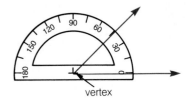

vertex

POSTULATE
8

The Angle Measure Postulate

To each angle there corresponds exactly one number n, called its *measure*, such that $0° < n \leq 180°$.

For the measure of ∠ABC we write "*m* ∠ABC."

Example   1. Read the measures of ∠ABC, ∠ABD, and ∠ABE.

$m \angle ABC = 30°$
$m \angle ABD = 75°$
$m \angle ABE = 120°$

Try This...   1. Read the measures of ∠PQR, ∠PQS, and ∠PQT.

Example   2. Use a protractor to measure ∠JKL.

Step 1

Place the protractor so that the vertex mark is at K and the bottom edge is along $\overrightarrow{KL}$.

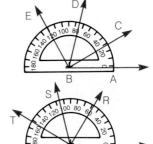

Step 2   Find the point where $\overrightarrow{KJ}$ intersects the edge of the protractor.

Step 3   Read the measurement: $m \angle JKL = 52°$.

Try This...   Use a protractor to measure these angles.

2.

3.

▲▲ Drawing Angles

We can also use a protractor to draw an angle with a specific measure.

Example   3. Draw an angle with measure 60°.

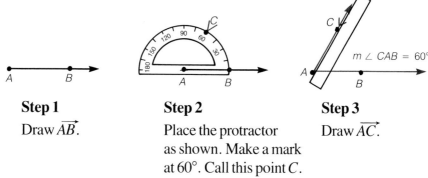

Step 1
Draw $\overrightarrow{AB}$.

Step 2
Place the protractor
as shown. Make a mark
at 60°. Call this point C.

Step 3
Draw $\overrightarrow{AC}$.

Try This...   Draw angles with these measures.

4.   70°   5.   95°   6.   132°

POSTULATE
9

The Protractor Postulate

Consider a ray, $\overrightarrow{AB}$, and a number n, such that $0° < n \le 180°$.
If $n < 180°$, there is exactly one ray $\overrightarrow{AC}$ or $\overrightarrow{AC'}$ on each side of $\overrightarrow{AB}$
such that $m \angle CAB = m \angle C'AB = n$.

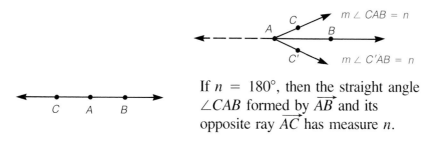

If $n = 180°$, then the straight angle
$\angle CAB$ formed by $\overrightarrow{AB}$ and its
opposite ray $\overrightarrow{AC}$ has measure n.

Classifying Angles

Angles are classified by their measures.

Acute $m\angle ABC < 90°$

Right $m\angle ABC = 90°$

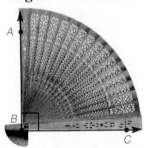

Obtuse $90° < m\angle ABC < 180°$

Straight $m\angle ABC = 180°$

Examples Classify these angles.

4.

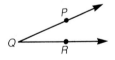

$\angle PQR$ is acute.

5.

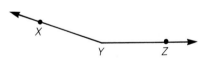

$\angle XYZ$ is obtuse.

6.

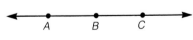

$\angle ABC$ is a straight angle.

Try This... Classify these angles.

7.

8.

9.

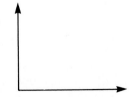

Exercises

▲ **Read the measure of each angle.**

1.

2.
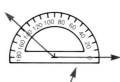

3.

4.
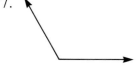

5.

6.
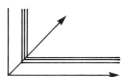

Use a protractor to measures these angles.

7.

8.

9.

10.
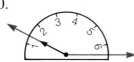

11.

12.
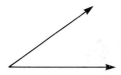

▲▲ **Draw angles with these measures.**

13. 75°   14. 105°   15. 15°

16. 65°   17. 135°   18. 25°

▲▲
▲ **Classify these angles.**

19.

20.
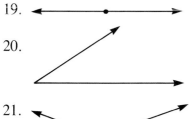

21.

22.   ∠ 1, ∠ 2, and ∠ 3 in the photograph
      at the right.

6 | Adding Angle Measures

After finishing Section 6, you should be able to

▲ *apply the Angle Addition Postulate in problems involving sums of angle measures.*

1. Draw a nonstraight angle ∠ *ABC*.
   Choose a point *D* in the interior
   of ∠ *ABC* and draw $\overrightarrow{BD}$.

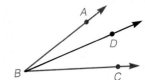

2. Measure ∠ *ABD*, ∠ *DBC*, and ∠ *ABC*.

3. Draw a straight angle ∠ *ABC*.
   Choose a point *D* not on
   the angle, and draw $\overrightarrow{BD}$.

4. Measure ∠ *ABD* and ∠ *DBC*.
   What is the sum of their measures?

POSTULATE
10

The Angle Addition Postulate

For any nonstraight angle ∠ *ABC*,
if *D* is a point in its interior, then
$m \angle ABD + m \angle DBC = m \angle ABC.$

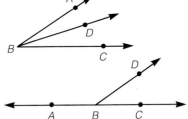

For any straight angle ∠ *ABC*, if *D*
is a point not on ∠ *ABC*, then
$m \angle ABD + m \angle DBC = m \angle ABC.$

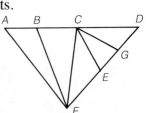

Examples

Refer to the figure to complete these statements.

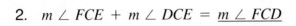

1. $m \angle AFB + m \angle BFC = \underline{m \angle AFC}$

2. $m \angle FCE + m \angle DCE = \underline{m \angle FCD}$

3. $m \angle BFD - m \angle CFD = \underline{m \angle BFC}$

Try This...   Refer to the figure to complete these statements.

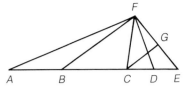

1. $m \angle BFC + m \angle CFD =$ _____

2. $m \angle FCG + m \angle GCD =$ _____

3. $m \angle AFD - m \angle AFB =$ _____

Examples   4. Find $m \angle ABC$.

$m \angle ABC = 30° + 80° = 110°$

5. $\angle ABC$ is a straight angle.
Find $m \angle ABD$.

$m \angle ABD = 180° - 45° = 135°$

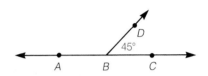

▲6. $m \angle ABC = 51°$. Find
$m \angle ABD$ and $m \angle DBC$.

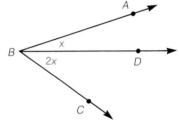

$m \angle ABC = 51°$. Thus, we have

$$x + 2x = 51$$
$$3x = 51$$
$$x = 17$$

Hence, $m \angle ABD = 17°$ and $m \angle DBC = 34°$.

Try This...   4. Find $m \angle PQR$.

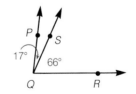

▲5. $m \angle DEF = 180°$. Find
$m \angle DEG$ and $m \angle GEF$.

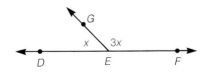

▲6. $m \angle TRS = 90°$. Find
$m \angle TRU$ and $m \angle URS$.

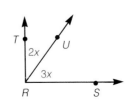

Just as every segment has a midpoint that bisects the segment, for every nonstraight angle there is a ray that bisects the angle.

<u>DEFINITION</u>

Given point D in the interior of $\angle ABC$, $\overrightarrow{BD}$ is a **bisector** of $\angle ABC$ whenever $m \angle ABD = m \angle DBC$ (or, $m \angle ABD = m \angle DBC = \frac{1}{2}m \angle (ABC)$.

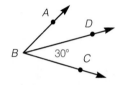

Examples   In each figure, $\overrightarrow{BD}$ is an angle bisector of $\angle ABC$.

7. Find $m \angle ABC$.

$m \angle ABC = 2m \angle DBC$
$= 2 \times 30°$
$= 60°$

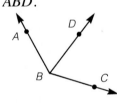

8. $m \angle ABC = 136°$. Find $m \angle DBC$ and $m \angle ABD$.

$m \angle DBC = \angle ABD = \frac{1}{2}m \angle ABC$

$= \frac{1}{2} \times 136°$

$= 68°$

▲9. $m \angle ABC = 7x + 10$ and $m \angle DBC = 3x + 15$. Find $m \angle ABC$, $m \angle DBC$, and $m \angle ABD$.

$m \angle ABC = m \angle ABD + m \angle DBC$
$= 2 \cdot m \angle DBC$

Thus,

$$\overbrace{7x + 10}^{m \angle ABC} = \overbrace{2(3x + 15)}^{m \angle DBC}$$
$$= 6x + 30$$
$$x = 20$$

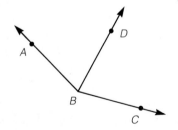

Hence, $m \angle ABC = (7 \cdot 20 + 10)° = 150°$

and, $m \angle ABD = m \angle DBC = \frac{1}{2}(150°) = 75°$

Exercises

▲ **Use the figures to complete these statements.**

1. $m \angle AFC + m \angle CFE =$ _____
2. $m \angle ACB + m \angle ACF =$ _____
3. $m \angle EFC + m \angle CFA =$ _____
4. $m \angle FCB + m \angle DCF =$ _____
5. $m \angle DCB - m \angle BCA =$ _____
6. $m \angle ACE - m \angle FCE =$ _____
7. $m \angle GPH + m \angle HPK =$ _____
8. $m \angle OPH + m \angle HPK =$ _____
9. $m \angle NPL - m \angle NPM =$ _____
10. $m \angle OPK - m \angle OPH =$ _____

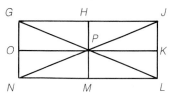

11. Find $m \angle PQR$. 12. Find $m \angle DEF$. 13. $\angle ABC$ is a straight angle. Find $m \angle ABD$.

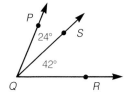 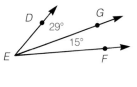 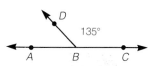

In each figure, $\overrightarrow{BD}$ is an angle bisector of $\angle ABC$.

14. Find $m \angle ABC$.

15. $m \angle ABC = 174°$. Find $m \angle DBC$ and $m \angle ABD$.

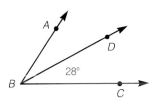

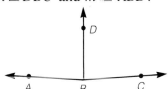

► Extension Exercises

▲16. $m \angle DEF = 90°$. Find $m \angle DEG$ and $m \angle GEF$.

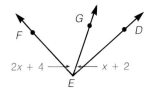

▲17. $m \angle DBF = 80°$. Find $m \angle ABC$.

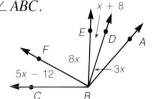

7   Bisecting and Copying Angles

After finishing Section 7, you should be able to
▲   *bisect an angle using compass and straightedge.*
▲▲   *copy a given angle using compass and straightedge.*

▲   Bisecting an Angle

In Chapter 1 we learned how to bisect a segment using a straightedge and compass. These tools can also be used to bisect angles.

Example   1. Use a straightedge and compass to bisect ∠ A.

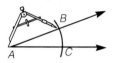 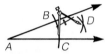 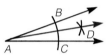

Step 1

Place the compass point on *A* and draw an arc, locating points *B* and *C*.

Step 2

Place the compass point on *B* and draw an arc. With the same compass setting, place the compass point on *C* and draw an arc, locating point *D*.

Step 3

Draw a ray, $\overrightarrow{AD}$, which is the angle bisector of ∠*A*.

Try This...   1. Draw a nonstraight angle. Use a compass and straightedge to bisect the angle.

       2. Draw a triangle and bisect each of its angles.

▲▲ Copying an Angle

When we copy an angle, we draw an angle that has the same measure as that of the given angle.

Example   2. Use a compass and straightedge to copy ∠*A*.

Step 1
Place the compass point on *A* and draw an arc, locating points *B* and *C*.

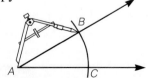

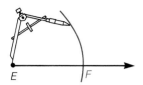

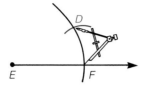

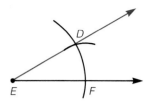

Step 2
Draw a ray with
endpoint E. Place
the compass point
on E. With the same
compass setting as in
Step 1, draw an arc,
locating point F.

Step 3
Place the compass
point on B and set the
opening so the pencil is
at C. With this setting,
place the compass
point on F and draw an
arc, locating point D.

Step 4
Draw a ray, $\overrightarrow{ED}$.
$\angle DEF$ has the same
measure as $\angle CAB$.

Try This...   3. Draw a nonstraight angle and copy it, using a compass and
straightedge.

By copying angles, we can find new angles with different measures.

Example   3. Given angles with measures a and b, and $a > b$, construct
angles with measures $(a + b)$ and $(a - b)$.

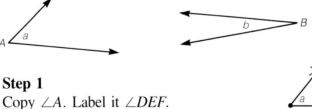

Step 1
Copy $\angle A$. Label it $\angle DEF$.

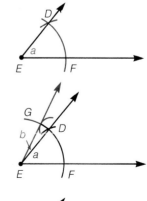

Step 2
Copy $\angle B$. Use one ray
of $\angle DEF$ as a common
side of both angles.
Label this $\angle GED$.

$\angle GEF$ has measure $(a + b)$.

Step 3
Again copy $\angle A$. Label it $\angle DEF$.

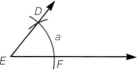

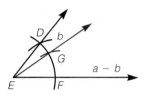

Step 4

Now copy $\angle B$. Use one ray of $\angle DEF$ as a common side of both angles and draw the other ray in the interior of $\angle DEF$. Label this $\angle DEG$.

$\angle GEF$ has measure $(a - b)$.

Note that bisecting a given angle is the same as constructing two angles with half the measure of the given angle.

Try This. ... Given angles with measures a and b, construct angles with these measures.

4. $a - b$
5. $2b$
6. $\frac{1}{2}a$

Exercises

▲ **Use a straightedge and compass to copy and bisect each angle.**

1.

2.

3.

4.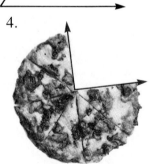

5.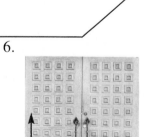

6.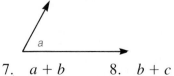

Given angles with measures a, b, and c, use a straightedge and compass to construct angles with these measures.

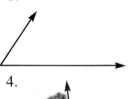   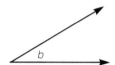

7. $a + b$ 8. $b + c$ 9. $c - b$ 10. $a - b$ 11. $2a$
12. $2b$ 13. $\frac{1}{2}c$ 14. $\frac{1}{2}a$ 15. $2a - b$ 16. $a + 2b$

8 | Complementary, Supplementary, and Adjacent Angles

After finishing Section 8, you should be able to
▲ *identify complementary angles and find the measure of a complement of a given angle.*
▲▲ *identify supplementary angles and find the measure of a supplement of a given angle.*
▲ *identify adjacent angles and linear pairs of angles.*
▲▲

▲ Complementary Angles

$\angle 1$ and $\angle 2$ are complementary angles.

$$m \angle 1 + m \angle 2 = 90°$$
$$45° + 45° = 90°$$

DEFINITION

Two angles are **complementary** whenever the sum of their measures is 90°. Each angle is called a *complement* of the other.

Example   1. Identify each pair of complementary angles.

$\angle 1$ and $\angle 2$
(because $25° + 65° = 90°$)
$\angle 1$ and $\angle 4$
$\angle 2$ and $\angle 3$
$\angle 3$ and $\angle 4$

Try This....   1. Identify each pair of complementary angles.

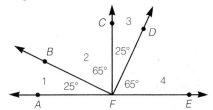

Example   2. Find the measure of a complement of an angle of 29°.

$90° - 29° = 61°$.
Thus, the measure of a complement is 61°.

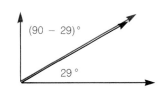

Try This...   Find the measures of complements of these angles.

2.   3.   4.

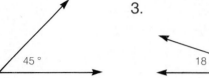      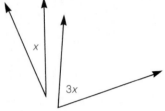

Example   ▲3. The measure of an angle is three times the measure of its complement. Find the measures of the angles.

Let the measure of the smaller angle be x. Then the measure of the larger angle is $3x$.

Because the angles are complementary, the sum of their measures is 90°.

$$x + 3x = 90$$
$$4x = 90$$
$$x = 22.5$$

Thus, the angles measure 22.5° and 3 × 22.5°, or 67.5°.

Try This...   ▲5. The measure of an angle is four times the measure of its complement. Find the measures of the angles.

Theorem 2.5 follows from the definitions and postulates in both Sections 5 and 6.

| THEOREM | If two angles are complementary, then they are acute angles. |
| 2.5 | |

▲▲ Supplementary Angles

∠1 and ∠2 are supplementary angles.

$$m \angle 1 + m \angle 2 = 180°$$
$$155° + 25° = 180°$$

DEFINITION

Two angles are **supplementary** whenever the sum of their measures is 180°. Each angle is called a *supplement* of the other.

Examples   4. Identify each pair of supplementary angles.

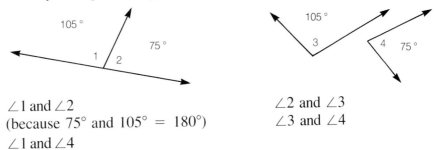

∠1 and ∠2
(because 75° and 105° = 180°)
∠1 and ∠4

∠2 and ∠3
∠3 and ∠4

5. Find the measure of a supplement of an angle of 112°.

180° − 112° = 68°.

Thus, the measure of a supplement is 68°.

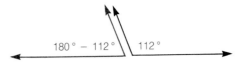

Try This...   6. Identify each pair of supplementary angles in the figure.

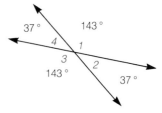

7. Find the measure of a supplement of an angle with this measure.

    a.   38°   b.   157°   c.   90°

Example   ▲6. The measure of an angle is 20° less than the measure of a supplement. Find the measures of the two angles.

Let x be the measure of the larger angle. Then the measure of a supplement is $x - 20$. Because the angles are supplementary,

$$x + (x - 20) = 180$$
$$2x - 20 = 180$$
$$2x = 200$$
$$x = 100$$

Thus, the angles measure 100° and (100 − 20)°, or 80°.

Adjacent Angles and Linear Pairs

In each drawing, $\angle ADB$ and $\angle BDC$
are *adjacent angles*.

 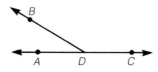

DEFINITION

> Two **angles are adjacent** whenever they have a common side and
> their interiors do not intersect.

Two adjacent angles that are supplementary are called a *linear pair*.

DEFINITION

> Two angles form a **linear pair** whenever they are adjacent and their
> noncommon sides are opposite rays.

Examples   Identify the adjacent angles. Tell which angles form a linear pair.

7.  $\angle 1$ and $\angle 2$ are adjacent and form a linear pair.

8. 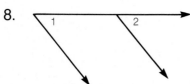 $\angle 1$ and $\angle 2$ have no common side. Their interiors also intersect. They are not adjacent and do not form a linear pair.

9. $\angle 1$ and $\angle 2$ are adjacent angles, but they do not form a linear pair.

10. 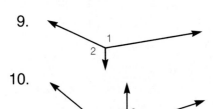 $\angle 1$ and $\angle 2$ are not adjacent because they do not have a common side. They do not form a linear pair.

Try This...   Identify the adjacent angles and tell which pairs of adjacent angles form linear pairs.

8.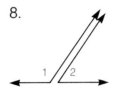

9.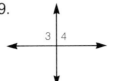

10.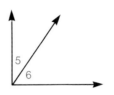

11.

The theorems below follow from the definitions and the postulates in this chapter.

THEOREM 2.6	If two angles form a linear pair, then they are supplementary.	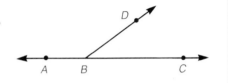

THEOREM 2.7	If two angles form a linear pair and have the same measure, then each is a right angle.

Exercises

▲   **Identify each pair of complementary angles.**

1.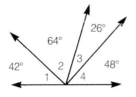

2.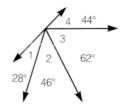

Find the measures of complements of angles with these measures.

3. $22°$ 4. $45°$ 5. $85°$ 6. $76°$ ▲7. t

▲8. s ▲9. $90 - n$ ▲10. $42 + y$ ▲11. $x + y$ ▲12. $p + q$

▲13. The measure of an angle is twice the measure of a complement. Find the measures of the two angles.

▲14. The measure of an angle is 15° less than the measure of a complement. Find the measures of the two angles.

▲▲ **Identify each pair of supplementary angles.**

15.

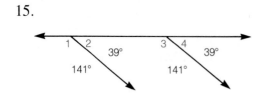

16.

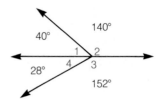

Find the measures of supplements of angles with these measures.

17. 119° 18. 114° 19. 143° 20. 157° 21. 74°

22. 59° ▲23. y ▲24. x ▲25. $a + b$ ▲26. $r + t$

▲27. The measure of an angle is 18° less than the measure of a supplement. Find the measures of the two angles.

▲28. The measure of an angle is three times the measure of a supplement. Find the measures of the two angles.

▲▲▲ **Identify all pairs of adjacent angles and linear pairs.**

29. *A-B-C*

30. *A-B-C* and *D-B-E*

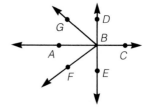

▶ Extension Exercises

Which definitions, postulates, or theorems explain these statements?

31. $m \angle ABD + m \angle DBC = 180°$.

32. $\angle BEH$ and $\angle FEH$ form a linear pair.

33. $\angle GEB$ and $\angle FEG$ are supplementary.

▲34. If $m \angle ABD = m \angle GEF$, then $m \angle ABE = \angle GEB$.

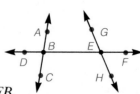

**In the drawing, *m* ∠ *AEB* = 57°, *m* ∠ *BEC* = 42°,
and *m* ∠ *CED* = 33°.**

35. Which postulate explains the conclusion that *m* ∠ *AEC* = 99°?

36. Which angles are complementary?

37. Name four acute angles.

38. Name two obtuse angles.

39. Name two pairs of adjacent angles.

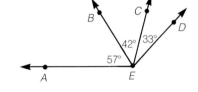

40. Two complementary angles have the same measure.
     What is the measure of each angle?

41. *m* ∠ *AEC* = *m* ∠ *BED*. What other angles
     have the same measure?

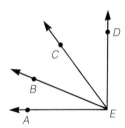

42. What can be concluded about the measure of a
     supplement of an acute angle?

43. ∠ *ABC* and ∠ *ADB* are right angles. Then *m* ∠ *ABD*
     is equal to the measure of which other angle?

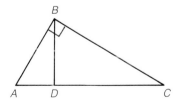

44. What is the difference between the
     measures of a supplement and a
     complement of an angle?

▶◀ Activity

Fold a square piece of paper in half. Unfold the square and label the endpoints of the fold *A* and *B*.

Now fold the square in half the other way. Unfold the paper and label the endpoints of this fold *C* and *D*.

Label the intersection of $\overline{AB}$ and $\overline{CD}$, *E*.

What is the measure of ∠ *DEB*?
What is the measure of ∠ *BEC*?
What can you conclude about ∠ *DEB* and ∠ *BEC*?

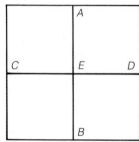

Now fold the square along a diagonal. Unfold the paper and label the endpoints of this fold *F* and *G*.

What is the measure of ∠ *DEG*?
What is the measure of ∠ *GEB*?
What can you conclude about ∠ *DEB* and ∠ *GEB*?

What can you conclude about $\overline{EG}$?

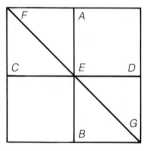

▶◀ Activity

On his way home from school, Benito needs to buy tickets for the local rodeo. Stores *A,B,C,D,* and *E* all sell tickets. At which store should he stop to make his trip as short as possible? (Measure the length in centimeters of each route.)

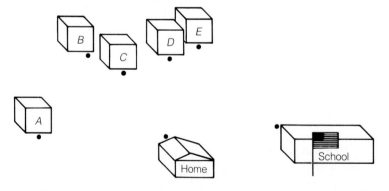

Calculator Application   Finding Coordinates

Use a calculator to find *c*, the coordinate of *C*. The coordinate of *C* is a positive number.

Example

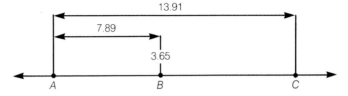

Find *BC* and add it to *b*, the coordinate of *B*.

$$BC = AC - AB$$
$$c = BC + b$$
$$c = (AC - AB) + b$$

Enter: 13.91 $\boxed{-}$ 7.89 $\boxed{+}$ 3.65 $\boxed{=}$

Display: 9.67

c = 9.67.

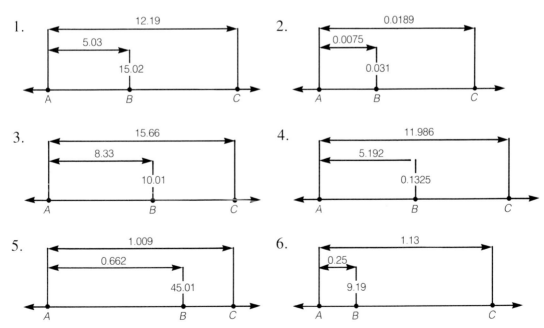

Chapter Review

 Use this number line for Exercises 1-3.

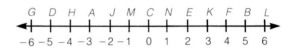

1. Name the coordinates of *A, B,* and *C.*

2. Name the points having coordinates −5 and 6.

3. Find the distances *DE, KJ,* and *GA.*

4. Let the coordinates of *P* and *Q* be *p* and *q,* respectively. Find the coordinate *q* if *PQ* = 8 and *p* = 3.

 5. Change −70°C to Kelvin.

6. *A, B,* and *C* are collinear. *AB* = 7, *BC* = 18, and *AC* = 11. Which point is between the other two?

7. Find the coordinate of the midpoint of $\overline{AB}$.

 Use the figure for Exercises 8 and 9.

8. Name three segments.

9. Name each angle in as many different ways as possible. Identify the vertex and sides of each angle.

10. Use a protractor to measure this angle.

11. Use a protractor to draw an angle with measure 125°.

12. $m \angle DEF = 70°$ and $m \angle CEF = 22°$. Find $m \angle DEC$.

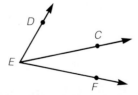

▲13. $m \angle ABC = 126°$. Find $m \angle ABD$ and $m \angle DBC$.

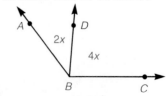

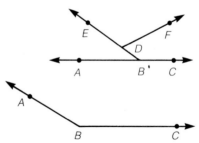

14. Given angles with measures a and b, use a straightedge and compass to construct an angle with measure $b - a$.

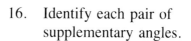
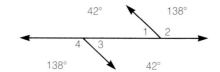

15. Identify each pair of complementary angles.

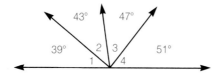

16. Identify each pair of supplementary angles.

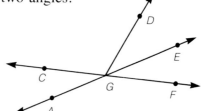

17. The measure of an angle is four times the measure of a supplement. Find the measures of the two angles.

18. Name two linear pairs of angles. Assume A-G-E and C-G-F.

Chapter Test

Use this number line for Exercises 1-3.

1. Name the coordinate of J.
2. Name the point having coordinate 4.
3. Find the distance KC.
4. Let the coordinates of A and B be a and b, respectively. Find the coordinate b if $AB = 7$, $a = 3$ and $b < 0$.
5. Change $-20°C$ to Kelvin.
6. P, Q, and R are collinear. If $RP = 12$, $PQ = 21$, and $QR = 9$, which point is between the other two?
7. Find the coordinate of the midpoint of $\overline{AB}$.

8. Name three segments shown in the drawing.

9. Name an obtuse angle, an acute angle, and a straight angle shown in the drawing.

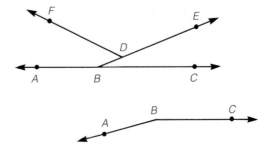

10. Use a protractor to measure this angle.

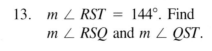

11. Use a protractor to draw an angle with measure 35°.

12. $m \angle ABC = 105°$ and $m \angle DBC = 32°$. Find $m \angle ABD$.

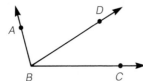

13. $m \angle RST = 144°$. Find $m \angle RSQ$ and $m \angle QST$.

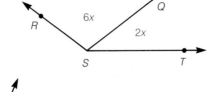

14. Given angles with measures a and b, use a straightedge and compass to construct an angle with measure $2a - b$.

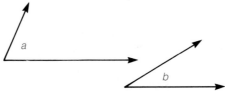

15. Identify each pair of complementary angles.

16. Identify each pair of supplementary angles.

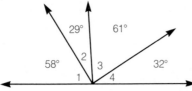

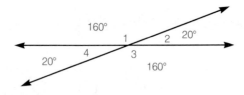

▲17. The measure of an angle is 15° less than twice the measure of a supplement. Find the measures of the two angles.

18. Name two linear pairs of angles. Assume *A-B-C*.

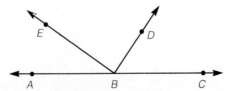

Skills Review				Addition

Add.

1.
$$\begin{array}{r} 47 \\ +69 \\ \hline \end{array}$$
2.
$$\begin{array}{r} 48 \\ +\ 5 \\ \hline \end{array}$$
3.
$$\begin{array}{r} 647 \\ +292 \\ \hline \end{array}$$
4.
$$\begin{array}{r} 843 \\ +\ 76 \\ \hline \end{array}$$

5.
$$\begin{array}{r} 9.8 \\ +6.7 \\ \hline \end{array}$$
6.
$$\begin{array}{r} 6.7 \\ +\ 0.8 \\ \hline \end{array}$$
7.
$$\begin{array}{r} 0.66 \\ +7.7 \\ \hline \end{array}$$
8.
$$\begin{array}{r} 8.94 \\ +0.47 \\ \hline \end{array}$$

9.
$$\begin{array}{r} 743 \\ +682 \\ \hline \end{array}$$
10.
$$\begin{array}{r} 579 \\ +78 \\ \hline \end{array}$$
11.
$$\begin{array}{r} 894 \\ +147 \\ \hline \end{array}$$
12.
$$\begin{array}{r} 137 \\ +979 \\ \hline \end{array}$$

13.
$$\begin{array}{r} \$4.98 \\ +3.71 \\ \hline \end{array}$$
14.
$$\begin{array}{r} \$7.90 \\ +6.82 \\ \hline \end{array}$$
15.
$$\begin{array}{r} \$8.73 \\ +5.69 \\ \hline \end{array}$$
16.
$$\begin{array}{r} \$0.89 \\ +6.29 \\ \hline \end{array}$$

17.
$$\begin{array}{r} 4,827 \\ +6,973 \\ \hline \end{array}$$
18.
$$\begin{array}{r} 6,324 \\ +3,816 \\ \hline \end{array}$$
19.
$$\begin{array}{r} 1,827 \\ +9,043 \\ \hline \end{array}$$
20.
$$\begin{array}{r} 67,892 \\ +43,215 \\ \hline \end{array}$$

21.
$$\begin{array}{r} 8.937 \\ +5.74 \\ \hline \end{array}$$
22.
$$\begin{array}{r} 29.863 \\ +80.18 \\ \hline \end{array}$$
23.
$$\begin{array}{r} 0.9 \\ +2.687 \\ \hline \end{array}$$
24.
$$\begin{array}{r} 63.482 \\ +19.689 \\ \hline \end{array}$$

25.
$$\begin{array}{r} 9,627 \\ 4,873 \\ +5,896 \\ \hline \end{array}$$
26.
$$\begin{array}{r} 46,274 \\ 90,296 \\ +57,851 \\ \hline \end{array}$$
27.
$$\begin{array}{r} 782,943 \\ 18,091 \\ +894,267 \\ \hline \end{array}$$
28.
$$\begin{array}{r} 78,257 \\ 115,587 \\ +\ 1,399 \\ \hline \end{array}$$

29.
$$\begin{array}{r} 8.273 \\ 0.08 \\ +2.5379 \\ \hline \end{array}$$
30.
$$\begin{array}{r} 7.64 \\ 8.9 \\ +4.764 \\ \hline \end{array}$$
31.
$$\begin{array}{r} 89.24 \\ 5.29 \\ +\ 6.2 \\ \hline \end{array}$$
32.
$$\begin{array}{r} 368.2 \\ 5.34 \\ +18.592 \\ \hline \end{array}$$

33. $976 + 22 + 80$

34. $720 + 7 + 611$

35. $878 + 17 + 1,004$

36. $\$15.38 + \$1.01 + \$0.03$

37. $\$84.73 + \$94.62 + \$7.15$

38. $\$14.87 + \$0.04 + \$101.00$

39. $2.65 + 0.093 + 38.1$

40. $0.3 + 30.2 + 5.11 + 0.456$

3 Congruence and Angles

1 Congruent Angles and Segments

After finishing Section 1, you should be able to
▲ *identify congruent segments.*
▲▲ *identify congruent angles.*

Congruent figures have the same size and shape.
They fit together exactly.

▲ Congruent Segments

DEFINITION
_____

Two segments are congruent whenever they have the same length.

Find some congruent segments in this photograph.

Example   1. Use a ruler to show that $\overline{PQ}$ and $\overline{RS}$ are congruent.

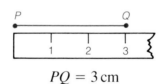

$PQ = 3\,\text{cm}$ $RS = 3\,\text{cm}$

Because $PQ = RS = 3$ cm, $\overline{PQ}$ and $\overline{RS}$ are congruent. To say that $\overline{PQ}$ and $\overline{RS}$ are congruent, we write
$$\overline{PQ} \cong \overline{RS}$$
To mean "not congruent," we write ≇ .

We can also use a compass to show that segments are congruent. Place the compass points on the endpoints of a segment. Then compare the opening with the other segment.

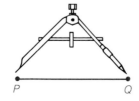
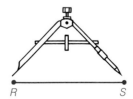

Example   2. Which pairs of segments are congruent? Use a compass.

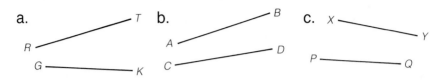

a.   b.   c.

$$\overline{AB} \cong \overline{CD} \text{ and } \overline{PQ} \cong \overline{XY}$$

Try This...   Which pairs of segments are congruent? Use a ruler or compass.

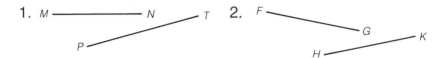

1.   2.

▲▲ Congruent Angles

___DEFINITION___

Two angles are congruent whenever they have the same measure.

Find some congruent angles formed in the photograph at the left.

Example   3. Use a protractor to show that $\angle P$ and $\angle Q$ are congruent.

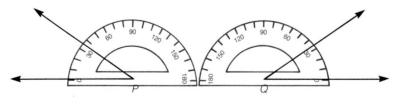

Because $m \angle P = m \angle Q = 34°$, $\angle P$ and $\angle Q$ are congruent. To say that $\angle P$ and $\angle Q$ are congruent, we write

$$\angle P \cong \angle Q$$

$m \angle P = m \angle Q$ is a statement about numbers. It says that the measures of $\angle P$ and $\angle Q$ are the same number.

$\angle P \cong \angle Q$ is a statement about two geometric figures.

$\angle ABC \cong \angle PQR$ says that $\angle ABC$ and $\angle PQR$ have the same measure.

Remember that angles and segments are sets of points, but their measures are numbers.

Example   4. Which pairs of angles are congruent? Use a protactor.

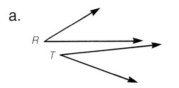

a.

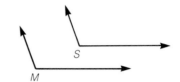

b.

$\angle M \cong \angle S$ because $m \angle M = m \angle S = 110°$.

Try This...   Which pairs of angles are congruent? Use a protractor.

3.

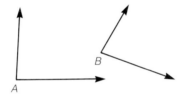

4.

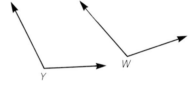

1. Use a protractor. Draw $\angle P$ and $\angle Q$, each with a measure of 36°.
2. Draw a complement of $\angle P$ and a complement of $\angle Q$.
3. Compare the measures of the two complements.
4. Draw a supplement of $\angle P$ and a supplement of $\angle Q$.
5. Compare the measures of the two supplements.

This drawing exercise suggest the following theorems.

THEOREM   If two angles are congruent, then their supplements are congruent.
3.1

THEOREM 3.2	If two angles are congruent, then their complements are congruent.

Exercises

▲ **Which pairs of segments are congruent? Use a ruler or compass.**

1. 2. 3. 4.

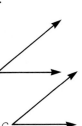

▲▲ **Which pairs of angles are congruent? Use a protractor.**

5. 6. 7. 8.

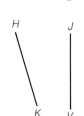 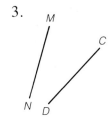 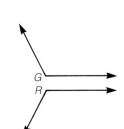 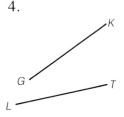 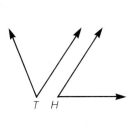

▶ Extension Exercises

9. $\angle A \cong \angle C$ and $m \angle A = 48°$. What is $m \angle C$?

10. $\overline{AB} \cong \overline{XY}$ and $AB = 15$ cm. What is the measure of XY?

11. $RS = 9$ cm and $TV = 9$ cm. $\overline{RS}$ is congruent to what segment?

12. If $m \angle B = 54°$ and $m \angle G = 54°$, then $\angle B \cong$ _____ .

13. If $\angle R \cong \angle T$ and $\angle T \cong \angle S$, then $\angle R \cong$ _____ .

14. If $\overline{AB} \cong \overline{CD}$ and $\overline{CD} \cong \overline{HK}$, then $\overline{AB} \cong$ _____ .

15. Explain the difference between the statements "$m \angle ABC = m \angle STR$" and "$\angle ABC \cong \angle STR$."

16. Explain the difference between the statements "$AB = CD$" and "$\overline{AB} \cong \overline{CD}$."

17. If $\angle A$ and $\angle B$ are complements and $m \angle A = 36°$, then what is $m \angle B$?

18. If $\angle P$ and $\angle Q$ are supplements and $m \angle P = 84°$, then what is $m \angle Q$?

19. If $\angle A \cong \angle B$ and $m \angle A = 63°$, then the measure of a complement of $\angle B =$ _____ .

20. If $\angle P \cong \angle Q$ and $m \angle P = 108°$, then the measure of a supplement of $\angle Q =$ _____ .

▶▶ Challenge Exercises

21. Suppose an angle is congruent to a supplement. Explain why the angle must be a right angle.

22. Suppose an angle is congruent to a complement. Explain why the angle has a measure of 45°.

▶◀ Activity

A billiard ball bounces off the sides of a billiard table at the same angle at which it arrives.

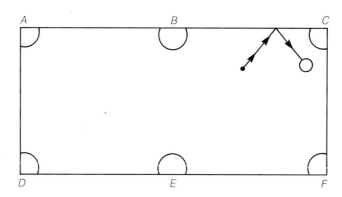

Into which pocket will the billiard ball fall?
(Use your protractor and straightedge to help you.)

2   Vertical Angles

After finishing Section 2, you should be able to
▲   *use the Vertical Angle Theorem to find measures of angles.*

When $\overleftrightarrow{RT}$ intersects $\overleftrightarrow{SQ}$ at P, four angles are formed: $\angle SPT$, $\angle RPQ$, $\angle SPR$, and $\angle QPT$.

Pairs of angles such as $\angle RPQ$ and $\angle SPT$ are called *vertical angles*.

Name another pair of vertical angles in the drawing.

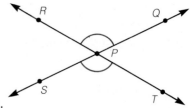

DEFINITION

Two non-straight angles are **vertical angles** whenever their sides form two pairs of opposite rays.

Find some pairs of vertical angles in this picture.

1. Draw four pairs of vertical angles.

2. Use a protractor to measure each pair of vertical angles.

3. Compare the measures of the angles of each pair.

THEOREM	*The Vertical Angle Theorem*
3.3	Vertical angles are congruent.

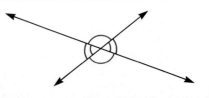

Examples

1. In the power line tower, $m \angle 1 = 124°$ and $m \angle 2 = 56°$.
   Find $m \angle 3$.

   $\angle 1$ and $\angle 3$ are vertical angles, so $m \angle 1 = m \angle 3$.
   Thus, $m \angle 3 = 124°$.

2. Find $m \angle APC$, $m \angle APD$, and $m \angle CPB$.

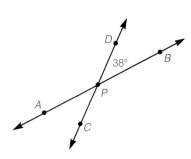

   $\angle APC$ and $\angle DPB$ are vertical angles.
   Thus, $m \angle APC = m \angle DPB$ and $m \angle APC = 38°$.

   Because $\angle APD$ and $\angle DPB$ are supplementary, we
   know that $m \angle APD + m \angle DPB = 180°$. Thus,
   $$m \angle APD = 180 - m \angle DPB$$
   $$= 180 - 38$$
   $$= 142°$$

   It then follows that $m \angle CPB = 142°$.

Try This... 1. In the fence, $m \angle 1 = 98°$
   and $m \angle 2 = 82°$.
   Find $m \angle 3$ and $m \angle 4$.

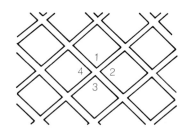

Example 3. In the drawing, $m \angle 1 = 23°$ and $m \angle 3 = 34°$.
   Find $m \angle 2$, $m \angle 4$, $m \angle 5$, and $m \angle 6$.

   Because $\angle 1$ and $\angle 4$ are vertical angles, $m \angle 4 = 23°$.
   Likewise, $\angle 3$ and $\angle 6$ are vertical angles, so $m \angle 6 = 34°$.

   $$m \angle 1 + m \angle 2 + m \angle 3 = 180$$
   $$23 + m \angle 2 + 34 = 180 \qquad \text{Substituting}$$
   $$m \angle 2 + 57 = 180$$
   $$m \angle 2 = 180 - 57$$
   $$m \angle 2 = 123°$$

   Because $\angle 2$ and $\angle 5$ are vertical angles, $m \angle 5 = 123°$.

Try This...   2. In the drawing, $m \angle 2 = 41°$ and $m \angle 4 = 10°$.

Find $m \angle 1$, $m \angle 3$, $m \angle 5$, and $m \angle 6$.

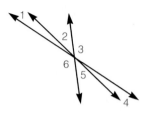

Example ▲4. Find $m \angle ABC$ and $m \angle DBE$.

Because $\angle ABC$ and $\angle DBE$ are vertical angles, $m \angle ABC = m \angle DBE$. Thus:

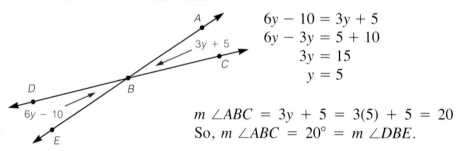

$$6y - 10 = 3y + 5$$
$$6y - 3y = 5 + 10$$
$$3y = 15$$
$$y = 5$$

$m \angle ABC = 3y + 5 = 3(5) + 5 = 20$
So, $m \angle ABC = 20° = m \angle DBE$.

Try This... ▲3. Find $m \angle PQR$ and $m \angle TQS$.

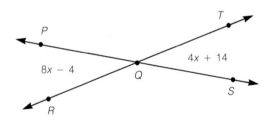

Exercises

▲ **Find the measures of the indicated angles.**

1. $m \angle 2$ and $m \angle 3$

2. $m \angle 1$ and $m \angle 2$

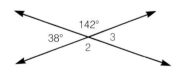

3. $m \angle 1, m \angle 2, m \angle 3,$ and $m \angle 4$

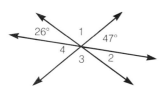

4. $m \angle 1, m \angle 2, m \angle 3,$ and $m \angle 4$

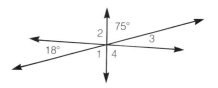

▲ 5. $m \angle PQR$ and $m \angle TQS$

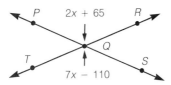

▲6. $m \angle ABC$ and $m \angle DBE$

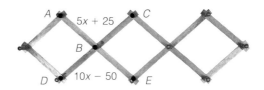

▲7. $m \angle TQS$ and $m \angle GQR$

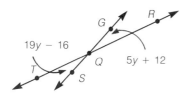

▲8. $m \angle VPS$ and $m \angle QPR$

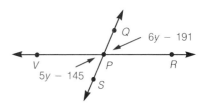

▲ 9. $m \angle ABC$ and $m \angle DBF$

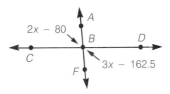

▲ 10. The photograph shows some vertical angles. Find $m \angle RST$ and $m \angle VSQ$.

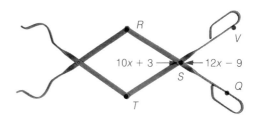

▶ Extension Exercises

11. Suppose $\angle 2 \cong \angle 3$. What can you conclude about $\angle 4$ and $\angle 1$? Explain how you know.

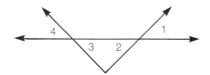

12. Suppose $\angle 1$ is a right angle. What can you conclude about $\angle 2, \angle 3,$ and $\angle 4$? Explain how you know.

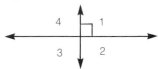

►► Challenge Exercises

13. Suppose two angles are both supplementary and vertical. Explain why both angles are right angles.

14. Suppose two angles are both complementary and vertical. Explain why each angle has a measure of 45°.

►◄ Activity

Estimate the length of $\overline{MT}$ in centimeters.
Estimate the length of $\overline{AH}$ in centimeters.
Which do you think is longer, $\overline{MT}$ or $\overline{AH}$?

Measure MT and AH with a ruler. How close were your estimates?
Which is longer, MT or AH?

Choose the appropriate metric unit of measure and then estimate the width of a paper clip, the length of your classroom, and the distance from your home to school. Measure and compare your answers.

Now estimate the length in centimeters around each of these figures.

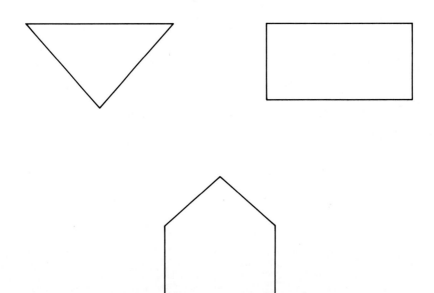

3 Perpendicular Lines

After finishing Section 3, you should be able to
▲   *identify perpendicular lines.*
▲▲   *identify perpendicular segments and rays.*

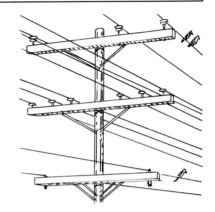

▲ Identifying Perpendiculars

The crosspieces and the telephone pole suggest
perpendicular lines.

DEFINITION

Two lines are perpendicular whenever they intersect to form a
right angle.

To say that $\overleftrightarrow{AB}$ is perpendicular to $\overleftrightarrow{RS}$, we write
$$\overleftrightarrow{AB} \perp \overleftrightarrow{RS}$$

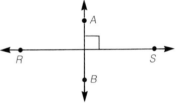

Example   1. Which pairs of lines are perpendicular? Use a protractor.

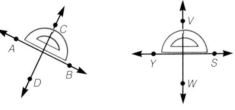

$$\overleftrightarrow{AB} \perp \overleftrightarrow{CD} \text{ and } \overleftrightarrow{VW} \perp \overleftrightarrow{YS}.$$

To say that $\overleftrightarrow{PQ}$ is not perpendicular to $\overleftrightarrow{TR}$, we write
$$\overleftrightarrow{PQ} \not\perp \overleftrightarrow{TR}$$

Try This...   1. Which pairs of lines are perpendicular? Use a protractor.

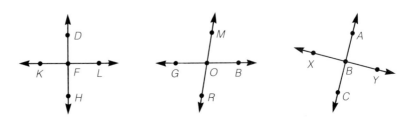

When two lines intersect and are perpendicular, one right angle is formed. What are the measures of the other three angles that are formed?

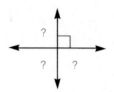

THEOREM **3.4**   If two lines intersect to form one right angle, then they form four right angles.

Proof   Suppose $\ell_1 \perp \ell_2$. Then they form a right angle. Suppose it is $\angle 1$.

Because $\angle 3$ and $\angle 1$ are vertical angles, $\angle 3 \cong \angle 1$. Thus, $m \angle 3 = m \angle 1$ and $m \angle 3 = 90°$.

Because $\angle 4$ and $\angle 1$ form a linear pair, they are supplementary. Hence, $m \angle 4 + m \angle 1 = 180°$.

Because $m \angle 1 = 90°$, then $m \angle 4 = 90°$. Thus, $\angle 4$ is a right angle.

Finally, $\angle 4 \cong \angle 2$ because they are vertical angles. This means that $\angle 2$ is a right angle.

▲▲ Perpendicular Segments and Rays

DEFINITION
_____

Rays and segments are perpendicular whenever they are contained in perpendicular lines.

Example   2. Which pairs of figures are perpendicular? Use a straightedge and a drawing triangle.

$\overline{TR} \perp \overline{MN}$

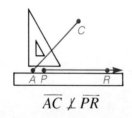

$\overline{AC} \not\perp \overline{PR}$

$\overline{GK} \perp \overline{AF}$

Try This... 2. Which pairs of figures are perpendicular? Use a straightedge and a drawing triangle.

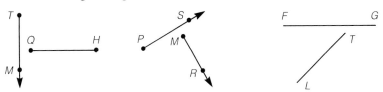

1. Draw a line, $\overleftrightarrow{PQ}$.
2. Choose a point T on $\overleftrightarrow{PQ}$. Use a ruler and drawing triangle. Draw a line perpendicular to $\overleftrightarrow{PQ}$ at T.
3. Try to draw a different line perpendicular to $\overleftrightarrow{PQ}$ at T. Is it possible?

A very important idea concerning perpendiculars is summarized in this theorem:

THEOREM
3.5

If a line ℓ is in a plane and A is any point on ℓ, then there is exactly one line in the plane that is perpendicular to ℓ at A.

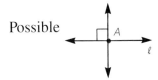

Possible

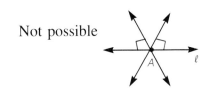

Not possible

Exercises

▲ **Which pairs of lines are perpendicular? Use a protractor.**

1.

2.

3.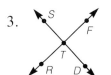

4.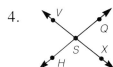

▲▲ **Which pairs of figures are perpendicular?
Use a straightedge and drawing triangle.**

5.

6.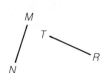

7.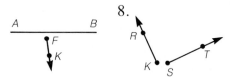

8.

► **Extension Exercises**

Find the measure of each angle.

9.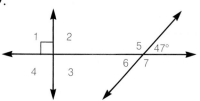

10.

11. Make drawings that illustrate the following.

   a. $\overleftrightarrow{AB} \perp \overline{CD}$ b. $\overrightarrow{RS} \perp \overline{GK}$
   c. $\overleftrightarrow{MN} \perp \overline{TV}$ d. $\overrightarrow{FL} \perp \overrightarrow{BD}$

12. Find some examples of perpendiculars in the physical world.

►► **Challenge Exercises**

13. Suppose two lines intersect to form congruent adjacent angles. What is
    the measure of each angle? Explain why the lines are perpendicular.

14. Suppose that at a point P on a line ℓ there are two different lines
    perpendicular to ℓ. Is this possible? Explain how you know.
    (Hint: Think of the Protractor Postulate.)

4 | Constructing Perpendiculars

After finishing Section 4, you should be able to
▲   *construct a perpendicular to a line from a point on the line,*
     using a compass and straightedge.
▲▲ *construct a perpendicular to a line from a point not on the*
     line, using a compass and straightedge.

▲   A Perpendicular from a Point on a Line

In Chapter 1, we drew perpendiculars using the drawing triangle.
Now, we will draw perpendiculars using a compass and straightedge.

Example   1. Consider point *P* on line *ℓ*. Construct a line perpendicular to *ℓ* at *P*.

Step 1

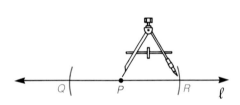

Place the compass
point on *P*. Using one
opening, draw arcs that
intersect *ℓ* at two points, *Q*
and *R*.

Step 2

Open the compass to about the length of $\overline{QR}$.
Place the point on *Q* and make an arc as shown.
Place the point on *R* and make another arc
so that the two arcs intersect at a point *S*.

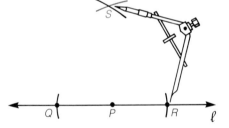

Step 3

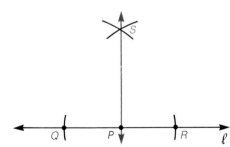

Use a straightedge to join
points *S* and *P*. $\overleftrightarrow{SP}$ is
perpendicular to *ℓ* at *P*.

Try This…   1. Draw a line, $\overleftrightarrow{BC}$. Choose a point *A* on $\overleftrightarrow{BC}$ and construct a line
               perpendicular to $\overleftrightarrow{BC}$ at *A*.

▲▲ A Perpendicular from a Point not on a Line

We can use a compass and straightedge to construct a perpendicular
from a point not on the line.

Example   2. Consider point P not on line ℓ. Construct a line perpendicular to ℓ
containing P.

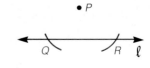

Step 1

Place the compass point on P.
Using one opening, draw arcs that
intersect ℓ at two points, Q and R.

Step 2

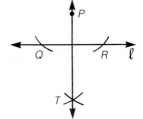

Open the compass to about the length of $\overline{QR}$. Place the point
on Q and make another arc as shown. Place the point on R
and make another arc so that the two arcs intersect in a point T.

Step 3

Use a straightedge to join points
T and P. $\overleftrightarrow{PT}$ is perpendicular to ℓ.

Try This...   2. Draw a line, $\overleftrightarrow{QR}$. Choose a point A not on $\overleftrightarrow{QR}$. Construct a line
containing A that is perpendicular to $\overleftrightarrow{QR}$.

►◄

Activity

Copy these triangles and use your straightedge to separate them by
drawing four straight lines.

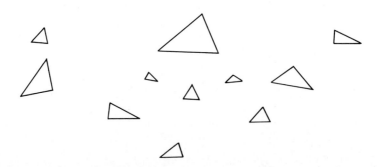

Exercises

▲ **Use a compass and straightedge for these exercises.**

1. Draw a line, $\overleftrightarrow{ST}$. Choose a point Q on $\overleftrightarrow{ST}$. Construct a line perpendicular to $\overleftrightarrow{ST}$ at Q.

2. Draw a line ℓ. Choose points R and P on ℓ. Construct perpendiculars to ℓ at R and P.

▲▲ **Use a compass and straightedge for the following.**

3. Draw a line, $\overleftrightarrow{AB}$. Choose a point C not on $\overleftrightarrow{AB}$. Construct a line containing C that is perpendicular to $\overleftrightarrow{AB}$.

4. Draw a line ℓ. Choose points X and Y not on ℓ. Construct lines containing X and Y that are perpendicular to ℓ.

▶◀ Activity

Fold a piece of paper in two. Label the endpoints of the fold R and S. Mark a point on the paper (not on $\overline{RS}$) and label it Q. Now join the edges of your fold to create a new fold that passes through Q. Unfold the paper.

What are the measures of the angles formed by the folded segments?

What can you conclude about the folded segment containing the point Q?

Try this activity again creating a new fold and marking a new point. Are your results the same?

Computer Application — Finding Supplementary Angles

BASIC (Beginner's All-purpose Symbolic Instruction Code) is a popular computer language that can be used to solve problems in mathematics. Many of the operation symbols in BASIC are similar to those in arithmetic.

ARITHMETIC	BASIC
+	+
−	−
×	*
÷	/
=	=

Find the supplement of an angle whose measure is greater than 0° and less than 180°.

Command	**Comments**
10 REM THIS PROGRAM FINDS SUPPLEMENTS	10 REM stands for "remark." This is not an instruction for the computer, but is an explanatory comment to make the program easier for the user to understand.
20 PRINT "ENTER AN ANGLE MEASURE."	
30 PRINT "IT SHOULD BE GREATER THAN 0 AND LESS THAN 180."	20 PRINT The computer prints everything between the quotation marks.
40 INPUT A	40 INPUT The computer accepts input from the user.
50 LET B = 180 − A	50 LET The computer assigns a value to the variable B.
60 PRINT "THE SUPPLEMENT OF "; A; "IS "; B	
70 PRINT "TO CONTINUE TYPE 1, TO STOP TYPE 0."	90 IF ... THEN The computer makes a decision based on information between the two commands.
80 INPUT C	
90 IF C = 1 THEN 20	
100 END	

Use the above program to find a supplement for each angle.

1. 37°   2. 153°   3. 16°   4. 13°   5. 137°

6. 115.7°   7. 90.5°   8. 48.6°   9. 103.9°   10. 163.8°

11. Write and run a program in BASIC that will find the complement of an angle whose measure is greater than 0° and less than 90°.

Chapter Review

❶ Which pairs of segments are congruent? Use a ruler or compass.

1. 2. 3. 4.

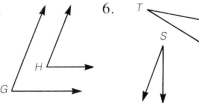

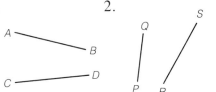

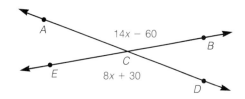

❷ Which pairs of angles are congruent? Use a protractor.

5. 6. 7. 8.

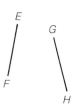

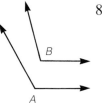

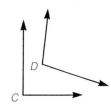

❸ 9. Find $m \angle 1$, $m \angle 2$, $m \angle 3$, and, $\angle 4$. **▲**10. Find $m \angle ACB$ and $m \angle ECD$.

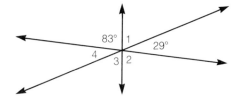

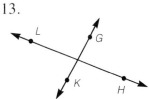

❹ Which pairs of lines are perpendicular? Use a protractor.

11. 12. 13.

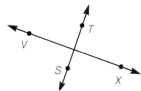

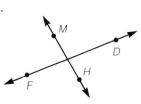

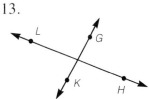

❺ 14. Use a compass and straightedge. Draw a line, $\overleftrightarrow{AB}$.
Choose a point D not on $\overleftrightarrow{AB}$.
Construct a line containing D that is
perpendicular to $\overleftrightarrow{AB}$.

Chapter Test

Which pairs of segments are congruent? Use a ruler or compass.

1.
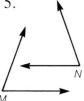

2.
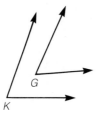

3.
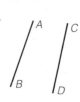

4.
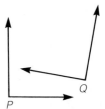

Which pairs of angles are congruent? Use a protractor.

5.
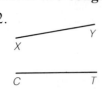

6.

7.
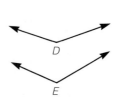

8.

9. Find $m \angle 1, m \angle 2, m \angle 3, m \angle 4.$

▲10. Find $m \angle RMP$ and $m \angle SMN.$

Which pairs of lines are perpendicular? Use a protractor.

11.
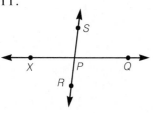

12.
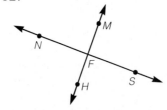

13.
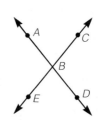

14. Use a compass and straightedge. Draw a line, $\overleftrightarrow{PQ}$. Choose a point F on $\overleftrightarrow{PQ}$. Construct a line perpendicular to $\overleftrightarrow{PQ}$ at F.

Skills Review   Subtraction

Subtract.

1.	58 − 32	2.	79 − 38	3.	65 − 26	4.	42 − 17
5.	5.3 − 3.8	6.	9.8 − 5.9	7.	8 − 6.1	8.	8.6 − 1.9
9.	345 − 266	10.	720 − 138	11.	345 − 69	12.	716 − 48
13.	$7.27 − 1.09	14.	$4.28 − 0.19	15.	$8.65 − 2.97	16.	$4.64 − 0.67
17.	3,176 − 2,085	18.	7,310 − 5,678	19.	5,315 − 4,129	20.	7,044 − 2,918
21.	6.531 − 3.87	22.	5.029 − 2.1	23.	400.1 − 128.6	24.	70.06 − 17.19
25.	72,189 − 28,177	26.	61,106 − 19,062	27.	50,080 − 13,245	28.	41,000 − 11,876
29.	$400.50 − 398.64	30.	$100.00 − 61.68	31.	$175.10 − 94.90	32.	$404.31 − 288.92

33. $5.68 - 3.9$ 34. $15.321 - 6$ 35. $5 - 1.79$

36. $16,471 - 762$ 37. $6,482 - 128$ 38. $85,041 - 42$

39. $18.43 - $9.00   40. $30.00 - $21.84   41. $65.01 - $0.05

4
Triangles and Congruence

1   Classifying Triangles

After finishing Section 1, you should be able to
▲   *identify included and opposite sides and angles.*
▲▲ *classify triangles by sides or angles.*

▲ Sides and Angles

A triangle consists of three segments determined by three
noncollinear points. The points are called *vertices* (plural of *vertex*)
and the segments are called *sides*.

> *P, Q,* and *R* are vertices.
> $\overline{PQ}$, $\overline{QR}$ and $\overline{PR}$ are sides.

In △ *PQR*, $\overline{QR}$, and ∠ *P* are opposite each other. $\overline{QR}$ is called the
included side of ∠ *Q* and ∠ *R*. Likewise, ∠ *P* is called the *included
angle* of $\overline{PQ}$ and $\overline{PR}$.

Examples   Consider △ *ABC*.

    1. What angle is included between $\overline{AB}$ and $\overline{BC}$?
       ∠ *B* is included between $\overline{AB}$ and $\overline{BC}$.

    2. What side is included between ∠ *B* and ∠ *C*?
       $\overline{BC}$ is included between ∠ *B* and ∠ *C*.

    3. What angle is opposite $\overline{BC}$?
       ∠ *A* is opposite $\overline{BC}$.

    4. What side is opposite ∠ *C*?
       $\overline{AB}$ is opposite ∠ *C*.

Try This...   Consider △ *ABC* above.

    1. What angle is included between $\overline{AB}$ and $\overline{AC}$?
    2. What side is included between ∠ *A* and ∠ *C*?
    3. What angle is opposite $\overline{AB}$?
    4. What side is opposite ∠ *B*?

▲▲ Classification of Triangles

Triangles may be classified by their angles.

Acute	Equiangular	Right	Obtuse
All angles acute	All angles congruent	One right angle	One obtuse angle
	congruent angles	right angle	obtuse angle

Example   5. Classify each triangle by its angles.

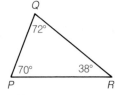

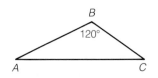

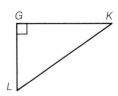

△ *PQR* is acute because all angles are acute.

△ *ABC* is obtuse because it has an obtuse angle.

△ *GKL* is right because it has a right angle.

Try This...   5. Classify each triangle by its angles.

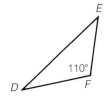

Triangles may also be classified by their sides.

Equilateral	Isosceles	Scalene
All sides congruent	At least two sides congruent	No sides congruent
congruent sides	two congruent sides	

Example   6. Classify each triangle by its sides.

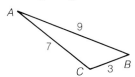

△ MNQ is isosceles
because two sides
are congruent.

△ ABC is scalene
because no sides
are congruent.

△ RST is equilateral
because all sides
are congruent.

Exercises

▲   **Refer to △QRS for Exercises 1-6.**

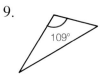

1.   What angle is included between $\overline{QR}$ and $\overline{QS}$?
2.   What angle is included between $\overline{QR}$ and $\overline{RS}$?
3.   What side is included between   4.   What side is included between
     ∠ Q and ∠ S?   ∠ S and ∠ R?
5.   What side is opposite ∠ Q?   6.   What angle is opposite $\overline{QR}$?

▲▲   **Classify each triangle by its angles.**

7.   8.   9.   10.

Classify each triangle by its sides.

11.   12.   13.   14.

▶▶   Challenge Exercises

15.   Draw an acute scalene triangle.   16.   Draw a right scalene triangle.

17.   Draw a right isosceles triangle.   18.   Try to draw an obtuse right triangle.

19.   Is an equilateral triangle also isosceles?
      Explain how you know.

2	Congruent Triangles

After finishing Section 2, you should be able to
▲   *identify the corresponding parts of*
    congruent triangles.

We know that congruent figures fit together
exactly.

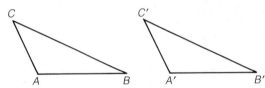

B′ is read "B prime."

These triangles will fit together exactly if we match A with A', B
with B', and C with C'. On the other hand, if we try to match
A with B', B with C', and C with A', the triangles will not fit together
exactly. The matching of vertices determines corresponding sides
and corresponding angles.

Examples   Consider $\triangle ABC$ and $\triangle A'B'C'$ above.

1. If we match A with A', B with B', and C with C', what are the
   corresponding sides?

   $\overline{AB} \longleftrightarrow \overline{A'B'}$
   $\overline{BC} \longleftrightarrow \overline{B'C'}$
   $\overline{AC} \longleftrightarrow \overline{A'C'}$

   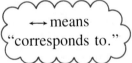

   ↔ means
   "corresponds to."

2. If we match A with A', B with B', and C with C', what are the
   corresponding angles?

   $\angle A \longleftrightarrow \angle A'$ $\angle B \longleftrightarrow \angle B'$ $\angle C \longleftrightarrow \angle C'$

If $A \longleftrightarrow A'$, $B \longleftrightarrow B'$, and $C \longleftrightarrow C'$, then we can write $ABC \longleftrightarrow A'B'C'$.

DEFINITION

Two triangles are congruent whenever their vertices can be matched
so that the corresponding sides and the corresponding angles are
congruent.

The corresponding sides and angles of two congruent triangles are called *corresponding parts of congruent triangles. Corresponding parts of congruent triangles are always congruent.*

We write $\triangle ABC \cong \triangle A'B'C'$ to say that $\triangle ABC$ and $\triangle A'B'C'$ are congruent. We agree that this symbol also tells us the way in which the vertices are matched.

$$ABC \cong A'B'C'$$

$\triangle ABC \cong \triangle A'B'C'$ means

$$\angle A \cong \angle A' \text{ and } \overline{AB} \cong \overline{A'B'}$$
$$\angle B \cong \angle B' \qquad \overline{AC} \cong \overline{A'C'}$$
$$\angle C \cong \angle C' \qquad \overline{BC} \cong \overline{B'C'}$$

Example   3. Suppose $\triangle PQR \cong \triangle STV$. What are the congruent corresponding parts?

Angles	Sides
$\angle P \cong \angle S$	$\overline{PQ} \cong \overline{ST}$
$\angle Q \cong \angle T$	$\overline{PR} \cong \overline{SV}$
$\angle R \cong \angle V$	$\overline{QR} \cong \overline{TV}$

Try This...   1. Suppose $\triangle ABC \cong \triangle DEF$. What are the congruent corresponding parts?

Example   4. Name the corresponding parts of these congruent triangles.

Angles	Sides
$\angle X \cong \angle U$	$\overline{XY} \cong \overline{UV}$
$\angle Y \cong \angle V$	$\overline{YZ} \cong \overline{VW}$
$\angle Z \cong \angle W$	$\overline{ZX} \cong \overline{WU}$

Try This...   2. Name the corresponding parts of these congruent triangles.

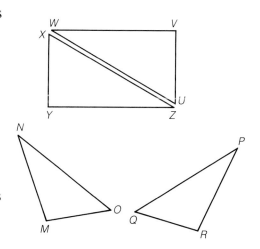

Exercises

▲ **Name the corresponding parts of these congruent triangles.**

1. $\triangle ABC \cong \triangle RST$
2. $\triangle DEF \cong \triangle GHK$
3. $\triangle XYZ \cong \triangle UVW$
4. $\triangle MNQ \cong \triangle HJK$
5. $\triangle ABC \cong \triangle ABC$
6. $\triangle ABC \cong \triangle ACB$

Name the corresponding parts of these congruent triangles.

7. 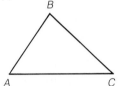 8.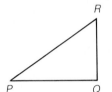

9. 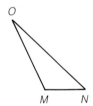 10.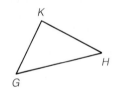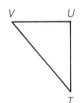

▶▶ Challenge Exercises

11. $\triangle ABC$ is both equilateral and equiangular. List all the possible matchings of vertices that show that $\triangle ABC$ is congruent to itself.

12. How many different matchings of vertices show a square congruent to itself?

13. Here are corresponding parts of two congruent triangles. Find a matching of vertices that shows the congruence.

$$\angle T \cong \angle S \qquad \overline{PT} \cong \overline{RS}$$
$$\angle P \cong \angle R \qquad \overline{TU} \cong \overline{SQ}$$
$$\angle U \cong \angle Q \qquad \overline{PU} \cong \overline{RQ}$$

3   SAS, SSS, and ASA Congruence

*After finishing Section 3, you should be able to
identify pairs of triangles that can be shown
congruent by*

▲   *the SAS Postulate.*

▲▲   *the SSS Theorem.*

▲▲▲   *the ASA Theorem.*

Sometimes we can show that triangles are
congruent without already knowing that all
six corresponding parts are congruent.

▲   The Side-Angle-Side (SAS) Postulate

1. On a full sheet of paper,
   draw △ *ABC*.

2. On another sheet of paper,
   make a copy of ∠ *A*. Label
   the copy ∠ *D*.

3. On the sides of ∠ *D*, copy
   both $\overline{AB}$ and $\overline{AC}$.

4. Cut out △ *DEF* and △ *ABC*. Place them together.
   What do you conclude?

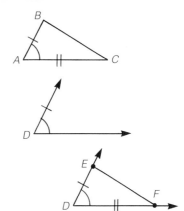

POSTULATE   *The SAS Postulate*

11   Two triangles are congruent if two sides and the included angle of
               one triangle are congruent to two sides and the included angle of the
               other triangle.

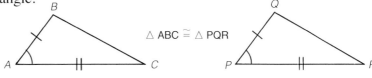

Example   1. Which pairs of triangles are congruent by the SAS Postulate?

a.   b.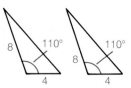

c. 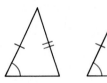   d.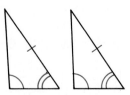

Pairs **b** and **c** are congruent by SAS.

Try This...   1. Which pairs of triangles are congruent by the SAS Postulate?

a. 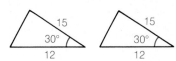   b.

c. 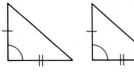   d.

▲▲ The Side-Side-Side (SSS) Theorem

In Chapter 1 you copied a triangle by copying each of its sides.
Obviously, a triangle and its copy are congruent. This suggests
the following theorem.

THEOREM   *The SSS Theorem*
4.1
           If three sides of one triangle are congruent to three sides of
           another triangle, then the triangles are congruent.

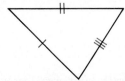   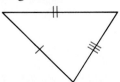

Example 2. Which pairs of triangles are congruent by the SSS Theorem?

a.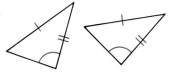

b.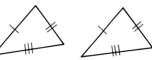

c.

d.

Pairs **b** and **d** are congruent by SSS.

Try This... 2. Which pairs of triangles are congruent by the SSS Theorem?

a.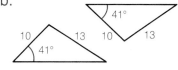

b.

▲▲ The Angle-Side-Angle (ASA) Theorem

We have shown triangles congruent by SAS and SSS. Here is a third way to show congruence.

1. On a full sheet of paper, draw a triangle, △ ABC.

2. On another sheet of paper, draw a segment, $\overline{DE}$ so that $DE = AB$.

3. At D, make a copy of ∠ A.

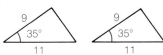

4. At E, make a copy of ∠ B. Label the third vertex of the copy F.

5. Cut out △ ABC and △ DEF. Place them together. What do you conclude?

THEOREM **The ASA Theorem**
4.2 If two angles and the included side of a triangle are congruent to two angles and the included side of another triangle, then the triangles are congruent.

Example 3. Which pairs of triangles are congruent by the ASA Theorem?

a. 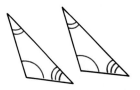 b. 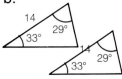 c.

Pairs **b** and **c** are congruent by ASA.

Try This... 3. Which pairs of triangles are congruent by the ASA Theorem?

a. 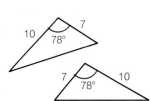 b. 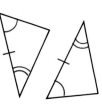 c.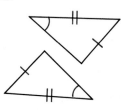

Exercises

▲ **Which pairs of triangles are congruent by the SAS Postulate?**

1. 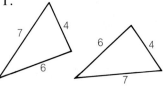 2. 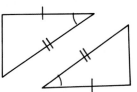 3.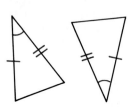

4. 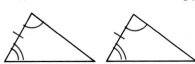 5. 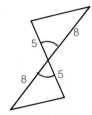 6.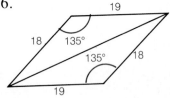

▲▲ **Which pairs of triangles are congruent by the SSS Theorem?**

7.
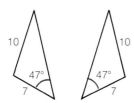

8.
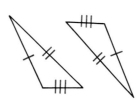

9.
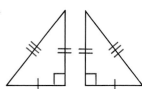

10.
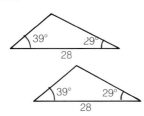

11.
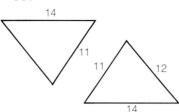

12.
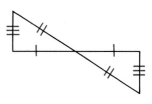

▲
▲▲ **Which pairs of triangles are congruent by the ASA Theorem?**

13.
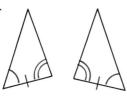

14.
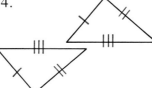

15.
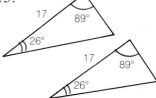

16.
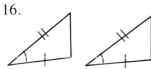

17.

18.
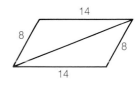

▶ Extension Exercises

19. If four rods are connected as shown, the figure "wobbles." Why does the addition of a fifth rod make the structure rigid?

20. How do you know that the faces of this pyramid are congruent triangles?

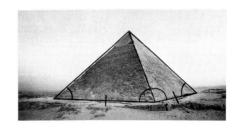

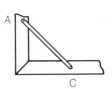

21. How can you find congruent triangles in the photograph on the left if all the tubes are the same size?

22. *M* is the midpoint of both crosspieces in the photograph on the right. Explain why the triangles are congruent.

23. A picture frame will not remain rectangular unless a brace $(\overline{AC})$ is added. Explain why.

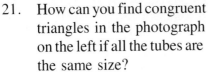

▶▶ Challenge Exercises

24. Draw $\triangle ABC$ where $m \angle A = 35°$, $AB = 6$ cm and $BC = 4$ cm. Try to draw another triangle, $\triangle A'B'C'$, with the same measurements but with a different shape. Is this possible? State an SSA Theorem. Is it true?

25. Draw $\triangle TOP$ where $m \angle T = 30°$, $m \angle O = 60°$, and $TP = 5$ cm. Try to draw another triangle, $\triangle T'O'P'$, with the same measurements but with a different shape. Is this possible? State an SAA Theorem. Is it true?

26. Draw $\triangle KMH$ where $m \angle K = 20°$, $m \angle M = 100°$, and $m \angle H = 60°$. Try to draw another triangle, $\triangle K'M'H'$, with the same measurements but with a different size. Is this possible? State an AAA Theorem. Is it true?

4	Which Postulate or Theorem?

After finishing Section 4, you should be able to
▲ *determine the postulate or theorem to use to show that triangles are congruent.*
▲▲ *determine information needed to use a certain postulate or theorem.*

▲ Selecting a Postulate or Theorem

When showing that triangles are congruent, we must first decide whether to use SAS, SSS, or ASA.

Examples | Which postulate or theorem (if any) should be used to tell whether these pairs of triangles are congruent?

1.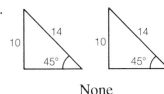

SAS Post.

2.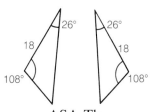

ASA Th.

3.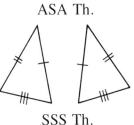

None

4.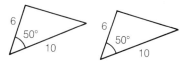

SSS Th.

Try This... | Which postulate or theorem (if any) should be used to tell whether these pairs of triangles are congruent?

1.

2.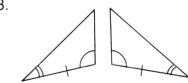

3.

4.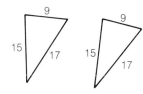

Examples Which postulate or theorem (if any) would you use to tell whether △ ABC ≅ △ PQR with the given information?

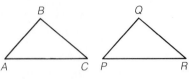

5. $\overline{AB} \cong \overline{PQ}$, $\overline{AC} \cong \overline{PR}$, and $\angle A \cong \angle P$.   Use SAS.
6. $\overline{AB} \cong \overline{PQ}$, $\overline{AC} \cong \overline{PR}$, and $\angle Q \cong \angle B$.   None
7. $\angle P \cong \angle A$, $\angle R \cong \angle C$, and $\overline{AC} \cong \overline{PR}$.   Use ASA.

Try This... Consider △ ABC and △ PQR above. Which postulate or theorem (if any) would you use to tell whether △ ABC ≅ △ PQR with the given information?

5. $\overline{AC} \cong \overline{PR}$, $\overline{AB} \cong \overline{PQ}$, $\overline{BC} \cong \overline{QR}$.
6. $\angle Q \cong \angle B$, $\angle P \cong \angle A$, and $\overline{PQ} \cong \overline{AB}$.
7. $\overline{AC} \cong \overline{PR}$, $\overline{AB} \cong \overline{PQ}$, and $\angle C \cong \angle R$.

▲▲ Determining Needed Information

It is important to know what information is needed to use a certain postulate or theorem.

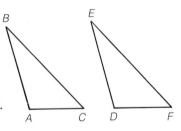

Examples We want to know if △ ABC ≅ △ DEF.

8. We know $\overline{AB} \cong \overline{DE}$ and $\overline{CB} \cong \overline{FE}$. What else must we know to use SSS?
    We must know $\overline{AC} \cong \overline{DF}$.
9. We know $\angle A \cong \angle D$. What else must we know to use SAS?
    We must know $\overline{AC} \cong \overline{DF}$ and $\overline{AB} \cong \overline{DE}$.
10. We know $\overline{AC} \cong \overline{DF}$. What else must we know to use ASA?
    We must know $\angle A \cong \angle D$ and $\angle C \cong \angle F$.

Try This... Refer to the triangles above. We want to know if △ ABC ≅ △ DEF.

8. We know $\angle D \cong \angle A$ and $\angle F \cong \angle C$. What else must we know to use ASA?
9. We know $\overline{AB} \cong \overline{DE}$ and $\overline{AC} \cong \overline{DF}$. What else must we know to to use SAS?

Exercises

▲ **Which postulate or theorem (if any) should be used to tell whether the following pairs of triangles are congruent?**

1.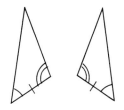

2.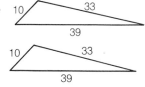

3.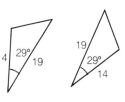

4.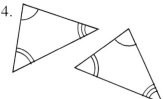

5.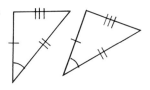

6.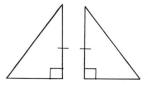

7. A toy arrangement

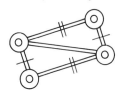

8. The flag of Grenada

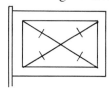

Which postulate or theorem (if any) would you use to tell whether △ RST ≅ △ DEF with the given information?

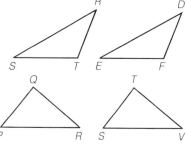

9. $\overline{RS} \cong \overline{DE}$, $\overline{RT} \cong \overline{DF}$, and $\angle R \cong \angle D$.

10. $\angle R \cong \angle D$, $\angle S \cong \angle E$, and $\angle T \cong \angle F$.

11. $\overline{RS} \cong \overline{DE}$, $\angle R \cong \angle D$, and $\angle S \cong \angle E$.

12. $\angle R \cong \angle D$, $\overline{RT} \cong \overline{DF}$, and $\overline{ST} \cong \overline{EF}$.

▲▲ **We want to know if △ PQR ≅ △ STV.**

13. We know $\overline{RQ} \cong \overline{VT}$. What else must we know to use ASA?

14. We know $\angle P \cong \angle S$. What else must we know to use SAS?

15. We know $\overline{PR} \cong \overline{SV}$ and $\overline{RQ} \cong \overline{VT}$. What else must we know to use SSS?

16. We know $\angle R \cong \angle V$ and $\angle Q \cong \angle T$. What else must we know to use ASA?

| **5** | Explaining Why Triangles are Congruent |

After finishing Section 5, you should be able to

▲   *explain why pairs of triangles are congruent in physical situations.*

▲▲ *explain why pairs of triangles are congruent in geometric situations.*

▲ Congruent Triangles in the World

We can use postulates and theorems to explain why triangles are congruent.

Many examples of congruent triangles appear in the physical world.

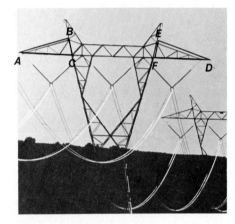

Examples   1. Explain why $\triangle ABC \cong \triangle DEF$ in this photograph.
$\angle A$ has the same measure as $\angle D$. Points B, C, E, and F are positioned so that $\overline{AC} \cong \overline{DF}$ and $\overline{AB} \cong \overline{DE}$.
Thus, $\triangle ABC \cong DEF$ by SAS.

2. In a racquetball game, a ball is hit from the right wall at C to the middle of the front wall at D. It rebounds to the left wall at E. Explain why $\triangle CPD \cong \triangle EQD$.

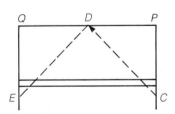

Because P and Q are corners of a room, they form right angles. So, $\angle Q \cong \angle P$. Point D is the midpoint of $\overline{QP}$, so $\overline{QD} \cong \overline{PD}$. The ball rebounds at the same angle at which it strikes the wall. Thus, $\angle PDC \cong \angle QDE$. Hence, $\triangle CPD \cong \triangle EQD$ by ASA.

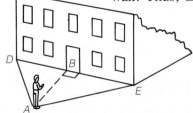

Try This...   1. A person standing at point A can see both ends of the building. The door is in the middle of the front wall. Explain why $\triangle ABD \cong \triangle ABE$.

▲▲ Congruent Triangles in Drawings

It is important to be able to explain why triangles are congruent.

Examples   3. In $\triangle ABC$ and $\triangle DEF$, $\overline{AB} \cong \overline{DE}$, $\overline{AC} \cong \overline{DF}$, and $\angle A \cong \angle D$. Explain why the triangles are congruent.

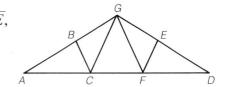

We have two sides and an included angle of $\triangle ABC$ congruent to the corresponding parts of $\triangle DEF$. Hence, $\triangle ABC \cong \triangle DEF$ by SAS.

4. In $\triangle CPD$ and $\triangle EQD$, $CP \perp \overline{QP}$ and $\overline{EQ} \perp \overline{QP}$. Also, $\angle QDE \cong \angle PDC$, and D is the midpoint of $\overline{QP}$. Explain why $\triangle CPD \cong \triangle EQD$.

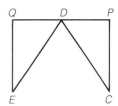

The perpendicular sides form right angles, which are congruent. Because D is the midpoint of $\overline{QP}$, we know $\overline{QD} \cong \overline{PD}$. With $\angle QDE \cong \angle PDC$, we have $\triangle CPD \cong \triangle EQD$ by ASA.

Try This...   2. In this figure, $\overline{AB} \perp \overline{ED}$ and B is the midpoint of $\overline{ED}$. Explain why $\triangle ABD \cong \triangle ABE$.

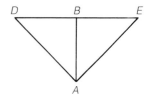

Exercises

▲   **In each physical setting, explain why the triangles indicated in parentheses are congruent.**

1.   In a bowtie, the indicated sides are congruent. ($\triangle PQR \cong \triangle STR$)

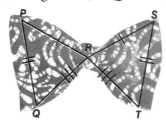

2.   On the flag of Jamaica, X marks the midpoint of QS and RP. ($\triangle RQX \cong \triangle PSX$)

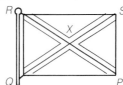

3. To brace a door, identical cross boards are spaced at equal distances perpendicular to the vertical boards on the door.

   Diagonal braces $\overline{AB}$ and $\overline{XZ}$ are also added. Find two congruent triangles. How do you know they are congruent?

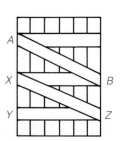

4. The photograph shows that $\overline{AB} \perp \overline{BC}$, $\overline{DE} \perp \overline{EF}$, $\overline{AB} \cong \overline{DE}$, and $\angle BAC \cong \angle EDF$. Find two congruent triangles. How do you know they are congruent?

▲▲ **Find two congruent triangles in each figure. Explain why they are congruent.**

5. R is the midpoint of both $\overline{PT}$ and $\overline{QS}$.
   ($\triangle PRQ \cong \triangle TRS$)

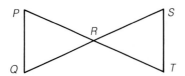

6. $\angle 1$ and $\angle 2$ are right angles, X is the midpoint of $\overline{AY}$, and $\overline{XB} \cong \overline{YZ}$.
   ($\triangle ABX \cong \triangle XZY$)

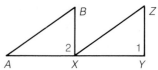

7. L is the midpoint of $\overline{KM}$ and $\overline{GL} \perp \overline{KM}$. ($\triangle KLG \cong \triangle MLG$)

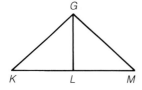

8. X is the midpoint of both $\overline{QS}$ and $\overline{RP}$ with $RQ = SP$.
   ($\triangle RQX \cong \triangle PSX$)

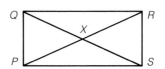

9. $\triangle AEB$ and $\triangle CDB$ are isosceles with $\overline{AE} \cong \overline{AB} \cong \overline{CB} \cong \overline{CD}$.
   Also, B is the midpoint of $\overline{ED}$.
   ($\triangle AEB \cong \triangle CDB$)

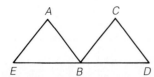

10. $\overline{AB} \perp \overline{BE}$ and $\overline{DE} \perp \overline{BE}$.
    $\overline{AB} \cong \overline{DE}$ and $\angle BAC \cong \angle EDC$.
    ($\triangle ABC \cong \triangle DEC$)

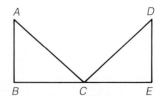

11. $\overline{GK} \cong \overline{ML}$ and $\angle GKM \cong \angle LMK$.
($\triangle GKM \cong \triangle LMK$)

12. $\overline{SX} \cong \overline{RX}$ and $\overrightarrow{XT}$ bisects $\angle SXR$.
($\triangle SXT \cong \triangle RXT$)

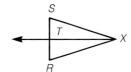

13. T is the midpoint of $\overline{RS}$ and $\angle AST$ is supplementary to $\angle 3$.
($\triangle AST \cong \triangle PRT$)

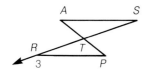

14. $\angle ATR \cong \angle STR$ and $\angle 1 \cong \angle 2$.
($\triangle ART \cong \triangle SRT$)

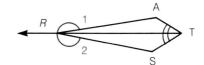

15. $\overline{FT} \cong \overline{FR}$ and $\overline{ST} \cong \overline{SR}$.
($\triangle FTS \cong \triangle FRS$)

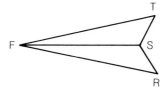

16. H is the midpoint of $\overline{QK}$, $\overline{QM} \cong \overline{KD}$, and $\overline{MH} \cong \overline{DH}$.
($\triangle QHM \cong \triangle KHD$)

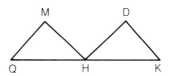

17. $\overline{TQ} \cong \overline{SQ}$, $\overline{TP} \cong \overline{SR}$, and Q is the midpoint of $\overline{PR}$.
($\triangle TQP \cong \triangle SQR$)

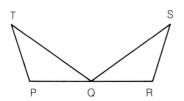

18. L is the midpoint of both $\overline{GN}$ and $\overline{KM}$ and $\overline{GK} \cong \overline{MN}$.
($\triangle GKL \cong \triangle NML$)

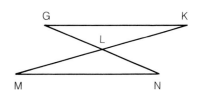

▶ Extension Exercises

19. On the sailboat pennants, $\angle 1 \cong \angle 2$, $\overline{AB} \cong \overline{DE}$, and $\overline{EF} \cong \overline{BC}$. Explain why $\triangle ABC \cong \triangle DEF$.

20. Suppose the sun is positioned behind a pyramid such that the indicated sides are congruent. Explain why the shadow is congruent to the face of the pyramid.

▶◀ Activity

A bricklayer often uses an instrument called a *level* to make a row of bricks horizontal. You can make a simple level based upon the principle of congruent triangles.

Cut out three congruent pieces of stiff cardboard in the shapes of rectangles. Tape the rectangles together, joining ends, to form an equilateral triangle. Draw a line through the midpoint of the triangle's base. Tie a large paper clip to a piece of string. Attach the string to the triangle's top vertex so that the paper clip hangs just above the base.

What will happen if the level is resting on a non-horizontal surface?

What will happen if the level is resting on a level surface?

If the surface is horizontal, what can you conclude about $\triangle ABD$ and $\triangle ACD$? If the surface is not horizontal, can you make the same conclusion? Explain how you know.

6 Drawings and Theorems

After finishing Section 6, you should be able to
▲   *tell what information is shown in a drawing.*
▲▲   *make drawings to illustrate a theorem.*

▲   Information in Drawings

It is important to know what information is shown in a drawing.
Markings show congruent angles, sides, right angles, and
perpendicular lines. Drawings can also show that points are
collinear; that angles are adjacent; that lines, rays, or segments
intersect; and that betweenness relationships hold.

Example   1. What information is shown in this drawing?

$\overline{DB} \perp \overline{AC}$
A-B-C
$\angle ADB$ and $\angle CDB$ are adjacent.
$\overline{AD} \cong \overline{CD}$

Try This...   1. What information is shown in this drawing?

Example   2. What information is shown in this drawing?
$\overline{AC} \perp \overline{CB}$
C-D-B
$\angle CAD \cong \angle DAB$
$\angle CAD$ and $\angle DAB$ are adjacent.

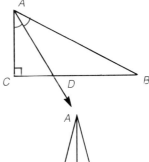

Try This...   2. What information is shown in this drawing?

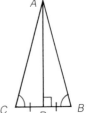

▲▲ Using Information to Make Drawings

It is helpful to be able to make an accurate drawing to show specific information.

Example   3. Make a drawing to show the information given in this theorem:
If $\angle R \cong \angle H$, $\overline{RS} \cong \overline{GH}$, and $\angle S \cong \angle G$, then
$\triangle RST \cong \triangle HGK$.
The theorem mentions two triangles, so we draw them.

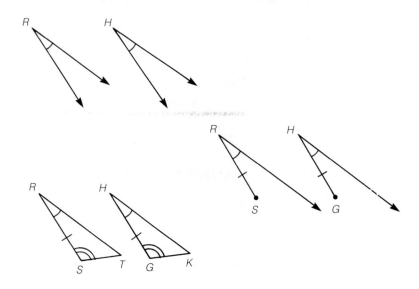

We know that $\angle R \cong \angle H$, $\overline{RS} \cong \overline{HG}$, and
$\angle S \cong \angle G$. We label the drawing accordingly.

Try This...   3. Make a drawing to show the information given in this theorem:
If $\angle C \cong \angle F$, $\overline{CB} \cong \overline{FE}$,
and $\angle B \cong \angle E$, then
$\triangle ABC \cong \triangle DEF$.

Example   4. Make a drawing to show the information given in this theorem:
If $\overline{AB} \cong \overline{SR}$, $\overline{AC} \cong \overline{SP}$, and $\overline{BC} \cong \overline{RP}$,
then $\triangle ABC \cong \triangle SRP$.

Draw two rays and
mark off $\overline{AB} \cong \overline{SR}$.

Set a compass opening of
AC (or SP) and draw arcs.

Set a compass opening of
BC (or RP) and draw arcs.

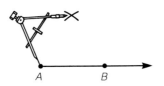 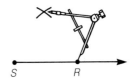

Label the intersections of the arcs
C and P and draw triangles.
Mark the congruent sides.

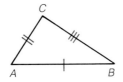 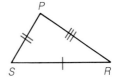

Try This...   4. Make a drawing to show the information given in this theorem:

$$\text{If } \overline{DE} \cong \overline{XY}, \overline{DF} \cong \overline{XZ}, \text{ and } \overline{EF} \cong \overline{YZ},$$
$$\text{then } \triangle DEF \cong \triangle XYZ.$$

Exercises

▲ **What information is shown in these drawings?**

1.

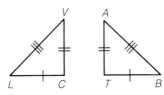

2.

3.

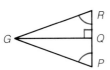

4.

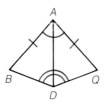

▲▲ **Make drawings to show the given information.**

5.   If $\angle S \cong \angle C, \overline{PS} \cong \overline{FC}$, and
$\angle P \cong \angle F$, then $\triangle PQS \cong \triangle FLC$.

6.   If $\overline{PL} \cong \overline{JR}, \angle L \cong \angle R$, and
$\angle P \cong \angle J$, then $\triangle PTL \cong \triangle JNR$.

7. If $\angle DEG \cong \angle KEG$ and $\angle DGE \cong \angle KGE$, then $\triangle DEG \cong \triangle KEG$.

8. If $\angle BAC \cong \angle DCA$ and $\angle BCA \cong \angle DAC$, then $\triangle ABC \cong \triangle CDA$.

9. If $\overline{ED}$ and $\overline{AC}$ intersect in a point B, $\overline{AB} \cong \overline{CB}$, and $\angle EAB \cong \angle DCB$, then $\triangle AEB \cong \triangle CDB$.

10. If $\overrightarrow{ST}$ is the bisector of $\angle PSQ$ and $\angle PTS \cong \angle QTS$, then $\triangle PST \cong \triangle QST$.

11. If $\overline{AD}$ and $\overline{CE}$ intersect at B, $\angle A \cong \angle C$, and $\overline{AB} \cong \overline{CB}$, then $\triangle AEB \cong \triangle CDB$.

12. If $\angle PTS \cong \angle QTS$ and $\overrightarrow{ST}$ is the bisector of $\angle PSQ$, then $\triangle PST \cong \triangle QST$.

13. If $\angle S \cong \angle C$, $\overline{PS} \cong \overline{FC}$, and $\angle P \cong \angle F$, then $\triangle PQS \cong \triangle FLC$.

14. If $\overline{PL} \cong \overline{JR}$, $\overline{PT} \cong \overline{JN}$, and $\angle P \cong \angle J$, then $\triangle PTL \cong \triangle JNR$.

15. If $\overline{AC}$ and $\overline{RS}$ bisect each other at Q, then $\triangle RQC \cong \triangle SQA$.

16. If $\overline{AR} \perp \overleftrightarrow{RQ}$, $\overline{BQ} \perp \overleftrightarrow{RQ}$, $\overline{AR} \cong \overline{BQ}$, and C is the midpoint of $\overline{RQ}$, then $\overline{AC} \cong \overline{BC}$.

▶◀ Activity

Arrange 13 straws to form six triangles as shown in this picture. Which three straws can be removed so that the remaining straws create only three triangles?

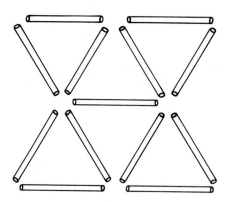

Now use nine of the straws to form the sides of an equilateral, an isosceles, and a scalene triangle. Cut the straws the appropriate lengths. Thread the three straws that form the sides of each triangle with string. Tie the string's ends together to form each triangle.

Historical Note

The Babylonians discovered many geometric rules through experimentation and intuition. The Romans used such rules for measuring land, surveying, and laying out cities. They were not very interested in proving rules discovered by experimentation, however.

The idea of proof was introduced by the Greeks. Thales (about 600 B.C.) proved geometric statements by deduction. Euclid (about 300 years later) extended this work by writing a book of geometric theorems. He was not interested in practical use as much as in proof. Therefore, he called his work the *Elements,* rather than "geometry," which means "earth measurement." The *Elements* also included number theory.

With the invention of the printing press, the first printed version of Euclid's *Elements* appeared in 1482. By 1570 the first English translation was printed. By that time, however, the word "geometry" began to appear as the title.

Today students around the world study theorems of geometry discovered through experimentation and proved through deduction.

▶◀ Activity

These logos are created by constructing equilateral triangles.

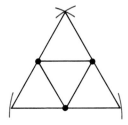

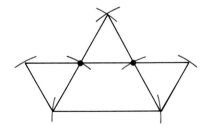

These logos are made up of equilateral triangles and arcs centered at various vertices.

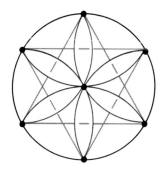

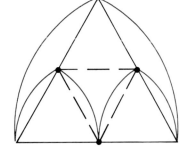

A six-leaved rose   An arch from Gothic architecture

Make your own design for a logo based on arcs and equilateral triangles.

Consumer Application   Using Solar Collectors

Solar collectors are instruments used to trap the sun's energy.
Many homeowners use solar energy to heat their water and/or their
living space. *Fixed solar collectors* typically are installed on roofs
at a fixed angle to the sun. To gather the most heat, the collectors
should be at right angles to the sun at noon. But, the sun changes
its noontime position during each season: It is in the south in the
winter and it is directly overhead in the summer. To be most
efficient, a fixed solar collector should be facing south at an angle
equal to the local latitude plus 15°.

Example   Find the best angle to position a fixed solar
                 collector given the local latitude.

                 Detroit, Michigan has a latitude of 42°20.0′.

                 42°20.0′ + 15°00.0′ = 57°20.0′   Add 15° to the local latitude
                                                    to find the best angle for the
                                                    solar collector.

                 A fixed solar collector should be angled at 57°20.0′ for best results.

**Find the best angle to position a fixed solar collector given the
local latitude.**

1. Spokane, Washington 47°40.3′   2. New Orleans, Louisiana 29°57.8′

3. San Diego, California 32°42.8′   4. Fairbanks, Alaska 64°50.8′

5. Miami, Florida 25°46.5′   6. Austin, Texas 30°16.9′

7. Billings, Montana 45°46.8′   8. Boston, Massachusetts 42°21.7′

9. Honolulu, Hawaii 21°18.8′   10. Burlington, Vermont 44°28.5′

11. Atlanta, Georgia 33°45.0′   12. Tulsa, Oklahoma 36°09.6′

13. Chicago, Illinois 41°35.0′   14. Denver, Colorado 39°44.4′

Chapter Review

1 **Classify each triangle by its angles.**

1.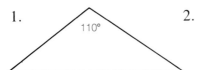

2.

3.

Classify each triangle by its sides.

4.

5.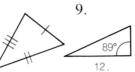

6.

2 7. Name the corresponding parts if $\triangle GKL \cong \triangle PTL$.

3 **Which pairs of triangles are congruent by the SAS Postulate?**

8.

9.

10.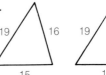

Which pairs of triangles are congruent by the SSS Theorem?

11.

12.

13.

Which pairs of triangles are congruent by the ASA Theorem?

14.

15.

16.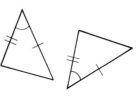

4 **Which postulate or theorem (if any) would you use to tell whether △BJC ≅ △KYL with the given information?**

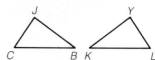

17. $\overline{BJ} \cong \overline{KY}$, $\overline{BC} \cong \overline{KL}$, and $\angle B \cong \angle K$.

18. $\overline{JC} \cong \overline{YL}$, $\angle J \cong \angle Y$, and $\angle C \cong \angle L$.

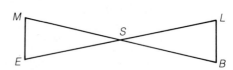

5 19. $\overline{MS} \cong \overline{LS}$ and $\overline{ES} \cong \overline{BS}$. Explain why △MES ≅ △LBS.

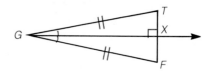

6 20. List four pieces of information shown in this drawing.

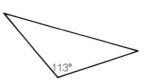

21. Make a drawing to illustrate this theorem: If X is the midpoint of $\overline{BD}$ and $\overline{AB} \cong \overline{AD}$, then △AXB ≅ △AXD.

Chapter Test

Classify each triangle by its angles.

1.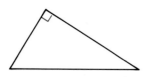

2.

3.

Classify each triangle by its sides.

4.

5.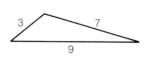

6.

7. Name the corresponding parts if △YAH ≅ △KEN.

Which pair of triangles are congruent by the SAS Postulate?

8.

9.

10.

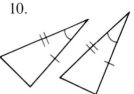

Which pair of triangles are congruent by the SSS Theorem?

11.

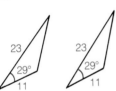

12.

13.

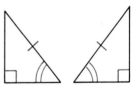

Which pair of triangles are congruent by the ASA Theorem?

14.

15.

16.

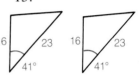

Which postulate or theorem (if any) would you use to tell whether △BRK ≅ △CHS with the given information?

17. ∠B ≅ ∠C, ∠R ≅ ∠H, and $\overline{BK} \cong \overline{CS}$.
18. ∠K ≅ ∠S, ∠R ≅ ∠H, and $\overline{KR} \cong \overline{SH}$.

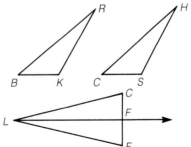

19. Explain why △CLF ≅ △ELF.
$\overrightarrow{LF}$ bisects ∠CLE and $\overline{CL} \cong \overline{EL}$.

20. List four pieces of information shown in this drawing.

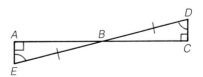

21. Make a drawing to illustrate this theorem: If $\overline{AB}$ and $\overline{DF}$ intersect at M, $\overline{AM} \cong \overline{MB}$, and ∠A ≅ ∠B, then △AMF ≅ △BMD.

Skills Review	Multiplication and Division

Multiply.

1.	42 × 6	2.	98 × 4	3.	148 × 8	4.	2,690 × 7
5.	$2.91 × 3	6.	$0.50 × 5	7.	$2.35 × 4	8.	$68.91 × 9
9.	60 × 30	10.	43 × 89	11.	400 × 80	12.	609 × 58
13.	5.88 × 11	14.	0.76 × 42	15.	8.47 × 6.9	16.	63.78 × 13.5
17.	7,243 × 36	18.	7,400 × 46	19.	658 × 600	20.	798 × 508

Divide.

21. $50 \div 7$ 22. $53 \div 8$ 23. $17 \div 6$ 24. $91 \div 5$

25. $2\overline{)\$8.90}$ 26. $7\overline{)\$64.26}$ 27. $5\overline{)\$1.50}$ 28. $5\overline{)\$35.20}$

29. $6\overline{)4,256}$ 30. $8\overline{)9,731}$ 31. $4\overline{)32,032}$ 32. $3\overline{)33,907}$

33. $11\overline{)786.5}$ 34. $31\overline{)106.64}$ 35. $42\overline{)71.4}$ 36. $60\overline{)7.62}$

37. $36\overline{)83,492}$ 38. $42\overline{)9,816}$ 39. $58\overline{)10,991}$ 40. $18\overline{)21,079}$

41. $0.02\overline{)1.942}$ 42. $7.3\overline{)0.511}$ 43. $0.28\overline{)100.8}$ 44. $0.004\overline{)0.696}$

45. $124\overline{)4,786}$ 46. $503\overline{)35,560}$ 47. $288\overline{)46,735}$ 48. $936\overline{)49,629}$

Cumulative Review: Chapters 1-4

1–3   1. Suggest a possible counterexample for the statement, "All triangles are isosceles."

1–4   2. Use the following assumptions. What can you conclude?
(a) If a number is even, then it has 2 as a factor.
(b) The number 56 is even.

1–7   3. Identify the hypothesis and the conclusion of "If the apple is red, then it is ripe."

4. Write the converse of "If $\triangle ABC$ is equilateral, then $\triangle ABC$ is equiangular."

2–1   **Use this number line for Exercises 5–7.**

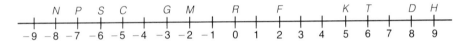

5. Name the coordinates of C, R, and T.

6. Name the points having coordinates −8 and 5.

7. Find the distances PF, TG, and HS.

8. Let the coordinates of A and B be a and b, respectively. Find the coordinate of b if $AB = 10$ and $a = -2$.

2–2   9. Using the coordinate system above, find a new coordinate system in which the coordinate of K is 0 and the coordinate of N is positive.

2–3   10. Points P, Q, and R are collinear. If $RP = 16$, $PQ = 23$, and $QR = 7$, which point is between the other two?

2–5   11. Use a protractor to draw an angle whose measure is 46°.

2–6   ▲12. $m \angle PQR = 172°$.
Find $m \angle PQS$ and $m \angle SQR$.

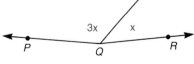

2–8   13.   The measure of an angle is three times the measure of its supplement. Find the measures of the angles.

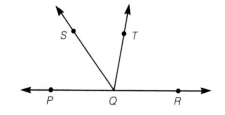

14.   Name two linear pairs of angles in the figure. Assume *P-Q-R*.

3–2   15.   Find $m \angle 1$, $m \angle 2$, $m \angle 3$, and $m \angle 4$.

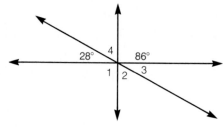

3–4   16.   Use a compass and straightedge. Draw $\overleftrightarrow{PQ}$. Choose a point *R* on $\overleftrightarrow{PQ}$. Construct a line containing *R* that is perpendicular to $\overleftrightarrow{PQ}$.

4–1   17.   Classify each triangle by its sides.

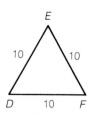
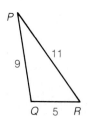
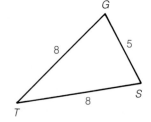

4–4   **Which postulate or theorem (if any) would you use to tell whether △ *PHD* ≅ △ *CLF* with the given information?**

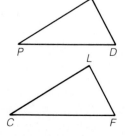

18. $\overline{PH} \cong \overline{CL}$, $\overline{HD} \cong \overline{LF}$, and $\angle H \cong \angle L$.

19. $\angle P \cong \angle C$, $\angle D \cong \angle F$, and $\overline{HD} \cong \overline{LF}$.

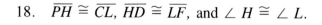

4–6   20. List four pieces of information
            shown in this drawing.

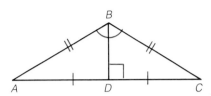

21. Find two congruent triangles. Explain why they are congruent.

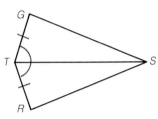

22. Make a drawing to illustrate this theorem:
     If $\angle P \cong \angle T$, $\angle Q \cong \angle S$, and $\overline{PQ} \cong \overline{TS}$,
     then $\triangle PQR \cong \triangle TSW$.

▶◀ Activity

Consider the equilateral triangle at the
right. Each side is divided into the same
number of congruent segments.

You can construct geometric patterns by
connecting corresponding points. The
pattern in black is formed by connecting
each point on the left side with the
corresponding point on the right side. By
connecting each point with the other
points having the same letter, we form the
pattern shown.

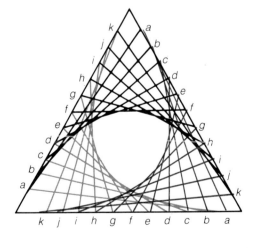

Draw a square 11 cm on a side. Mark off each side in 1 cm intervals.
Label the intervals. Create some geometric patterns.

5
Applying Congruent Triangles

1   Showing Corresponding Parts Congruent

After finishing Section 1, you should be able to
▲   *reach conclusions based on information about angles and segments.*
▲▲   *apply ideas about corresponding parts of congruent triangles in physical situations.*
▲▲   *explain why certain conclusions are reached.*

▲   Reaching Conclusions

Sometimes we can conclude that angles and segments are congruent by first showing that triangles are congruent.

Examples   1. $\angle 1 \cong \angle 2$ and $\overline{AB} \cong \overline{AD}$.
            What can you conclude?

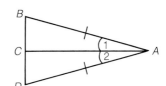

            We know $\angle 1 \cong \angle 2$.
            We know $\overline{AB} \cong \overline{AD}$.
            We know $\overline{AC} \cong \overline{AC}$.
            By SAS, $\triangle ABC \cong \triangle ADC$.
            Thus, we have these congruent, corresponding parts: $\angle B \cong \angle D$, $\overline{BC} \cong \overline{DC}$, and $\angle BCA \cong \angle DCA$.
            Because $\angle BCA \cong \angle DCA$, it follows that $\overline{AC} \perp \overline{BD}$.

     2. $\angle 1 \cong \angle 4$ and $\overline{BC} \cong \overline{CD}$.
            What can you conclude?

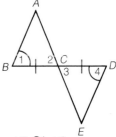

            We know $\angle 1 \cong \angle 4$.
            We know $\overline{BC} \cong \overline{CD}$.
            Because $\angle 2$ and $\angle 3$ are vertical angles, $\angle 2 \cong \angle 3$.
            By ASA, $\triangle ABC \cong \triangle EDC$.
            Thus, we have these congruent, corresponding parts: $\overline{AB} \cong \overline{ED}$, $\angle A \cong \angle E$, and $\overline{AC} \cong \overline{EC}$.

Try This...   1. $\overline{RS} \cong \overline{RT}$ and $\overline{SQ} \cong \overline{QT}$.
What can you conclude?

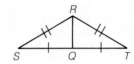

▲▲ Applying Corresponding Parts

We can use corresponding parts of congruent triangles to solve problems.

Example   3. Explain how you could use congruent triangles to find the
distance across a marsh.

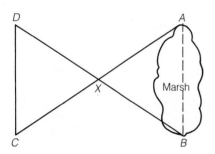

Mark off distances AX and BX. Extend
$\overline{AX}$ and $\overline{BX}$ so that point X becomes
the midpoint of $\overline{AC}$ and $\overline{BD}$. Then
$\triangle ABX \cong \triangle CDX$ by SAS.
Thus, $\overline{DC} \cong \overline{AB}$ as corresponding parts. Then
we can measure $\overline{DC}$ knowing $DC = AB$.

Try This...   2. Explain how you could
use congruent triangles
to find the distance PQ
across a lake.

▲▲ Explaining Conclusions

Our knowledge of congruent triangles can help us to explain how certain
conclusions are reached.

Example 4. $\angle 1 \cong \angle 2$ and $\overline{AB} \cong \overline{AD}$.
Explain why $\overline{BC} \cong \overline{DC}$.

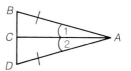

We know $\angle 1 \cong \angle 2$.

We know $\overline{AB} \cong \overline{AD}$.

We know $\overline{AC} \cong \overline{AC}$.

By SAS, $\triangle ABC \cong \triangle ADC$.

Thus, by corresponding parts of congruent triangles, $\overline{BC} \cong \overline{DC}$.

Try This... 3. $\overline{RS} \cong \overline{RT}$ and $\overline{SQ} \cong \overline{QT}$.
Explain why $\angle RSQ \cong \angle RTQ$.

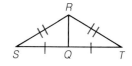

Example 5. $\overrightarrow{QS}$ bisects $\angle PQR$ and $\overline{RQ} \cong \overline{PQ}$.
Explain why $\angle R \cong \angle P$.

We know $\overrightarrow{QS}$ bisects $\angle PQR$,
so $\angle RQS \cong \angle PQS$.

We know $\overline{RQ} \cong \overline{PQ}$.

We know $\overline{QS} \cong \overline{QS}$.

By SAS, $\triangle SRQ \cong \triangle SPQ$.

Thus, by corresponding parts of congruent triangles, $\angle R \cong \angle P$.

Try This... 4. T is the midpoint of $\overline{AG}$,
$\overline{AB} \cong \overline{FG}$ and $\overline{BT} \cong \overline{FT}$.
Explain why $\angle B \cong \angle F$.

Exercises

▲ **Tell what you can conclude about each figure.**

1. $\overline{AB} \cong \overline{BC}$ and $\overline{EB} \cong \overline{DB}$

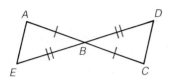

2. $\angle R \cong \angle T$, $\angle W \cong \angle V$ and $\overline{RW} \cong \overline{TV}$

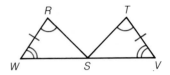

3. $\overline{GK} \perp \overline{LJ}$, $\overline{HK} \cong \overline{KJ}$, and $\overline{GK} \cong \overline{LK}$

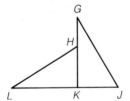

4. $\overline{AB} \cong \overline{DC}$ and $\angle BAC \cong \angle DCA$

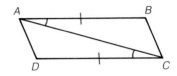

5. $\overline{AR} \cong \overline{AK}$ and $\overline{RT} \cong \overline{KT}$

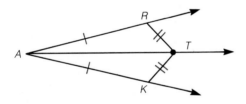

6. $\overline{RH} \cong \overline{CM}$, $\overline{TH} \cong \overline{LM}$, and $\angle 1$ is supplementary to $\angle 3$

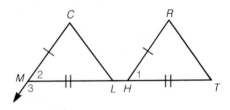

▲▲ **Use corresponding parts to solve these problems.**

7. On a pair of pinking shears, the indicated angles and sides are congruent. Explain why P is the midpoint of $\overline{GR}$.

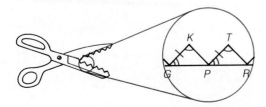

8. On this national flag, the indicated segments and angles are congruent. Explain why P is the midpoint of $\overline{EF}$.

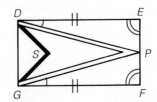

9. The indicated sides of a kite are congruent. Explain why $\angle 1 \cong \angle 2$.

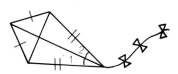

10. On an arrowhead, the indicated angles are congruent. Explain why $\angle R \cong \angle M$.

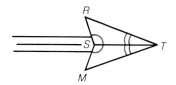

11. According to legend, an officer of Napoleon used the following method to determine the width of a river.

He looked across the river at point Q by sighting under the visor of his cap. He then turned and sighted up the river to point S. Pacing the distance BS, he announced that BS was the river's width. Explain his method.

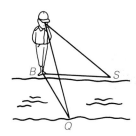

▲▲▲ **Explain each conclusion.**

12. $\angle K \cong \angle T$, $\angle G \cong \angle R$, and $\overline{GK} \cong \overline{RT}$. Explain why P is the midpoint of $\overline{GR}$.

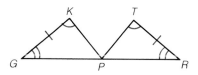

13. $\overline{PQ} \cong \overline{ST}$, $\angle P \cong \angle S$, and $\angle Q \cong \angle T$. Explain why $\overline{PR} \cong \overline{SV}$.

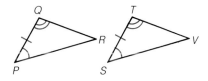

14. $\overline{AR} \cong \overline{AK}$ and $\overline{RT} \cong \overline{KT}$. Explain why $\overrightarrow{AT}$ bisects $\angle RAK$.

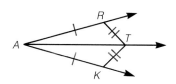

15. $\overline{PU} \cong \overline{PT}$ and $\angle 1 \cong \angle 2$. Explain why $\overline{US} \cong \overline{TS}$.

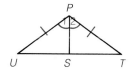

16. $\angle CAB \cong \angle DAB$ and $\angle CBA \cong \angle DBA$. Explain why $\overline{CB} \cong \overline{DB}$.

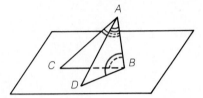

17. $\overline{RH} \cong \overline{CM}$, $\overline{TH} \cong \overline{LM}$, and $\angle 1$ is supplementary to $\angle 3$. Explain why $\overline{RT} \cong \overline{CL}$.

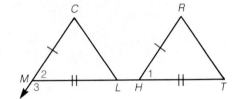

▶◀ Activity

How many different triangles can you find in this figure?

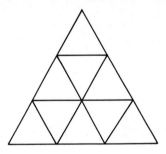

How many different triangles can you find in this figure?

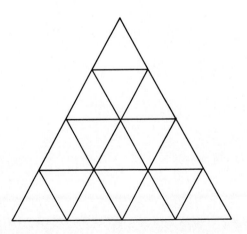

2   Overlapping Triangles

After finishing Section 2, you should be able to
▲   *identify overlapping triangles.*
▲▲   *reach conclusions based on overlapping triangles.*
▲▲   *explain conclusions based on overlapping triangles.*

▲   Identifying Overlapping Triangles

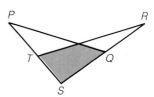

We call the shaded region the *interior* of △ *ABC*.
Triangles whose interiors overlap are called *overlapping triangles*.

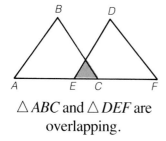

△ *ABC* and △ *DEF* are
overlapping.

△ *PQS* and △ *RTS* are
overlapping.

Examples   Identify the overlapping triangles.

1. △ *QPT* and △ *STP* are overlapping.

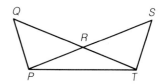

2. △ *RSW* and △ *QTV* are overlapping.

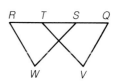

Try This...   Identify the overlapping triangles.

1.

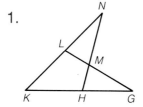

2.

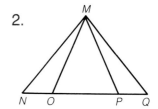

▲▲ Reaching Conclusions Based on Overlapping Triangles

We can reach conclusions by examining overlapping triangles.

Examples 3. $\overline{QP} \cong \overline{ST}$ and $\angle QPT \cong \angle STP$.
What can you conclude?

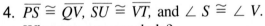

We know $\overline{QP} \cong \overline{ST}$.
We know $\angle QPT \cong \angle STP$.
We know $\overline{PT} \cong \overline{PT}$.
By SAS, $\triangle QPT \cong \triangle STP$.
Thus, we have these congruent, corresponding parts:
$\angle Q \cong \angle S$, $\angle QTP \cong \angle SPT$, and $\overline{QT} \cong \overline{SP}$.

4. $\overline{PS} \cong \overline{QV}$, $\overline{SU} \cong \overline{VT}$, and $\angle S \cong \angle V$.
What can you conclude?

We know $\overline{PS} \cong \overline{QV}$.
We know $\overline{SU} \cong \overline{VT}$.
We know $\angle S \cong \angle V$.
By SAS, $\triangle PSU \cong \triangle QVT$.
Thus, we have these congruent, corresponding parts:
$\angle P \cong \angle Q$, $\angle SUP \cong \angle VTQ$, and $\overline{PU} \cong \overline{QT}$.

Try This... 3. $\overline{TV} \cong \overline{SW}$, $\overline{RS} \cong \overline{QT}$, and
$\angle RSW \cong \angle QTV$. What
can you conclude?

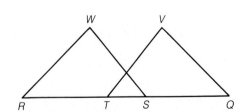

▲▲ Explaining Conclusions

When we solve problems involving overlapping triangles, it may be
helpful to draw the triangles separately.

Example   5. $\overline{QP} \cong \overline{ST}$ and $\angle QPT \cong \angle STP$.
Explain why $\triangle QPT \cong \triangle STP$.

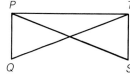

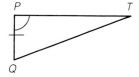

When we look at the triangles separately, we see that $\overline{QP} \cong \overline{ST}$
and $\angle QPT \cong \angle STP$. We also know $\overline{PT} \cong \overline{PT}$. This means that
$\triangle QPT \cong \triangle STP$ by SAS.

Try This...   4. $\overline{AB} \cong \overline{DF}$, $\overline{AC} \cong \overline{EF}$,
and $\overline{BC} \cong \overline{DE}$. Explain
why $\triangle ABC \cong \triangle FDE$.

Example   6. $\overline{TV} \cong \overline{SW}$, $\overline{RT} \cong \overline{QS}$,
and $\angle RSW \cong \angle QTV$.
Explain why $\angle W \cong \angle V$.

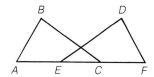

First we draw the triangles
separately and label our drawings.

We know that $\overline{SW} \cong \overline{TV}$ and $\angle RSW \cong \angle QTV$. $\overline{TS}$ is common to both
$\overline{RS}$ and $\overline{QT}$. Because we know that $\overline{RT} \cong \overline{QS}$, we can think of "adding"
the common segment, $\overline{TS}$, to $\overline{RS}$ and to $\overline{QT}$. This means $\overline{RS} \cong \overline{QT}$.
Thus, by SAS, $\triangle RSW \cong \triangle QTV$. Then we know that $\angle W \cong \angle V$
by corresponding parts.

Try This...   5. $\overline{RT} \cong \overline{QS}$, $\overline{RW} \cong \overline{QV}$, and $\overline{WS} \cong \overline{VT}$. Explain why $\angle R \cong \angle Q$.

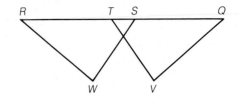

Exercises

▲   **Identify the overlapping triangles.**

1.
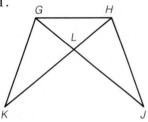

2.
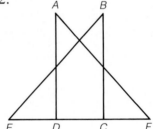

3.
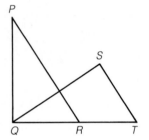

▲▲ **Tell what you can conclude from the given information. Explain how you know.**

4. $\overline{MN} \cong \overline{MQ}$, $\overline{MO} \cong \overline{MP}$, and $\angle NMP \cong \angle QMO$

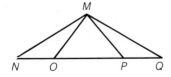

5. $\overline{PO} \cong \overline{RQ}$, $\overline{VP} \cong \overline{TR}$, and $\angle P \cong \angle R$

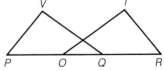

6. $\angle N \cong \angle G$ and $\overline{NK} \cong \overline{GK}$

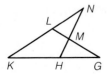

7. $\overline{RK} \cong \overline{LP}$ and $\angle KRL \cong \angle PLR$

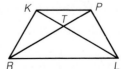

8. $\angle A \cong \angle D$, $\overline{AC} \cong \overline{DB}$, and $\angle ACE \cong \angle DBE$.

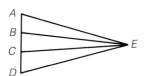

9. $\overline{PS} \cong \overline{PT}$ and $\angle RTP \cong \angle QSP$.

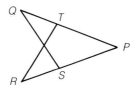

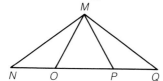 **Explain each conclusion.**

10. $\overline{MN} \cong \overline{MQ}$, $\overline{MO} \cong \overline{MP}$, and $\angle NMP \cong \angle QMO$. Explain why $\angle MNP \cong \angle MQO$.

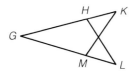

11. $\angle N \cong \angle G$ and $\overline{NK} \cong \overline{GK}$. Explain why $\triangle NKH \cong \triangle GKL$.

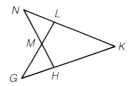

12. $\overline{GH} \cong \overline{GM}$ and $\overline{HK} \cong \overline{ML}$. Explain why $\angle K \cong \angle L$.

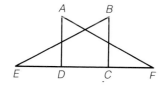

13. $\angle D \cong \angle K$, $\overline{DF} \cong \overline{KE}$, and $\angle DFS \cong \angle KES$. Explain why $\angle DSF \cong \angle KSE$.

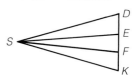

14. $\overline{AD} \perp \overline{EF}$, $\overline{BC} \perp \overline{EF}$, $\overline{AD} \cong \overline{BC}$, and $\angle A \cong \angle B$. Explain why $\angle E \cong \angle F$.

15. $\angle P \cong \angle T$, $\overline{PQ} \cong \overline{TS}$, and $\overline{PR} \cong \overline{TQ}$. Explain why $\angle QST \cong \angle RQP$.

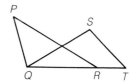

▶ Extension Exercises

16. All the triangles in the geodesic dome are congruent. What is true of the sides of all the triangles?

17. The bridge shown below is constructed with triangular supports. All the overlapping triangles are congruent. What can you conclude about ∠1, ∠2, and ∠3? Explain how you know.

18. In the offshore drilling platform, $\overline{RK} \cong \overline{LP}$ and $\angle KRL \cong \angle PLR$. Explain why $\overline{KL} \cong \overline{PR}$.

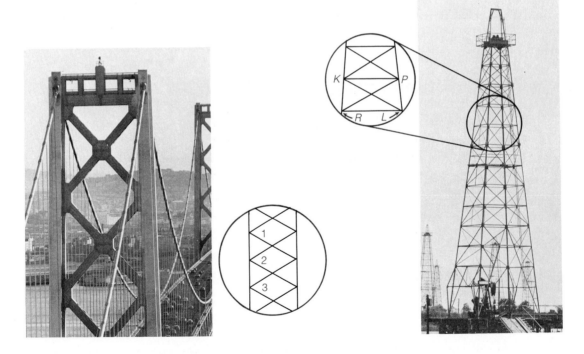

3	## The Isosceles Triangle Theorem

After finishing Section 3, you should be able to
▲   *solve problems involving the Isosceles Triangle Theorem.*
▲▲   *reach conclusions based on isosceles triangles.*

▲
▲▲   *explain conclusions based on isosceles triangles.*

▲ ## Isosceles Triangles

We know that isosceles triangles have at least
two congruent sides. The third side is called
the *base*. The angles opposite the congruent
sides are called the *base angles*. The angle
opposite the base is called the *vertex angle*.

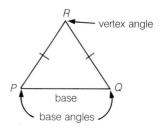

1. Draw △*ABC* such that
    AB = *BC* = 5 cm.
2. Cut out △*ABC* and fold
    as shown.
3. What is true of both ∠*A*
    and ∠*C*?
4. Draw △*PQR* such that
    ∠*P* ≅ ∠*R*.
5. Cut out △*PQR* and fold
    as shown.
6. What is true of $\overline{PQ}$ and $\overline{QR}$?

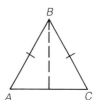

The drawing exercise suggests that whenever two sides of a triangle are congruent, the
angles opposite them are congruent. Conversely, it seems that whenever two angles of
a triangle are congruent, the sides opposite them are congruent.

THEOREM
5.1

The Isosceles Triangle Theorem

Two sides of a triangle are congruent whenever the angles opposite them are congruent.

Two angles of a triangle are congruent whenever the sides opposite them are congruent.

Example 1. Find $m \angle S$.

Because $\overline{TS} \cong \overline{TR}$, we know $m \angle S = m \angle R$. Thus, $m \angle S = 65°$

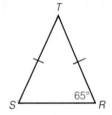

In Example 1 we used the fact that if two sides of a triangle are congruent, then the angles opposite them are congruent.

Example 2. In $\triangle GHK$, $GK = 27$. Find GH.

Because $\angle H \cong \angle K$, we know $\overline{GH} \cong \overline{GK}$. Thus, because $GK = 27$, we know $GH = 27$.

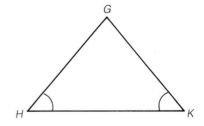

In Example 2 we used the fact that if two angles of a triangle are congruent, then the sides opposite them are congruent.

Try This... 1. Find $m \angle A$.

2. In $\triangle PQR$, $PR = 16$.
Find PQ.

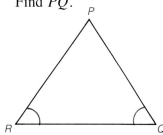

Example ▲3. Find x.

Because $MN = QN$, we know
$m \angle M = m \angle Q$. Thus,

$$3x = 51 \qquad \text{Solving for } x$$
$$x = 17$$

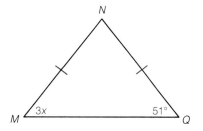

Example ▲4. Find y.

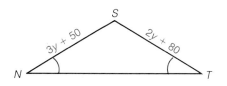

Because $\angle N \cong \angle T$, we know $NS = TS$. Thus
$$3y + 50 = 2y + 80$$
$$3y = 2y + 30 \qquad \text{Solving for } y$$
$$y = 30$$

Try This... ▲3. Find x.

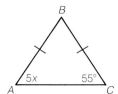

▲4. Find y.

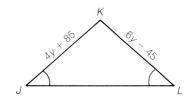

▲▲ Reaching Conclusions Based on Isosceles Triangles

We can also reach conclusions based on isosceles triangles.

Examples   5. $\angle 1 \cong \angle 4$. What can you conclude?

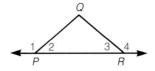

We know $\angle 1 \cong \angle 4$.
$\angle 1$ and $\angle 2$ form a linear pair as do $\angle 3$ and $\angle 4$.
Thus, $\angle 1$ is supplementary to $\angle 2$ and $\angle 3$ is
supplementary to $\angle 4$.
Now we know $\angle 2 \cong \angle 3$ because supplements
of congruent angles are congruent.
By the Isosceles Triangle Theorem, $\overline{PQ} \cong \overline{QR}$.
Hence, $\triangle PQR$ is an isosceles triangle.

6. $\overline{ST} \cong \overline{SV}$. What can you conclude?

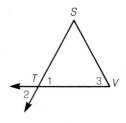

We know $\overline{ST} \cong \overline{SV}$.
By the Isosceles Triangle Theorem,
$\angle 1 \cong \angle 3$.
$\angle 1 \cong \angle 2$ because they are vertical angles.
Thus, $\angle 2 \cong \angle 3$.

Try This...   5. $\overline{AB} \cong \overline{CB}$. What can you conclude?

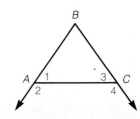

▲▲ Explaining Conclusions

The Isosceles Triangle Theorem can be used to help explain conclusions.

Example   7. $\angle 1 \cong \angle 4$. Explain why $\triangle PQR$ is isosceles.

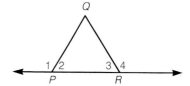

We know $\angle 1 \cong \angle 4$.
$\angle 1$ is supplementary to $\angle 2$ and $\angle 3$ is supplementary to $\angle 4$ because each pair of angles forms a linear pair.
We know $\angle 2 \cong \angle 3$ by Theorem 3.1.
Because $\angle 2 \cong \angle 3$, $\overline{RQ} \cong \overline{RQ}$ by the Isosceles Triangle Theorem.
Thus, $\triangle PQR$ is an isosceles triangle.

Try This...   6. $\triangle ABC$ is isosceles with $\overline{AB} \cong \overline{CB}$. Explain why $\angle 2 \cong \angle 4$.

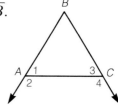

A theorem that is proved easily from another theorem can be called a *corollary*. "Corollary" comes from the Greek word that means "gift."

A corollary that follows easily from the Isosceles Triangle Theorem is stated below.

COROLLARY   A triangle is equilateral whenever it is equiangular.
  5.2

Exercises

▲ **Solve.**

1. Find $m\angle Q$.

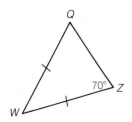

2. Find $m\angle T$.

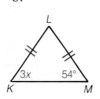

3. In $\triangle ABC$, $AB = 62$. Find AC.

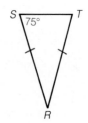

4. In $\triangle DEF$, $DE = 78$.
   Find DF.

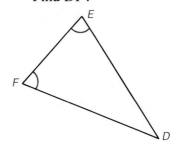

▲ **Find x for each figure.**

5.

6.

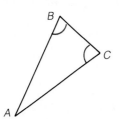

7.

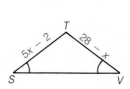

8.

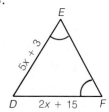

9.

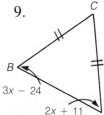

10.

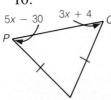

11.

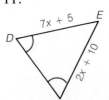

12.

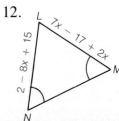

▲▲ **What can you conclude from the given information? Explain how you know.**

13. $\overline{GR} \cong \overline{PR}$.

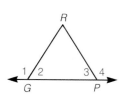

14. $\angle 1 \cong \angle 4$.

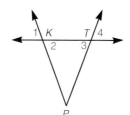

15. $\overline{RS} \cong \overline{WS}$ and $\overline{RT} \cong \overline{WV}$.

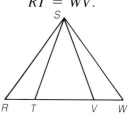

▲▲ **Explain each conclusion.**

16. $\overline{FD} \cong \overline{ED}$. Explain why $\angle 3 \cong \angle 2$.

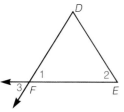

17. $\overline{GR} \cong \overline{PR}$. Explain why $\angle 1 \cong \angle 4$.

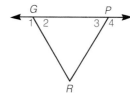

18. $\overline{MN} \cong \overline{MQ}$. Explain why $\angle 2 \cong \angle 3$.

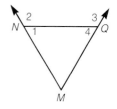

19. $\angle 1 \cong \angle 4$. Explain why $\triangle KPT$ is isosceles.

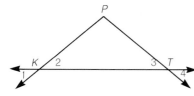

20. $\overline{RS} \cong \overline{WS}$ and $\overline{RT} \cong \overline{VW}$. Explain why $\triangle STV$ is isosceles.

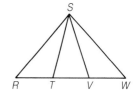

▶◀ Activity

Connect two congruent cardboard strips at one end with a paper fastener. Punch a hole at the other end of each strip.
(The holes should be the same distance from the end of each strip.)
Securely tie a string through one hole and then thread the string through the second hole. Pull the string taut.

What kind of triangle does *CAT* form?

Slide *T* away from *C* along the string, keeping the string taut. What kind of triangle does *CAT* form now?

Does changing the distance between *C* and *T* affect the type of triangle formed? Explain how you know.

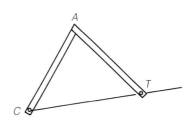

4	The Perpendicular Bisector Theorem

After finishing Section 4, you should be able to
▲ *solve problems using the Perpendicular Bisector Theorem.*

We already know that for any point on a segment there is exactly one line in a plane that is perpendicular to the segment at that point.

DEFINITION

The line that is perpendicular to a segment at its midpoint is the **perpendicular bisector** of the segment.

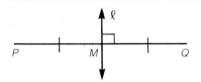

1. Draw $\overline{PQ}$.

2. Use a compass to find points that are equidistant from P and Q.

> A point is **equidistant** from P and Q if it is the same distance from P and Q.

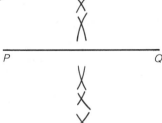

3. Find at least ten such points.

4. Describe the entire set of such points.

THEOREM

5.3

The Perpendicular Bisector Theorem

In a plane, a point is on the perpendicular bisector of a segment whenever it is equidistant from the endpoints of the segment.

Any point on the perpendicular bisector of a segment is equidistant from the endpoints of the segment.

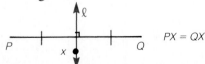

Example   1. $\overleftrightarrow{HG}$ is the perpendicular bisector of $\overline{AB}$. $HA = 9$ and $GB = 7$. Find HB and GA.

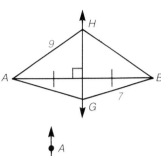

Because $HA = 9$, we know $HB = 9$.
Because $GB = 7$, we know $GA = 7$.

Try This...   1. $\overleftrightarrow{AP}$ is the perpendicular bisector of $\overline{DF}$. $DA = 10$ and $PF = 6$. Find DP and FA.

Example   ▲2. On the windmill, $\overleftrightarrow{RS}$ is the perpendicular bisector of $\overline{TV}$. $RT = 42$ and $RV = 3y - 21$. Find y.

Because R is on the perpendicular bisector of $\overline{TV}$, we know $RT = RV$. Thus,

$$42 = 3y - 21$$
$$63 = 3y$$
$$21 = y$$

Try This... ▲2. On the windmill, $SV = 74$ and $ST = 5x - 1$. Find x.

The perpendicular bisector of a segment is an example of a locus. A **locus** is the set that contains all the points that satisfy a given condition.

The following corollary is a direct result of the Perpendicular Bisector Theorem.

COROLLARY 5.4   In a plane, if points P and Q are equidistant from the endpoints of $\overline{XY}$, then $\overleftrightarrow{PQ}$ is the perpendicular bisector of $\overline{XY}$.

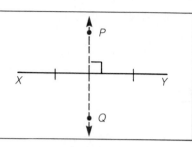

Exercises

▲ **Refer to the drawing for Exercises 1-10. Line ℓ is the perpendicular bisector of $\overline{TS}$.**

1. If $RS = 20$, what is RT?

2. If $HT = 11$, what is HS?

3. If $QS = 17$, what is QT?

4. If $PT = 10.5$, what is PS?

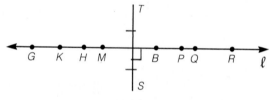

▲5. If $KT = 3x + 7$ and $KS = 19$, what is x?

▲6. If $RT = 9y + 2$, and $RS = 29$, what is y?

▲7. If $QT = 8x$ and $QS = 2(x + 6)$, what is x?

▲8. If $MT = 8y$ and $MS = 3(y + 5)$, what is y?

▲9. If $GT = 7$ and $GS = \frac{d}{5} + 2$, what is d?

▲10. If $BS = 38$ and $BT = 4m - 6$, what is m?

▶ Extension Exercises

11. $\triangle XYZ$ is isosceles with $\overline{XY} \cong \overline{XZ}$. Explain why X is on the perpendicular bisector of $\overline{YZ}$.

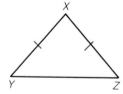

12. M is the midpoint of $\overline{AB}$ and $\overrightarrow{MN} \perp \overline{AB}$. Explain why $\triangle ABN$ is isosceles.

13. $\overline{RS} \cong \overline{ST}$ and $\overline{RV} \cong \overline{VT}$. Explain why $\angle SRV \cong \angle STV$.

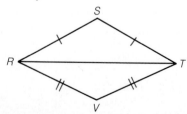

►► Challenge Exercises

14. Sketch the locus of points that are equidistant from the sides of an angle.

15. Sketch the locus of points that are equidistant from the endpoints of a segment.

►◄ Activity

The set of all points that are equidistant from the endpoints of a segment is the perpendicular bisector of the segment.

Demonstrate this by creating a series of index cards, each with segment $\overline{AB}$ and a point equidistant from the endpoints of $\overline{AB}$. Hold one end of the stack of cards firmly in one hand. Flip through the other end with your thumb. What do you see?

Sample cards

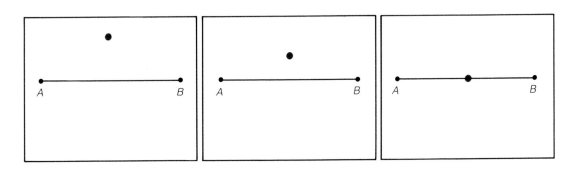

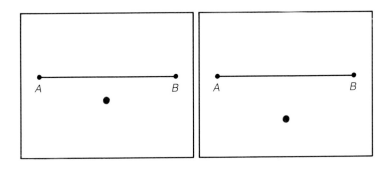

5 | Explaining Constructions

After finishing Section 5, you should be able to
▲ *explain a construction.*

We have done many constructions using a compass and straightedge. We sometimes use congruent triangles to show that a construction actually works. We call this *explaining a construction*.

Example | 1. Explain the construction for copying an angle.

In copying ∠ *ABC*, the compass makes sure that $\overline{BP} \cong \overline{DM}$, $\overline{BQ} \cong \overline{DS}$, and $\overline{PQ} \cong \overline{MS}$.

By SSS, we have △ *PBQ* ≅ △ *MDS*. That means that ∠ *B* ≅ ∠ *D*.

Therefore, ∠ *MDS* is a copy of ∠ *ABC*.

Try This... | 1. Explain the construction for bisecting an angle. See page 56 to review the construction.

Exercises

▲ **Explain these constructions. Refer to the page number in parentheses to review each construction.**

1. Copying a triangle. (page 7)

2. Constructing the perpendicular bisector of a segment. (page 3)

3. Constructing the perpendicular to a line from a point on the line. (page 87)

4. Constructing the perpendicular to a line from a point not on the line. (page 88)

▶▶ Challenge Exercises

5. Devise a construction for a non-perpendicular bisector of a segment. Explain your construction.

▶◀ Activity

Fold a piece of paper in two. Label the endpoints of the fold S and T.

Fold $\overline{ST}$ in half. Unfold the paper and label the endpoints of this new segment P and Q. Label the intersection of $\overline{ST}$ and $\overline{PQ}$, R. Measure $\overline{SR}$ and $\overline{RT}$. Measure $\angle PRS$ and $\angle PRT$. What can you conclude about $\overline{PQ}$?

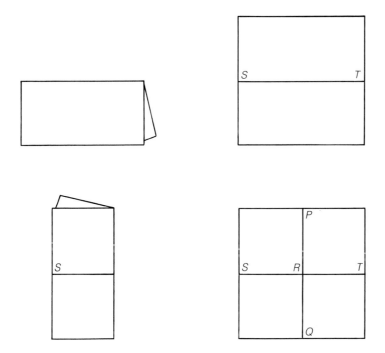

Calculator Application   Finding Lengths of Segments

Some calculators follow different rules for the order of operations
involving addition, subtraction, multiplication, and division.

Calculators with Algebraic Logic   **Calculators without Algebraic Logic**

These calculators do multiplication
and division operations before
addition and subtraction.

These calculators compute numbers
in the order in which they are entered.

Example ℓ is the perpendicular
bisector of $\overline{BD}$. $AB = 4$
and $BD = 12$. Find AC.

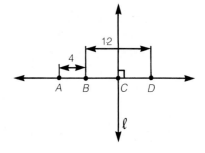

Because ℓ is the perpendicular
bisector of $\overline{BD}$, we know
$BC = BD \div 2$. Thus,

$AB + BC = AC$ Adding to find AC
$AB + (BD \div 2) = AC$ Substituting for BC

Calculators with Algebraic Logic   **Calculators without Algebraic Logic**

Enter: $4 \boxed{+} 12 \boxed{\div} 2 \boxed{=}$ Enter: $4 \boxed{+} 12 \boxed{\div} 2 \boxed{=}$
Display: 10   Display: 8

We are trying to compute $4 + (12 \div 2)$ and *not* $(4 + 12) \div 2$. On a calculator
without algebraic logic, enter $12 \boxed{\div} 2$ first and then add 4. $AC = 10$.

Use your calculator to find the length of each segment.

1. k is the perpendicular bisector of $\overline{SU}$.
    $RS = 4.2$ and $SU = 16.04$. Find RT.

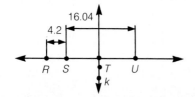

2. m is the perpendicular bisector of $\overline{QS}$.
    $PQ = 0.562$ and $QS = 1.1236$.
    Find PR.

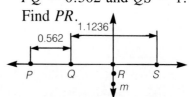

Chapter Review

1 1. P is the midpoint of $\overline{RS}$ and $\angle R \cong \angle S$. What can you conclude?

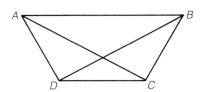

2. $\overline{TF} \perp \overline{SM}$ and F is the midpoint of $\overline{SM}$. Explain why $\angle S \cong \angle M$.

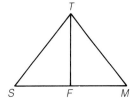

2 3. Identify the overlapping triangles.

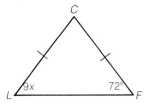

4. $\angle E \cong \angle H$, $\overline{EG} \cong \overline{HF}$, and $\angle DGE \cong \angle DFG$. Explain why $\overline{DG} \cong \overline{DF}$.

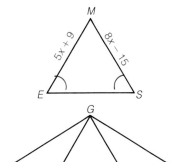

3 **Find x.**

⚠ 5.

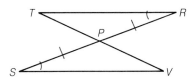

⚠ 6.

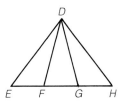

7. $\overline{GK} \cong \overline{GN}$ and $\overline{KM} \cong \overline{NL}$. Explain why $\overline{GM} \cong \overline{GL}$.

4 **Line ℓ is the perpendicular bisector of $\overline{LN}$.**

⚠ 8. If $KL = 5x + 7$ and $KN = 3x + 35$, what is x?

⚠ 9. If $TL = 3(x + 9)$ and $TN = 57$, what is x ?

10. $\overrightarrow{BT}$ is the perpendicular bisector of $\overline{HQ}$. Explain why $\angle H \cong \angle Q$.

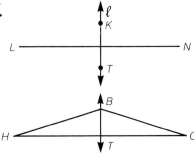

Chapter Test

1. M is the midpoint of both $\overline{DK}$ and $\overline{RP}$. What can you conclude?

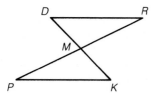

2. $\angle 1 \cong \angle 2$ and $\angle 3 \cong \angle 4$. Explain why $\angle S \cong \angle F$.

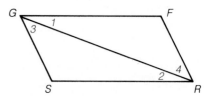

3. Identify the overlapping triangles.

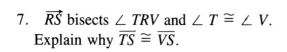

4. $\overline{AD} \cong \overline{BC}$ and $\angle ADC \cong \angle BCD$. Explain why $\overline{AC} \cong \overline{BD}$.

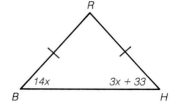

Find x.

▲5.

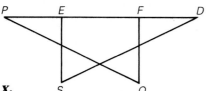

▲6.

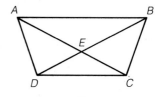

7. $\overrightarrow{RS}$ bisects $\angle TRV$ and $\angle T \cong \angle V$. Explain why $\overline{TS} \cong \overline{VS}$.

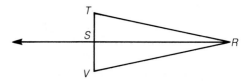

Line ℓ is the perpendicular bisector of $\overline{AB}$.

▲8. If $CA = 2(x + 7)$ and $CB = 5x + 2$, what is x?

▲9. If $RA = 7x - 9$ and $RB = 2(x + 8)$, what is x?

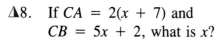

10. $CA = CB$ and $DA = DB$. Explain why F is the midpoint of $\overline{AB}$.

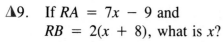

Skills Review   Rounding

Round to the nearest ten.

1.	47	2.	269	3.	595	4.	1,411
5.	3,254	6.	6,246	7.	13,497	8.	83,013

Round to the nearest hundred.

9.	541	10.	352	11.	2,739	12.	42,462
13.	89,910	14.	132,850	15.	770,770	16.	999,999

Round to the nearest thousand.

17.	6,482	18.	5,583	19.	8,701	20.	3,009
21.	42,750	22.	70,991	23.	69,299	24.	132,500

Round to the nearest tenth.

25.	8.72	26.	0.65	27.	3.44	28.	0.09
29.	499.012	30.	24.98	31.	3.6099	32.	7.052

Round to the nearest hundredth.

33.	3.0144	34.	9.745	35.	0.524	36.	8.912
37.	16.396	38.	0.0092	39.	0.0075	40.	4.0156

Round to the nearest whole number.

41.	6.3	42.	8.7	43.	25.43	44.	2.299
45.	307.51	46.	81.476	47.	14.72	48.	69.6

6
Triangles and Inequalities

1   Exterior Angles of a Triangle

After finishing Section 1, you should be able to

▲   *insert the proper symbol, >, <, or =, between measures of segments or angles.*

▲▲   *identify exterior angles and remote interior angles of a triangle.*

▲▲   *solve problems related to the Exterior Angle Theorem.*

▲   Segment and Angle Inequalities

The properties of inequalities can be applied to measures of geometric figures.

	Picture	Measure
Segment	P Q R S	$PQ < RS$
Angle	2 3	$m \angle 2 < m \angle 3$

The table says that $\overline{PQ}$ is shorter than $\overline{RS}$ if the length of $\overline{PQ}$ is less than the length of $\overline{RS}$. Likewise, $\angle 2$ is smaller than $\angle 3$ if the measure of $\angle 2$ is less than the measure of $\angle 3$.

Examples   Insert < or > in each blank to make a true statement.

    1. $AB \underline{\ >\ } CD$ 2. $m \angle 1 \underline{\ <\ } m \angle 3$

Try This...   Insert < or > in each blank to make a true statement.

    1. $BC \underline{\ \ \ \ } GH$ 2. $m \angle 4 \underline{\ \ \ \ } m \angle 5$

The properties of geometric inequalities together with the concept of betweenness and the Angle Addition Postulate lead to some basic theorems.

THEOREM **6.1**	If A, B, and C are any points and A-B-C, then $AC > AB$ and $AC > BC$.	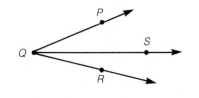
THEOREM **6.2**	If $\angle PQR$ is any angle and S is a point in the interior of $\angle PQR$, then $m \angle PQS < m \angle PQR$ and $m \angle SQR < m \angle PQR$.	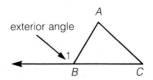

▲▲ Exterior Angles

DEFINITION

An angle that forms a linear pair with an angle of a triangle is an **exterior angle** for the triangle.

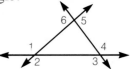

There are two exterior angles at each vertex of a triangle.

$\angle 1$, $\angle 2$, $\angle 3$, $\angle 4$, $\angle 5$, and $\angle 6$ are exterior angles.

The angles of the triangle that are *not* adjacent to a specific exterior angle are called *remote interior angles*.

$\angle 2$ and $\angle 3$ are remote interior angles for $\angle 1$.

Example 3. Name the remote interior angles for the given exterior angles of $\triangle BCD$.

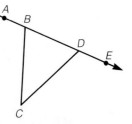

Exterior Angle	Remote Interior Angles
$\angle ABC$	$\angle BCD$ and $\angle BDC$
$\angle CDE$	$\angle BCD$ and $\angle CBD$

Try This... 3. Name the remote interior angles for the exterior angles drawn on the building.

 The Exterior Angle Theorem

We can compare the measure of an exterior angle to the measures of its remote interior angles.

1. Draw △ ABC. Draw $\overrightarrow{BC}$ to form an exterior angle, ∠ ACD.

2. Measure ∠ ACD, ∠ ABC, and ∠ BAC.

3. Compare the measure of ∠ ACD with the measures of its two remote interior angles.

4. Repeat these steps for several triangles.

THEOREM 6.3	*The Exterior Angle Theorem* The measure of an exterior angle of a triangle is greater than the measure of either of its remote interior angles.

Example 4. Consider the triangle formed by a nautical identification flag. What is the relationship between ∠ ACD and ∠ ABC? Explain how you know.

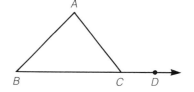

$m \angle ACD > m \angle ABC$ because ∠ ACD is an exterior angle of △ ABC and ∠ ABC is one of its remote interior angles.

Try This... 4. What is the relationship between $m \angle R$ and $m \angle RTQ$ in this triangular shelf brace?

Look at right triangle △ *ABC*.
What is the measure of ∠ *DCA*?
What does the Exterior Angle
Theorem tell us about the measures
of ∠ *A* and ∠ *B* in this triangle?

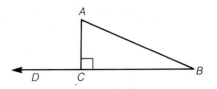

| THEOREM **6.4** | If one angle of a triangle is a right angle, then the other two angles are both acute. |

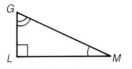

Could there be more than one
perpendicular from point *D* to line ℓ,
as shown at the right?
What is the measure of ∠ *CAD*?
What is the measure of ∠ *DBA*?

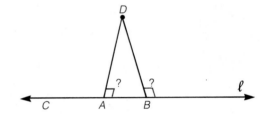

| THEOREM **6.5** | If ℓ is any line and *A* is a point not on ℓ, then there is exactly one line containing *A* that is perpendicular to ℓ. |

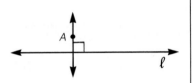

Exercises

▲ **Insert < or > in each blank to make a true statement.**

1. *AB* _____ *RS*

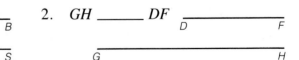

2. *GH* _____ *DF*

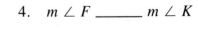

3. *m* ∠ *C* _____ *m* ∠ *B*

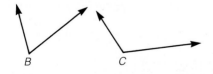

4. *m* ∠ *F* _____ *m* ∠ *K*

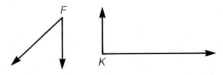

▲▲ **For each exterior angle, name its remote interior angles.**

5.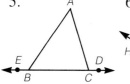

6.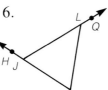

7.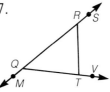

8.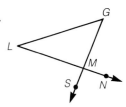

▲
▲▲ **What are the relationships between the measures of the indicated angles?**

9. ∠*AFC* and ∠*D*

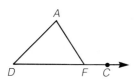

10. ∠*TVR* and ∠*S*

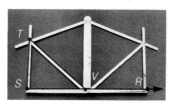

11. ∠*K* and ∠*KSH*

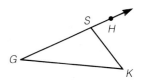

▶ **Extension Exercises**

Insert <, >, or = in each blank to make a true statement about the figure.

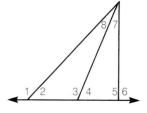

12. *m* ∠8 _____ *m* ∠4

13. *m* ∠1 _____ *m* ∠3

14. *m* ∠3 _____ *m* ∠7

15. *m* ∠1 _____ *m* ∠5

16. How are the exterior angles of an equilateral triangle related to each other?

17. Explain why a triangle with an obtuse angle must have two other angles that are both acute.

18. Which is greater, *m* ∠*DCE* or *m* ∠*ABD*? Explain how you know.

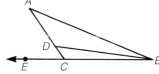

19. Can a triangle have two right angles? Explain how you know.

20. Explain why the sum of the measures of any two angles of a triangle is less than 180°.

| **2** | The Opposite Parts Theorem |

After finishing Section 2, you should be able to

▲ *solve problems using the Opposite Parts Theorem and its converse.*

We can relate the measure of each angle of a triangle to the measure of the side opposite the angle.

1. Draw a large scalene triangle.
2. Measure each side.
3. List the sides from largest to smallest.
4. Measure each angle.
5. List the angles from largest to smallest.

THEOREM 6.6 *The Opposite Parts Theorem* In any △ *ABC*, if *CA* > *CB*, then *m ∠B* > *m ∠A.*

Example   1. In △ *PQR, PR* > *PQ*. What is true of ∠*Q* and ∠*R?*

$$m \angle Q > m\angle R$$

Try This...   1. In △ *RST, RS* > *RT*. What is true of ∠*T* and ∠*S?*

Example   2. Jordan (*J*), Cohagen (*C*), and Sand Springs (*S*) are three towns in Garfield County, Montana. They form the vertices of △ *JCS*. List the angles of △ *JCS* from smallest to largest.

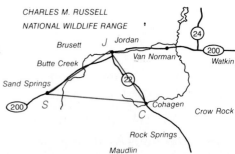

∠*S*, ∠*C*, ∠*J*

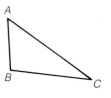

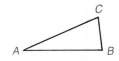

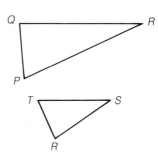

Try This... 2. In △ *ABC*, *AB* = 9, *BC* = 18, and *AC* = 24. List the angles from smallest to largest.

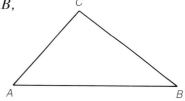

The converse of the Opposite Parts Theorem is also true.

| THEOREM 6.7 | In any △ *ABC*, if *m∠C* > *m* ∠*B*, then *AB* > *AC*. |

Example 3. In △*GKH*, *m* ∠ *G* = 55°
m ∠ *H* = 61°
m ∠ *K* = 64°.
List the sides from shortest to longest.

$\overline{KH}$, $\overline{GK}$, $\overline{GH}$

Try This... 3. Three stars determine △ *LMN*, with *m* ∠*L* = 45°, *m∠M* = 55°, and *m∠N* = 80°. List the sides from shortest to longest.

Two corollaries follow from Theorems 6.6 and 6.7.

COROLLARY **6.8** No two angles of a scalene triangle are congruent.

COROLLARY **6.9** In a right triangle, the hypotenuse is the longest side.

The **hypotenuse** is the side opposite the right angle.

Exercises

▲ 1. In △GHK, GH > GK. What is true of the angles?

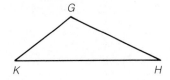

2. On the road sign, KJ > KH. What is true of ∠J and ∠H?

List the angles from smallest to largest.

3.
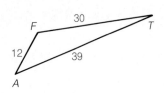

4.
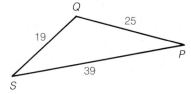

List the sides from shortest to longest.

5.
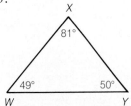

6.
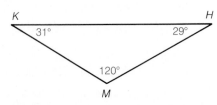

► **Extension Exercises**

7. Restate Theorems 6.6 and 6.7 replacing all symbols with words.
8. Is any equilateral triangle also equiangular? Explain how you know.
9. Is any equiangular triangle also equilateral? Explain how you know.
10. $m\angle2 > m\angle1$. What can you conclude about $m\angle2$ and $m\angle3$? About $\overline{AC}$ and $\overline{BC}$?

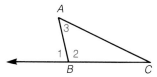

11. $m\angle G > m\angle N$. What can you conclude about $\overline{NK}$ and $\overline{MK}$? (Hint: Consider exterior angle $\angle KMN$.)

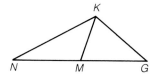

12. $m\angle S < m\angle Q$ and $PR < PQ$. What can you conclude about $m\angle S$ and $m\angle PRS$?

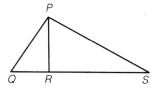

►► Challenge Exercises

13. $\overline{DE} \cong \overline{DF}$, *E-B-S*, and *D-B-F*. Compare $\overline{ES}$ and $\overline{FS}$. What theorems did you use to make the comparison?

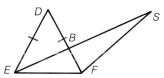

14. $\overline{PQ} \cong \overline{PR}$ and *Q-R-S*. Compare $\overline{PS}$ and $\overline{PQ}$. What theorems did you use to make the comparison?

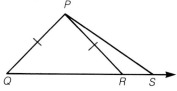

3 | The Triangle Inequality

After finishing Section 3, you should be able to
▲ *solve problems related to the Triangle Inequality.*

Crows fly from one point to another in a straight
line. Thus, we can speak of the distance between
two cities "as the crow flies." We can prove that
the length of the crow's path is the shortest
distance between two points.

THEOREM 6.10	The sum of the lengths of any two sides of a triangle is greater than the length of the third side.

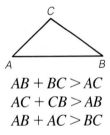

$$AB + BC > AC$$
$$AC + CB > AB$$
$$AB + AC > BC$$

To go from Kingsville to Perryville
by way of Essex is longer than
going directly from Kingsville to
Perryville.

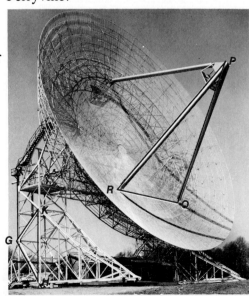

Example 1. Consider △ *PQR* in the radar
scanner. List three true state-
ments of inequality.

$$PQ + QR > PR$$
$$QP + PR > QR$$
$$PR + RQ > PQ$$

Try This... 1. Consider △*GKH* in the
scanner. List three true
statements of inequality
about △*GKH*.

If the sum of the lengths of any two segments is not greater than the length of a third segment, then the segments cannot form a triangle.

Examples   Can these triples of numbers be the lengths of the sides of a triangle?

2. 5, 7, 9

   Yes, because 5 + 7 > 9, 5 + 9 > 7, and 9 + 7 > 5.

3. 2, 3, 7

   No, because 2 + 3 < 7.

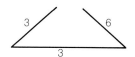

4. 3, 3, 6

   No, because 3 + 3 = 6.

Try This...   Can these triples of numbers be the lengths of the sides of a triangle?

2. 5, 6, 9   3. 2, 2, 4   4. 7, 2, 11

Proof of Theorem 6.10

Consider △ *ABC*. We shall prove that *AB* + *BC* > *CA*. On the ray opposite $\overrightarrow{BC}$, find point *D* such that *AB* = *DB*. Because *D-B-C*, it follows that *DC* = *DB* + *BC*. Thus, *DC* = *AB* + *BC*.

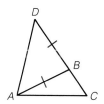

B is in the interior of ∠*DAC*. So we know *m* ∠*DAC* > *m* ∠*DAB* by Theorem 6.2.

Because *AB* = *DB*, the Isosceles Triangle Theorem states that *m* ∠*D* = *m* ∠*DAB*. Hence *m* ∠*DAC* > *m* ∠*D*.

Thus, by Theorem 6.7, we have *DC* > *CA*. Because *DC* = *AB* + *BC*, it follows that *AB* + *BC* > *CA*, which is what we want to prove.

Exercises

▲ **Make three true statements of inequality for each triangle.**

1.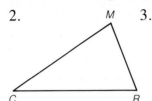
2.
3.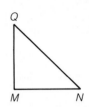
4.

Can these triples of numbers be the lengths of the sides of a triangle?

5. $8, 9, 10$

6. $1, 1, 2$

7. $6.2, 9.3, 8.6$

8. $2.4, 5.2, 7.6$

9. $9.4, 0.8, 10.1$

10. $0.5, 8.3, 1.03$

11. $3\frac{1}{2}, 5\frac{1}{8}, 6$

12. $7\frac{1}{4}, 9\frac{1}{2}, 2\frac{3}{4}$

13. $8\frac{5}{8}, 3, 6\frac{1}{4}$

▶ **Extension Exercises**

14. Suppose the lengths of the sides of a triangle are 8, 5, and x. What can you conclude about x?

15. What is the relationship between the difference of the lengths of any two sides of a triangle and the third side?

16. In square $ABCD$, explain why the length of the diagonal $\overline{BD}$ must be greater than 3 and less than 6.

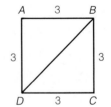

17. In rectangle $PQRS$, compare $PQ + QR + RS + SP$ and $QS + PR$.

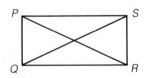

▶◀ **Activity**

Cut three straws with the following lengths: $3\frac{1}{2}$ inches, $3\frac{1}{2}$ inches, and 7 inches. Put the ends of the straws together to form a triangle.

What happened? Why?

Cut off one inch from the 7-inch straw. Now put the ends of the straws together to form a triangle.

What happened? Why?

4   Inequalities in Two Triangles

After finishing Section 4, you should be able to
▲ *reach conclusions about pairs of triangles.*

We can compare the measures of sides and angles of two triangles.

1. Draw $\triangle PQR$.

2. Draw another triangle, $\triangle P'Q'R'$. Make $m\angle P' > m\angle P$, $P'Q' = PQ$, and $P'R' = PR$.

3. Compare RQ and $R'Q'$.

THEOREM   *The Derrick Theorem*

6.11   In $\triangle PQR$ and $\triangle P'Q'R'$, if $\overline{PQ} \cong \overline{P'Q'}$, $\overline{PR} \cong \overline{P'R'}$, and $m\angle P < m\angle P'$, then $RQ < R'Q'$.

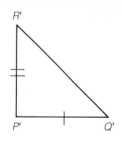

Example   1. In $\triangle ABC$ and $\triangle GHK$, $\overline{AB} \cong \overline{GH}$, $\overline{AC} \cong \overline{GK}$, and $m\angle A < m\angle G$. What can you conclude?

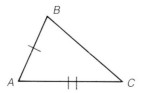
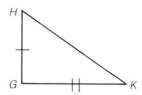

By the Derrick Theorem, $BC < HK$.

Try This... 1. In $\triangle DEF$ and $\triangle RST$, $\overline{DE} \cong \overline{RS}$, $\overline{DF} \cong \overline{RT}$, and $m \angle D < m \angle R$. What can you conclude?

Example 2. Consider $\triangle CLF$ and $\triangle HJK$. What can you conclude?

 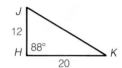

Because $CL = HJ = 12$, we know $\overline{CL} \cong \overline{HJ}$. Also, $CF = HK = 20$, so $\overline{CF} \cong \overline{HK}$. Because $m \angle C = 32°$ and $m \angle H = 88°$, we know $m\angle C < \angle H$. Thus, by the Derrick Theorem, $LF < JK$.

Try This... 2. Consider $\triangle XYZ$ and $\triangle MNK$. What can you conclude?

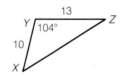

A converse of the Derrick Theorem is also true.

THEOREM **6.12** In $\triangle PQR$ and $\triangle P'Q'R'$, if $\overline{PQ} \cong \overline{P'Q'}$, $\overline{PR} \cong \overline{P'R'}$, and $RQ < R'Q'$, then $m\angle P < m\angle P'$.

Example 3. Consider $\triangle ABC$ and $\triangle GHK$. What can you conclude?

$AB = GH = 10$, so $\overline{AB} \cong \overline{GH}$.
$AC = GK = 15$, so $\overline{AC} \cong \overline{GK}$.
$BC = 17$ and $HK = 23$, so $BC < HK$.

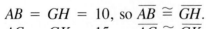  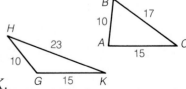

Thus, by Theorem 6.12, we know $m\angle A < m\angle G$.

Try This...   3. Consider △ *PQR* and △ *TUV*.
What can you conclude?

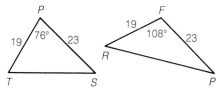

Exercises

▲   **What can you conclude about each pair of triangles?**

1. In △*GHK* and △*DEF*, $\overline{GH} \cong \overline{DE}$, $\overline{GK} \cong \overline{DF}$, and $m\angle G < m\angle D$.

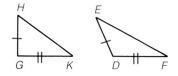

2. In △*PRS* and △*FQT*, $\overline{PR} \cong \overline{FQ}$, $\overline{PS} \cong \overline{FT}$, and $m\angle P < m\angle F$.

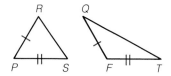

3. △*TPS* and △*RFP*

4. △*WFG* and △*TMS*

5. What does the Derrick Theorem indicate about two circles that are drawn with a compass using different settings?

6. What does the Derrick Theorem indicate about two triangles formed by the tone arm and stacking arm on a turntable?

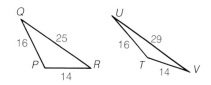

For exercises 7-11, insert <, >, or = in each blank to make a true statement about the figure.

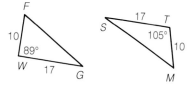

7. If $m\angle 1 = 30°$ and $m\angle 2 = 43°$, then *AC* _____ *CD*.
8. If $\angle 1 \cong \angle 2$, then *AC* _____ *CD*.
9. If $AC = 14$ and $CD = 20$, then $m\angle 1$ _____ $m\angle 2$.
10. If $\overline{AC} \cong \overline{CD}$, then $m\angle 1$ _____ $m\angle 2$.
11. If $m\angle 1 = 29°$ and $m\angle 2 = 26°$, then *AC* _____ *CD*.
12. △ *ABC* is a scalene triangle, and $\overline{AD}$ is a median.
    Could $\overline{AD}$ be perpendicular to side $\overline{BC}$? Explain how you know.

5   The SAA and HL Theorems

After finishing Section 5, you should be able to
▲   *identify pairs of triangles that are congruent by either SAA or HL.*
▲▲   *solve problems involving SAA or HL congruence.*

▲   Side-Angle-Angle and Hypotenuse-Leg Congruence

We can use inequalities to show that triangles are congruent.

THEOREM 6.13

The Side-Angle-Angle (SAA) Theorem

If two angles and a non-included side of one triangle are congruent to two angles and a non-included side of another triangle, then the triangles are congruent.

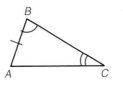 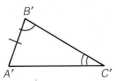

$$\triangle ABC \cong \triangle A'B'C'$$

Example   1. Which pairs of triangles are congruent by the SAA Theorem?

a. 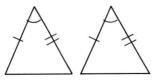   b.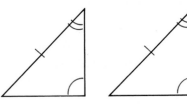

c. 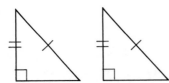   d.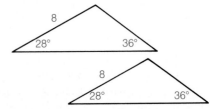

Pairs **b** and **d** are congruent by SAA.

Try This... 1. Which pairs of triangles are congruent by SAA?

a.
b.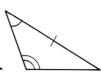

In the triangles below, $\overline{AB} \cong \overline{A'B'}$, $\overline{BC} \cong \overline{B'C'}$, and $\angle A \cong \angle A'$.

 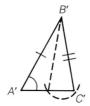

But $\triangle ABC$ is *not* congruent to $\triangle A'B'C'$.

Triangles are not necessarily congruent if SSA holds. However, if the angles involved are right angles, then they are congruent.

In a right triangle, the two sides that are not the hypotenuse are called *the legs*.

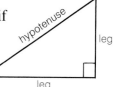

THEOREM
6.14

The Hypotenuse-Leg (HL) Theorem

If the hypotenuse and a leg of one right triangle are congruent to the hypotenuse and a leg of another right triangle, then the two right triangles are congruent.

 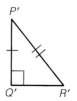

Example 2. Which pairs of triangles are congruent by HL?

a.
b.

15   15
18   18

c.
d.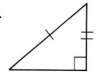

Pairs **c** and **d** are congruent by HL.

Try This... 2. Which pairs of triangles are congruent by HL?

a. 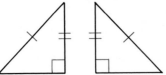 b.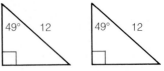

▲▲ Using SAA and HL

Both the SAA and HL Theorems can be used to show that two triangles are congruent.

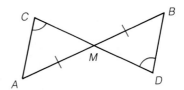

Example 3. *M* is the midpoint of $\overline{AB}$ and $\angle C \cong \angle D$.
Explain why $\overline{AC} \cong \overline{BD}$.

Because *M* is the midpoint of $\overline{AB}$, we know $\overline{AM} \cong \overline{BM}$.
We know $\angle C \cong \angle D$.
$\angle CMA \cong \angle DMB$ by Vertical Angle Theorem.
Thus, by SAA, $\triangle ACM \cong \triangle BDM$.
$\overline{AC} \cong \overline{BD}$ as corresponding parts of congruent triangles.

Try This... 3. $\overline{AL}$ is the bisector of $\angle GAK$ and $\angle G \cong \angle K$.
Explain why $\overline{GL} \cong \overline{KL}$.

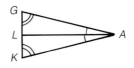

Example 4. $\overline{QR} \perp \overline{PS}$ and $\overline{PQ} \cong \overline{SQ}$.
Explain why $\angle PQR \cong \angle SQR$.

Because $\overline{QR} \perp \overline{PS}$, both $\triangle PRQ$ and $\triangle SRQ$ are right triangles.
We know $\overline{PQ} \cong \overline{SQ}$.
We know $\overline{QR} \cong \overline{QR}$.
By HL, $\triangle PRQ \cong \triangle SRQ$.
Thus, $\angle PQR \cong \angle SQR$ as corresponding parts of congruent triangles.

Try This...   4. $\overline{MN} \perp \overline{RT}$ at P, $\overline{RM} \cong \overline{TN}$
and $\overline{RP} \cong \overline{TP}$. Explain why
$\overline{MP} \cong \overline{NP}$.

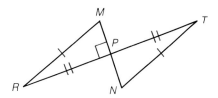

Exercises

▲   **Which pairs of triangles are congruent by SAA?**

1.

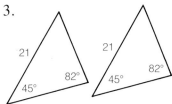

2.

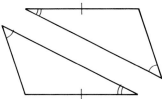

3.

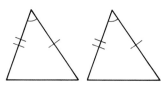

4.

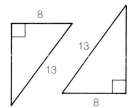

Which pairs of triangles are congruent by HL?

5.

6.

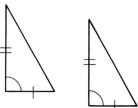

7.

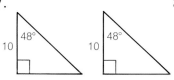

8.

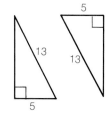

▲▲ **Explain each conclusion.**

9. $\overline{PQ} \cong \overline{TS}$ and $\angle Q \cong \angle S$.
   Explain why $\triangle PQR \cong \triangle TSR$.

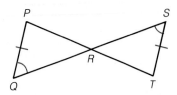

10. $\angle G \cong \angle H$ and $\angle GLK \cong \angle HLK$.
    Explain why $\overline{GL} \cong \overline{HL}$.

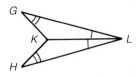

11. C is the midpoint of $\overline{AE}$,
    $\overline{BA} \perp \overline{AE}$, $\overline{DE} \perp \overline{AE}$, and $\overline{BC} \cong \overline{DC}$.
    Explain why $\triangle BAC \cong \triangle DEC$.

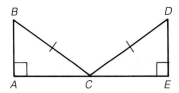

12. $\angle A$ and $\angle L$ are right angles and
    E is the midpoint of $\overline{BF}$ and $\overline{AL}$.
    Explain why $\angle B \cong \angle F$.

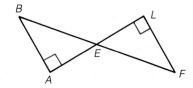

13. Y is the midpoint of $\overline{RS}$ and
    $\angle T \cong \angle Q$. Explain why $\overline{TS} \cong \overline{QR}$.

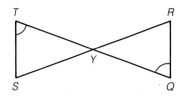

14. $\overline{BD} \cong \overline{CD}$ and $\angle A \cong \angle F$.
    Explain why $\triangle ABC \cong \triangle FCB$.

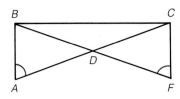

15. $\overline{JT} \cong \overline{RT}$, $\overline{TK} \perp \overline{DJ}$, $\overline{TS} \perp \overline{DR}$,
    and $\overline{TK} \cong \overline{TS}$. Explain why $\triangle DJR$
    is isosceles.

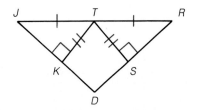

16. $\overline{YM} \perp \overline{MS}$, $\overline{XS} \perp \overline{MS}$, and
    $\overline{MY} \cong \overline{SX}$. Explain why $\overline{MS}$ and $\overline{YX}$
    bisect each other.

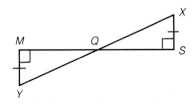

6	Angle Bisectors

After finishing Section 6, you should be able to
▲   *solve problems using the Angle Bisector Theorem.*
▲▲   *construct the incenter of a triangle.*

▲   The Angle Bisector Theorem

The SAA and HL Theorems help us illustrate a theorem about angle bisectors.

THEOREM 6.15	*The Angle Bisector Theorem* The bisector of an angle is the set of interior points equidistant from the sides of the angle.	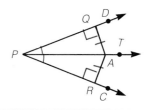

Theorem 6.15 describes a locus. It says that if A is any point on $\overrightarrow{PT}$ except P, then $AQ = AR$. It also says that if A is in the interior of the angle and $AQ = AR$, then A is on the angle bisector.

Note that when we talk of the distance from a point to a line, we mean the length of the perpendicular segment from the point to the line.

Example   ▲1. $\overrightarrow{RS}$ is the bisector of $\angle QRF$.
$MN = 3x + 5$ and
$NG = 8x - 10$. Find x. Then
find MN and NG.

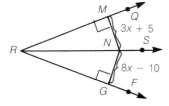

Because N is on the bisector of $\angle QRF$, $MN = NG$. Thus,
$$3x + 5 = 8x - 10$$
$$15 = 5x$$
$$3 = x$$

Then $MN = NG = 14$.

Try This...   ▲1. $\overrightarrow{AB}$ is the bisector of $\angle GAT$.
$MR = 3x + 8$ and $MS = 9x - 4$.
Find x. Then find MR and MS.

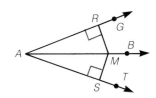

▲▲ The Incenter

In $\triangle GHK$, a ray such as $\overrightarrow{HJ}$ is called an
angle bisector of the triangle.

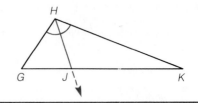

1. Draw a large triangle.
2. Use a compass and straightedge to bisect each angle of the triangle.
3. What do you observe?

Lines are **concurrent** if they intersect in a single point.
That point is called the *point of concurrency.*
Segments or rays are concurrent if they are contained
in concurrent lines.

point of concurrency

THEOREM 6.16   The angle bisectors of a triangle are concurrent in a point that is equidistant from the sides of the triangle.

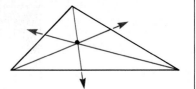

DEFINITION

The **incenter** of a triangle is the point of concurrency of the angle bisectors.

Example   2. Construct the incenter of $\triangle PQR$.

Construct the angle bisector of each angle. The point of intersection is the incenter.

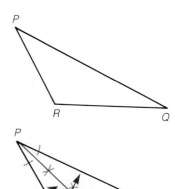

Try This...   2. Draw a triangle. Construct its incenter.

Exercises

▲ **Use the figure for Exercises 1-6. $\overrightarrow{RM}$ bisects $\angle TRK$. Find x
in each case. Then find MG and MQ.**

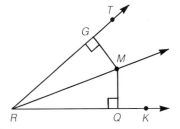

▲1. $MG = 5x + 9$
$MQ = 7x - 3$

▲2. $MG = 8x - 10$
$MQ = 3x + 5$

▲3. $MG = -5x + 6$
$MQ = -7x - 18$

▲4. $MG = 6x + 7$
$MQ = -10x + 9$

▲5. $MG = 1.5x + 12.5$
$MQ = 3.5x + 13.5$

▲6. $MG = 2.5x + 16.5$
$MQ = 4.5x - 8.5$

▲▲ **Draw the indicated triangle and construct its incenter.**

7. An obtuse triangle

8. A right isosceles triangle

9. An acute triangle

10. An obtuse scalene triangle

▶◀ Activity

The set of all points that are equidistant from the sides of an angle is the bisector
of the angle.

Demonstrate this by creating a series of index cards each with $\angle SET$ and a point
that is equidistant from the sides of $\angle SET$. Hold one end of the stack of cards firmly
in one hand. Flip through the other end with your thumb.
What do you see?

Sample cards

▶ **Extension Exercises**

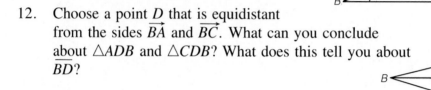

11. *D* is on the angle bisector $\overrightarrow{BD}$ and we draw perpendiculars to the sides as shown. How do you know that *D* is equidistant from the sides?

12. Choose a point *D* that is equidistant from the sides $\overrightarrow{BA}$ and $\overrightarrow{BC}$. What can you conclude about △*ADB* and △*CDB*? What does this tell you about $\overrightarrow{BD}$?

13. Is any angle bisector of an equilateral triangle also a median of the triangle? Explain how you know.

▶▶ **Challenge Exercises**

14. Can the incenter of a triangle ever be in the exterior of a triangle? Explain how you know.

15. Is it possible for two planes to be concurrent? Explain how you know.

16. In a plane there are exactly four points, each of which is equidistant from the three lines determined by the sides of a triangle. Find them.

▶◀ **Activity**

Draw the following three triangles. Find each incenter.

△*ABC*	△*JKL*	△*PQR*
AB = 6 cm	*JK* = 5 cm	*PQ* = 12 cm
BC = 10 cm	*KL* = 5 cm	*QR* = 8 cm
CA = 8 cm	*LJ* = 5 cm	*RP* = 6 cm

Computer Application   Forming Triangles

Find out whether three given segments can form a triangle.

Command	**Comments**

```
10 PRINT "ENTER THE MEASURES OF THE
        THREE SEGMENTS."
20 INPUT X, Y, Z
```
20 The computer accepts the three inputs.

```
30 IF X + Y < = Z THEN 80
```
30 < = means *less than or equal to*.

```
40 IF X + Z < = Y THEN 80
50 IF Y + Z < = X THEN 80
60 PRINT "THE SEGMENTS FORM
        A TRIANGLE."
70 GOTO 90
```
70 GOTO This command sends the computer to the indicated line.

```
80 PRINT "THE SEGMENTS DO NOT FORM
        A TRIANGLE."
90 END
```

Use the program above to determine if a triangle can be formed from the three segments given in exercises 1-12.

1. $3, 5, 8$ 2. $6, 10, 12$ 3. $53, 10, 25$ 4. $6, 50, 12$

5. $6.5, 8.3, 12.4$ 6. $11.5, 25.3, 14.2$ 7. $23.5, 24.6, 23.7$ 8. $17.9, 10.4, 5.1$

9. $111, 21, 32.9$ 10. $62, 35.9, 30$ 11. $50, 50, 100$ 12. $27, 37.9, 62.8$

13.   Write a program in BASIC that will find the perimeter of a triangle.

Chapter Review

 Insert $<$ or $>$ in each blank to make a true statement.

1. *AR* _____ *TQ*

2. *m ∠B* _____ *m ∠C*

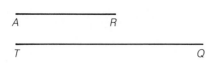

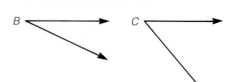

3. For each exterior angle, name its remote interior angles.

4. What is the relationship between ∠*HTJ* and ∠*V*?

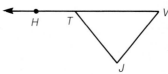

 5. In △*MES*, *ME* = 21, *MS* = 8, and *SE* = 16. List the angles from largest to smallest.

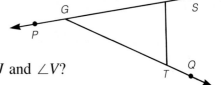

6. In △*RST*, *m ∠R* = 119°, *m ∠S* = 31°, and *m ∠T* = 30°. List the sides from largest to smallest.

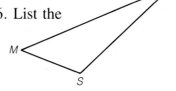

 7. Make three true statements of inequality for △*JLK*.

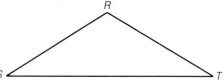

Can these triples of numbers be the lengths of the sides of a triangle?

8. 5, 9, 11

9. 2.3, 2.5, 4.8

4 **What can you conclude about each pair of triangles?**

10. △*TFS* and △*PRM*

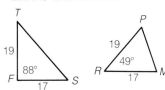

11. △*WAV* and △*PLG*

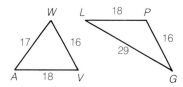

5 **Explain each conclusion.**

12. $\overline{AF}$ is the perpendicular bisector of $\overline{CD}$ and $\overline{AD} \cong \overline{CB}$. Explain why $\overline{AF} \cong \overline{BF}$.

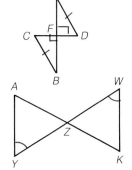

13. $\angle Y \cong \angle W$ and *Z* is the midpoint of $\overline{AK}$. Explain why $\overline{AY} \cong \overline{KW}$.

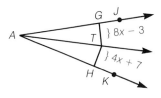

6 **△**14. $\overrightarrow{AT}$ bisects $\angle JAK$. Find *x*. Then find *GT* and *TH*.

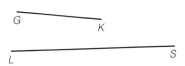

Chapter Test

Insert < or > in each blank to make a true statement.

1. $m \angle F$ _____ $m \angle P$

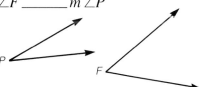

2. *GK* _____ *LS*

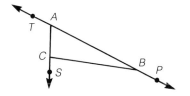

3. For each exterior angle, name its remote interior angles.

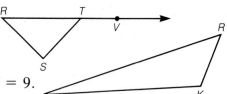

4. What is the relationship between ∠S and ∠STV?

5. In △ARK, AR = 31, AK = 26, and RK = 9. List the angles from largest to smallest.

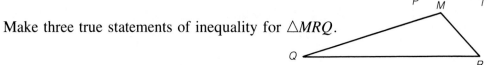

6. In △PET, m ∠P = 111°, m ∠E = 33°, and m ∠T = 36°. List the sides from largest to smallest.

7. Make three true statements of inequality for △MRQ.

Can these triples of numbers be the lengths of the sides of a triangle?

8. 3.9, 5.1, 9.9

9. 17, 13, 33

What can you conclude about each pair of triangles?

10. △GRS and △FCT

11. △STN and △CLF

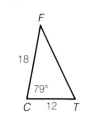

12. $\overrightarrow{TK}$ bisects ∠RTG and ∠R ≅ ∠G. Explain why $\overrightarrow{KT}$ bisects ∠RKG.

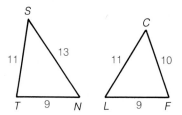

13. $\overline{PR}$ ⊥ $\overline{RM}$, $\overline{SM}$ ⊥ $\overline{RM}$, and $\overline{PM}$ ≅ $\overline{SR}$. Explain why ∠P ≅ ∠S.

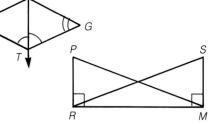

▲14. $\overrightarrow{RK}$ bisects ∠NRS. Find x. Then find MK and KA.

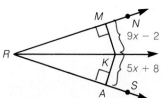

Skills Review   Estimating

Estimate the sums.

1.	37 +44	2.	638 +257	3.	9,148 + 286	4.	3,701 + 3,098
5.	8.8 +6.5	6.	5.743 +3.289	7.	16.88 + 8.3	8.	35.739 +15.35
9.	$7.58 +1.89	10.	$7.16 +9.56	11.	$36.19 +24.78	12.	$58.72 +73.68

Estimate the differences.

13.	82 −24	14.	661 −385	15.	8,631 − 807	16.	5,984 −3,012
17.	9.3 −6.4	18.	8.094 −3.9	19.	3.056 −2.4	20.	7.4 −3.885
21.	$6.89 −1.56	22.	$9.15 −1.23	23.	$34.15 − 7.63	24.	$98.95 −30.13

Estimate the products.

25.	66 × 8	26.	310 × 7	27.	51 ×22	28.	580 × 28
29.	4.8 × 4	30.	7.12 × 3	31.	2.907 × 51	32.	6.378 ×5.501
33.	$2.74 × 210	34.	$7.78 × 392	35.	$6.66 × 413	36.	$5.09 × 868

Estimate the quotients.

37.	$8\overline{)465}$	38.	$5\overline{)312}$	39.	$6\overline{)3,586}$	40.	$8\overline{)43,987}$
41.	$4.5\overline{)39.82}$	42.	$8.1\overline{)28.7}$	43.	$3.63\overline{)37.2}$	44.	$6.6\overline{)51.17}$
45.	$8\overline{)\$34.80}$	46.	$6\overline{)\$42.75}$	47.	$4\overline{)\$22.81}$	48.	$7\overline{)\$39.13}$

7
Parallel Lines

1 Parallel Lines

After finishing Section 1, you should be able to
▲ *distinguish between parallel and skew lines and segments.*
▲▲ *draw parallel lines and segments using a straightedge and either a compass or drawing triangle.*

▲ Parallel and Skew Lines

If two lines in a plane do not intersect, we call them *parallel lines*.

DEFINITION

Two lines are parallel whenever they are in the same plane and do not intersect.

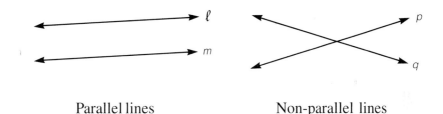

Parallel lines   Non-parallel lines

To say that ℓ is parallel to m, we write $\ell \parallel m$. We can also talk about parallel segments.

DEFINITION

Two segments are parallel whenever the lines containing them are parallel.

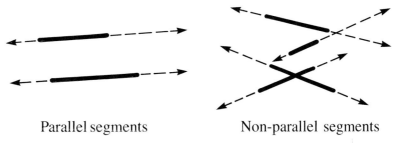

Parallel segments   Non-parallel segments

This highway interchange suggests that there are lines in space that neither intersect nor lie in the same plane. Such lines are **noncoplanar.**

DEFINITION

Any two noncoplanar lines are called *skew lines*. Two segments contained in two skew lines are called *skew segments*.

Note that skew lines cannot intersect. If they did intersect, then they would be coplanar by Theorem 1.4.

Examples
1. Name three pairs of parallel segments in this cube.

There are many pairs. Three of them are $\overline{AB}$ and $\overline{DC}$, $\overline{DH}$ and $\overline{AE}$, and $\overline{BC}$ and $\overline{EH}$.

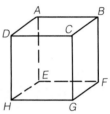

2. Name three pairs of skew segments in the cube.

There are many pairs. Three of them are $\overline{AB}$ and $\overline{DH}$, $\overline{HG}$ and $\overline{AE}$, and $\overline{EF}$ and $\overline{BC}$.

Try This...   Refer to the cube above.

1. Name three other pairs of parallel segments.

2. Name three other pairs of skew segments.

▲▲ Drawing Parallel Lines

We can use a straightedge and compass to draw parallel lines.

Example
3. Use a straightedge and compass to draw a line that contains point P and is parallel to $\overleftrightarrow{AB}$.

Step 1   Draw any line that contains P and intersects $\overleftrightarrow{AB}$ at Q.

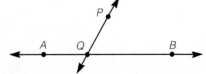

Step 2 With the vertex at P, copy $\angle PQB$. $\overrightarrow{PR}$ is parallel to $\overleftrightarrow{AB}$.

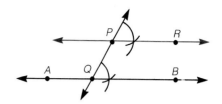

Try This... 3.

Draw a line $\overleftrightarrow{AB}$ on a sheet of paper. Choose a point P not on $\overleftrightarrow{AB}$. Then use a straightedge and compass to draw a line that contains P and is parallel to $\overleftrightarrow{AB}$.

Parallel lines can also be drawn using a straightedge and drawing triangle.

Example 4. Use a straightedge and drawing triangle to draw a line that contains P and is parallel to $\overleftrightarrow{AB}$.

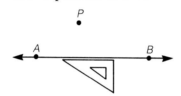

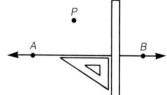

Step 1

Place the drawing triangle so that one edge lies on $\overleftrightarrow{AB}$.

Step 2

Place the straightedge along another edge of the drawing triangle, as shown.

Step 3

Holding the straightedge in place, slide the drawing triangle up until its edge reaches point P.

Then use the edge to draw $\overleftrightarrow{PQ}$, which is parallel to $\overleftrightarrow{AB}$.

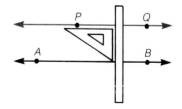

Try This... 4.

Draw a line $\overleftrightarrow{AB}$ on a sheet of paper. Choose a point P not on $\overleftrightarrow{AB}$. Then use a straightedge and drawing triangle to draw a line that contains P and is parallel to $\overleftrightarrow{AB}$.

Exercises

▲ Use the cube for Exercises 1-8. For the given segment name two other segments in the cube that are parallel to it.

1. $\overline{PQ}$ 2. $\overline{JK}$ 3. $\overline{PS}$ 4. $\overline{LK}$

Name a line in the cube that forms a pair of skew lines with the line given below.

5. $\overleftrightarrow{PS}$ 6. $\overleftrightarrow{PQ}$ 7. $\overleftrightarrow{JK}$ 8. $\overleftrightarrow{SL}$

Tell whether the lines in these pictures are parallel or skew lines.

9.

10.

11.

12.

▲▲ Copy ∠ABC. Use a straightedge and compass to draw a line parallel to $\overleftrightarrow{BC}$ at A. Then draw a line parallel to $\overleftrightarrow{AB}$ at C.

13.

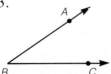

14.

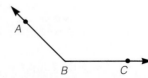

Copy $\angle ABC$**. Use a straightedge and drawing triangle to draw a line parallel to** $\overleftrightarrow{BC}$ **at** A**. Then draw a line parallel to** $\overleftrightarrow{AB}$ **at** C**.**

15.

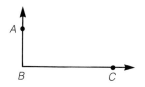

16.

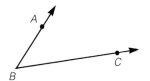

▶◀ Activity

Fold an $8\frac{1}{2}$- by 11-inch piece of paper in half crosswise. Label the endpoints of the fold A and B. Now fold the paper in half the other way. Label the endpoints C and D.

What can you conclude about $\overline{AB}$ and $\overline{CD}$? (Measure the angles formed.)

Fold over the top edge of the paper so that $\overline{CD}$ aligns with itself. Label the endpoints of this new fold E and F.

Is $\overline{EF} \perp \overline{CD}$? Measure the angles formed by their intersection.

Now what can you conclude about $\overline{EF}$ and $\overline{AB}$?

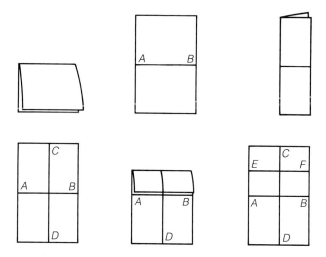

2   When Are Lines Parallel?

After finishing Section 2, you should be able to
▲   *identify pairs of corresponding angles, interior angles, and alternate interior angles.*
▲▲   *identify conditions that enable you to conclude that two lines are parallel.*

▲   Transversals and Angles

Our definition of parallel lines is difficult to use. We need to find some practical way to tell whether two lines are parallel.
In the figure, line *t* is called a *transversal*.

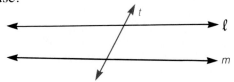

DEFINITION

A **transversal** is a line that intersects two or more coplanar lines in different points.

When a transversal intersects a pair of lines, eight angles are formed. Certain pairs of these angles have special names.

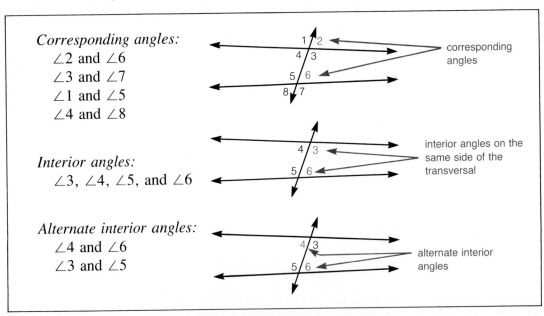

Corresponding angles:
    ∠2 and ∠6
    ∠3 and ∠7
    ∠1 and ∠5
    ∠4 and ∠8

corresponding angles

Interior angles:
    ∠3, ∠4, ∠5, and ∠6

interior angles on the same side of the transversal

Alternate interior angles:
    ∠4 and ∠6
    ∠3 and ∠5

alternate interior angles

Examples   Identify each pair of angles as corresponding angles, interior angles, or alternate interior angles.

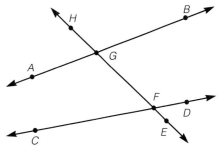

1. $\angle AGH$ and $\angle CFG$
   corresponding angles

2. $\angle BGF$ and $\angle GFC$
   alternate interior angles

3. $\angle AGF$ and $\angle CFG$
   interior angles

Try This...   Identify each pair of angles as corresponding angles, interior angles, or alternate interior angles.

1. $\angle DEB$ and $\angle EBC$
2. $\angle FEB$ and $\angle CBE$
3. $\angle HED$ and $\angle EBA$

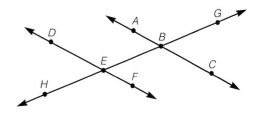

▲▲ Conditions for Parallel Lines

We are now ready to answer the question, "When are lines parallel?"

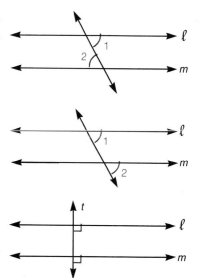

THEOREM 7.1	If two lines and a transversal form congruent alternate interior angles, then the lines are parallel.
	If $\angle 1 \cong \angle 2$, then $\ell \parallel m$.
COROLLARY 7.2	If two lines and a transversal form congruent corresponding angles, then the lines are parallel.
	If $\angle 1 \cong \angle 2$, then $\ell \parallel m$.
COROLLARY 7.3	If two lines are perpendicular to a transversal, then the two lines are parallel.
	If $\ell \perp t$ and $m \perp t$, then $\ell \parallel m$.

COROLLARY   If two lines and a transversal form supplementary interior angles on
   7.4   the same side of the transversal, then the lines are parallel.

Examples

4. Which lines are parallel?
   Explain how you know.

   $\ell \parallel n$ by Corollary 7.2 or 7.4.

   $m \parallel p$ by Theorem 7.1.

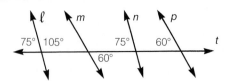

5. Vertical boards in walls are often
   called studs. Why are studs
   parallel? Explain how you know.

   They are parallel because
   they are all perpendicular
   to the floor (Corollary 7.3).
   They are also parallel by
   Corollary 7.2 or 7.4.

6. $\triangle ABC$ and $\triangle BCD$ are
   equilateral triangles. Which
   segments in the figure are
   parallel? Explain how you know.

Equilateral triangles are also equiangular.
Because $\angle ABC \cong \angle BCD$, $\overline{AB} \parallel \overline{CD}$ by Theorem 7.1.
Because $\angle ACB \cong \angle CBD$, $\overline{AC} \parallel \overline{BD}$, also by Theorem 7.1.
In this example, BC is a transveral for each pair of sides.

Try This...

4. Which lines are parallel?
   Explain how you know.

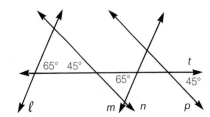

5. $\triangle ABC$ and $\triangle BCD$ are
   isosceles, and $\angle A \cong \angle D$.
   Which segments are parallel?
   Explain how you know.

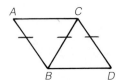

6. Why is the top of the window
frame parallel to the bottom?

Exercises

▲ **Identify each pair of angles as corresponding angles,
interior angles, or alternate interior angles.**

1. ∠ABH and ∠DEB
2. ∠CBE and ∠DEB
3. ∠BEF and ∠CBE
4. ∠ABE and ∠DEB
5. ∠HBC and ∠BEF
6. ∠ABE and ∠BEF

7. Name a pair of alternate interior angles formed
by $\overline{BC}$, $\overline{AD}$, and transversal $\overline{AC}$.

8. Name a pair of alternate interior angles formed by
$\overline{AB}$, $\overline{CD}$, and transversal $\overline{AC}$.

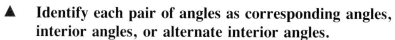

Identify the transversal associated with each pair of angles.

9. ∠QPS and ∠RSP are interior angles.

10. ∠RPQ and ∠PRS are alternate
interior angles.

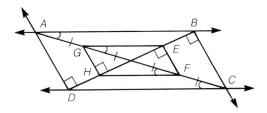

11. ∠RQS and ∠PSQ are alternate
interior angles.

12. ∠SPQ and ∠RQP are interior
angles.

13. ∠TPQ and ∠PSR are
corresponding angles.

14. ∠PQU and ∠SRQ are
corresponding angles.

▲▲ **Identify the parallel lines and segments. Explain how you know.**

15.

16.

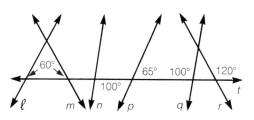

Explain why $\overleftrightarrow{AB} \parallel \overleftrightarrow{CD}$.

17.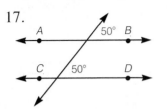

18.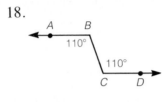

19.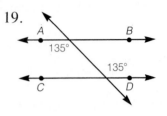

▶ Extension Exercises

Explain why $\overleftrightarrow{AB} \parallel \overleftrightarrow{DC}$.

20.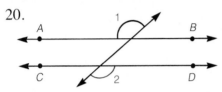

21. $m \angle 1 + m \angle 2 = 180°$

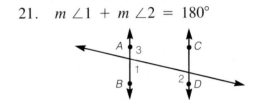

▶▶ Challenge Exercise

22. $\overline{RS} \cong \overline{RT}$, and
$\angle RQP \cong \angle S$.
Explain why $\overline{PQ} \parallel \overline{ST}$.

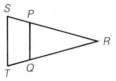

▶◀ Activity

Fold a piece of tracing paper in half and then fold it in half again. Unfold the paper and label the folded segments *l, m,* and *n.* Now fold the paper along a diagonal. Unfold the paper and label the diagonal *p.* Make a cut across the paper (the short way) between *l* and *m* and then between *m* and *n.*

Align *l* and *p* with *m* and *p.* What can you conclude about the angles formed by the intersection of *l* and *m* with *p*?

Align *m* and *p* with *n* and *p.* What can you conclude about the angles formed by the intersection of *m* and *n* with *p*?

What does this tell us about *l, m,* and *n* before the paper was cut?

   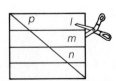

3	The Parallel Postulate

After finishing Section 3, you should be able to
▲   *identify congruent pairs of angles associated*
     with parallel lines and transversals.

▲ Some Consequences of the Parallel Postulate

We know that parallel lines exist. That is, if P is any point in a plane
not on a line ℓ, we can find *at least one* line that contains P and is
parallel to ℓ.

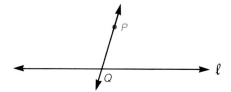 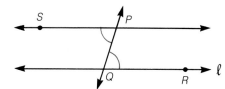

Consider $\overrightarrow{PQ}$ where Q is on ℓ.   Find $\overrightarrow{PS}$ so that $\angle PQR \cong \angle SPQ$.

By Corollary 7.2 it follows that $\overleftrightarrow{SP} \parallel \ell$.

Is this the *only* line that contains P and is parallel to ℓ? It may seem obvious that the
answer is "yes." Many mathematicians tried to show this, but none succeeded. Today
we know that it is not possible to show that parallels are *unique* by means of postulates
and theorems from our geometry. (See the Historical Note, page 203.)

We therefore make the following assumption.

POSTULATE   *The Parallel Postulate*
   12   Given a line ℓ and a point P not
              on ℓ, there is at most one line
              that contains P and is parallel to ℓ.

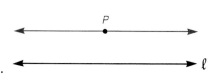

In Section 2, we proved that if certain relations between angles held, then lines were
parallel. We shall now consider the converse situation. That is, if two lines are parallel,
what relations hold between the angles?

THEOREM 7.5	If a transversal intersects two parallel lines, then the corresponding angles are congruent. If $\ell \parallel m$, then $\angle 1 \cong \angle 2$.	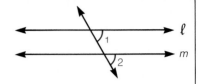
COROLLARY 7.6	If a transversal intersects two parallel lines, then the alternate interior angles are congruent. If $\ell \parallel m$, then $\angle 1 \cong \angle 2$.	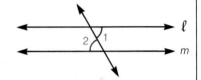
COROLLARY 7.7	In a plane, if two lines are parallel to a third line, then the two lines are parallel to each other. If $\ell \parallel p$ and $m \parallel p$, then $\ell \parallel m$.	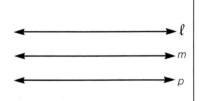

Examples

1. If $\ell \parallel m$ and $m\angle 1 = 40°$, what are the measures of the other angles? Explain how you know.

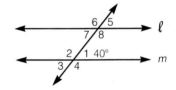

$m\angle 7 = 40°$ by Corollary 7.6.
$m\angle 5 = 40°$ by Theorem 7.5.

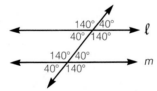 Because $\angle 7$ and $\angle 8$ form a linear pair, they are supplementary, and $\angle 8 = 140°$.
By similar reasoning, we have the measures of the other angles as shown.

2. $\overline{PT} \parallel \overline{SR}$. Which pairs of angles are congruent? Explain how you know.

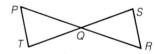

By Corollary 7.6, $\angle TPQ \cong \angle SRQ$ and $\angle PTQ \cong \angle RSQ$. $\angle PQT \cong \angle SQR$, because they are vertical angles.

3. $\overline{DE} \parallel \overline{BC}$. Which pairs of angles are congruent? Explain how you know.

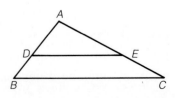

By Theorem 7.5, $\angle ADE \cong \angle ABC$ and $\angle AED \cong \angle ACB$.

Try This... $\overleftrightarrow{AB} \parallel \overleftrightarrow{CD}$. Identify congruent pairs of angles and find their measures when possible.

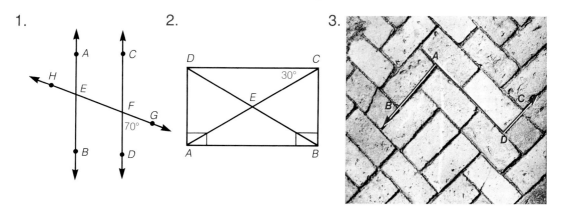

1.   2.   3.

Recall that when a theorem can be illustrated easily from another theorem we often call it a *corollary*.

COROLLARY **7.8**   In a plane, if a line intersects one of two parallel lines, then it intersects the other.

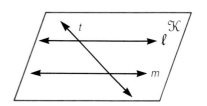

COROLLARY **7.9**   If a transversal intersects two parallel lines, then the interior angles on the same side of the transversal are supplementary.

$$m \angle 1 + m \angle 2 = 180°$$

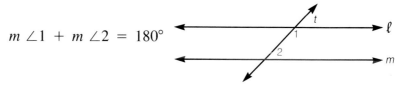

COROLLARY **7.10**   If a transversal is perpendicular to one of two parallel lines, then it is perpendicular to the other.

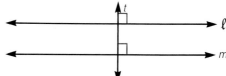

Exercises

▲ In each drawing, $\overline{AB} \parallel \overline{CD}$. Identify pairs of congruent angles and supplementary angles. When possible, find the measures of the angles.

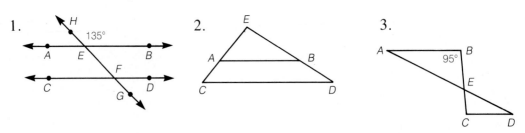

1.

2.

3.

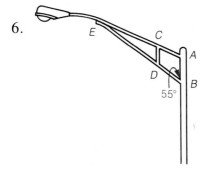

4.

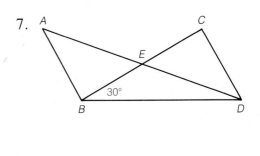

5.

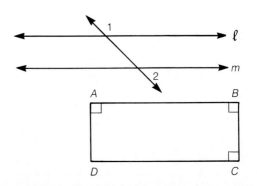

6.

7.

▶ Extension Exercises

8. $\ell \parallel m$. Is $\angle 1$ supplementary to $\angle 2$? Explain how you know.

9. $\angle A$, $\angle B$, and $\angle C$ are right angles. Is $\angle D$ a right angle? Explain how you know.

10. $\overline{AB} \cong \overline{AC}$, and $\overrightarrow{DE} \parallel \overline{AB}$. Is $\triangle CDE$ isosceles? Explain how you know.

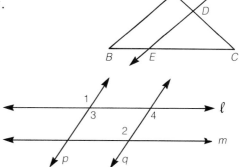

▶▶ Challenge Exercise

11. $\ell \parallel m$ and $p \parallel q$. Is $\angle 1 \cong \angle 2$? Explain how you know.

Historical Note

For more than 2,000 years, many mathematicians tried to prove the Parallel Postulate from the other postulates. It probably seemed obvious to them that there should be only one parallel to a line containing a point not on the line. All of their efforts failed, however, until two mathematicians, Janos Bolyai (1802-1860) in Hungary and Nicolai Lobachevsky (1793-1856) in Russia, independently made the same surprising discovery.

Each had been trying to prove parallels are unique by assuming that there was more than one. They thought that this would lead to a contradiction. To their amazement, instead of finding a contradiction, they discovered a new geometry with some very interesting properties.

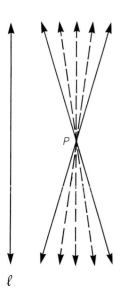

One of their first discoveries was that if you assume there are two parallel lines containing a point P as shown, then there have to be an infinite number of such parallel lines.

A third mathematician, Georg Riemann (1826-1866) from Germany, developed a second new geometry in which there are no parallels. To do this he had to make some changes in the other postulates. This is not surprising since we have established that, with our postulates, parallels do exist.

As a result of these developments, mathematicians now realize that for a point P not on line ℓ there are three possibilities.

(1) Point P is not on a line parallel to ℓ.
(2) Point P is on exactly one line parallel to ℓ.
(3) Point P is on an infinite number of lines parallel to ℓ.

All three possibilities are equally correct.

4	The Angle Sum Theorem

After finishing Section 4, you should be able to
- ▲ *use the Angle Sum Theorem to find measures of angles of triangles.*
- ▲▲ *apply corollaries of the Angle Sum Theorem to solve problems.*

▲ The Angles of a Triangle

The following theorem is already familiar to you.

THEOREM
7.11

The Angle Sum Theorem

The sum of the measures of the angles of a triangle is 180°.

$$m \angle A + m \angle B + m \angle C = 180°$$

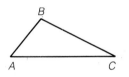

Examples

1. Find $m \angle C$.

$$m \angle A + m \angle B + m \angle C = 180$$
$$80 + 30 + m \angle C = 180$$
$$110 + m \angle C = 180$$
$$m \angle C = 70°$$

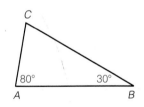

▲2. Find the measure of each angle.

$$m \angle A + m \angle B + m \angle C = 180$$
$$x + 2x + 3x = 180$$
$$6x = 180$$
$$x = 30$$

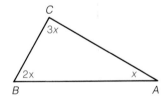

$$m \angle A = 30°, m \angle B = 60°, \text{ and } m \angle C = 90°.$$

Try This...   1. Find $m \angle A$.

▲2. Find the measure of each angle.

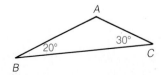

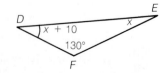

Example   3. If $m \angle 1 = m \angle 2$, what are $m \angle 3$ and $m \angle 4$?

In $\triangle ABC$,

$$35 + m \angle B + 25 = 180$$
$$m \angle B = 120°$$

Thus, $m \angle 1 = m \angle 2 = 60°$.

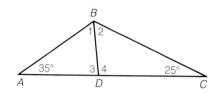

In $\triangle ABD$,

$$m \angle A + m \angle 1 + m \angle 3 = 180$$
$$35 + 60 + m \angle 3 = 180$$
$$m \angle 3 = 85°$$

In $\triangle BCD$,

$$60 + 25 + m \angle 4 = 180$$
$$m \angle 4 = 95°$$

Try This...   3. If $m \angle 1 = m \angle 2$, what are $m \angle 3$ and $m \angle 4$?

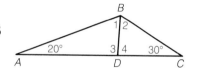

▲▲ Some Corollaries of the Angle Sum Theorem

There are several corollaries to the Angle Sum Theorem.

COROLLARY
7.12
If two angles of one triangle are congruent to two angles of another triangle, then the third angles are congruent.

Example   4. $\angle 1 \cong \angle 2$. How are $\angle A$ and $\angle C$ related? Explain how you know.

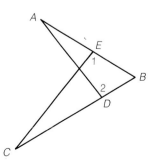

$\angle 1$, $\angle B$, and $\angle C$ are angles of $\triangle CBE$.
$\angle 2$, $\angle B$, and $\angle A$ are angles of $\triangle ABD$.

We know $\angle 1 \cong \angle 2$.
We know $\angle B \cong \angle B$.

Thus, by Corollary 7.12, $\angle A \cong \angle C$.

Try This...   4. How are $\angle 1$ and $\angle 2$
related? Explain how you know.

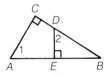

COROLLARY The acute angles of a right triangle are complementary.
7.13

Example   5. Find $m \angle 1$ and $m \angle 2$.

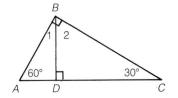

By Corollary 7.13,
$m \angle A + m \angle 1 = 90°$. Thus,
$m \angle 1 = 30°$.

By Corollary 7.13,
$m \angle C + m \angle 2 = 90°$.
Thus, $m \angle 2 = 60°$.

Try This...   5. $\triangle ABC$ is a right triangle, $\overline{BC} \cong \overline{BD}$,
and $m \angle BDC = 55°$.

Find the measures of all the angles
in the figure.

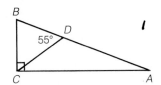

COROLLARY The measure of an exterior angle of a triangle is the
7.14   sum of the measures of the two remote interior angles.

Example   ▲6. Find $m \angle A$ and $m \angle ACB$ in $\triangle ABC$.

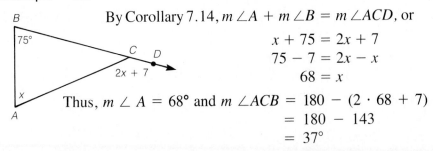

By Corollary 7.14, $m \angle A + m \angle B = m \angle ACD$, or

$$x + 75 = 2x + 7$$
$$75 - 7 = 2x - x$$
$$68 = x$$

Thus, $m \angle A = 68°$ and $m \angle ACB = 180 - (2 \cdot 68 + 7)$
$$= 180 - 143$$
$$= 37°$$

Try This... ▲6. Find $\angle A$ and $m \angle C$ in $\triangle ABC$.

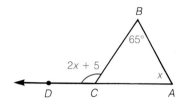

Exercises

▲ **Find $m \angle A$ in each figure.**

1.

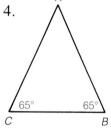

2.

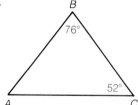

3.

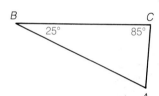

4.

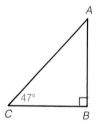

5.

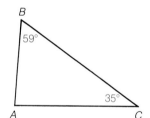

6.

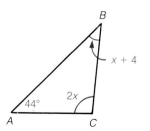

Find the measure of each angle.

▲7.

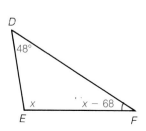

8.

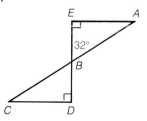

▲9.

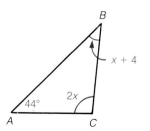

10. $\overline{AB} \parallel \overline{DE}$

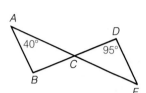

11. $\angle 1 \cong \angle 2$

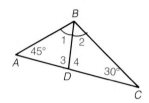

12. $m\angle 1 = m\angle 2 = 62°$

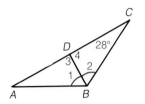

▲▲ **Find the measure of each angle.**

13. Find $m\angle P$, $m\angle 1$, and $m\angle 2$.

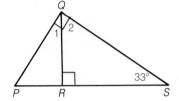

14. Find $m\angle 1$ and $m\angle 2$.

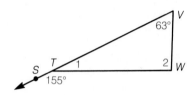

15. Find $m\angle F$.

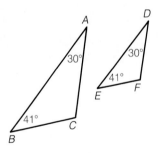

16. Find $m\angle 1$ and $m\angle 2$.

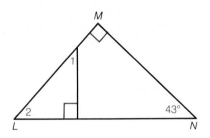

▲ **Solve for x and find the measure of each angle.**

17.

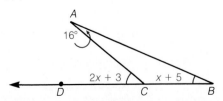

18.

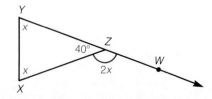

► Extension Exercises

19. ∠1 ≅ ∠2. Is ∠A ≅ ∠C?
   Explain how you know.

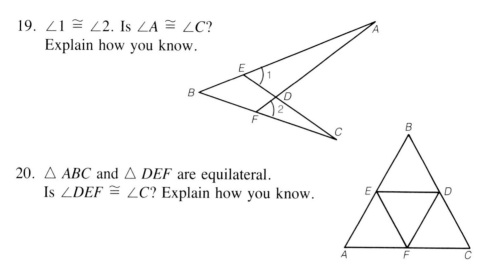

20. △ ABC and △ DEF are equilateral.
   Is ∠DEF ≅ ∠C? Explain how you know.

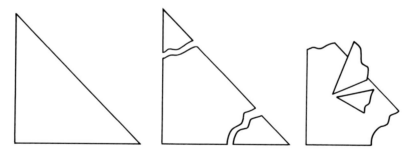

►◄ Activity

Draw a right triangle and cut it out. Tear off the acute angles. Place the two angles side by side and position them over the right angle. Do the two angles fit within the right angle? What can you conclude from this activity?

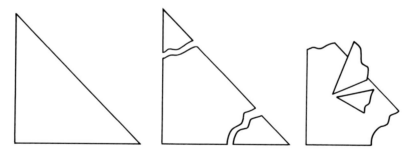

Now copy the figure below on another piece of paper. Tear ∠CAB and ∠ABC as shown. Place the two angles side by side and position them over ∠BCD. Do ∠CAB and ∠ABC fit within ∠BCD? What can you conclude from this activity?

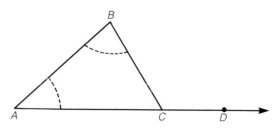

Calculator Application　　　　Finding Measures of Angles

Memory keys can be helpful when doing calculations that involve more than one operation. The following keys appear on some calculators.

MS or STO stores the display in the memory.

M+ adds the display number to the memory.

M− subtracts the display number from the memory.

MR , RM , or RCL recalls the number in the memory.

MC or CM clears the memory.

Example

$\overrightarrow{AD}$ bisects $\angle BAC$.
Find $m\,\angle DAC$.

Find $m\,\angle BAC$ and
then divide by 2.

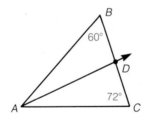

$m\,\angle BAC = 180 - (m\,\angle ABC + m\,\angle ACB)$

$m\,\angle DAC = \dfrac{180 - (m\,\angle ABC + m\,\angle ACB)}{2}$

Enter: 60 [+] 72 [=] [MS] 180 [−] [RM] [=] [÷] 2 [=]

Display: 24

$m\,\angle DAC = 24°$

Find the measure of each angle.

1.　$\overrightarrow{RP}$ bisects $\angle SRT$.
　　Find $m\,\angle PRT$.

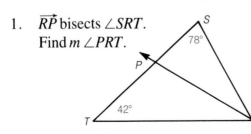

2.　$\overrightarrow{MN}$ bisects $\angle PMO$.
　　Find $m\,\angle PMN$.

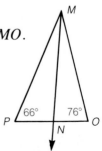

Chapter Review

1 **Use the cube for Exercises 1–2.**

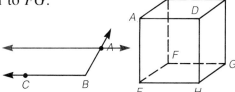

1. Name two segments that are parallel to $\overline{FG}$.

2. Name one pair of skew lines.

3. Use a straightedge and compass to draw a line parallel to $\overleftrightarrow{BC}$ at A.

2 **Use the drawing for Exercises 4–7.**

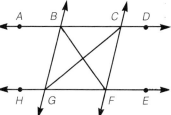

4. Name one pair of corresponding angles.

5. Name one pair of alternate interior angles.

6. Identify the transversal associated with interior angles $\angle CBG$ and $\angle BCF$.

7. If $\angle GBC \cong \angle FCD$, what lines are parallel?

3 **In each drawing, *AB* ∥ *CD*. Identify pairs of congruent angles and supplementary angles. When possible, find the angle measures.**

8.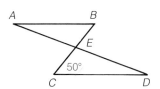

9.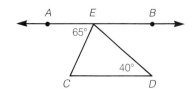

4 **Find the measure of each angle.**

10.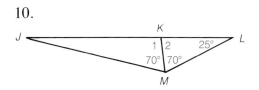

▲11.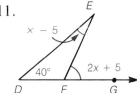

Chapter Test

Use the cube for Exercises 1-2.

1. Name two segments that are parallel to $\overline{BF}$.

2. Name one pair of skew lines.

3. Use a straightedge and drawing triangle to draw a line parallel to $\overleftrightarrow{BC}$ at A.

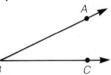

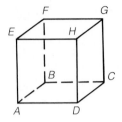

Use the drawing for Exercises 4-7.

4. Name one pair of corresponding angles.

5. Name one pair of alternate interior angles.

6. Identify the transversal associated with interior angles $\angle 4$ and $\angle 5$.

7. If $m \angle 4 = m \angle 6$, what lines are parallel?

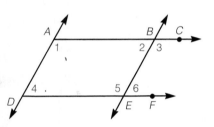

In each drawing, $\overline{AB} \parallel \overline{CD}$. Identify pairs of congruent angles and supplementary angles. When possible, find the angle measures.

8.

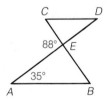

9.

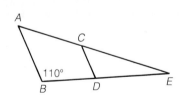

Find the measure of each angle.

10.

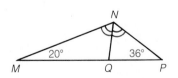

▲11.

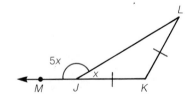

Skills Review	Converting Metric Units

Write the missing numbers.

1. 3 km = _____ m   2. 4 m = _____ cm   3. 7 mm = _____ cm

4. 72.1 m = _____ cm   5. 620 m = _____ km   6. 45 mm = _____ cm

7. 3,521 mm = ___ m   8. 7.5 m = _____ cm   9. 9.9 cm = ____ mm

10. 836 m = _____ km   11. 3.4 cm = _____ m   12. 130 mm = ____ cm

13. 1.39 m = ____ mm   14. 86.2 km = _____ m   15. 52 cm = _____ m

16. 7 L = _____ mL   17. 4,528 mL = ___ L   18. 6,000 L = _____ kL

19. 4 L = _____ kL   20. 14 L = _____ mL   21. 2.5 L = _____ mL

22. 2,013 mL = ___ L   23. 630 mL = _____ L   24. 0.003 L = _____ mL

25. 13,000 mL = ___ L   26. 4.8 L = _____ mL   27. 0.01 L = _____ mL

28. 1,000 L = _____ kL   29. 500 mL = _____ L   30. 3,901 L = _____ kL

31. 4,792 mg = ___ g   32. 320 mg = _____ g   33. 1,428 g = _____ kg

34. 200 g = _____ kg   35. 4 t = _____ kg   36. 3.51 t = _____ kg

37. 8,420 kg = _____ t   38. 4.6 kg = _____ g   39. 3.3 g = _____ mg

40. 14 kg = _____ g   41. 13 kg = _____ t   42. 4 g = _____ mg

43. 0.006 kg = _____ g   44. 13 t = _____ kg   45. 1 mg = _____ g

8
Quadrilaterals

1	Classifying Quadrilaterals

After finishing Section 1, you should be able to
▲   *identify parts of quadrilaterals.*
▲▲   *identify special types of quadrilaterals.*

▲ Parts of a Quadrilateral

DEFINITION

A **quadrilateral** consists of four coplanar segments that intersect only at their endpoints. Each endpoint belongs to exactly two segments.

In quadrilateral *ABCD*,
$\overline{AB}$, $\overline{BC}$, $\overline{CD}$, and $\overline{DA}$ are the **sides,**
A, *B*, *C*, and *D* are the **vertices,**
and $\angle A$, $\angle B$, $\angle C$, and $\angle D$ are the **angles.**

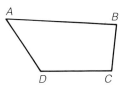

Two sides, angles, or vertices of a quadrilateral are either **opposite** or **consecutive.**

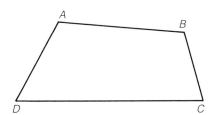   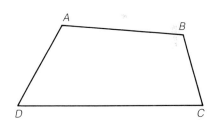

$\overline{AB}$ and $\overline{CD}$ are opposite sides. $\overline{AB}$ and $\overline{BC}$ are consecutive sides.
$\angle A$ and $\angle C$ are opposite angles. $\angle A$ and $\angle B$ are consecutive angles.
A and *C* are opposite vertices.   *A* and *B* are consecutive vertices.

Six segments are determined by the four vertices of a quadrilateral.
Four of these are sides. The other two are **diagonals.**

DEFINITION

A **diagonal** of a quadrilateral is a segment that joins two opposite vertices.

$\overline{AC}$ and $\overline{BD}$ are diagonals.

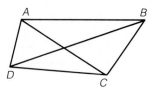

Example 1. Name the diagonals and the pairs of opposite sides and angles in quadrilateral *PQRS*.

The diagonals are $\overline{PR}$ and $\overline{QS}$.
The pairs of opposite sides are:

$$\overline{PQ} \text{ and } \overline{RS}$$
$$\overline{QR} \text{ and } \overline{PS}$$

The pairs of opposite angles are:

$$\angle P \text{ and } \angle R$$
$$\angle Q \text{ and } \angle S$$

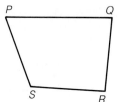

Try This... 1. Name the diagonals and the pairs of opposite sides and angles in quadrilateral *DEFG*.

Example 2. Name the pairs of consecutive sides and angles in quadrilateral *WXYZ*.

Consecutive sides

$$\overline{WX} \text{ and } \overline{XY}$$
$$\overline{XY} \text{ and } \overline{YZ}$$
$$\overline{YZ} \text{ and } \overline{ZW}$$
$$\overline{ZW} \text{ and } \overline{WX}$$

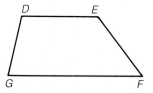

Consecutive angles

$$\angle W \text{ and } \angle X$$
$$\angle X \text{ and } \angle Y$$
$$\angle Y \text{ and } \angle Z$$
$$\angle Z \text{ and } \angle W$$

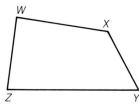

Try This... 2. Name the pairs of consecutive sides and angles in quadrilateral *MNOP*.

The two quadrilaterals on the left differ from the two on the right. The two on the left are *convex* quadrilaterals. The other two are *concave* quadrilaterals.

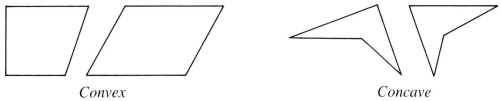

Convex   *Concave*

One way to distinguish between convex and concave quadrilaterals is by their diagonals. In convex quadrilaterals both diagonals (except for their endpoints) are in the interior. In concave quadrilaterals, one of the diagonals (except for its endpoints) is in the exterior.

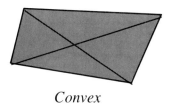   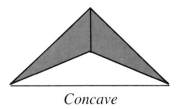

Convex   *Concave*

From now on, when we refer to quadrilaterals, we will mean convex quadrilaterals.

THEOREM **8.1**   The sum of the measures of the angles of a quadrilateral is 360°.

Example   3. Find $m \angle D$.

By Theorem 8.1,

$$m \angle A + m \angle B + m \angle C + m \angle D = 360$$
$$90 + 115 + 95 + m \angle D = 360$$
$$m \angle D = 60°$$

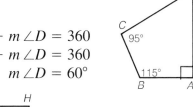

Try This...   3. Find $m \angle F$.

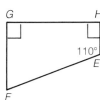

▲▲ Classification

Some special types of quadrilaterals are defined in the table.

Type of Quadrilateral	Definition	Picture
Kite	Two pairs of congruent consecutive sides	
Trapezoid	At least one pair of parallel sides	
Parallelogram	Two pairs of parallel sides	
Rectangle	A parallelogram with four right angles	
Rhombus	A parallelogram with four congruent sides	
Square	A rectangle with four congruent sides or A rhombus with four right angles	

Examples   Classify each quadrilateral.

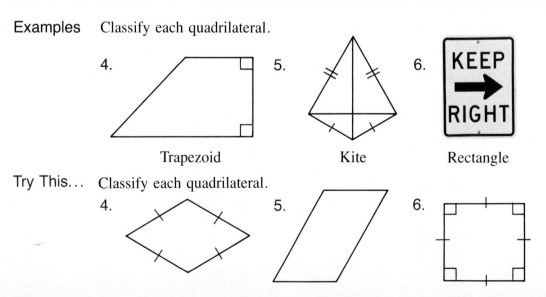

4.   Trapezoid   5.   Kite   6.   Rectangle

Try This...   Classify each quadrilateral.

4.   5.   6.

Exercises

▲ **Name the pairs of opposite sides and angles in each quadrilateral.**

1.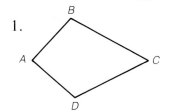

2.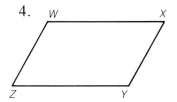

3.

Name the pairs of consecutive sides and angles in each quadrilateral.

4. W X Z Y

5. D E G F

6.

7. Name the diagonals of each quadrilateral in Exercises 1-3.
8. Name the diagonals in each quadrilateral in Exercises 4-6.

▲▲ 9-14. Classify each quadrilateral in Exercises 1-6.

▶ Extension Exercises

Try to draw a quadrilateral with the following properties. Then classify it.

15. Exactly two right angles
16. Exactly one pair of parallel sides
17. Exactly three right angles
18. Exactly one right angle
19. Four right angles and four congruent sides
20. Exactly one pair of sides parallel and the other two sides congruent
21. Two pairs of parallel sides and no congruent sides
22. Four congruent sides and no right angles

▶▶ Challenge Exercises

23. Draw several different quadrilaterals. In each, connect the midpoints of consecutive sides to obtain a new quadrilateral. Try to discover something about this new quadrilateral.

24. Draw several different quadrilaterals. In each, connect the midpoints of opposite sides. Try to discover something about the relationship between these two segments.

2 | Properties of Parallelograms

After finishing Section 2, you should be able to
▲ *apply the properties of parallelograms to solve problems.*

Recall that a parallelogram is a quadrilateral with two pairs of parallel sides. For parallelogram *ABCD* we will write "□ *ABCD*."

1. Draw two pairs of parallel lines to form □ *ABCD*.

2. Compare the lengths of opposite sides.

3. Compare the measures of opposite angles.

4. Compare the measures of consecutive angles.

5. Draw diagonal $\overline{AC}$. How are △*ADC* and △*CBA* related?

6. Draw diagonal $\overline{BD}$, intersecting $\overline{AC}$ at point *E*. What is special about point *E*?

THEOREM	A diagonal of a parallelogram determines two congruent triangles.	
8.2	△*ADC* ≅ △*CBA*	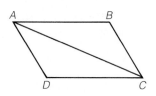

Because corresponding parts of congruent triangles are also congruent, we can state the following corollaries.

COROLLARY	The opposite angles of a parallelogram are congruent.
8.3	

COROLLARY	The opposite sides of a parallelogram are congruent.
8.4	

Examples   1. $m \angle A = 120°$. Find the measures of the other angles of $\square ABCD$.

By Corollary 8.3, $m \angle C = 120°$.

By Theorem 8.1,

$m \angle A + m \angle B + m \angle C + m \angle D = 360°$.

Because $m \angle B = m \angle D$, we have

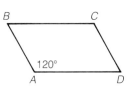

$120 + 120 + 2m \angle B = 360$

$2m \angle B = 360 - 240$

$= 120$

Thus, $m \angle B = m \angle D = 60°$.

▲2. $m \angle A = 2x$ and $m \angle B = x - 15$. Find the measures of other angles of $\square ABCD$.

By Corollary 8.3, $m \angle A = m \angle C$ and $m \angle B = m \angle D$.

By Theorem 8.1, $2m \angle A + 2m \angle B = 360°$. Substituting, we can solve for x:

$2(2x) + 2(x - 15) = 360$

$4x + 2x - 30 = 360$

$6x = 390$

$x = 65$

Thus, $m \angle A = m \angle C = 2 \times 65 = 130°$ and $m \angle B = m \angle D = 65 - 15 = 50°$.

Try This...   Find the measure of each angle.

1.

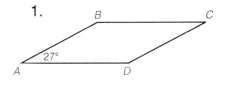

▲2.

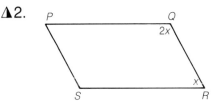

Examples   3. Find AB and BC.

By Corollary 8.4, $AB = 18$ and $BC = 7$.

▲4. Recall that the perimeter of a polygon is the distance around it. The perimeter of ▱ *MNOP* is 144. One side is twice as long as a consecutive side. Find the length of each side.

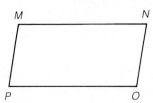

Let *MP* = *x*. Then *MN* = 2*x*. Because the perimeter is 144, we have

$$x + 2x + x + 2x = 144$$
$$6x = 144$$
$$x = 24$$

Thus, *MP* = *NO* = 24, and *MN* = *PO* = 48.

Try This...　Find the length of each side.

3.

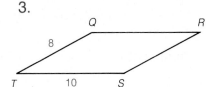

▲4. Perimeter of ▱ *DEFG* is 68.

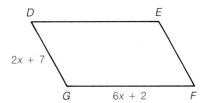

From Theorems 2.6 and 7.5, we obtain the following corollary.

COROLLARY　Consecutive angles of a
8.5　　　parallelogram are supplementary.

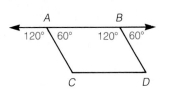

From Corollaries 7.6 and 8.4 and the ASA Theorem, we obtain the following corollary.

COROLLARY　The diagonals of a parallelogram
8.6　　　bisect each other.

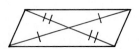

Example   5. $m \angle A = 32°$.
Find $m \angle B$ and $m \angle D$.

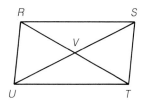

By Corollary 8.5, $m \angle A + m \angle B = 180°$.

Hence, $32 + m \angle B = 180$,
$$m \angle B = 148°.$$

Similarly, $m \angle D = 148°$.

6. $RV = 12$ and $VS = 13$. Find the
length of each diagonal.

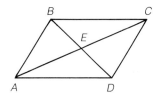

By Corollary 8.6, V is the midpoint of $\overline{RT}$ and $\overline{US}$.
Thus, $VT = 12$, $UV = 13$, $RT = 24$, and $US = 26$.

Try This...   5. Find $m \angle D$ and $m \angle F$.   6. $AC = 14$ and $BD = 8$.
Find $AE, BE, CE,$ and DE.

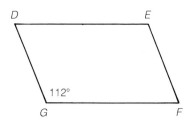

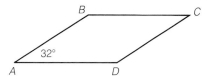

A familiar statement about parallel lines is that they are equidistant.
This means that if we choose *any* pair of points on one of the parallel
lines, the points will be the same distance from the other line. This
theorem follows from Corollary 8.4.

| THEOREM
 8.7 | Parallel lines are equidistant. | 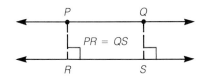 |

Exercises

▲ **Find the measures of the angles of each parallelogram.**

1.

A *B*

D 70° *C*

2.

E

F

H 110°

G

3.

M 71° *K*

J *L*

▲4.

P

2*x* − 3

S

Q

x + 9

R

Find the lengths of the sides of each parallelogram.

5.

T

U

15

O

9

N

6.

32

F

E

G

16

H

▲7.

K

W

J *P* = 64 *L*

x

3*x* − 4

M

▲8.

X

W

x − 6

P = 76

Y

Z *x* + 8

Find m ∠B and m ∠D in each parallelogram.

9.

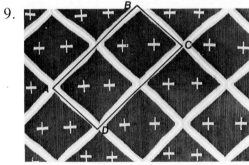

10.

11. *AB* = 14 and *BD* = 19. Find the length of each diagonal.

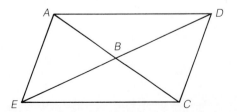

12. *EJ* = 23 and *GJ* = 13. Find the length of each diagonal.

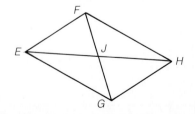

▶ Extension Exercises

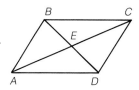

13. Name four pairs of congruent triangles in □ *ABCD*.
    Explain how you know.

14. The perimeter of □ *ABDC* is 60. *AD* = 12, *DB* = 16,
    and *EC* = 11. Find *AB*, *EB*, and *AC*.

15. Can two parallelograms have congruent sides but different
    angle measures? Support your answer with drawings.

16. Parallel rulers are often used in navigation.
    The rulers pivot at points *A*, *B*, *C*, and *D*.
    Explain how the parallel ruler works.

17. One angle of a parallelogram is a
    right angle. What can you conclude about the
    other angles? Explain how you know.

Exercises 18–20 refer to □ *ABCD*.

18. Name three pairs of parallel
    segments. Explain how you know.

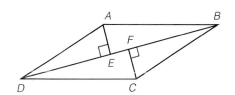

19. Name three pairs of congruent
    triangles. Explain how you know.

20. Name three pairs of congruent
    segments (other than the sides).
    Explain how you know.

3   Determining Parallelograms

After finishing Section 3, you should be able to
▲   *tell whether a given quadrilateral is a parallelogram.*

If quadrilateral *ABCD* is a parallelogram,
then we know that

opposite angles are congruent.

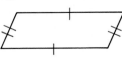

opposite sides are congruent.

diagonals bisect each other.

a diagonal determines two congruent triangles.

The converses of some of these statements are also true.

THEOREM 8.8	If the opposite angles of a quadrilateral are congruent, then the quadrilateral is a parallelogram. If $\angle A \cong \angle C$ and $\angle B \cong \angle D$, then *ABCD* is a parallelogram.	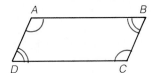
THEOREM 8.9	If the opposite sides of a quadrilateral are congruent, then the quadrilateral is a parallelogram. If $\overline{AB} \cong \overline{DC}$ and $\overline{AD} \cong \overline{BC}$, then *ABCD* is a parallelogram.	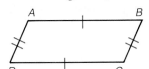
THEOREM 8.10	If the diagonals of a quadrilateral bisect each other, then the quadrilateral is a parallelogram. If $\overline{AE} \cong \overline{EC}$ and $\overline{BE} \cong \overline{ED}$, then *ABCD* is a parallelogram.	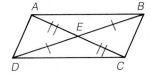

A parallelogram can be determined by one pair of sides.

> THEOREM
> **8.11**
>
> If two sides of a quadrilateral are both parallel and congruent, then the quadrilateral is a parallelogram.
>
> If $\overline{AB} \parallel \overline{DC}$ and $\overline{AB} \cong \overline{DC}$,
> then *ABCD* is a parallelogram.

Examples   Which figures are parallelograms? Explain how you know.

1.

Because $\angle D$ and $\angle C$ are supplementary angles, $\overline{AD} \parallel \overline{BC}$ by Corollary 7.4. Also, $AD = BC$. Thus, by Theorem 8.11, *ABCD* is a parallelogram.

2.

EFGH is not necessarily a parallelogram because all we know is that one pair of opposite angles are congruent.

Try This...   Which figures are parallelograms? Explain how you know.

1.

2.

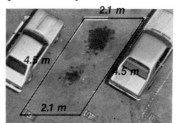

Example   3. Diagonal $\overline{AC}$ determines two congruent triangles. Is *ABCD* a parallelogram? Explain how you know.

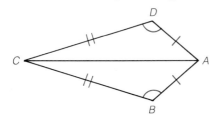

Although $\triangle ADC \cong \triangle ABC$, this quadrilateral is not a parallelogram.

Thus, the converse of Theorem 8.2 is not true. If a diagonal determines two congruent triangles, the quadrilateral is not necessarily a parallelogram.

Exercises

▲ **Tell which quadrilaterals are parallelograms. Explain how you know.**

1.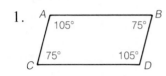

2.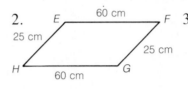

3.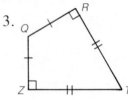

4.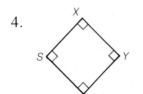

5.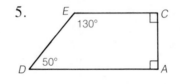

6.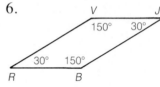

7.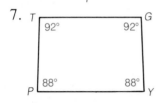

8.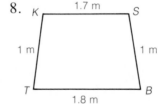

9.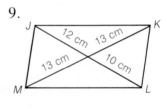

10.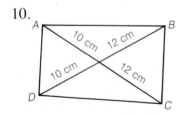

11.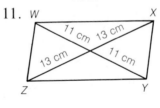

12.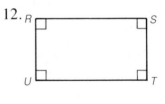

▶ Extension Exercises

13. △ *ZWX* ≅ △ *YXW*. Explain why *WXYZ* is a parallelogram.

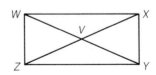

14. Draw a parallelogram with diagonals measuring 5 cm and 7 cm.

15. Draw a quadrilateral with diagonals measuring 5 cm and 7 cm that is *not* a parallelogram.

16. Explain how the design of these pliers guarantees that the jaws will always be parallel.

►► Challenge Exercises

17. *ABCD* is a parallelogram, $\overline{AD} \cong \overline{DE}$, and $\overline{BC} \cong \overline{BF}$.

    What can you conclude about *AFCE*?
    Explain how you know.

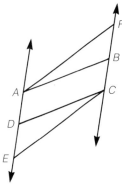

18. Draw a parallelogram *ABCD*. Let *E* and *F* be the midpoints of $\overline{AB}$ and $\overline{CD}$. What can you conclude about *AEFD*? Explain how you know.

19. Draw ▱*ABCD* and diagonal $\overline{BD}$. Bisect ∠*A* and ∠*C*, with the bisectors meeting $\overline{DB}$ at points *E* and *F*, respectively. Draw $\overline{AF}$ and $\overline{CE}$. What can you conclude about quadrilateral *AFCE*? Explain how you know.

►◄ Activity

Make twelve copies of this quadrilateral.

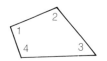

Cut them out and piece them together so that no two figures overlap and any two adjacent figures have one side in common. Such arrangements are called *tesselations*.

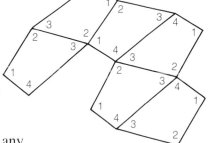

1. Which angles must meet at a common point in the tessellation so that there are no gaps?

2. What is the sum of the measures of the angles that meet at a common point in the tessellation?

3. Can a tessellation be made with copies of any quadrilateral? How do you know?

4. Can a tessellation be made with copies of any triangle? How do you know?

| 4 | The Triangle Midpoint Theorem |

After finishing Section 4, you should be able to
▲   *apply the Triangle Midpoint Theorem to solve problems.*

1. Draw an obtuse, an acute, and a right triangle. Label each $\triangle ABC$.

2. Using a ruler, find the midpoints of $\overline{AC}$ and $\overline{AB}$. Label them E and D.

3. Measure $\overline{ED}$ and $\overline{CB}$ in each triangle. Is $\overline{ED} \parallel \overline{CB}$?

THEOREM **8.12**

The Triangle Midpoint Theorem
The segment determined by the midpoints of two sides of a triangle is parallel to and is half as long as the third side.

$$\overline{ED} \parallel \overline{CB} \text{ and } ED = \frac{1}{2}CB$$

Examples   1. Find EB.

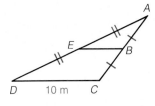

$$EB = \frac{1}{2}DC$$
$$= \frac{1}{2} \cdot 10$$
$$= 5 \text{ m}$$

2. Find QP in the compass.

$$RN = \frac{1}{2}QP$$
$$3.5 = \frac{1}{2}QP$$
$$QP = 7 \text{ cm}$$

Try This...   1. Find *DE*.   2.   Find *ML*.

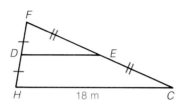

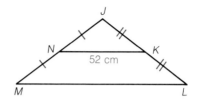

Example   ▲3. Find *DE* and *BC*.

Because *BC* = 2*DE*, we have
$$3x - 1 = 2(x + 2)$$
$$3x - 1 = 2x + 4$$
$$x = 5$$

Thus, *DE* = 7 and *BC* = 14.

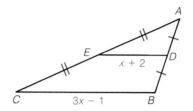

Try This... ▲3. Find *QR* and *ST*.

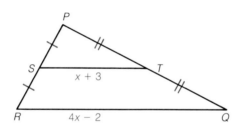

Example   4. *D*, *E*, and *F* are midpoints, *m* ∠*C* = 53°,
and *m* ∠*A* = 47°. Find m ∠1, *m* ∠2, and *m* ∠3.

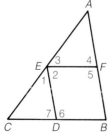

Because $\overline{EF} \parallel \overline{CB}$, *m* ∠*C* = *m* ∠3 by corresponding angles,
and *m* ∠3 = 53°.
Because $\overline{DE} \parallel \overline{AB}$, *m* ∠*A* = *m* ∠1 by corresponding angles,
and *m* ∠1 = 47°.
Because *m* ∠1 + *m* ∠2 + *m* ∠3 = 180
$$47 + m \angle 2 + 53 = 180$$
$$m \angle 2 + 100 = 180$$

Thus,   *m* ∠2 = 80°

Try This...   4. Find *m* ∠*B*, *m* ∠4, *m* ∠5, *m* ∠6, and *m* ∠7 in △ *ABC* of
Example 4.

Exercises

▲ **In each figure, find *DE*, *BC*, or both.**

1.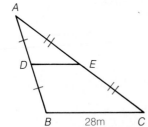

▲2.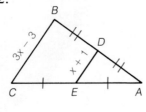

▲3.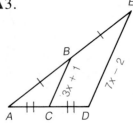

4.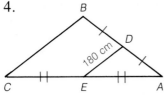

▲5.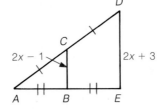

▲6.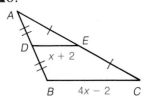

D, E, and F are midpoints, m ∠A = 73°, and m ∠B = 54°. Find the indicated angle measures.

7. *m* ∠1, *m* ∠2, *m* ∠3, and *m* ∠4

8. *m* ∠5, *m* ∠6, *m* ∠7, *m* ∠8, and *m* ∠9

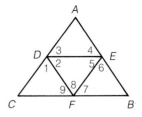

▶ Extension Exercises

Find the lengths of as many sides as you can from the given information.

9.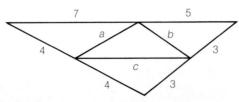

10.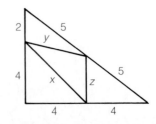

▶▶ Challenge Exercises

Exercises 11-13 refer to △ ABC.

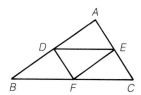

11. D, E, and F are midpoints of $\overline{AB}$, $\overline{AC}$, and $\overline{BC}$. Name as many parallelograms as you can. Explain how you know.

12. Name all of the triangles that are congruent to each other. Explain how you know.

13. Compare the perimeters of △ DEF and △ ABC. Explain how you know.

14. Draw any quadrilateral and find the midpoints of the sides. Connect the midpoints of consecutive sides to form a new quadrilateral. What kind of quadrilateral did you get? Explain how you know.

15. Draw any quadrilateral and find the midpoints of the sides. Connect the midpoints of opposite sides. Where do they intersect each other? Explain how you know.

16. $\overrightarrow{SW}$ and $\overrightarrow{TX}$ are medians of △RST with $SW = WY$, and $TX = XZ$. What can you conclude about segments $\overline{YR}$ and $\overline{RZ}$? Explain how you know.

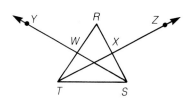

▶◀ Activity

Copy this Chinese Tangram puzzle and cut it into seven pieces as shown. Now arrange the seven pieces to form a rectangle. See if you can form a parallelogram and a trapezoid, too.

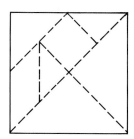

5 | Parallels and Transversals

After finishing Section 5, you should be able to
▲ *find lengths of segments intercepted by parallel lines.*
▲▲ *use a straightedge and compass to divide a segment into a given number of congruent segments.*

▲▲▲ *use a ruler to divide a sheet of paper with a given number of equally-spaced parallel lines.*

▲ Intercepted Segments

Parallel lines m, ℓ, and p intersect the transversal t at points A, B, and C. We say that the parallel lines **intercept** the segments $\overline{AB}$ and $\overline{BC}$.

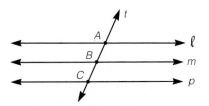

1. Draw several transversals on a sheet of lined notebook paper.

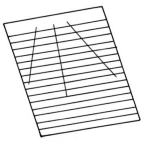

2. Measure the intercepted segments for each transversal.

| THEOREM 8.13 | If three or more parallel lines intercept congruent segments on one transversal, then they intercept congruent segments on every transversal. |

Examples $\ell \parallel m \parallel p$, $AB = BC = 5$, $DH = 10$, and $DE = 7$.

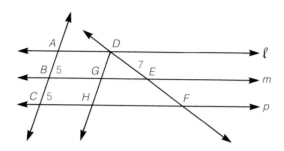

1. Find EF.

   By Theorem 8.13, $DE = EF = 7$.

2. Find DG.

   By Theorem 8.13, $DG = GH$, and $DG + GH = 10$. Thus, $DG = 5$.

Try This... $j \parallel k \parallel \ell$, $PQ = QR = 3$, $ST = 6$, and $WY = 16$.

1. Find TU.

2. Find WX.

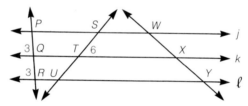

Example   ▲3. $a \parallel b \parallel c$, $\overline{TR} \cong \overline{RS}$, $PQ = x + 3$, and $QM = 2x - 7$.
Find PQ and QM.

By Theorem 8.13, we know $PQ = QM$.

Thus, $x + 3 = 2x - 7$

$\qquad\qquad 10 = x$

Hence, $PQ = QM = 13$.

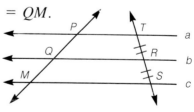

Try This...   ▲3. $x \parallel y \parallel z$, $\overline{AB} \cong \overline{BC}$, $DE = 2x - 4$, and $EF = x + 6$. Find DE and EF.

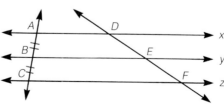

▲▲ Dividing a Segment

We can apply Theorem 8.13 to divide a segment into any number
of congruent segments.

Example   4. Use a straightedge and compass to divide $\overline{AB}$ into three congruent
segments. That is, find two points C and D such that $\overline{AC} \cong \overline{CD} \cong \overline{DB}$.

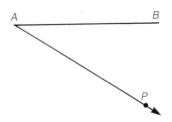 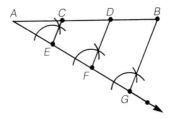

Step 1

Draw a ray, $\overrightarrow{AP}$, forming
an acute angle with $\overline{AB}$.

Step 2

Choose a convenient
compass opening and
mark off three congruent
segments, $\overline{AE}$, $\overline{EF}$, and
$\overline{FG}$.

Step 3

Draw $\overline{BG}$. Construct
segments $\overline{CE}$ and $\overline{DF}$
such that $\overline{CE} \parallel \overline{FD} \parallel \overline{GB}$.

By Theorem 8.13, because the parallel lines intercept congruent
segments on transversal $\overleftrightarrow{AP}$, they also intercept congruent segments
on transversal $\overleftrightarrow{AB}$.

Try This...   4. Draw a segment 7 cm long. Use a straightedge and compass to divide
the segment into 5 congruent segments.

▲▲ Drawing Equally-Spaced Parallel Lines

Here is another use of parallel lines and transversals.

Example   5. Suppose you have a sheet of paper
22 cm wide that you want to divide
equally into five vertical columns. How
can you do it with only a ruler?

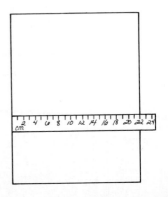

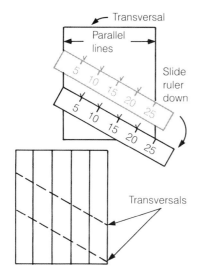

Transversal
Parallel lines
Slide ruler down
Transversals

Step 1

Position your ruler on a diagonal so that you can mark off 5 congruent segments along the ruler.

Step 2

Slide your ruler down and repeat Step 1.

Step 3

Use each pair of vertical marks to draw a segment.

The vertical segments are parallel. You can think of the marks on the diagonals as points on two transversals.

Try This... 5. Use a ruler to divide a sheet of paper equally into eight vertical columns.

Exercises

▲ **Use the figure for Exercises 1-10.** $\ell \parallel m \parallel n$ and $\overline{AB} \cong \overline{BC}$.

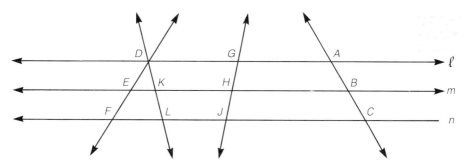

1.   If $DE = 7$, then $EF =$ _____ .
2.   If $GH = 3$, then $HJ =$ _____ .
3.   If $DF = 13$, then $DE =$ _____ .
4.   If $GJ = 23$, then $HJ =$ _____ .
5.   If $DK = 3$, then $DL =$ _____ .
6.   If $DL = 34$, then $DK =$ _____ .
▲7.   If $DE = x + 8$ and $EF = 2x + 5$, what is DE and EF?
▲8.   If $AB = 4x - 3$ and $BC = 5x - 7$, what is AB and BC?
▲9.   If $DL = 3x + 6$ and $DK = x + 7$, what is KL?
▲10.   If $DF = x + 9$ and $EF = x - 3$, what is DE?

11. Draw a segment 8 cm long. Divide it into five congruent segments.

12. Draw a segment 9 cm long. Divide it into seven congruent segments.

Use a ruler.

13. Divide a sheet of paper equally into seven vertical columns.

14. Divide a sheet of paper equally into eight vertical columns.

▶◀ Activity

A pentomino is made up of five connecting squares, all congruent. Copy the six pentominoes shown here on paper or cardboard and cut them out. Arrange the pentominoes to form two congruent rectangles.

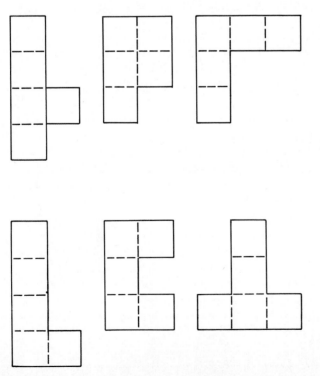

6 | Rhombuses, Rectangles, and Squares

After finishing Section 6, you should be able to
▲ *identify properties of rhombuses, rectangles, and squares, and conversely, identify rhombuses, rectangles, and squares by their properties.*

Rhombuses, rectangles, and squares are special kinds of parallelograms. Thus, each one has all the properties of a parallelogram. This is shown in the figure.

These special parallelograms have some additional properties that involve diagonals.

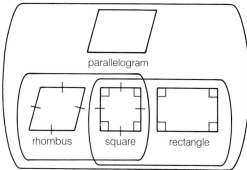

parallelogram

rhombus | square | rectangle

1. Draw a rhombus on a sheet of paper. Follow the directions below.

①

A   D

Step 1.

Draw a segment, $\overline{AD}$. Use a compass setting of AD to draw all the arcs. Draw arc ①.

②

A   D

Step 2

Choose any point B on arc ① and draw arc ②.

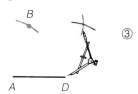

③

A   D

Step 3

Draw arc ③ from point D. Point C is the intersection of arcs ② and ③.

A   D

Step 4

Draw rhombus $ABCD$.

1. Draw several rhombuses.
2. Draw the diagonals of each rhombus.
3. Use a protractor to measure the angles of intersection of the diagonals of each rhombus. What do you observe?
4. Now draw several pairs of non-perpendicular segments that bisect each other. Join the endpoints. Describe the quadrilaterals formed.
5. Draw several pairs of perpendicular segments that bisect each other. Join the endpoints. Describe the quadrilaterals formed.

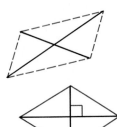

THEOREM
8.14   A parallelogram is a rhombus whenever its diagonals are perpendicular.

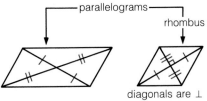

The diagonals of a rectangle are also related in a special way.

1. Draw several rectangles on a sheet of paper.
2. Draw the diagonals and measure them. Compare the lengths of each pair of diagonals.

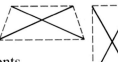

3. Draw some pairs of intersecting segments that are congruent and bisect each other.
4. Join the endpoints. Describe the quadrilaterals formed.
5. Repeat Steps 3 and 4 for pairs of congruent segments that do *not* bisect each other.

THEOREM
8.15
A parallelogram is a rectangle whenever its diagonals are congruent.

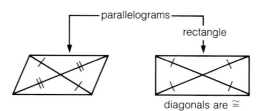

A square is both a rhombus and a rectangle. Hence, its diagonals bisect each other and are perpendicular and congruent.

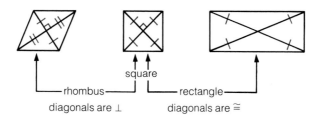

THEOREM
8.16
A parallelogram is a square whenever its diagonals are perpendicular and congruent.

Examples   Which type of quadrilateral is described by each pair of diagonals?

1.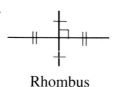

Rhombus

2.

Parallelogram

3.

Square

Try This...   Which type of quadrilateral is described by each pair of diagonals?

1.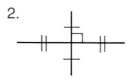

2.

3.

Examples   Consider rhombus *ABCD*.

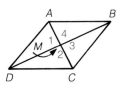

4. Which triangle is congruent to △*AMB*? Why?
Because the diagonals bisect each other,

$$\overline{AM} \cong \overline{MC} \text{ and } \overline{DM} \cong \overline{MB}.$$

∠1 ≅ ∠2 ≅ ∠3 ≅ ∠4 (right angles).

Hence, by SAS, △*AMB* ≅ △*CMD* ≅ △*CMB* ≅ △*AMD*.
Because the sides of a rhombus are congruent, the triangles are also congruent by SSS.

5. If *AM* + *DM* = 17, then what is *AC* + *BD*?
Because the diagonals bisect each other,

$$2(AM + DM) = AC + BD = 2 \cdot 17 = 34.$$

6. If $\overline{AC} \cong \overline{BD}$, then what do we know about the rhombus?
If the diagonals are congruent, then by Theorem 8.16 the rhombus is a square.

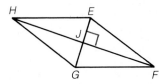

Try This...   Consider rhombus *EFGH*.

4. If *m* ∠*HEF* = 90°, then what do we know about the rhombus?
5. If *m* ∠*EHG* = 53°, then what is *m* ∠*HEF*?
6. Name all of the right triangles.

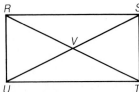

Examples   Consider rectangle *RSTU*.

7. What type of triangle is △*RVS*?
$\overline{RT} \cong \overline{SU}$ and *V* bisects $\overline{RT}$ and $\overline{SU}$. Thus, $\overline{RV} \cong \overline{VS}$ and △*RVS* is isosceles.

8. If *RV* = 4, then what is *SU*?
If *RV* = 4, then *RT* = *SU* = 8.

9. If $\overline{RS} \cong \overline{ST}$, then what do we know about the rectangle?
If $\overline{RS} \cong \overline{ST}$, then all four sides are congruent, and *RSTU* is a square.

Try This... Consider rectangle *JKLM*.

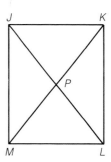

7. If *m* ∠*JPK* = 90°, then what do we know about the rectangle?

8. What type of triangle is △*JML*?

9. If *MP* + *PL* = 14, then what is *JL*?

Exercises

▲ **What type of quadrilateral is described by each pair of diagonals?**

1.

2.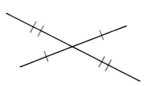

3.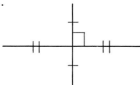

4.

5.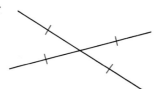

6.

Use rhombus *ABCD* for Exercises 7-14.

7. If *BM* = 6, then what is *DM*?

8. If *AC* = 13, then what is *AM*?

9. If *AD* = 10, then what is *BC* ?

10. If *BC* = 12, then what is *DC*?

11. What triangle is congruent to △*ADC*?

12. What triangle is congruent to △*ADB*?

13. If the rhombus is a square, then what is *m* ∠*DAB*?

14. If the rhombus is a square, then what is *AC*?

Use rectangle *PQRS* for Exercises 15-22.

15. If $PR = 12$, then what is SQ?

16. If $SQ = 13$, then what is PR?

17. Name three other triangles congruent to $\triangle PSR$.

18. What triangle is congruent to $\triangle PQT$?

19. $\triangle PTS$, $\triangle PTQ$, $\triangle QTR$, and $\triangle STR$ are what type of triangles?

20. Name four right triangles.

21. If the rectangle is a square, then what is $m \angle PTQ$?

22. If the rectangle is a square, then how are $\overline{PS}$ and $\overline{PQ}$ related?

▶ Extension Exercises

23. Name the properties of a square that are not properties of every parallelogram.

24. Name the properties of a rectangle that are not properties of every parallelogram.

25. Name the properties of a rhombus that are not properties of every parallelogram.

▶▶ Challenge Exercises

26. Draw any rhombus and find the midpoint of each side. Connect the midpoints of consecutive sides to form a quadrilateral. What kind of quadrilateral did you get? Explain how you know.

27. Suppose that $ABCE$ is a rectangle, and $ACDE$ is a parallelogram. Find as many isosceles triangles as you can. Explain how you know.

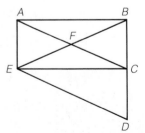

28. Draw $\square ABCD$ with $AB > AD$. Bisect $\angle A$ and $\angle D$. Extend the bisectors to intersect $\overline{DC}$ and $\overline{AB}$ at E and F, respectively. What can you conclude about $AFED$? Explain how you know.

7	Trapezoids

After finishing Section 7, you should be able to
▲ *identify parts of trapezoids.*
▲▲ *apply the theorem about medians of trapezoids.*
▲▲ *identify properties of isosceles trapezoids and apply them in solving problems.*

▲ Parts of Trapezoids

A trapezoid is a quadrilateral that has at least one pair of parallel sides.

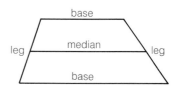

DEFINITIONS

The **bases of a trapezoid** are the pair of parallel sides.
The **legs of a trapezoid** are the other two sides.
A **median of a trapezoid** is the segment determined by the midpoints of the legs.

Examples   Name the bases, legs, and median of each trapezoid. The points between the vertices are midpoints of the sides.

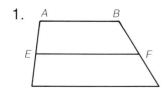

1.
Bases: $\overline{AB}$ and $\overline{CD}$
Legs: $\overline{AD}$ and $\overline{BC}$
Median: $\overline{EF}$

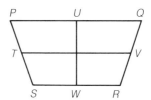

2.
Bases: $\overline{PQ}$ and $\overline{SR}$
Legs: $\overline{PS}$ and $\overline{QR}$
Median: $\overline{TV}$

3.
Bases: $\overline{AD}$ and $\overline{BC}$
Legs: $\overline{AB}$ and $\overline{CD}$
Median: $\overline{MN}$

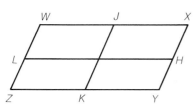

4.
Bases: $\overline{WX}$ and $\overline{ZY}$ ⎱ ⎰ $\overline{WZ}$ and $\overline{XY}$
Legs: $\overline{WZ}$ and $\overline{XY}$ ⎰or⎱ $\overline{WX}$ and $\overline{ZY}$
Medians: $\overline{LH}$ ⎰ ⎱ $\overline{JK}$

Try This…   Name the bases, legs, and median of each trapezoid. The points
between the vertices are midpoints of the sides.

1. 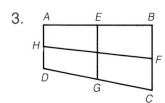   2.

3.    4.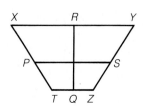

▲▲ Medians of Trapezoids

1. Draw several trapezoids and their medians.

2. Measure each median and
    the two bases. What is the
    relationship between their
    lengths?

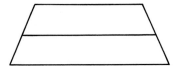

3. Think of one leg as a transversal. Measure the angles
    formed by that transversal with the median and each base.
    How is the median related to the two parallel bases?

THEOREM
8.17

A median of a trapezoid is parallel to the bases and is half as long
as the sum of the lengths of the two bases.

$\overline{MN} \parallel \overline{AB} \parallel \overline{DC}$

$MN = \frac{1}{2}(AB + DC)$

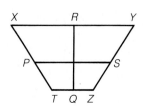

Examples 5. Find *MN*.

$$MN = \frac{1}{2}(6 + 12) = 9$$

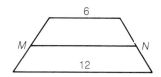

6. Find *RS* and *m* ∠*STU*.

$$\frac{1}{2}(PQ + RS) = TU$$
$$\frac{1}{2}(18 + RS) = 22$$
$$18 + RS = 44$$
$$RS = 26$$

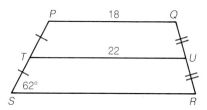

Because $\overline{TU} \parallel \overline{SR}$ and interior angles ∠*S* and ∠*STU* are supplementary, *m* ∠*STU* = 180 − 62 = 118°.

▲7. Find the lengths of the bases and the median.

$$FC = \frac{1}{2}(ED + AB)$$
$$x + 2 = \frac{1}{2}(x + 2x + 3)$$
$$2(x + 2) = 3x + 3$$
$$2x + 4 = 3x + 3$$
$$1 = x$$

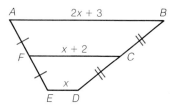

Substituting, we get *AB* = 5, *ED* = 1, and *FC* = 3.

Try This... 5. Find *MN*.

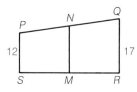

6. Find *DE* and *m* ∠*GFE*.

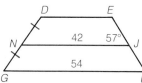

▲7. Find the length of the bases and the median.

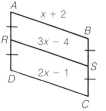

▲▲ Isosceles Trapezoids

If we "cut off" part of an isosceles triangle, we would have an isosceles trapezoid.

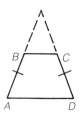

DEFINITION

An **isosceles trapezoid** is a trapezoid with two congruent, non-parallel sides.

The following theorems describe some properties of isosceles trapezoids.

THEOREM **8.18** In an isosceles trapezoid, each pair of base angles is congruent.

THEOREM **8.19** The diagonals of an isosceles trapezoid are congruent.

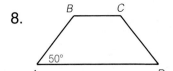

Examples Find the missing angle measures in each isosceles trapezoid.

8.

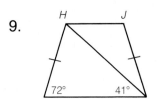

$m \angle D = 50°$. So $m \angle B = m \angle C = 130°$ because they are supplementary to $\angle A$.

9.

$m \angle HKJ = 72 - 41 = 31°$
$m \angle J = 180 - 72 = 108°$
$m \angle GHK = 180 - 72 - 41 = 67°$
$m \angle JHK = m\angle J - 67$
$\qquad = 108 - 67 = 41°$

Try This... Find the missing angle measures in each isosceles trapezoid.

8.

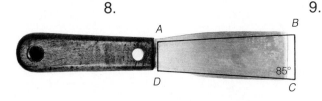

9.

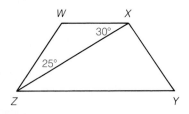

Examples 10. Name all pairs of congruent triangles.

$\triangle DEF \cong \triangle GFE$
$\triangle DEH \cong \triangle GFH$
$\triangle DEG \cong \triangle GFD$

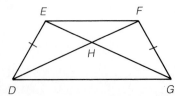

11. Find the missing angle measures.

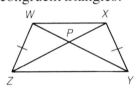

$m \angle ECD = 40°$ $m \angle EDA = 65°$
$m \angle ECB = 65°$ $m \angle DAE = 35°$
$m \angle BEC = 80°$ $m \angle ABE = m \angle BAE = 40°$
$m \angle AED = 80°$ $m \angle AEB = m \angle DEC = 100°$

Try This... 10. Name all pairs of
congruent triangles.

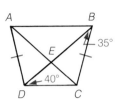

11. Find the missing angle
measures.

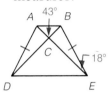

Exercises

▲ **Name the base, legs, and median of each trapezoid. The points between the vertices are midpoints of the sides.**

1.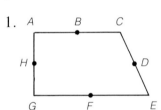

2.

3.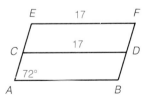

▲▲ **Find the indicated lengths and angle measures.**

4. Find *MN*.

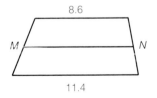

5. Find *PQ*.

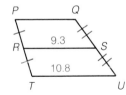

6. Find *AB* and $m \angle F$.

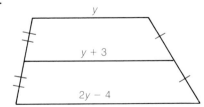

Find the lengths of the bases and the median.

▲7.

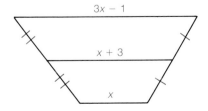

▲8.

Find the missing angle measures in these isosceles trapezoids. Name all pairs of congruent triangles in Exercises 13 and 14.

9.

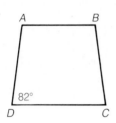

10.

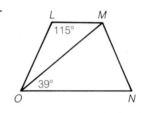

11.

12.

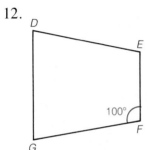

13.

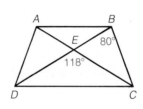

14.

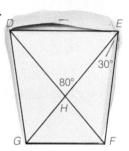

▶ Extension Exercises

15. Consider this wooden A-frame. Suppose that you wish to put up a horizontal brace parallel to the line containing the bases. How can this be done?

16. Draw any isosceles trapezoid and measure the vertex angles. What can you conclude about these angles? Explain how you know.

17. Draw any trapezoid, a median, and the diagonals. Where does the median intersect each of the diagonals? Explain how you know.

Computer Application   Missing Angle Measures

Find the missing angle in a quadrilateral.

Command	**Comments**
10 FOR X = 1 TO 3	**10 and 50 FOR...NEXT** This creates a loop in the program. The computer reads through the program returning to **X** the indicated number of times.
20 READ A, B, C	
30 LET D = 360 − (A + B + C)	
40 PRINT " THE MISSING ANGLE IS "; D	**20 READ** The computer reads the first three angle values from the DATA statement (line 60).
50 NEXT X	**30** The computer finds the measure of the missing angle and assigns the value to the variable **D**.
60 DATA 36, 72, 54, 26, 100, 82, 140, 36, 75	
70 END	**50 NEXT** Next, the computer returns to line 10, continuing through the program until it reaches the final value of the variable **X**.
	60 DATA The computer finds the data here for three quadrilaterals.

Run the program above, replacing line 60 with new data.

1. 50 DATA 126, 37, 52, 90, 90, 90, 85, 95, 105

2. 50 DATA 76, 75, 89, 29, 140, 45, 122, 17, 86

3. 50 DATA 25, 35, 145, 60, 70, 80, 110, 105, 56

4. 50 DATA 35.5, 62.7, 136.1, 152.5, 63.9, 17.4, 18.9, 99.2, 101

5. 50 DATA 57.5, 89.2, 44.4, 104.6, 121.3, 17.2, 91, 87.9, 113

6. 50 DATA 120, 80, 30.4, 111.5, 33.3, 66.6, 119, 37, 42

7. Write and run a program in BASIC that will find the missing angle in a triangle.

Chapter Review

1 1. For quadrilateral *KLMN*, name one pair of opposite angles and one pair of consecutive angles.

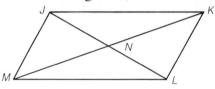

2 ⚠ 2. The perimeter of ▱ *DEFG* is 62. Find the measures of the angles and the lengths of the sides.

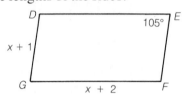

3. In ▱ *JKLM*, *JN* = 3.2 and *KN* = 3. Find the lengths of the diagonals, $\overline{LJ}$ and $\overline{KM}$.

3 **Tell why each figure is a parallelogram.**

4.

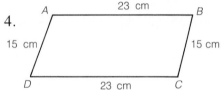

5.

4 **Use the figure for Exercises 6 and 7.**

⚠ 6. Find *BC* and *DE*.

7. *m* ∠*A* = 65° and *m* ∠*AED* = 45°. Find *m* ∠*ABC*.

5 8. *k* ∥ *ℓ* ∥ *m* ∥ *n* and $\overline{AB} \cong \overline{BC} \cong \overline{CD}$. If *GF* = 3.4, then what is *AG*?

9. Divide $\overline{CD}$ into three congruent segments.

C _____ D

6 **Which type of quadrilateral is described by each pair of diagonals?**

10.

11.

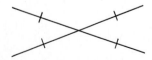

12. What triangles in rhombus *ABCD* are congruent to △*AEB*?

13. If *BE* = 4.5, then what is *DB* in *ABCD*?

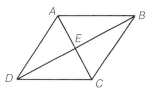

14. If *MK* = 17 in rectangle *JKLM*, then what is *JN*?

15. Name two triangles in rectangle *JKLM* that are congruent to △*MKJ*.

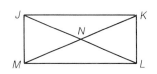

16. Find the lengths of the bases and the median in trapezoid *ABCD*.

17. Find the missing angle measures in isosceles trapezoid *QRST*.

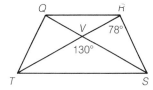

Chapter Test

1. For quadrilateral *ABCD*, name one pair of opposite sides and one pair of consecutive angles.

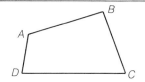

2. The perimeter of ▱ *RSTV* is 98. Find the measures of the angles and the lengths of the sides.

3. In ▱ *DEFG*, *GH* = 3.5 and *HF* = 4.8. Find the lengths of the diagonals, $\overline{DF}$ and $\overline{GE}$.

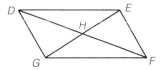

Tell why each figure is a parallelogram.

4.

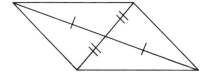

5.

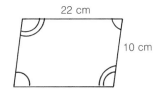

Use the figure for Exercises 6 and 7.

▲6. Find *DE* and *BC*.

7. Name one pair of congruent angles.

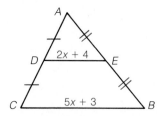

8. *m* ∥ *n* ∥ *p* ∥ *q* and $\overline{AB} \cong \overline{BC} \cong \overline{CD}$. If *AF* = 12.2, then what is *AG*?

9. Divide $\overline{AB}$ into five congruent segments.

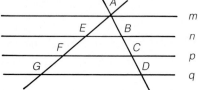

Which type of quadrilateral is described by each pair of diagonals?

10.

11.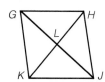

12. Name two triangles in rhombus *GHJK* that are congruent to △*GLK*.

13. In rhombus *GHJK*, *GH* = 5. What is *HJ*?

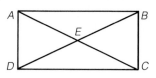

14. In rectangle *ABCD*, if *AE* = 6.3, then what is *DE*?

15. If *m* ∠*AEB* = 90°, then what type of rectangle is *ABCD*?

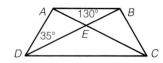

▲16. Find the lengths of the bases and the median in trapezoid *JKLM*.

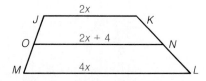

17. Find the missing angle measures in isosceles trapezoid *ABCD*.

Skills Review   Converting Customary Units

Write the missing number.

1. 4 ft = _____ in.

2. 2 yd = _____ in.

3. 3 mi = _____ yd

4. 6 pt = _____ c

5. 8 qt = _____ pt

6. 5 T = _____ lb

7. 5 yd = _____ ft

8. 2 c = _____ fl oz

9. 8 gal = _____ qt

10. 3 lb = _____ oz

11. 15 ft = _____ yd

12. 40 fl oz = _____ c

13. 52 qt = _____ gal

14. 18 in. = _____ ft

15. 24 in. = _____ yd

16. 7 c = _____ pt

17. 14 qt = _____ gal

18. 32 oz = _____ lb

19. 8 yd = _____ ft

20. 7 gal = _____ qt

21. 20 pt = _____ qt

22. $2\frac{1}{3}$ yd = _____ in.

23. 3,000 lb = _____ T

24. 32 fl oz = _____ c

25. 2 mi = _____ ft

26. 144 in. = _____ yd

27. 4 lb = _____ oz

28. 36 in. = _____ ft

29. $1\frac{1}{4}$ T = _____ lb

30. 30 pt = _____ qt

31. 6 yd = _____ ft

32. 54 in. = _____ yd

33. 1.5 lb = _____ oz

34. 10,560 ft = _____ mi

35. $1\frac{1}{2}$ qt = _____ pt

36. $2\frac{1}{2}$ lb = _____ oz

37. 1 mi = _____ in.

38. 3,520 yd = _____ mi

39. 10,000 T = _____ lb

40. 2 qt = _____ c

41. 64 oz = _____ lb

42. 40 pt = _____ gal

43. 5,000 lb = _____ T

44. 7 pt = _____ qt

45. 64 fl oz = _____ qt

Cumulative Review: Chapters 5–8

5–1   1. $\overline{AB} \cong \overline{AD}$ and $\overline{BC} \cong \overline{DC}$.
What can you conclude?

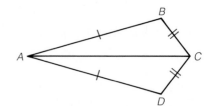

5–2   2. $\angle G \cong \angle M$, $\overline{GL} \cong \overline{MK}$,
and $\overline{MN} = \overline{GP}$. Explain why
$\angle P \cong \angle N$.

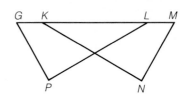

5–3   **Find x in each figure.**

▲3.

▲4.

5–4   ▲5. Line ℓ is the perpendicular bisector
of $\overline{CF}$. If $CH = 2(y - 10)$ and
$FH = 8y - 140$, what is y?

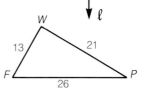

6–2   6. List the angles in $\triangle WFP$ from largest
to smallest.

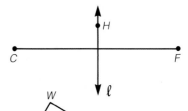

6–3   7. Can 6, 8, and 15 be the lengths of sides of a triangle?

6–4   8. Consider $\triangle DGT$ and $\triangle RSV$.
What can you conclude?

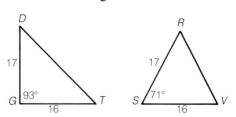

6–5   9. $\overrightarrow{SV}$ bisects $\angle RST$ and $\angle R \cong \angle T$.
Explain why $\overline{RV} \cong \overline{TV}$.

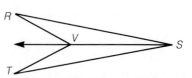

7–2   **Identify each pair of angles as corresponding angles, interior angles, or alternate interior angles.**

      10. $\angle 1$ and $\angle 6$

      11. $\angle 4$ and $\angle 5$

      12. $\angle 3$ and $\angle 5$

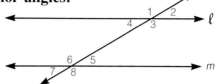

7–3   13. Consider the figure in Exercises 10-12 with $\ell \parallel m$. Identify all pairs of congruent and supplementary angles.

7–4   **Find the measure of each angle.**

      14.

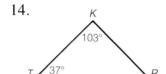

      15.

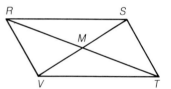

8–2   16. In $\square$ $RSTV$, $RM = 3.6$ and $SM = 2.8$. Find RT and VS.

8–3   **Tell why each figure is a parallelogram.**

      17.

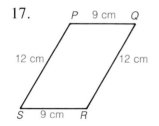

      18.

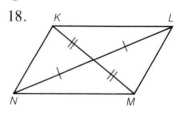

8–4   ▲19. S and T are midpoints of $\overline{PR}$ and $\overline{PW}$. Find ST and RW.

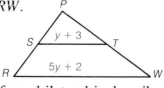

8–6   20. Which type of quadrilateral is described by this pair of diagonals?

8–7   ▲21. Find the lengths of the bases and the median in trapezoid $RVGT$.

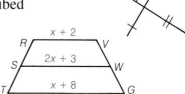

9
Similarity

1   Ratio and Proportion

After finishing Section 1, you should be able to
▲   *find the ratio of one quantity to another.*
▲▲   *solve proportions.*

▲   Ratio

We often find the ratio of one quantity to another. In the measuring cup, there is twice as much oil as vinegar. We say the ratio of oil to vinegar is 2 to 1.

DEFINITION

The **ratio** of two numbers, a and b, is their quotient, $\dfrac{a}{b}$.

Examples   Find these ratios.

1. 75 meters to 10 meters.

   $\dfrac{75}{10} = \dfrac{15}{2}$, so the ratio of 75 meters to 10 meters is $\dfrac{15}{2}$.

2. 28 years to 7 years.

   $\dfrac{28}{7} = 4$, so the ratio of 28 years to 7 years is 4.

3. 18 kg to 76 kg.

   $\dfrac{18}{76} = \dfrac{9}{38}$, so the ratio of 18 kg to 76 kg is $\dfrac{9}{38}$.

Try This...   Find these ratios.

1. 15 days to 45 days.

2. 82 cm to 144 cm.

3. 19 liters to 38 liters.

▲▲ Solving Proportions

<u>DEFINITION</u>

A **proportion** is a statement that two ratios are equal. For any numbers a, b, c, and d,

$$\frac{a}{b} = \frac{c}{d} \quad (b \neq 0,\ d \neq 0)$$

is a proportion.

In a proportion, if the cross products are the same, the proportion is true. If the cross products are different, the proportion is false.

$$\frac{a}{b} \diagdown\kern-1.2em\diagup \frac{c}{d}$$

If $ad = bc$, then the proportion is true.

Examples   Tell whether each proportion is true.

4. $\dfrac{7}{8} = \dfrac{21}{24}$

   Find the cross products.

   $$7 \cdot 24 = 168$$
   $$8 \cdot 21 = 168$$
   $$168 = 168$$

   The cross products are the same, so the proportion is true.

5. $\dfrac{4}{5} = \dfrac{8}{12}$

   Find the cross products.

   $$4 \cdot 12 = 48$$
   $$5 \cdot 8 = 40$$
   $$48 \neq 40$$

   The cross products are not the same, so the proportion is false.

Try This...   Tell whether each proportion is true.

4. $\dfrac{4}{5} = \dfrac{20}{25}$ 5. $\dfrac{75}{25} = \dfrac{3}{2}$

The numbers in a true proportion are said to be **proportional.**

If $\dfrac{a}{b} = \dfrac{c}{d}$ is true, then we say that a and c are proportional to b and d.

Example   6. Tell which numbers are proportional:

$$\dfrac{2}{3} = \dfrac{4}{6}$$

2 and 4 are proportional to 3 and 6, respectively.

Try This...   Tell which numbers are proportional.

6. $\dfrac{5}{8} = \dfrac{15}{24}$ 7. $\dfrac{8}{3} = \dfrac{32}{12}$

We can use the cross product property to solve proportions.

Examples   Solve these proportions. Find what x represents.

7. $\dfrac{x}{72} = \dfrac{9}{12}$

$x \cdot 12 = 72 \cdot 9$ Finding the cross products

$12x = 648$

$x = \dfrac{648}{12}$ Because 648 is 12 times x, we can find x by dividing by 12.

$x = 54$

8. $\dfrac{24}{3} = \dfrac{66}{x}$

$24 \cdot x = 3 \cdot 66$ Finding the cross products

$24x = 198$

$x = \dfrac{198}{24}$

$x = \dfrac{33}{24}$ or $8\dfrac{1}{4}$

Try This...   Solve these proportions. Find what y and x represent.

8. $\dfrac{y}{8} = \dfrac{6}{4}$ 9. $\dfrac{20}{7} = \dfrac{80}{x}$

Example   9. On a map the scale is 1 cm to 12 m. How many meters does 2.5 cm represent?

$\dfrac{1\,\text{cm}}{2.5\,\text{cm}} = \dfrac{12\,\text{m}}{x}$

$1 \cdot x = 2.5 \cdot 12$ Finding the cross products

$x = 30$

2.5 cm represents 30 m.

Distances on a map and their actual distances are proportional.

Try This...   10. On a map the scale is 2 cm to 20 m. How many meters does 5 cm represent?

Exercises

▲ **Find these ratios.**

1. 4 weeks to 18 weeks
2. 9 minutes to 30 minutes
3. 12 years to 60 years
4. 28 cm to 50 cm
5. 9 km to 54 km
6. 54 km to 9 km
7. 125 peanuts to 700 peanuts
8. 96 apples to 168 apples

▲▲ **Solve these proportions. Find what x and y represent.**

9. $\dfrac{x}{5} = \dfrac{3}{15}$ 10. $\dfrac{y}{7} = \dfrac{3}{21}$ 11. $\dfrac{32}{y} = \dfrac{8}{9}$ 12. $\dfrac{45}{x} = \dfrac{15}{16}$

13. $\dfrac{16}{y} = \dfrac{1}{4}$ 14. $\dfrac{25}{75} = \dfrac{1}{x}$ 15. $\dfrac{5}{x} = \dfrac{10}{20}$ 16. $\dfrac{5}{8} = \dfrac{10}{y}$

17. $\dfrac{12}{9} = \dfrac{x}{7}$ 18. $\dfrac{16}{15} = \dfrac{y}{20}$ 19. $\dfrac{24}{x} = \dfrac{4}{7}$ 20. $\dfrac{18}{x} = \dfrac{3}{5}$

21. $\dfrac{125}{y} = \dfrac{35}{7}$ 22. $\dfrac{100}{80} = \dfrac{25}{y}$ 23. $\dfrac{11}{x} = \dfrac{2}{7.1}$ 24. $\dfrac{10}{x} = \dfrac{3.4}{1.2}$

25. On a map the scale is 1.5 cm to 25 m. How many meters does 8 cm represent?

26. The scale of a model of an airplane is $\dfrac{1}{4}$ in. to 1 ft. The wing span of the actual plane is 50 ft. What is the wing span of the model?

▶ **Extension Exercises**

27. Find the ratio of a to b.

    a. $3a = 8b$ b. $4a = 5b$ c. $xa = yb$

28. Two complementary angles have measures whose ratio is $\dfrac{2}{3}$. Find the measure of each angle.

29. Two supplementary angles have measures whose ratio is $\dfrac{4}{5}$. Find the measure of each angle.

▶◀ **Activity**

This is an old map. Much of it is unreadable, including the scale and most of the distances. This map is drawn to scale. Find the distances to the other towns using the information shown.

How far is it from Mudville to Starville?

How far is it from Squareville to Curve Lake?

How far is it from Starville to Triville?

How far is it from Starville to Squareville?

How far is it from Curve Lake to Mudville?

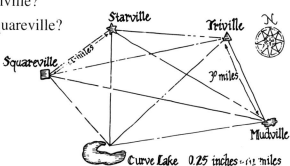

2 | Similar Triangles

After finishing Section 2, you should be able to
▲ *identify corresponding parts of similar triangles.*
▲▲ *determine which sides of a given pair of triangles have lengths that are proportional.*
▲ *find lengths of sides of similar triangles.*
▲▲

▲ Identifying Corresponding Parts

We know that congruent figures have the same shape and size.
Similar figures have the same shape, but are not necessarily the same size.

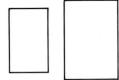

Similar Figures

Example 1. Which pairs of triangles appear to be similar?

a.  b.

c.  d.

Pairs **a**, **c**, and **d** appear to be similar.

Try This... 1. Which pairs of triangles appear to be similar?

a.  b.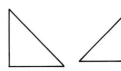

c.  d.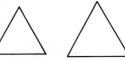

 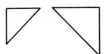

Similar triangles have corresponding sides and angles.

Example   2. $\triangle ABC$ and $\triangle DEF$ are similar. Name their corresponding sides and angles.

$\overline{AB} \longleftrightarrow \overline{DE}$ $\angle A \longleftrightarrow \angle D$

$\overline{AC} \longleftrightarrow \overline{DF}$ $\angle B \longleftrightarrow \angle E$

$\overline{BC} \longleftrightarrow \overline{EF}$ $\angle C \longleftrightarrow \angle F$

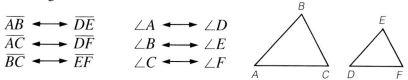

Try This...   2. $\triangle PQR$ and $\triangle GHK$ are similar. Name their corresponding sides and angles.

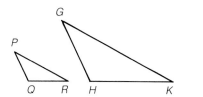

DEFINITION

Two **triangles are similar** whenever their vertices can be matched so that the corresponding angles are congruent and the lengths of corresponding sides are proportional.

▲▲ Finding Proportional Lengths

To say that $\triangle ABC$ and $\triangle DEF$ are similar, we write "$\triangle ABC \sim \triangle DEF$." We shall agree that this symbol also tells us the way in which the vertices are matched.

$$\triangle A \; B \; C \sim \triangle D \; E \; F$$

Thus, $\triangle ABC \sim \triangle DEF$ means

$\angle A \cong \angle D$

$\angle B \cong \angle E$ and $\dfrac{AB}{DE} = \dfrac{AC}{DF} = \dfrac{BC}{EF}$

$\angle C \cong \angle F$

Let us agree to talk of "proportional sides" instead of "sides whose lengths are proportional." We understand that it is lengths that are proportional, not the sets of points.

Example   3. Suppose $\triangle PQR \sim \triangle STV$. Which angles are congruent? Which sides are proportional?

Angles	*Sides*
$\angle P \cong \angle S$	
$\angle Q \cong \angle T$	$\dfrac{PQ}{ST} = \dfrac{PR}{SV} = \dfrac{QR}{TV}$
$\angle R \cong \angle V$	

Try This... 3. Suppose $\triangle JKL \sim \triangle ABC$. Which angles are congruent? Which sides are proportional?

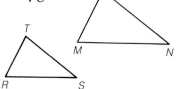

Example 4. These triangles are similar. Which sides are proportional?

It appears that if we match X with U, Y with W, and Z with V, the corresponding angles will be congruent. Thus,

$$\frac{YZ}{WV} = \frac{YX}{WU} = \frac{ZX}{VU}$$

Try This... 4. These triangles are similar. Which sides are proportional?

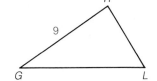

▲▲ Finding Missing Lengths

We can find lengths of sides in similar triangles.

Example 5. $\triangle RAE \sim \triangle GRL$. Find RL and GL.

Because $\triangle RAE \sim \triangle GRL$, the corresponding sides are proportional. Thus,

$$\frac{6}{9} = \frac{4}{RL} \quad \text{and} \quad \frac{6}{9} = \frac{7}{GL}$$

We use the cross product property to solve the proportions.

$$6(RL) = 9 \cdot 4 \qquad 6(GL) = 9 \cdot 7$$
$$6(RL) = 36 \qquad 6(GL) = 63$$
$$RL = 6 \qquad GL = 10\tfrac{1}{2}$$

Try This... 5. $\triangle WNE \sim \triangle CBT$. Find BT and CT.

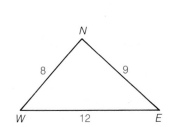

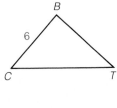

Example ▲6. $\triangle JKH \sim \triangle WTR$. Find KH and TR.

In $\triangle JKH$ and $\triangle WTR$,

$$\frac{JK}{WT} = \frac{KH}{TR}$$

$$\frac{4}{12} = \frac{x+2}{2x+5}$$

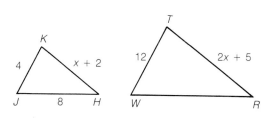

$$4(2x+5) = 12(x+2)$$
$$8x + 20 = 12x + 24$$
$$-4 = 4x$$
$$-1 = x$$

If $x = -1$, then $KH = 1$ and $TR = 3$.

Try This... ▲6. $\triangle LUK \sim \triangle ZEN$.
Find UK and EN.

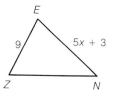

Example 7. The pitch of a roof is the **rise** divided by the **span.** A roof with a
rise of 8 feet has a pitch of $\frac{1}{3}$.   What is the span?

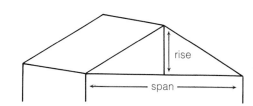

$$\frac{\text{rise}}{\text{span}} = \frac{1}{3}$$

$$\frac{8}{\text{span}} = \frac{1}{3}$$

$$\text{Span} = 24 \text{ feet.}$$

Try This... 7. A roof with a rise of 9 feet has a pitch of $\frac{3}{8}$. Find the span.

Exercises

▲ **For each pair of similar triangles, name the corresponding sides and angles.**

1.

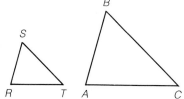

2.

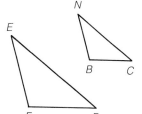

3.

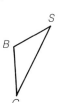

▲▲ **For each pair of similar triangles, name the congruent angles and proportional sides.**

4. $\triangle ABC \sim \triangle RST$ 5. $\triangle PQR \sim \triangle STV$

6. $\triangle MES \sim \triangle CLF$ 7. $\triangle SMH \sim \triangle WLK$

Name the proportional sides in these similar triangles.

8.   9.

▲▲ **Find the missing lengths.**

10. $\triangle ABC \sim \triangle PQR$ 11. $\triangle MAC \sim \triangle GET$ 12. $\triangle RST \sim \triangle WYZ$

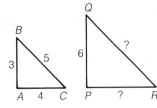   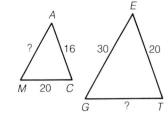   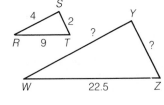

13. $\triangle DEF \sim \triangle KGH$ ▲14. $\triangle REG \sim \triangle CUP$.   ▲15. $\triangle MNP \sim \triangle SQV$
Find RE and CU.

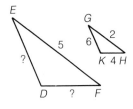   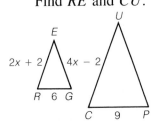   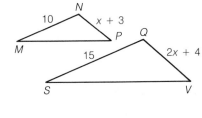

▶ **Extension Exercises**

16. Three cities on a map are 9 cm, 10 cm, and 8 cm apart. The map scale is 3.8 cm to 75 km. How far apart are the cities?

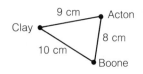

17. A roof with a rise of 7 feet has a pitch of $\frac{3}{8}$. What is its span?

18. A roof with a span of 5 feet has a pitch of $\frac{1}{3}$. What is its rise?

▶▶ **Challenge Exercise**

19. Explain why any two congruent triangles are also similar.

| **3** | The AA Similarity Theorem |

After finishing Section 3, you should be able to
▲ *use the AA Similarity Theorem to identify pairs of similar triangles.*
▲▲ *solve problems using the AA Theorem.*

▲ The AA Similarity Theorem

Sometimes we can show that triangles are similar without knowing that the corresponding angles are congruent and that the lengths of corresponding sides are proportional.

1. On a full sheet of paper, draw △*ABC*.

2. On another full sheet of paper, draw $\overline{PQ}$ so that *PQ* < *AB*.

3. Use a compass. At *P*, make a copy of ∠*A*, and at *Q*, make a copy of ∠*B*. Extend the sides to meet at a point *R*.

4. What is true of ∠*R* and ∠*C*?

5. Describe the two triangles.

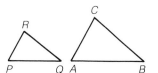

POSTULATE
13

The AAA Similarity Postulate
For any two triangles, if the corresponding angles are congruent, then the triangles are similar.

△*ABC* ~ △*PQR*

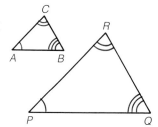

A theorem follows immediately from this postulate.

THEOREM
9.1

The AA Similarity Theorem

For any two triangles, if two pairs of corresponding angles are congruent, then the triangles are similar.

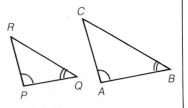

$\triangle PQR \sim \triangle ABC$

Example   1. Which pairs of triangles are similar by the AA Theorem?

a.
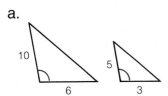

b.
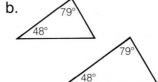

c.
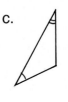

Pairs **b** and **c** are similar by the AA Theorem.

Try This...   1. Which pairs of triangles are similar by the AA Theorem?

a.
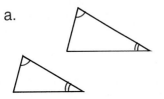

b.
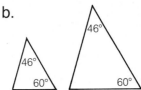

c.

▲▲ Using the AA Theorem

The AA Theorem can help us find lengths of sides of triangles.

Example   2. In $\triangle RST$, $\overline{GH} \parallel \overline{RS}$, $RS = 18$, $GH = 6$, and $GT = 9$. Find ST.

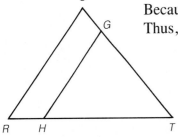

Because $\overline{GH} \parallel \overline{RS}$, $\angle SRT \cong \angle GHT$. Also, $\angle T \cong \angle T$. Thus, $\triangle RST \sim \triangle HGT$ by the AA Theorem. Hence,

$$\frac{18}{6} = \frac{ST}{9}$$

$$6(ST) = 162$$

$$ST = 27$$

Try This...   2. In $\triangle TAR$ and $\triangle MSR$, $\overline{TA} \parallel \overline{SM}$, $TA = 21$, $SM = 14$, and $TR = 18$. Find MR.

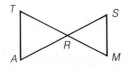

Example 3. A rod 3 m tall casts a shadow 5 m long. At the same time, the shadow of a tower is 110 m long. How tall is the tower?

The rod and the tower form right angles with the ground. The sun's rays form congruent angles with both the rod and the tower. Thus, $\triangle ABC \sim \triangle PQR$ by the AA Theorem. Hence,

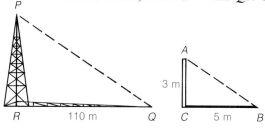

$$\frac{PR}{QR} = \frac{AC}{BC}$$

$$\frac{PR}{110} = \frac{3}{5}$$

$$5(PR) = 110 \cdot 3$$

$$5(PR) = 330$$

The tower is 66 m tall. $PR = 66$

Try This... 3. The shadow of a tree is 25 m long. At the same time, a person who is 180 cm tall casts a shadow 240 cm long. How tall is the tree?

▶◀ Activity

To find out how tall a tree is, stand back from the tree. Place a mirror on the ground so that you can see the top of the tree reflected in the mirror. (If you cannot see the top of the tree, you will have to relocate the mirror.)

Measure the distance from the tree to the mirror and the distance from the mirror to yourself. Then measure the height of your eye level above the ground.

As $\triangle CED \sim \triangle AEB^*$, the distance of AB can be found by using the fact that corresponding sides of similar triangles are proportional.

$$\frac{AB}{CD} = \frac{EB}{ED}$$

$$\frac{AB}{5.25} = \frac{20}{2}$$

$$(AB)2 = 5.25 \cdot 20$$

$$(AB)2 = 105$$

$$AB = 52.5 \text{ feet}$$

Measure the height of a flagpole or tree.

*$\angle D \cong \angle B$ as both are right angles. A law of physics tells us that $\angle CED \cong \angle AEB$ as they are angles of incidence and reflection of light striking a mirror. $\triangle CED \sim \triangle AEB$ by AA Theorem.

Exercises

▲ **Which pairs of triangles are similar by the AA Theorem?**

1.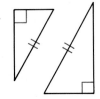

2.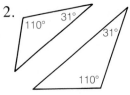

3.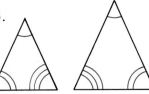

4.

5.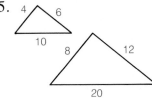

6.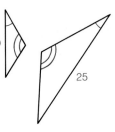

▲▲ **Find the missing lengths.**

7. In $\triangle CLF$, $\overline{EM} \parallel \overline{CF}$, $LC = 12$, $LF = 16$, $CF = 22$, and $CE = 3$. Find EM.

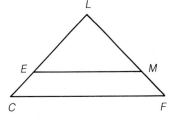

8. In $\triangle WJD$, $\overline{LG} \perp \overline{WJ}$, $\overline{DJ} \perp \overline{WJ}$, $LG = 4$, $WJ = 20$, and $DJ = 15$. Find GW.

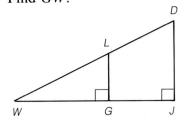

9. $\overline{JG} \perp \overline{RC}$, $\overline{RD} \perp \overline{JC}$, $GC = 9$, $JC = 15$, and $DC = 6$. Find RC.

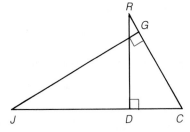

10. $\overline{AT} \perp \overline{SP}$, $\overline{SL} \perp \overline{PA}$, $ST = 4$, $TN = 3$, and $NL = 5$. Find LA.

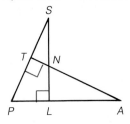

11. A lens that enlarges and inverts the image of $\overline{PQ}$ is placed at point R such that $\overline{PQ} \parallel \overline{ST}$. Find ST.

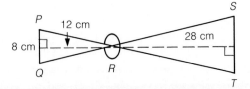

▶ Extension Exercises

12. $\angle A \cong \angle H$. What can you conclude about $\dfrac{EH}{EA}$ and $\dfrac{EG}{EB}$? Explain how you know.

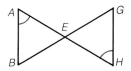

13. $RK \parallel ST$. What can you conclude about $\dfrac{MR}{MK}$ and $\dfrac{MS}{MT}$? Explain how you know.

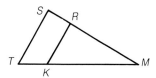

14. $ME \parallel CS$. What can you conclude about $\dfrac{MN}{NS}$ and $\dfrac{EN}{NC}$? Explain how you know.

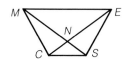

15. $PQ \parallel AB$. What can you conclude about $\triangle CPQ$ and $\triangle CAB$? Explain how you know.

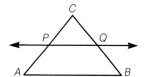

16. Consider two similar triangles. One triangle has sides whose lengths are 6, 8, and 9. The longest side of the second triangle has length 14. Find the lengths of the other two sides of the second triangle.

▶▶ Challenge Exercise

17. State two AA Theorems that apply to right triangles and to isosceles triangles.

▶◀ Activity

Draw any triangle ABC. Select a point P and draw PA, PB, and PC. Locate points A', B', C' so that $AA' = 2PA$, $BB' = 2PB$, and $CC' = 2PC$. Connect points $A'B'C'$. How are triangles ABC and $A'B'C'$ related?

Try locating P in a different position.

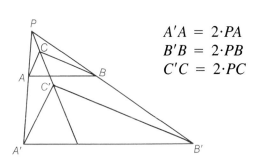

$A'A = 2 \cdot PA$
$B'B = 2 \cdot PB$
$C'C = 2 \cdot PC$

4	Parallel Lines and Proportional Segments

After finishing Section 4, you should be able to
▲ *solve proportions related to a triangle and
a line parallel to a side of the triangle.*

The triangles in this roof suggest an
important theorem about similar triangles.

Because $\overleftrightarrow{DE} \parallel \overline{BC}$, then $\angle 1 \cong \angle 2$ and $\angle 3 \cong \angle 4$.
Thus, $\triangle ADE \sim \triangle ABC$ by the AA Theorem.

THEOREM 9.2 — If a line is parallel to one side of a triangle and intersects the other
sides at any points except a vertex, then a triangle similar to the
given triangle is formed and the line divides the sides proportionally.

$$\frac{QP}{QA} = \frac{QR}{QB}$$

$$\frac{QA}{AP} = \frac{QB}{BR}$$

An important corollary follows from Theorem 9.2.

COROLLARY 9.3 — For any $\triangle ABC$, if a line intersects
$\overline{AB}$ and $\overline{AC}$ at D and E, respectively,
and $\overleftrightarrow{DE} \parallel \overline{BC}$, then $\dfrac{AB}{DB} = \dfrac{AC}{EC}$.

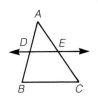

Examples 1. $RP = 6$, $RT = 4$, and $RQ = 9$. Find SR.

By Theorem 9.2, $\dfrac{RP}{RT} = \dfrac{RQ}{RS}$.

Thus,

$$\frac{6}{4} = \frac{9}{SR}.$$

$$6(SR) = 36$$

$$SR = 6$$

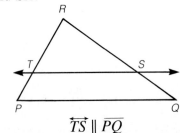

$\overleftrightarrow{TS} \parallel \overline{PQ}$

2. $TP = 4$, $RT = 7$, and $SQ = 5$. Find RS.

By Theorem 9.2, $\dfrac{RT}{TP} = \dfrac{RS}{SQ}$.

Thus,
$$\frac{7}{4} = \frac{RS}{5}.$$
$$35 = 4(RS)$$
$$8.75 = RS$$

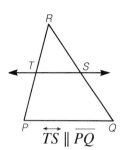

$\overleftrightarrow{TS} \parallel \overline{PQ}$

Try This... Consider $\triangle PQR$ in Example 2.

1. $RP = 8$, $RT = 6$, $RQ = 12$. Find RS.
2. $TP = 10$, $RT = 8$, $SQ = 12$. Find RS.

Example 3. In $\triangle ABC$, $\overleftrightarrow{DE} \parallel \overline{AB}$. $CA = 6$, $DA = 4$, $CB = 9$. Find EB.

By Corollary 9.3, $\dfrac{CA}{DA} = \dfrac{CB}{EB}$.
$$\frac{6}{4} = \frac{9}{EB}.$$
$$6(EB) = 36$$
$$EB = 6$$

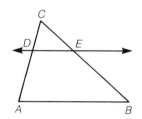

Try This... 3. Consider $\triangle ABC$ in Example 3. $CA = 8$, $DA = 6$, $CB = 10$. Find EB.

The converse of Theorem 9.2 is also true.

THEOREM 9.4 If a line divides two sides of a triangle into proportional segments, then the line is parallel to the third side.

$\overleftrightarrow{DE}$ intersects $\overline{AB}$ at D and $\overline{AC}$ at E such that $\dfrac{AD}{DB} = \dfrac{AE}{EC}$.

Hence, $\overleftrightarrow{DE} \parallel \overline{BC}$.

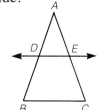

Exercises

▲ **In △ABC, $\overleftrightarrow{DE} \parallel \overline{AB}$. From the given information, find the missing lengths.**

1. $CD = 12$, $CA = 18$, $CE = 8$, $CB = ?$

2. $CD = 10$, $CA = 24$, $CE = 12$, $CB = ?$

3. $CD = 9$, $DA = 12$, $CE = 6$, $EB = ?$

4. $CD = 8$, $DA = 14$, $CE = 7$, $EB = ?$

5. $DA = 4$, $CE = 9$, $EB = 15$, $CD = ?$

6. $DA = 8$, $CE = 10$, $EB = 16$, $CD = ?$

7. $AC = 12$, $DC = 8$, $BC = 10$, $BE = ?$

8. $AC = 18$, $DC = 10$, $BC = 12$, $BE = ?$

9. $CD = 4$, $DA = 8$, $CB = 18$, $EB = ?$

10. $CD = 3$, $DA = 9$, $CB = 15$, $EB = ?$

11. $CD = 3\sqrt{3}$, $CE = 2\sqrt{2}$, $DA = 4$, $EB = ?$

12. $CD = 2\sqrt{3}$, $CE = 4\sqrt{2}$, $DA = 8$, $EB = ?$

▶ **Extension Exercises**

Explain each conclusion.

13. $\overline{SW} \parallel \overline{TV}$ and $\overline{UW} \parallel \overline{RT}$. What can you conclude about $\dfrac{RS}{ST}$ and $\dfrac{TU}{UV}$? Explain how you know.

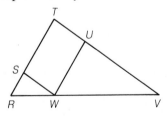

14. $\angle 1 \cong \angle 2$ and $\angle 3 \cong \angle 4$. What can you conclude about $\dfrac{AC}{TC}$ and $\dfrac{BC}{FC}$? Explain how you know.

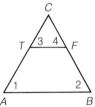

15. $\angle 1 \cong \angle 2$. What can you conclude about $\dfrac{PQ}{QR}$ and $\dfrac{PT}{TS}$? Explain how you know.

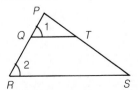

16. $\overline{SV} \perp \overline{MV}$ and $\overline{UY} \perp \overline{MV}$. What can you conclude about $\triangle RST$ and $\triangle RUW$? Explain how you know.

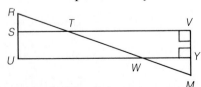

5 SAS and SSS Similarity

After finishing Section 5, you should be able to
▲ *use the SAS and SSS Similarity Theorems to identify pairs of similar triangles.*
▲▲ *reach conclusions based on the SAS and SSS Theorems.*
▲▲ *explain conclusions using the SAS and SSS Theorems.*

▲ Similarity Theorems

In addition to the AA Theorem, there are two more ways to show that triangles are similar.

1. On a full sheet of paper, draw any △*ABC*.

2. On another sheet of paper, draw △*PQR* with ∠*P* ≅ ∠*A*, *PQ* = 2*AB*, and *PR* = 2*AC*.

3. Describe the two triangles.

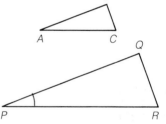

THEOREM
9.5

The SAS Similarity Theorem

For any two triangles, if one pair of corresponding angles is congruent and the sides that include these angles are proportional, then the triangles are similar.

$$\frac{AB}{PQ} = \frac{AC}{PR}.$$

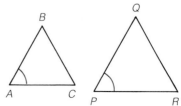

△*ABC* ~ △*PQR*

Example   1. Which pairs of triangles are similar by the SAS Similarity Theorem?

a.
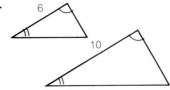

b.
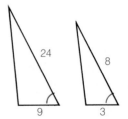

c.
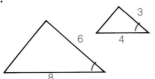

d.
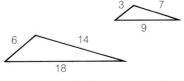

Pairs **b** and **c** are similar by the SAS Similarity Theorem.

An SSS Theorem also holds for similar triangles.

THEOREM **9.6**   *The SSS Similarity Theorem*

For any two triangles, if all three pairs of corresponding sides are proportional, then the triangles are similar.

$$\frac{AB}{PQ} = \frac{AC}{PR} = \frac{BC}{QR}$$

$$\triangle ABC \sim \triangle PQR$$

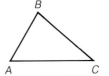

Example   2. Which pairs of triangles in Example 1 are similar by the SSS Similarity Theorem?

The triangles in pair **d** are similar by the SSS Similarity Theorem.

Try This...   1. Determine whether the triangles in each pair are similar by the SAS or the SSS Similarity Theorem.

a.
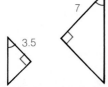

b.
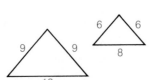

c.
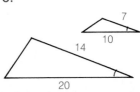

▲▲ Reaching Conclusions

We can reach conclusions by examining similar triangles.

Example   3. In the figure, $\dfrac{PR}{RS} = \dfrac{QR}{RT}$.

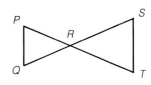

What can we conclude?

We know $\dfrac{PR}{RS} = \dfrac{QR}{RT}$.

$\angle\, PRQ \cong \angle\, SRT$ by the Vertical Angle Theorem.
It follows that $\triangle\, PQR \sim \triangle\, STR$ by the SAS Similarity Theorem.
Thus, as corresponding angles, $\angle P \cong \angle S$ and $\angle Q \cong \angle T$.

Also, $\dfrac{PQ}{ST} = \dfrac{PR}{RS} = \dfrac{QR}{RT}$.

Try This...   2. In the figure, $\dfrac{AB}{AD} = \dfrac{AE}{AC}$.

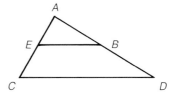

What can you conclude?

▲▲ Using SAS and SSS

We can use the SAS and SSS Similarity Theorems to help explain conclusions.

Example   4. $\dfrac{PR}{RT} = \dfrac{QR}{RS}$.

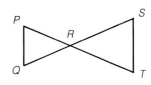

What can you conclude about
$\triangle PQR$ and $\triangle TSR$?
Explain how you know.

We know that $\dfrac{PR}{RT} = \dfrac{QR}{RS}$.

$\angle PRQ \cong \angle TRS$ by Vertical Angle Theorem.

Thus, $\triangle PQR \sim \triangle TSR$ by SAS Similarity Theorem.

Try This...   3. $\dfrac{AD}{AB} = \dfrac{AC}{AE}$.

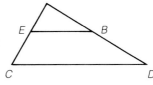

What can you conclude about
$\triangle AEB$ and $\triangle ACD$?

Explain how you know.

Example   5. $AP = \frac{1}{3}QS$, $AC = \frac{1}{3}QA$, and $PC = \frac{1}{3}AS$. What can you conclude about $\angle Q$ and $\angle A$? Explain how you know.

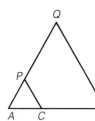

We know that $AP = \frac{1}{3}QS$, $AC = \frac{1}{3}QA$, and $PC = \frac{1}{3}AS$.

Thus, $\dfrac{AP}{QS} = \dfrac{AC}{QA} = \dfrac{PC}{AS} = \dfrac{1}{3}$.

The SSS Similarity Theorem tells us that $\triangle APC \sim \triangle QSA$. This means $\angle Q \cong \angle A$ as corresponding angles of similar triangles.

Try This...   4. $MF = 2GK$, $MT = 2GR$, and $TF = 2RK$. What can you conclude about $\angle F$ and $\angle K$? Explain how you know.

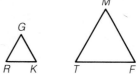

Exercises

▲ **Which pairs of triangles are similar by the SAS Similarity Theorem?**

1.
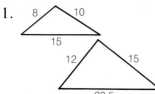

2.
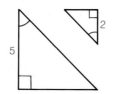

3.
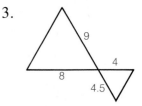

4.
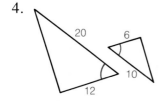

5.
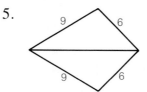

6.
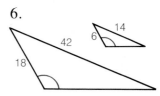

7. Which pairs of triangles in Exercises 1-6 are similar by the SSS Similarity Theorem?

▲▲ **What can you conclude about each figure from the given information?**

8. $MH = \frac{1}{4}MG$, $ML = \frac{1}{4}MK$, $HL = \frac{1}{4}GK$.

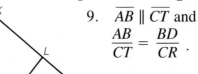

9. $\overline{AB} \parallel \overline{CT}$ and $\dfrac{AB}{CT} = \dfrac{BD}{CR}$.

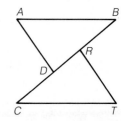

10. $\dfrac{GR}{GZ} = \dfrac{GT}{GM}.$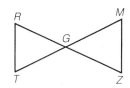

11. $\dfrac{MC}{MG} = \dfrac{ME}{MS}.$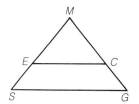

▲▲ Explain each conclusion.

12. $ML = \frac{1}{4}MG$, $MH = \frac{1}{4}MK$, and $HL = \frac{1}{4}KG$. What can you conclude about $\triangle MLH$ and $\triangle MGK$? Explain how you know. Use the figure in Exercise 8.

13. $\overline{AB} \parallel \overline{CT}$ and $\dfrac{AB}{CT} = \dfrac{BD}{CR}$. What can you conclude about $\triangle ABD$ and $\triangle TCR$? Explain how you know. Use the figure in Exercise 9.

14. $\dfrac{GR}{GZ} = \dfrac{GT}{GM}$. What can you conclude about $\overline{RT}$ and $\overline{MZ}$? Explain how you know. Use the figure in Exercise 10.

15. $\dfrac{ME}{MS} = \dfrac{MC}{MG}$. What can you conclude about $\overline{EC}$ and $\overline{SG}$? Explain how you know. Use the figure in Exercise 11.

▶ Extension Exercise

16. An adjustable ironing board is constructed so that $PR = QR$ and $SR = TR$ as shown. Explain why the board will always remain parallel to the floor.

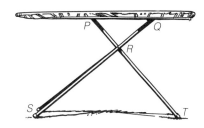

▶◀ Activity

A pantograph is an instrument used to reduce or enlarge a drawing to scale. You can construct your own pantograph by cutting four congruent strips of heavy cardboard and attaching them with paper fasteners as shown. $\overline{AT}$ is parallel to $\overline{BU}$ and $\overline{BS}$ is parallel to $\overline{UT}$. Place a paper fastener through A and securely tape the ends of the paper fastener to an even surface. Place a pointer through B and a pencil through C. As you trace a figure with the pointer, the pencil enlarges the figure to scale. To reduce the figure, simply interchange the pointer and pencil.

Explain why $\triangle ATC \sim \triangle ASB$.

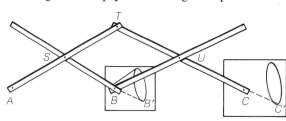

Consumer Application   Finding Unit Prices

A unit price is a price for one unit of measurement of an item, for example, one ounce of orange juice. It is the ratio of the price of an item to the number of units of measurement the item contains. The unit price helps consumers compare the costs of similar products. The product with the smaller unit price is less expensive.

Example   Find the unit price
of a 20 oz box of cereal
for $2.09.

$$\frac{\$2.09}{20} = \text{price of product per}$$
$$\qquad\qquad \text{number of units}$$

$$\$0.1045 = \text{price per ounce}$$
$$\$0.105 = \text{unit price rounded to the nearest tenth}$$
$$\qquad\qquad\;\; \text{of a cent}$$

Find the unit price for each item. Round your answer to the nearest tenth of a cent.

1. 6.5 oz box of rice for $2.59

2. 32 oz jar of jam for $2.58

3. 64 fl oz bottle of apple juice for $2.05

4. 1.80 lb of ground hamburger for $3.50

5. 6.5 oz can of tuna for $0.89

6. 10.5 oz can of soup for $0.45

Find the lowest unit price. Round your answer to the nearest tenth of a cent.

7. Brand A
    6 fl oz of
    orange juice
    for $0.75

    Brand B
    12 fl oz of
    orange juice
    for $1.29

    Brand C
    16 fl oz of
    orange juice
    for $1.79

8. Brand A
    9 oz box of raisins
    for $1.19

    Brand B
    15 oz box of raisins
    for $1.25

    Brand C
    24 oz box of raisins
    for $2.19

9. Brand A
    8 oz can of green
    beans for $0.49

    Brand B
    16 oz can of green
    beans for $0.65

    Brand C
    28 oz can of green
    beans for $0.99

Chapter Review

 Solve these proportions. Find what _y_ and _x_ represent.

1. $\dfrac{y}{9} = \dfrac{8}{72}$

2. $\dfrac{50}{x} = \dfrac{2}{5}$

 3. $\triangle ERS \sim \triangle TGF$. Name the congruent angles and the proportional lengths.

Find the missing lengths.

4. $\triangle GTR \sim \triangle ZEK$.
   Find _EK_ and _ZK_.

▲5. $\triangle JAK \sim \triangle VYS$.
   Find _JA_ and _VY_.

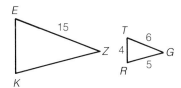

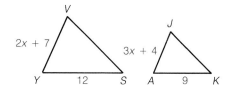

 6. In $\triangle ABC$, $\overline{DE} \parallel \overline{BC}$, $AB = 18$, $AC = 20$, $BC = 16$, and $BD = 4$. Find _DE_.

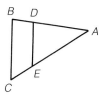

 Find the missing lengths from the given information. $\overleftrightarrow{DE} \parallel \overline{AB}$.

7. $CD = 6$, $CA = 10$, $CE = 7$, $CB = $?

8. $AC = 16$, $DC = 10$, $BC = 14$, $BE = $?

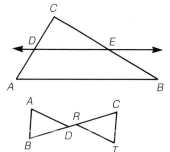

5 9. In the figure, $\overline{AB} \parallel \overline{CT}$ and $\dfrac{AB}{CT} = \dfrac{BD}{CR}$.
   What can you conclude?

10. $\angle S \cong \angle V$. What can you conclude about $\triangle RST$ and $\triangle WVT$?
    Explain how you know.

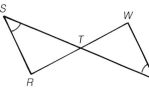

Chapter Test

Solve these proportions. Find what *x* represents.

1. $\dfrac{x}{18} = \dfrac{4}{6}$

2. $\dfrac{14}{18} = \dfrac{24}{x}$

3. $\triangle PTL \sim \triangle CSM$. Name the congruent angles and the proportional lengths.

Find the missing lengths.

4. $\triangle HEK \sim \triangle QAL$. Find QL and AL.

▲5. $\triangle SUE \sim \triangle PAM$. Find UE and AM.

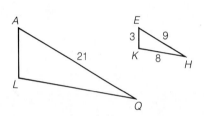

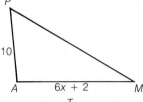

6. In $\triangle TES$, $\overline{TE} \perp \overline{ES}$, $\overline{GM} \perp \overline{ES}$, $GM = 6$, $ST = 24$, and $TE = 14$. Find GS.

Find the missing lengths from the given information. $\overleftrightarrow{DE} \parallel \overline{AB}.$

7. $DE = 9$, $AB = 15$, $DC = 6$, $DA = $?

8. $CE = 10$, $EB = 4$, $AB = 18$, $DE = $?

9. In the figure, $\dfrac{EC}{CB} = \dfrac{DC}{CA}$.

   What can you conclude?

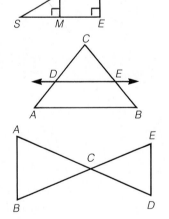

10. $\overline{PQ} \parallel \overline{RM}$. What can you conclude about $\triangle PQG$ and $\triangle MRG$? Explain how you know.

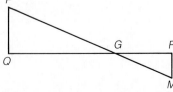

Skills Review   Squares and Square Roots

Find each square root.

1. $\sqrt{49}$ 2. $-\sqrt{16}$ 3. $\sqrt{100}$ 4. $-\sqrt{9}$ 5. $-\sqrt{25}$

6. $\sqrt{64}$ 7. $-\sqrt{400}$ 8. $-\sqrt{1}$ 9. $\sqrt{2,500}$ 10. $-\sqrt{36}$

11. $\sqrt{8,100}$ 12. $\sqrt{1,600}$ 13. $-\sqrt{900}$ 14. $\sqrt{10,000}$ 15. $-\sqrt{6,400}$

Use the table on page 564 to find the square roots.

16. $\sqrt{62}$ 17. $\sqrt{78}$ 18. $\sqrt{20}$ 19. $\sqrt{46}$ 20. $\sqrt{35}$

21. $\sqrt{80}$ 22. $\sqrt{12}$ 23. $\sqrt{55}$ 24. $\sqrt{86}$ 25. $\sqrt{37}$

26. $\sqrt{64}$ 27. $\sqrt{32}$ 28. $\sqrt{59}$ 29. $\sqrt{99}$ 30. $\sqrt{169}$

31. $\sqrt{8}$ 32. $\sqrt{900}$ 33. $\sqrt{484}$ 34. $\sqrt{3,721}$ 35. $\sqrt{2,209}$

36. $\sqrt{4,356}$ 37. $\sqrt{7,569}$ 38. $\sqrt{1,681}$ 39. $\sqrt{8,464}$ 40. $\sqrt{9,801}$

Use the table on page 564 to find n.

41. $\sqrt{n} \approx 2.646$ 42. $\sqrt{n} \approx 8.124$ 43. $\sqrt{n} \approx 6.633$ 44. $\sqrt{n} \approx 1.414$ 45. $\sqrt{n} \approx 9.747$

46. $\sqrt{n} \approx 6.083$ 47. $\sqrt{n} \approx 7.550$ 48. $\sqrt{n} \approx 3.742$ 49. $\sqrt{n} \approx 5.099$ 50. $\sqrt{n} \approx 9.644$

51. $\sqrt{n} \approx 2.236$ 52. $\sqrt{n} \approx 8.000$ 53. $\sqrt{n} \approx 4.123$ 54. $\sqrt{n} \approx 1.732$ 55. $\sqrt{n} \approx 10.000$

10
Using Similar Triangles

1 | Similar Right Triangles

After finishing Section 1, you should be able to
▲ *identify the similar triangles formed by the altitude to the hypotenuse of a right triangle.*
▲▲ *solve problems involving the geometric mean of two numbers.*

▲ Finding Similar Triangles

The altitude to the hypotenuse of a right triangle forms three similar triangles.

$\triangle PQR$ is a right triangle with right angle at Q. $\overline{QS}$ is an altitude.

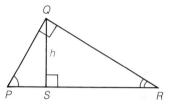

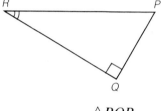  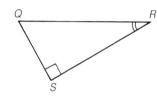

$$\triangle PQR \quad \sim \quad \triangle PSQ \quad \sim \quad \triangle QSR$$

THEOREM 10.1 | In a right triangle the altitude to the hypotenuse forms two triangles, each similar to the right triangle and similar to each other.

Example 1. Name the similar triangles in $\triangle GHK$.

The right angles are congruent.
The common angles are congruent.
Thus, $\triangle GHK \sim \triangle GTH \sim \triangle HTK$.

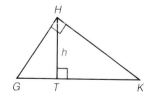

Try This... 1. Name the similar triangles in $\triangle PFS$.

▲▲ The Geometric Mean

The following table summarizes some important proportions related to triangles formed by the altitude to the hypotenuse of a right triangle.

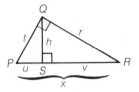

Similar Triangles	Proportion
$\triangle PSQ \sim \triangle QSR$	$\dfrac{u}{h} = \dfrac{h}{v}$
$\triangle PQR \sim \triangle PSQ$	$\dfrac{x}{t} = \dfrac{t}{u}$
$\triangle PQR \sim \triangle QSR$	$\dfrac{x}{r} = \dfrac{r}{v}$

In each proportion, the means are the same. When this is true, a mean is called the *geometric mean* of the two numbers.

DEFINITION

For any positive numbers p, q, and r, q is the **geometric mean** of p and r whenever

$$\frac{p}{q} = \frac{q}{r}$$

Skills Refresher

To solve an equation such as $x^2 = 16$, take the principal (non-negative) square root of each side.

Example: $x^2 = 16$
$\sqrt{x^2} = \sqrt{16}$
$|x| = 4$ Recall $\sqrt{x^2} = |x|$.
Thus, $x = 4$ or $x = -4$.

1. $x^2 = 25$
2. $y^2 = 36$
3. $y^2 = 4$
4. $x^2 = 11$
5. $x^2 = 64$
6. $a^2 = 9$
7. $n^2 = 81$
8. $a^2 = 49$
9. $x^2 = 5$
10. $y^2 = 7$
11. $b^2 = 6$
12. $c^2 = 13$

Example   2. Find the geometric mean of 3 and 5.

$$\frac{3}{x} = \frac{x}{5}$$

$$x^2 = 15$$

$$|x| = \sqrt{15}$$

$$x = \sqrt{15} \text{ or } x = -\sqrt{15}$$

The geometric mean of 3 and 5 is $\sqrt{15}$.

Try This...   Find the geometric mean of these numbers.

2.   1 and 25   3.   7 and 2

The proportions stated in the table on page 288 are restated in the following corollaries.

COROLLARY   In a right triangle, the length of the altitude to the hypotenuse is the
10.2   geometric mean of the lengths of the segments on the hypotenuse.

$$\frac{a}{h} = \frac{h}{b}$$

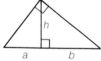

COROLLARY   In a right triangle with the altitude to the hypotenuse, the length of
10.3   each leg is the geometric mean of the length of the hypotenuse and
the length of the segment of the hypotenuse that is adjacent to
the leg.

$$\frac{c}{e} = \frac{e}{a} \quad \text{and} \quad \frac{c}{d} = \frac{d}{b}$$

Example   3. $GL = 9$ and $LK = 25$. Find HL.

From Corollary 10.2, we know

$$\frac{GL}{HL} = \frac{HL}{LK}$$

$$\frac{9}{HL} = \frac{HL}{25}$$

$$225 = (HL)^2$$

$$\sqrt{225} = (HL)$$

$$15 = HL$$

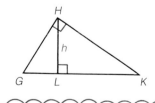

Because *HL* is a distance it cannot be negative.

Try This...   4. Use $\triangle GHK$. $GL = 4$ and $LK = 9$.
Find HL.

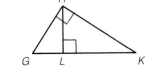

Example   4. $AC = 9$ and $DC = 5$. Find BC.

From Corollary 10.3 we know

$$\frac{AC}{BC} = \frac{BC}{DC}$$

$$\frac{9}{BC} = \frac{BC}{5}$$

$$(BC)^2 = 45$$

$$BC = \sqrt{45} = 3\sqrt{5}$$

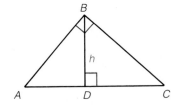

Try This...   5. Use $\triangle ABC$ in Example 4. $AC = 10$ and $DC = 4$. Find BC.

Exercises

▲   **Name the similar triangles.**

1.

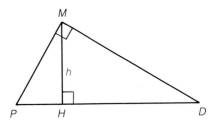

2.

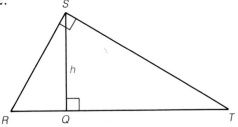

▲▲ **Find the geometric mean of these numbers.**

3.   4 and 25   4.   1 and 16   5.   9 and 49

6.   36 and 25   7.   0.3 and 0.12   8.   0.3 and 1.2

Use $\triangle TFR$ for Exercises 9–22.

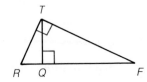

Find the missing lengths.

9. $RQ = 4, QF = 25, TQ = ?$ 10. $RQ = 4, QF = 36, TQ = ?$

11. $RQ = 6, QF = 15, TQ = ?$ 12. $RQ = 11, QF = 17, TQ = ?$

13. $FQ = 3, QR = 19, TQ = ?$ 14. $FQ = 5, QR = 21, TQ = ?$

15. $FQ = 5, FR = 20, FT = ?$

16. $QR = 10, FR = 18, TR = ?$

17. $RQ = 4, RT = 7, RF = ?$

18. $QF = 10, TF = 20, RF = ?$

19. $FT = 11, FR = 23, FQ = ?$

20. $RT = 16, RF = 26, RQ = ?$

21. $RQ = 5, FQ = 7, QT = ?$

22. $RQ = 11, TQ = 9, QF = ?$

▶▶ Challenge Exercises

23. y is the geometric mean of x and z with $x > 0$ and $z > 0$. Compare x, y, and z. Explain how you know.

24. If $x = z$, what can you conclude about y? Explain how you know.

Skills Refresher

To simplify a radical expression such as $\sqrt{18}$, recall that $\sqrt{a \cdot b} = \sqrt{a} \cdot \sqrt{b}$.

$$\text{Example:} \quad \sqrt{18} = \sqrt{9 \cdot 2}$$
$$= \sqrt{9} \cdot \sqrt{2}$$
$$= 3\sqrt{2}$$

1. $\sqrt{32}$ 2. $\sqrt{50}$ 3. $\sqrt{160}$

4. $\sqrt{90}$ 5. $\sqrt{72}$ 6. $\sqrt{144}$

7. $\sqrt{75}$ 8. $\sqrt{200}$ 9. $\sqrt{24}$

10. $\sqrt{12}$ 11. $\sqrt{54}$ 12. $\sqrt{45}$

2	The Pythagorean Theorem

After finishing Section 2, you should be able to

▲ *solve problems using the Pythagorean Theorem.*

The Pythagorean Theorem relates the measures of the three sides of a right triangle.

$3^2 + 4^2 = 5^2$
$9 + 16 = 25$

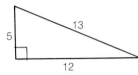

$5^2 + 12^2 = 13^2$
$25 + 144 = 169$

THEOREM
10.4

The Pythagorean Theorem

In a right triangle, the sum of the squares of the lengths of the two legs is the square of the length of the hypotenuse.

$$a^2 + b^2 = c^2$$

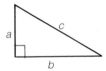

We can use the Pythagorean Theorem to find the lengths of sides of right triangles.

Example   1. Find b.

$a^2 + b^2 = c^2$
$6^2 + b^2 = 10^2$
$36 + b^2 = 100$
$b^2 = 64$
$b = \sqrt{64} = 8$

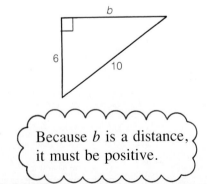

Because b is a distance, it must be positive.

Example   2. Find a.

$$a^2 + b^2 = c^2$$
$$a^2 + 7^2 = 9^2$$
$$a^2 + 49 = 81$$
$$a^2 = 32$$
$$a = \sqrt{32} = 4\sqrt{2}$$

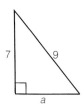

Try This...   Find a in each triangle.

1.

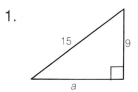

2.

Example   3. Find c.

$$a^2 + b^2 = c^2$$
$$7^2 + 24^2 = c^2$$
$$49 + 576 = c^2$$
$$625 = c^2$$
$$\sqrt{625} = c$$
$$25 = c$$

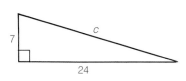

Try This...   3. Find c.

Proof of the Pythagorean Theorem

Consider $\triangle ABC$ with right angle at C.
Let $\overline{CD}$ be the altitude. We want to show that
$a^2 + b^2 = c^2$.

By Corollary 10.3, we know $\dfrac{c}{a} = \dfrac{a}{e}$. Thus, $a^2 = ce$.
Likewise, $\dfrac{c}{b} = \dfrac{b}{d}$.

Thus, $cd = b^2$.

Hence, $a^2 + b^2 = ce + cd = c(e + d)$. But $e + d = c$.
So, $a^2 + b^2 = c^2$.

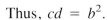

Example   4. $AB = BC = 18$ dm.
$AC = 30$ dm. Find x.

The length y is half of 30, or 15.

Thus, $15^2 + x^2 = 18^2$

$225 + x^2 = 324$

$x^2 = 99$

$x = \sqrt{99} = 3\sqrt{11}$ dm

Try This...   4. In the photograph above, $AB = BC = 15$ dm. $AC = 28$ dm. Find x.

Exercises

▲   **Use the information given to find the missing lengths in $\triangle ABC$.**

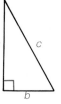

1. $b = 40, c = 50, a = ?$ 2. $a = 24, c = 40, b = ?$

3. $a = 8, c = 17, b = ?$ 4. $b = 16, c = 34, a = ?$

5. $a = 36, b = 15, c = ?$ 6. $a = 16, b = 30, c = ?$

7. $b = 5, c = 9, a = ?$ 8. $a = 8, c = 19, b = ?$

9. $a = 10, b = 7, c = ?$ 10. $a = 5, b = 3, c = ?$

Use the figure for Exercises 11 and 12.

11.   The distance between bases on a regular baseball diamond is 90 feet. About how far is it from home plate to second base?

12.   On a little league diamond, the distance between bases is 60 feet. About how far is it from home plate to second base?

▶   Extension Exercises

13.   A rectangular field is 70 meters by 155 meters. About how much shorter is it to walk diagonally from one corner to another than to walk along the edge (around the corners)?

14.   An outfielder catches the ball on the first baseline about 40 feet beyond first base. About how far would he have to throw the ball to third base? (See Exercise 11.)

15. Find the length of altitude $\overline{SM}$ in isosceles $\triangle RST$.

16. Find the length of the sides of rhombus $PQRS$.

$$PR = 18$$
$$SQ = 26$$

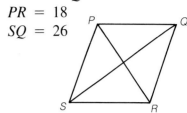

17. $ABCD$ is a rectangle. Find BD.

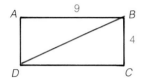

18. $GHKL$ is a square. Find GK.

▶▶ Challenge Exercises

Three positive integers that can be the lengths of sides of a right triangle are called a *Pythagorean triple*. For example, 3, 4, and 5 form a Pythagorean triple because $3^2 + 4^2 = 5^2$.

19. Find five other Pythagorean triples.

20. How can you use a Pythagorean triple to find another Pythagorean triple?

21. Substitute several pairs of positive integers $(x > y)$ in the expressions $x^2 + y^2$, $2xy$, and $x^2 - y^2$. What can you conclude about each triple of numbers?

22. Find PQ.

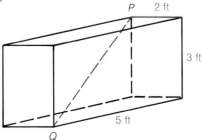

▶◀ Activity

Use $\frac{1}{4}$-inch graph paper to enlarge or to reduce these figures. Count the number of squares used along the vertical and the horizontal edges of the figures, find the number of squares needed for the enlargement or the reduction, plot the new points, and then connect them.

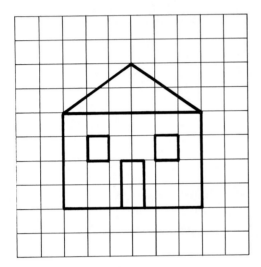

Enlarge $1\frac{1}{2}$ the size.

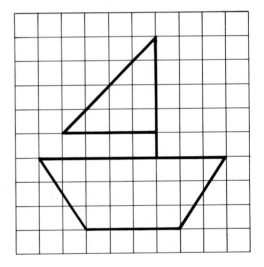

Reduce $\frac{1}{2}$ the size.

Historical Note

Pythagoras, a Greek mathematician and philosopher who lived more than 2500 years ago, proved a Babylonian rule for right triangles. This rule bears his name: the Pythagorean Theorem.

A right triangle whose legs have length 1 has a hypotenuse of length $\sqrt{2}$. He proved that $\sqrt{2}$ could not be rational. This challenged his theory that rational numbers caused order in the world.

By his discovery, however, the mathematical world of numbers began to expand. It came to include irrational numbers and real numbers, and eventually imaginary numbers.

| **3** | The Converse of the Pythagorean Theorem |

After finishing Section 3, you should be able to
▲   *determine whether a triangle is a right triangle by the lengths of its sides.*

We can use the converse of the Pythagorean Theorem to determine whether a triangle is a right triangle.

THEOREM
10.5

The Converse of the Pythagorean Theorem

If the lengths of the sides of a triangle are a, b, and c and $a^2 + b^2 = c^2$, then the triangle is a right triangle with right angle opposite the longest side, whose length is c.

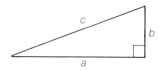

Examples   Determine whether these are right triangles.

1. If $4^2 + 9^2 = 10^2$, then $\triangle ABC$ is a right triangle. But $16 + 81 = 97$ and $97 \neq 100$. So $\triangle ABC$ is not a right triangle.

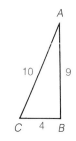

2. If $12^2 + 16^2 = 20^2$, then $\triangle RST$ is a right triangle. $144 + 256 = 400$. So $\triangle RST$ is a right triangle with right angle opposite RT.

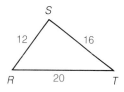

Try This...   Determine whether these are right triangles.

1.

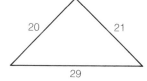

2.

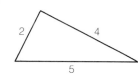

▶◀ Activity

The Möbius strip, introduced by the German mathematician and astronomer Augustus Ferdinand Möbius (1790-1868), can fool you.

Cut out a strip of paper about 11 inches long and 1 inch wide.

1. Take the strip, and turn one end over. (Give the loop a half twist.) Tape the ends together.

    Draw a pencil line down the middle, and shade one side of the strip until you come back to your original point. Cut the strip in half along its center line. What happens?

2. Cut the strip in half again. What happens?

3. Take a second strip and connect it as you did with the first one. Cut parallel to one edge and about one-third of the way from that edge. Continue cutting until you come back to your original position. What happens?

Exercises

▲ **Determine whether these measurements can be the lengths of the sides of a right triangle.**

1.	$d = 7$	$e = 5$	$f = 9$	2.	$d = 5$	$e = 2$	$f = 8$

1. $d = 7$ $e = 5$ $f = 9$ 2. $d = 5$ $e = 2$ $f = 8$

3. $d = 40$ $e = 2$ $f = 8$ 4. $d = 5$ $e = 5$ $f = 5\sqrt{2}$

5. $d = \sqrt{5}$ $e = \sqrt{4}$ $f = \sqrt{7}$ 6. $d = 30$ $e = 16$ $f = 34$

7. $d = 1.2$ $e = 0.5$ $f = 1.3$ 8. $d = 1.8$ $e = 1.2$ $f = 1.9$

9. $d = 48$ $e = 20$ $f = 52$ 10. $d = 16$ $e = 2$ $f = 11$

11. Is quadrilateral *ABCD* a rhombus?   12. Is quadrilateral *GTRM* a square?

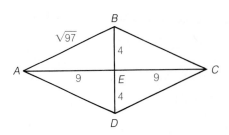

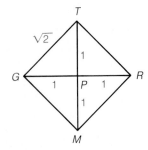

▶ Extension Exercises

13. Carpenters sometimes use the following test to determine whether two pieces of wood are perpendicular. The 6″ and 8″ measurements are made as shown. Then the distance *AB* is checked. Explain this method.

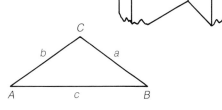

▶▶ Challenge Exercises

14. Draw several triangles like △*ABC* where ∠*C* is obtuse. Find measures *a*, *b*, *c*, and compare $a^2 + b^2$ and c^2. What can you conclude?

15. Draw several triangles like △*ABC* where ∠*C* is acute. Find measures *a*, *b*, *c*, and compare $a^2 + b^2$ and c^2. What can you conclude?

Skills Refresher

To simplify a radical expression such as $\dfrac{4}{\sqrt{3}}$, rationalize the denominator. We do this by multiplying the expression by a form of 1.

Example: $\dfrac{4}{\sqrt{3}} = \dfrac{4}{\sqrt{3}} \cdot \dfrac{\sqrt{3}}{\sqrt{3}}$ Multiplying by $\dfrac{\sqrt{3}}{\sqrt{3}}$, a form of 1.

$= \dfrac{4\sqrt{3}}{3}$ or $\dfrac{4}{3}\sqrt{3}$

1. $\dfrac{5}{\sqrt{3}}$ 2. $\dfrac{6}{\sqrt{2}}$ 3. $\dfrac{1}{\sqrt{5}}$

4. $\dfrac{5}{\sqrt{6}}$ 5. $\dfrac{3}{\sqrt{2}}$ 6. $\dfrac{7}{\sqrt{3}}$

7. $\dfrac{8}{\sqrt{7}}$ 8. $\dfrac{6}{\sqrt{3}}$ 9. $\dfrac{6}{\sqrt{5}}$

10. $\dfrac{\sqrt{2}}{\sqrt{3}}$ 11. $\dfrac{\sqrt{7}}{\sqrt{8}}$ 12. $\dfrac{\sqrt{5}}{\sqrt{25}}$

13. $\dfrac{\sqrt{11}}{\sqrt{2}}$ 14. $\dfrac{\sqrt{13}}{\sqrt{5}}$ 15. $\dfrac{\sqrt{7}}{\sqrt{2}}$

<table>
<tr><td>**4**</td><td colspan="2" align="center">Special Right Triangles</td></tr>
</table>

After finishing Section 4, you should be able to
▲   *find lengths of sides in a 30°–60° right triangle.*
▲▲   *find lengths of sides in isosceles right triangles.*

▲   30°–60° Right Triangles

The Pythagorean Theorem helps us determine the relationship
between the lengths of sides in a 30°–60° right triangle.

1.   Use a protractor. Draw $\triangle ABC$ with
     angle measures 30°, 60°, and 90°.
2.   On $\overrightarrow{AC}$ find a point D such that
     $AD = 2AC$. Draw $\overline{BD}$.
3. $\triangle ABC \cong \triangle DBC$. Why? What kind of triangle is $\triangle ABD$?
4.   Suppose $AC = a$. What is AB?
5.   Use the Pythagorean Theorem to find BC.

THEOREM
10.6

The 30°–60° Right Triangle Theorem

For any 30°–60° right triangle, the hypotenuse is twice as long as
the shorter leg, and the longer leg is $\sqrt{3}$ times as long as the shorter
leg.

Examples   Find the missing lengths in each triangle.

1.

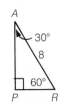

By the 30°–60° Right Triangle Theorem,
$2 \cdot PR = AR$ and $AP = \sqrt{3} \cdot PR$
$2 \cdot PR = 8$ $AP = \sqrt{3} \times 4$
$PR = 4$ $AP = 4\sqrt{3}$

2.

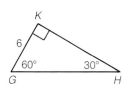

By the $30° - 60°$ Right Triangle Theorem,

$$2 \cdot GK = GH \quad \text{and} \quad KH = \sqrt{3} \cdot GK$$
$$2 \times 6 = GH \qquad KH = \sqrt{3} \times 6$$
$$12 = GH \qquad KH = 6\sqrt{3}$$

3.

By the $30° - 60°$ Right Triangle Theorem,

$$MA = \sqrt{3} \cdot KA \quad \text{and} \quad MK = 2 \cdot KA$$
$$5\sqrt{3} = \sqrt{3} \cdot KA \qquad MK = 2 \times 5$$
$$5 = KA \qquad MK = 10$$

Try This... Find the missing lengths in each triangle.

1.

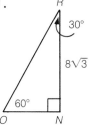

2.

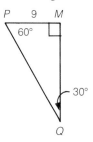

3.

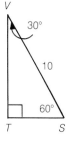

Example 4. Find BC and AC.

By the $30° - 60°$ Right Triangle Theorem,

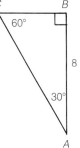

$$AB = BC \cdot \sqrt{3} \qquad\qquad AC = 2 \cdot BC$$

$$8 = BC \cdot \sqrt{3} \qquad\qquad AC = 2 \cdot \frac{8\sqrt{3}}{3}$$

$$\frac{8}{\sqrt{3}} = BC \qquad\qquad AC = \frac{16\sqrt{3}}{3}$$

$$\frac{8}{\sqrt{3}} \cdot \frac{\sqrt{3}}{\sqrt{3}} = BC$$

$$\frac{8\sqrt{3}}{3} = BC$$

Try This... 4. Find QR and PR.

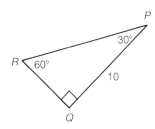

▲▲ Isosceles Right Triangles

An isosceles right triangle is called a $45°-45°$ right triangle.
There is a special relationship between the lengths of the
sides in isosceles right triangles.

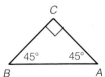

1. Use a protractor. Draw
   an isosceles right triangle, $\triangle ABC$.

2. Suppose $AC = BC = n$. Use the
   Pythagorean Theorem to find AB in terms of n.

THEOREM **10.7**	*The Isosceles Right Triangle Theorem*
	For any isosceles right triangle, the hypotenuse is $\sqrt{2}$ times as long as either leg.

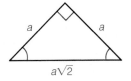

Examples   Find the missing lengths in each triangle.

5.

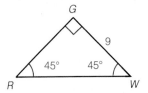

Because $\triangle RGW$ is isosceles, $RG = 9$.
By Theorem 10.7, $RW = 9\sqrt{2}$.

6.

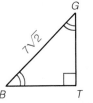

By Theorem 10.7, $GB = GT \cdot \sqrt{2}$.
Thus, $7\sqrt{2} = GT \cdot \sqrt{2}$.

$$7 = GT$$

Because $\triangle GTB$ is isosceles, $BT = 7$.

Try This...   Find the missing lengths in each triangle.

5.

6.

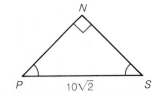

Example   7. Find *CE*.

By Theorem 10.7,

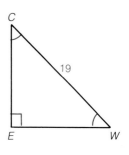

$$CW = CE\sqrt{2}$$
$$19 = CE\sqrt{2}$$
$$\frac{19}{\sqrt{2}} = CE$$
$$\frac{19}{\sqrt{2}} \cdot \frac{\sqrt{2}}{\sqrt{2}} = CE$$
$$\frac{19\sqrt{2}}{2} = CE$$

Try This...   7. Find *GK*.

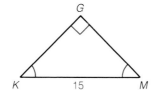

Exercises

▲ **From the information given, find the lengths of the other two sides of △ *PRT*.**

1. $p = 10$ 2. $p = 18$

3. $p = 27$ 4. $p = 35$

5. $t = 5$ 6. $t = 11$

7. $t = 24$ 8. $t = 5.6$

9. $r = 6\sqrt{3}$ 10. $r = 10\sqrt{3}$

11. $r = 19\sqrt{3}$ 12. $r = 15\sqrt{3}$

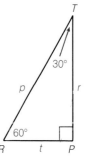

▲▲ **From the information given, find the lengths of the other two sides of △ *MRS*.**

13. $r = 2$ 14. $s = 7$

15. $r = 4.5$ 16. $r = 8.4$

17. $m = 14\sqrt{2}$ 18. $m = 16\sqrt{2}$

19. $m = 3.5\sqrt{2}$ 20. $m = 4.7\sqrt{2}$

▶ Extension Exercises

21. The base of a ladder is placed 0.9 m from a wall. If the angle between the ladder and the ground is 60°, to what length must the ladder be extended? At what height does the ladder touch the wall?

22. Square plugs are often used to check the diameter of a hole. What must the length of the side of a square be to test a hole with diameter 3.15 cm? (Allow 0.1 mm for clearance.)

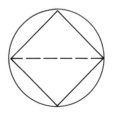

23. The arch in the photograph shows an equilateral triangle, △ABC. The sides of △ ABC measure 3.6 m. How high is the arch?

24. This toy is a series of isosceles right triangles. If AB = 1, find AC, BC, CD, CE, BD, DE, EF, and DF.

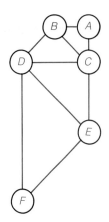

25. A hockey player is 5 m from the center of the rink. The angle to the center of the goal is 30°. How far must she hit the puck to reach the goal?

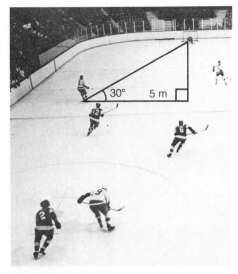

26. ℓ is the length of the diagonal of a square with side s. Find ℓ in terms of s.

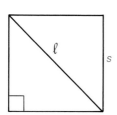

27. s is the length of the side of an equilateral triangle and h is the length of an altitude. Find h in terms of s.

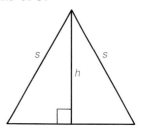

▶▶ Challenge Exercises

28. One angle of a rhombus has a measure of 120° and the length of each side is 18. Find the length of the longer diagonal.

29. Refer to Exercise 24. Simplify the following ratios using the lengths you found.

$$\frac{BC}{AB}, \frac{CD}{BD}, \frac{DE}{CE}, \frac{DF}{EF}$$

30. The isosceles right triangle is used as the basis of this parquet floor design. In the drawing below, $PS = ST$, $\overline{PR} \perp \overline{QV}$, and $\overline{TS} \parallel \overline{PQ}$. Devise a procedure for constructing $\overline{TS} \parallel \overline{PQ}$ so that $PS = ST$.

31. In this enlarged drawing of a bolt, the angle has a measure of 60° and the distance from thread to thread is 12 mm. Find the depth of each thread.

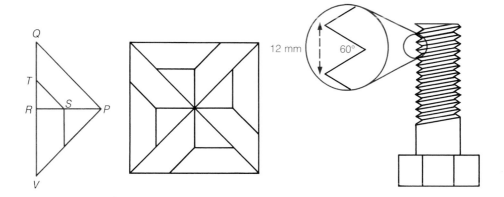

Calculator Application   Finding Missing Lengths

To find a square root, simply enter the number and
then press the square root key.

Example   Find c. Round your answer
                    to the nearest tenth.

$$a^2 + b^2 = c^2$$
$$8^2 + 11^2 = c^2$$
$$64 + 121 = c^2$$
$$185 = c^2$$
$$\sqrt{185} = c$$

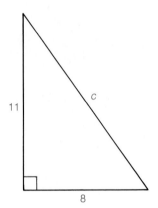

Enter: 185 $\boxed{\sqrt{}}$

Display: 13.60147

$c = 13.6$

Find the missing lengths. Round your answer to the nearest tenth.

1.

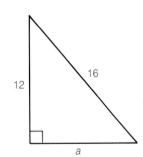

2.

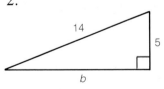

3.

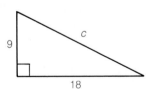

4.

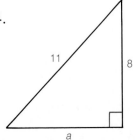

5.

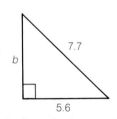

6.

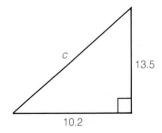

Chapter Review

① **Name the similar triangles.**

1.

2.
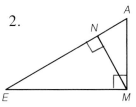

Find the geometric mean of these numbers.

3. 4 and 16

4. 7 and 10

Find the missing lengths.

5. $RQ = 9, QF = 36, TQ = ?$

6. $XT = 6, XY = 9, XZ = ?$

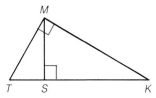

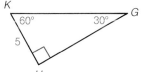

② **Use the given information to find the missing lengths.**

7. $a = 20, b = 15, c = ?$

8. $b = 4, c = 5, a = ?$

③ **Determine whether these measurements can be the lengths of sides of a right triangle.**

9. $p = 24, q = 36, r = 40$

10. $p = 5, q = 8, r = 10$

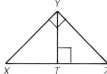

④ **Find the missing lengths in each triangle.**

11.

12.

13.

14.
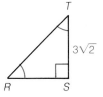

15.
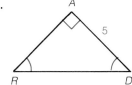

16.
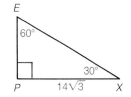

Chapter Test

Name the similar triangles.

1.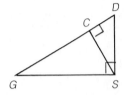

2.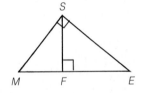

Find the geometric mean of these numbers.

3. 9 and 36

4. 11 and 15

Find the missing lengths.

5. $MF = 16, FE = 25, SF = ?$

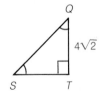

6. $RH = 5, RT = 8, RB = ?$

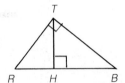

Use the given information to find the missing lengths.

7. $b = 70, c = 74, a = ?$

8. $a = 8, b = 2, c = ?$

Determine whether these measurements can be the lengths of sides of a right triangle.

9. $p = 16, q = 12, r = 20$

10. $p = 10, q = 15, r = 29$

Find the missing lengths in each triangle.

11.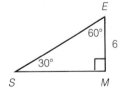

12.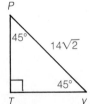

13.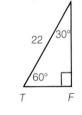

14.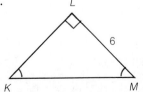

15.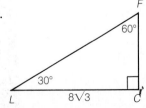

16.

Skills Review   Fractions

Compare each pair of numbers. Use <, >, or =.

1. $\frac{5}{8}$ and $\frac{4}{8}$ 2. $\frac{2}{9}$ and $\frac{5}{9}$ 3. $\frac{1}{4}$ and $\frac{1}{3}$ 4. $\frac{1}{8}$ and $\frac{1}{6}$

5. $\frac{11}{16}$ and $\frac{2}{3}$ 6. $\frac{5}{6}$ and $\frac{4}{5}$ 7. $\frac{3}{4}$ and $\frac{5}{8}$ 8. $\frac{7}{10}$ and $\frac{69}{100}$

9. $\frac{3}{9}$ and $\frac{1}{3}$ 10. $\frac{3}{2}$ and $\frac{14}{10}$ 11. $\frac{3}{8}$ and $\frac{2}{5}$ 12. $\frac{3}{7}$ and $\frac{5}{9}$

Convert to fractional notation.

13. 0.2   14. 0.9   15. 3.8   16. 6.9

17. 0.13   18. 0.09   19. 1.49   20. 13.98

21. 1.007   22. 342.011   23. 0.0001   24. 21.0003

Convert to fractional notation.

25. $5\frac{1}{3}$ 26. $3\frac{1}{4}$ 27. $8\frac{3}{4}$ 28. $22\frac{1}{2}$

29. $5\frac{7}{8}$ 30. $3\frac{5}{6}$ 31. $1\frac{1}{8}$ 32. $10\frac{1}{100}$

33. $3\frac{3}{4}$ 34. $5\frac{9}{10}$ 35. $2\frac{7}{10}$ 36. $16\frac{1}{2}$

Convert each improper fraction to a mixed number or whole number.

37. $\frac{7}{4}$ 38. $\frac{13}{3}$ 39. $\frac{9}{5}$ 40. $\frac{23}{2}$

41. $\frac{17}{6}$ 42. $\frac{83}{10}$ 43. $\frac{58}{7}$ 44. $\frac{22}{7}$

45. $\frac{221}{100}$ 46. $\frac{18}{2}$ 47. $\frac{49}{12}$ 48. $\frac{37}{10}$

Convert to decimal notation. Round to the nearest thousandth.

49. $\frac{1}{8}$ 50. $\frac{13}{4}$ 51. $\frac{7}{5}$ 52. $\frac{11}{6}$

53. $\frac{9}{10}$ 54. $\frac{39}{10}$ 55. $\frac{236}{100}$ 56. $\frac{1,728}{100}$

57. $1\frac{3}{9}$ 58. $3\frac{5}{6}$ 59. $7\frac{2}{11}$ 60. $8\frac{11}{12}$

11
Polygons

1   Identifying Polygons

After finishing Section 1, you should be able to
▲   *determine whether a figure is a polygon.*
▲▲   *classify polygons by their sides and as convex or concave.*

▲   Sides and Vertices

We have already studied two types of polygons: triangles and quadrilaterals.

DEFINITION

A **polygon** is a figure formed by the segments connecting three or more coplanar points. The segments are called *sides* and the endpoints are called *vertices*. No three consecutive vertices can be collinear. Any two sides can intersect only at vertices.

We usually name a polygon by naming its vertices in order.

In polygon *QRSTV*, $\overline{QR}$, $\overline{RS}$, $\overline{ST}$, $\overline{TV}$, and $\overline{VQ}$ are sides.
Points *Q, R, S, T,* and *V* are vertices.

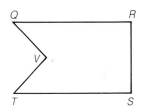

Examples   Which figures are polygons? Tell why the others are not.

1.   2.   3.

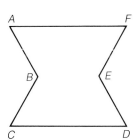   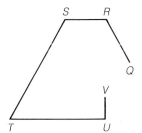   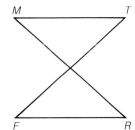

Polygon

Not a polygon.
Endpoints *V* and *Q* are not shared by exactly two sides.

Not a polygon.
$\overline{MR}$ and $\overline{FT}$ intersect in a point that is not a vertex.

Try This... Which figures are polygons? Tell why the others are not.

1.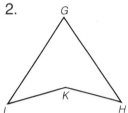
2.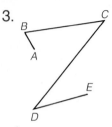
3.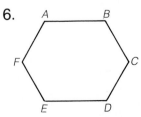

A property about the number of sides and vertices in a polygon is stated below.

THEOREM **11.1**	A polygon has *n* sides whenever it has *n* vertices.

▲▲ Classifying Polygons

We can classify polygons by the number of sides.

Number of Sides	Name of Polygon
3	Triangle
4	Quadrilateral
5	Pentagon
6	Hexagon
7	Heptagon
8	Octagon
9	Nonagon
10	Decagon
11	Undecagon
12	Dodecagon
n	*n*-gon

Examples Classify each polygon by the number of sides.

4.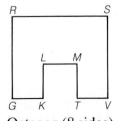

Pentagon (5 sides)

5.

Octagon (8 sides)

6.

Hexagon (6 sides)

Try This... Classify each polygon by the number of sides.

4.

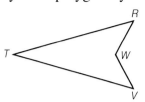

5.

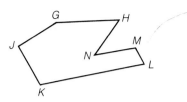

Polygons can also be classified as convex or concave.

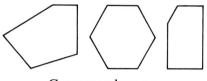

Convex polygons

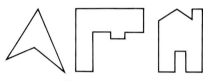

Concave polygons

DEFINITION

A **polygon is convex** whenever no line containing a side of the polygon intersects the interior of the polygon. If a polygon is not convex, then it is **concave.**

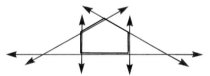

Convex: No lines contain points in the interior.

Concave: The line intersects the interior.

Examples Classify each polygon as convex or concave.

7.

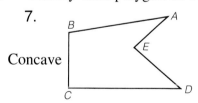

Concave

8.

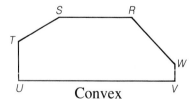

Convex

Try This... Classify each polygon as convex or concave.

6.

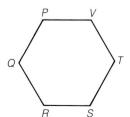

7.

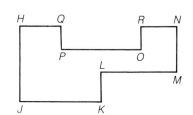

Exercises

▲ **Which figures are polygons? Tell why the others are not.**

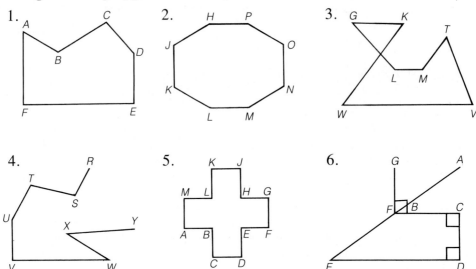

1.
2.
3.
4.
5.
6.

▲▲ **Classify each polygon by the number of sides.**

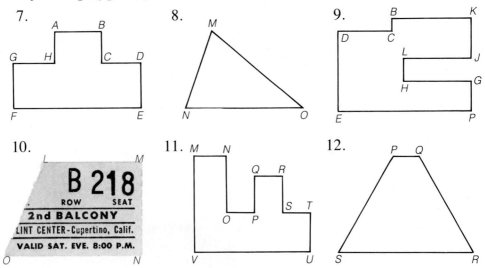

7.
8.
9.
10.
11.
12.

13–18. **Classify each polygon as convex or concave in Exercises 7-12.**

▶▶ Challenge Exercise

19. Does a concave triangle exist?

2   Diagonals and Perimeter of a Polygon

After finishing Section 2, you should be able to
▲   *calculate the number of diagonals in a polygon given the number of sides.*
▲▲ *find the perimeter of a polygon.*

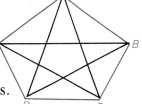

▲   Finding the Number of Diagonals

In pentagon *ABCDE*, $\overline{AC}$, $\overline{AD}$, $\overline{BD}$, $\overline{BE}$, and $\overline{CE}$ are diagonals.

DEFINITION

> A **diagonal of a polygon** is a segment that has vertices as endpoints and that is not a side.

1. Copy the following chart.

Polygon	Number of Vertices	Number of Diagonals
Triangle		
Quadrilateral		
Pentagon		
Hexagon		
Heptagon		
Octagon		

2. Make a drawing of each type of polygon listed.

3. For each polygon, draw all the diagonals and complete the chart.

4. Use the chart to predict the number of diagonals in a nonagon.

We can find the number of diagonals of a polygon with any number of sides.

THEOREM
11.2   For any polygon with *n* sides, the number of diagonals is $\frac{1}{2}n(n-3)$.

Examples   1. How many diagonals does a 25-gon have?

The number of diagonals is $D = \frac{1}{2} n(n - 3)$. Substituting 25 for n, we have

$$D = \frac{1}{2} \cdot 25 \, (25 - 3)$$
$$= \frac{25}{2} \, (22)$$
$$= 25 \times 11 = 275$$

A 25-gon has 275 diagonals.

▲2. Find the number of diagonals in a polygon with $(x - 4)$ sides. The number of diagonals is

$$D = \frac{1}{2} \cdot n \, (n - 3)$$
$$= \frac{1}{2} \cdot (x - 4)[(x - 4) - 3] \qquad \text{Substituting } x - 4 \text{ for } n$$
$$= \frac{(x - 4)}{2} \cdot (x - 7) \qquad \text{Simplifying}$$
$$= \frac{x^2 - 11x + 28}{2}$$

A polygon with $x - 4$ sides has $\dfrac{x^2 - 11x + 28}{2}$ diagonals.

Try This...   Find the number of diagonals in a polygon with:

1. 20 sides   2. 35 sides

▲3. $x - 2$ sides   ▲4. $x + 5$ sides

▲▲ Perimeter of a Polygon

DEFINITION

The **perimeter of a polygon** is the sum of the lengths of its sides.

Examples   Find the perimeter of each polygon.

3.

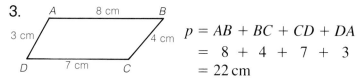

$p = AB + BC + CD + DA$
$= 8 + 4 + 7 + 3$
$= 22 \text{ cm}$

The perimeter of polygon *ABCD* is 22 cm.

4.

$p = PQ + QR + RS + ST + TP$
$= 12 + 7 + 15 + 5 + 8$
$= 47 \text{ cm}$

The perimeter of polygon *PQRST* is 47 cm.

Try This...   Find the perimeter of each polygon.

5.

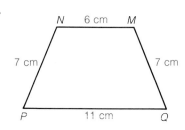

6.

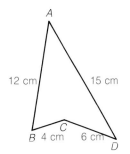

Exercises

▲ **Find the number of diagonals in each polygon.**

1. 15-gon   2. 18-gon
3. 40-gon   4. 27-gon
5. 31-gon   6. 50-gon

7. 70-gon
8. 63-gon
9. 100-gon
10. 81-gon
△11. An x^2-sided polygon
△12. A y^3-sided polygon
△13. An $(x - 5)$-sided polygon
△14. An $(x - 3)$-sided polygon
△15. An $(a + 1)$-sided polygon
△16. An $(a + 4)$-sided polygon
△17. A $(1 - x)$-sided polygon
△18. A $(2 - y)$-sided polygon

▲▲ **Find the perimeter of each polygon.**

19.
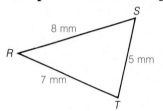

20.
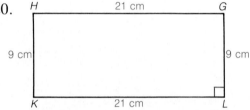

21.
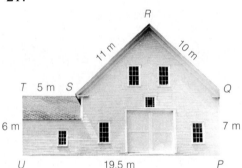

22.

►◄ Activity

Cut three 11-inch by 2-inch strips of paper. You can use a sheet of notebook paper and cut it into fourths lengthwise.

Now use one strip of paper to make a pentagon.

1. Tie a knot in the strip.
2. Carefully pull the ends tight and flatten the knot.
3. Cut off the extra paper.

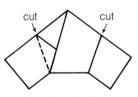

Use two strips of paper to make a hexagon.

1. Tie a square knot with the two strips.
2. Carefully pull the end tight and flatten the knot.
3. Cut off the extra paper.

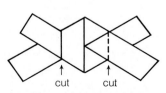

23.

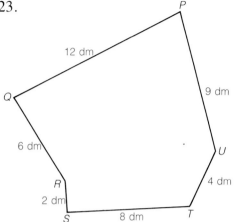

24.

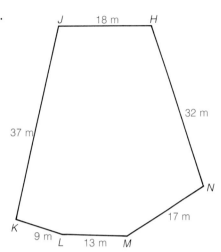

► **Extension Exercises**

25. Find the cost of fencing the yard pictured. The fencing costs $1.35 per meter.

26. Find the cost of baseboard for the room pictured. Omit 0.6 m for a doorway. The baseboard costs $1.94 per meter.

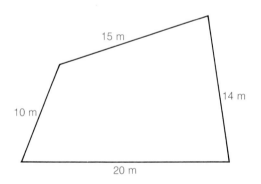

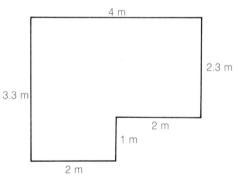

►► **Challenge Exercises**

27. Find the number of sides in a polygon with no diagonals.

28. Find the number of sides in a polygon with 405 diagonals.

▲**29.** Find the number of sides in a polygon with $\frac{1}{2}(a^2 - a - 2)$ diagonals.

30. Explain why the ratio of the perimeters of two similar triangles is the same as the ratio of the lengths of any two corresponding sides.

---

3 Angles of a Polygon

After finishing Section 3, you should be able to
▲   *solve problems involving the measures
    of the angles of a convex polygon.*
▲▲ *solve problems involving the exterior
    angles of a polygon.*

▲   Interior Angles

We know that the sum of the measures of the angles of a triangle is
180°. We can also find the sum of the angle measures of other types
of convex polygons.

1. Draw a pentagon *ABCDE*.
2. Draw all diagonals from *A*.
3. How many triangles are formed?
4. What is the sum of the measures
    of the angles of pentagon *ABCDE*?
5. Repeat this procedure for a hexagon
    ABCDEF. What can you conclude
    about the sum of the angle measures
    of a polygon?

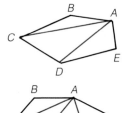

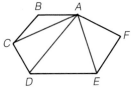

We can state a formula for the sum of the angle measures of any polygon.

THEOREM **11.3**	The sum *S* of the angle measures of any convex polygon with *n* sides is given by the formula

$$S = (n - 2)180$$

Examples   1. Find the sum of the angle measures of a 50-gon.

$$S = (n - 2)180$$
$$= (50 - 2)180 \quad \text{Substituting 50 for } n$$
$$= 48 \cdot 180$$
$$= 8{,}640$$

The sum of the angle measures of a 50-gon is 8,640°.

▲2. Find the sum of the angle measures of a polygon with $x - 2$ sides.

$$S = (n - 2)180$$
$$= [(x - 2) - 2]180 \qquad \text{Substituting } x - 2 \text{ for } n$$
$$= (x - 4)180$$
$$= 180x - 720$$

The sum of the angle measures is $180x - 720$.

Try This... Find the sum of the angle measures of each polygon.

1. 70-gon
2. 57-gon
▲3. A polygon with $x - 3$ sides

Example 3. The sum of the angle measures of a polygon is 7,020°. How many sides does the polygon have?

$$S = (n - 2)180$$
$$7,020 = (n - 2)180 \qquad \text{Substituting } 7,020 \text{ for } S$$
$$39 = n - 2 \qquad \text{Dividing by } 180$$
$$41 = n$$

The polygon has 41 sides.

Try This... 4. The sum of the angle measures of a polygon is 14,760°. How many sides does the polygon have?

▲▲ Exterior Angles

We have already discussed exterior angles of triangles. In the drawing, $\angle CBF$ is an exterior angle of pentagon $ABCDE$.

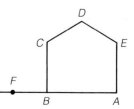

DEFINITION

An angle is an **exterior angle of a convex polygon** whenever it forms a linear pair with an angle of the polygon.

1. Draw several triangles and one exterior angle at each vertex.
2. For each triangle, find the sum of the measures of the three exterior angles.
3. Repeat this procedure for several hexagons.
   What can you conclude about the sum of the angle measures of a polygon?

Theorem 11.4 summarizes the results of this drawing exercise.

THEOREM **11.4**   For a convex polygon, the sum of the measures of the exterior angles, one at each vertex, is 360°.

For the heptagon shown,
$$a + b + c + d + e + f + g = 360°$$

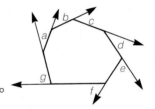

Example   4. Three of the four exterior angles of a quadrilateral have measures 45°, 73°, and 174°. Find the measure of the fourth exterior angle.

$$45 + 73 + 174 = 292$$

The sum of the three exterior angles is 292°.

By Theorem 11.4, we know that the sum of all four angles is 360°.

$$360 - 292 = x$$
$$68 = x$$

So, the measure of the fourth exterior angle is 68°.

Try This...   5. Four of the five exterior angles of a pentagon have measures 53°, 26°, 84°, and 103°. Find the measure of the fifth exterior angle.

Example △5. The measures of the exterior angles of a hexagon are x, $2x$, $3x$, $3x$, $4x$, and $5x$. Solve for x and find the measure of each exterior angle.

$$x + 2x + 3x + 3x + 4x + 5x = 360$$
$$18x = 360$$
$$x = 20$$

The measures of the exterior angles of the hexagon are $20°$, $40°$, $60°$, $60°$, $80°$, and $100°$.

Try This... △6. The measures of the exterior angles of a pentagon are $5x$, $6x$, $7x$, $8x$, and $10x$. Solve for x and find the measure of each exterior angle.

Exercises

▲ **Find the sum of the angle measures of each polygon.**

1. Decagon
2. Octagon
3. 40-gon
4. 38-gon
5. 100-gon
6. 200-gon
△7. $(x - 5)$-gon
△8. $(x + 4)$-gon

If S is the sum of the measures of the angles in a polygon, find the number of sides in the polygon.

9. $S = 1{,}980°$
10. $S = 6{,}120°$

▲▲ **Solve.**

11. Six of the seven exterior angles of a heptagon have measures $18°$, $12°$, $42°$, $75°$, and $87°$. Find the measure of the seventh exterior angle.

12. Nine of the ten exterior angles of a decagon have measures $12°$, $22°$, $16°$, $20°$, $10°$, $18°$, $23°$, $40°$, and $51°$. Find the measure of the tenth exterior angle.

13. Seven of the eight exterior angles of an octagon have measures $24°$, $36.5°$, $29.5°$, $51.5°$, $73°$, $16°$, and $38°$. Find the measure of the eighth exterior angle.

14. Five of the six exterior angles of a hexagon have measures $83°$, $24.5°$, $75.75°$, $39.6°$, and $112.2°$. Find the measure of the sixth exterior angle.

Solve for x and find the measures of the exterior angles in each polygon.

▲15. The measures of the exterior angles of a pentagon are x, $2x$, $3x$, $4x$, and $5x$.

▲16. The measures of the exterior angles of a hexagon are x, $3x$, $5x$, $6x$, $7x$, and $8x$.

▲17. The measures of the exterior angles of a heptagon are $2x$, $3x$, $4x$, $5x$, $7x$, $9x$, and $10x$.

▲18. The measures of the exterior angles of a nonagon are $6x$, $7x$, $8x$, $9x$, $10x$, $11x$, $12x$, $13x$, and $14x$.

▲19. The measures of the exterior angles of a hexagon are $4x$, $3x - 2$, $7x + 10$, $8x + 6$, $5x - 6$, and $2x + 4$.

▲20. The measures of the exterior angles of a pentagon are $3x$, $4x + 7$, $7x - 2$, $x + 12$, and $2x + 3$.

▶ Extension Exercises

21. A hexagon is equiangular. Find the measure of each of its interior and exterior angles.

22. The sum of the measures of an equiangular polygon is $5{,}040°$. Find the measure of an exterior angle.

▶▶ Challenge Exercises

23. Determine whether Theorems 11.3 and 11.4 hold true for concave polygons.

24. Develop a formula for finding the measure of one angle of an n-sided equiangular polygon.

4   Concurrent Lines in Triangles

After finishing Section 4, you should be able to
▲   *find the circumcenter of a triangle.*
▲▲   *find the centroid of a triangle.*

▲   The Circumcenter

In Chapter 6, we saw that the angle bisectors of a triangle are concurrent in a point that is called the incenter. We will talk about two more types of concurrent lines in triangles.

1. Draw a large triangle.

2. Draw the perpendicular bisector of each side.

3. Extend the bisectors. What do you observe?

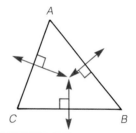

THEOREM 11.5	The perpendicular bisectors of the sides of a triangle are concurrent at a point that is equidistant from the vertices of the triangle.

DEFINITION

The point of concurrency of the perpendicular bisectors of the sides of a triangle is called the *circumcenter* of the triangle.

Example   1. Draw an acute triangle. Then draw its circumcenter.

Draw the perpendicular bisectors of the sides. Their point of intersection is the circumcenter.

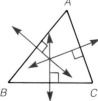

Try This...   1. Draw an obtuse triangle. Find its circumcenter.

▲▲ The Centroid

In Chapter 1 we found that the medians of a triangle appear concurrent. It can be shown that they are always concurrent.

THEOREM **11.6** The medians of a triangle are concurrent at a point whose distance from each vertex is $\frac{2}{3}$ the length of the corresponding median.

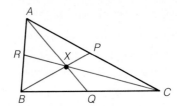

$$AX = \frac{2}{3}AQ$$

$$BX = \frac{2}{3}BP$$

$$CX = \frac{2}{3}CR$$

DEFINITION

The point of concurrency of the medians of a triangle is called the *centroid* of the triangle.

Example 2. Draw an acute triangle. Find its centroid.

Draw the medians of the triangle. Their point of intersection is the centroid.

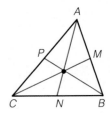

Try This... 2. Draw an obtuse triangle. Find its centroid.

Exercises

▲ **Draw each triangle and find its circumcenter.**

1. Isosceles
2. Scalene
3. Equilateral
4. Obtuse isosceles

▲▲ Draw each triangle and find its centroid.

5. Scalene

6. Equilateral

7. Acute isosceles

8. Right

▶ Extension Exercises

9. For what kinds of triangles is the circumcenter in the interior of the triangle? In the exterior? On the triangle?

10. For what kinds of triangles is the centroid in the interior of the triangle? In the exterior? On the triangle?

11. When (if ever) are the circumcenter, the centroid, and the incenter of a triangle the same point?

▶▶ Challenge Exercises

12. The point of concurrency of the altitudes of a triangle is called the *orthocenter*. Draw the altitudes of a triangle to find its orthocenter.

13. Of the four points of concurrency (incenter, circumcenter, centroid, and orthocenter), three are collinear. The line that contains them is called the *Euler line*. Determine which three points are collinear.

▶◀ Activity

Flexagons are polygons, folded from strips of paper, that change their faces when they are "flexed."

Make your own flexagon, like this:

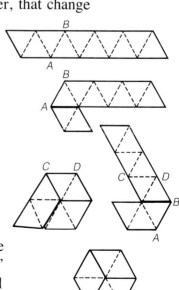

1. Prepare a strip of paper marked with equilateral triangles as shown.

2. Fold the strip backward along $\overline{AB}$.

3. Turn the figure upside down as shown.

4. Fold it backward again along $\overline{CD}$.

5. Fold and paste or tape the last triangle on top of the first triangle.

6. Fold repeatedly along the dotted lines. Then pinch two adjacent triangles together and force them upward to turn the hexagon "inside out." If you mark the triangles with colors, you will see the changes that occur when you flex it.

5   Similar Polygons

After finishing Section 5, you should be able to
▲   *identify pairs of similar polygons.*
▲▲   *find lengths of sides in similar polygons.*

▲ Identifying Similar Polygons

The properties of similar triangles can be applied
to other figures.

DEFINITION

Two polygons are similar whenever their vertices can be matched
so that the corresponding angles are congruent and the lengths of
corresponding sides are proportional.

Examples   Which pairs of polygons are similar? Tell why the others are not.

1.

Similar

2.

Not similar. The vertices of the second polygon cannot be matched
with the vertices of the first polygon.

Try This...   Which pairs of polygons are similar? Tell why the others are not.

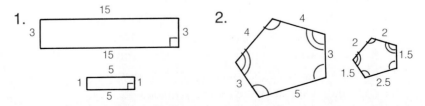

▲▲ Finding Missing Lengths

Similarity can be used to find lengths of sides of polygons.

Example 3. Rectangle $ABCD \sim$ rectangle $PQRS$. Find PQ.

Because the rectangles are similar, the lengths of corresponding sides are proportional.

Thus, $\dfrac{3}{6} = \dfrac{5}{PQ}$

$3(PQ) = 6 \cdot 5$
$3(PQ) = 30$
$PQ = 10$

Try This... 3. Trapezoid $RSTV \sim$ trapezoid $DEFG$. Find DE and GF.

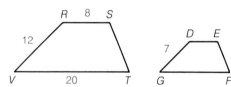

Example ▲4. Quadrilateral $ABCD \sim$ quadrilateral $GHJK$. Find DC and JK.

$$\dfrac{AD}{GK} = \dfrac{DC}{JK}$$

$$\dfrac{8}{10} = \dfrac{x + 5}{3x + 1}$$

$$8(3x + 1) = 10(x + 5)$$
$$24x + 8 = 10x + 50$$
$$14x = 42$$
$$x = 3$$

If $x = 3$, then $DC = 8$ and $JK = 10$.

Try This... ▲4. Pentagon $ABCDE \sim$ pentagon $PQRST$. Find ED and TS.

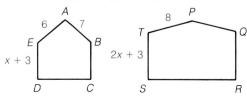

Exercises

▲ **Which pairs of polygons are similar? Tell why the others are not.**

1.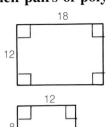

2.

3.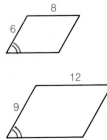

▲▲ **Find the indicated lengths.**

4. Kite *RSTV* ~ kite *ABCD*. Find *BC*.

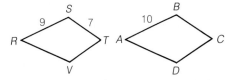

5. ▱*GHJK* ~ ▱*TVWX*. Find *TV*.

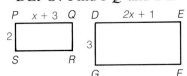

6. Trapezoid *FRDY* ~ trapezoid *CHPS*. Find *CS*.

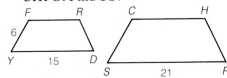

▲7. Rectangle *PQRS* ~ rectangle *DEFG*. Find *PQ* and *DE*.

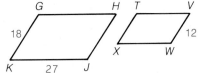

8. Pentagon *DEFGH* ~ pentagon *RSTUV*. Find *RS* and *UV*.

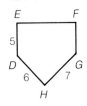

▲9. Hexagon *FGHJKL* ~ hexagon *XRSTVW*. Find *FG* and *RX*.

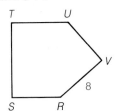
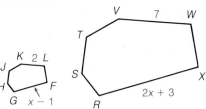

▶ Extension Exercises

10. Are all squares similar? Explain how you know.

11. Can two polygons be similar if they do not have the same number of sides? Explain how you know.

6   Regular Polygons

After finishing Section 6, you should be able to
▲   *find angle measures of regular polygons.*
▲▲   *draw regular polygons using a protractor,*
    compass, and straightedge.

▲   Angle Measures in Regular Polygons

Some polygons are equilateral.

Some polygons are
equiangular.

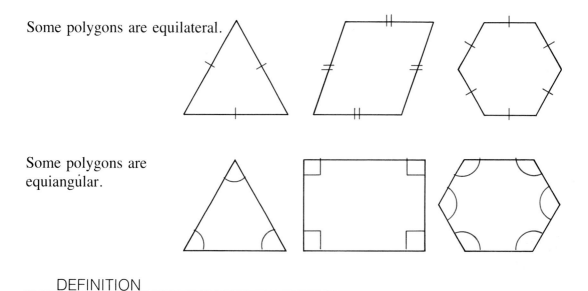

DEFINITION

A **convex polygon is regular** whenever it is both equilateral and
equiangular.

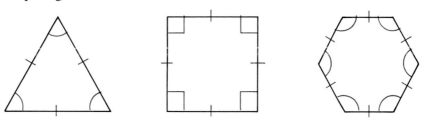

All angles of a regular polygon have the same measure. Thus, to
find the measure of each angle, we can divide the sum of the
angle measures by the number of angles. Recall from Theorem 11.3
that the sum of the angle measures of an *n*-sided polygon is
$(n - 2)180°$.

THEOREM   The measure of an interior angle of a regular polygon with n sides is

11.7
$$\frac{(n-2)180}{n}$$

Example   1. Find the measure of each interior angle of a regular decagon.

Substituting 10 for n, we have

$$\frac{(n-2)180}{n} = \frac{(10-2)180}{10}$$

$$= \frac{8 \times 180}{10}$$

$$= \frac{1440}{10} = 144$$

Each angle measures 144°.

Try This...   1. Find the measure of each interior angle of a regular octagon.

A corollary about exterior angles follows directly from Theorem 11.7.

COROLLARY   The measure of each exterior angle of a regular polygon of n

11.8   sides is

$$\frac{360}{n}$$

Example   2. Find the measure of each exterior angle of a regular heptagon.

$$\frac{360}{n} = \frac{360}{7} = 51\frac{3}{7}$$

Each exterior angle measures $51\frac{3}{7}$°.

Try This...   2. Find the measure of each exterior angle of a regular nonagon.

▲▲ Drawing Regular Polygons

Regular polygons can be drawn using a protractor, compass, and straightedge.

Example   3. Draw a regular octagon.

Step 1
Draw a circle.

Step 2
Because an octagon has eight sides, we divide 360 by 8:
$$360 \div 8 = 45$$

Draw eight angles, each with measure 45° and vertex at the center of the circle.

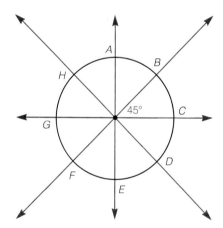

Step 3
Connect the points where the rays intersect the circle.

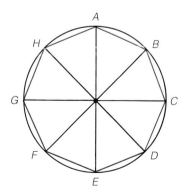

Try This...   3. Draw a regular pentagon. Use the method in Example 3.

Exercises

▲ **Find the measure of each interior angle of these regular polygons.**

1. Hexagon
2. Pentagon
3. Triangle
4. Quadrilateral
5. Heptagon
6. Nonagon
7. 20-gon
8. 50-gon
9. 100-gon
10. 1,000–gon

11–20. Find the measure of each exterior angle of the polygons in Exercises 1–10.

▲▲ **Draw these regular polygons.**

21. Hexagon
22. Decagon
23. Nonagon
24. Quadrilateral
25. Dodecagon
26. 15-gon

▶ Extension Exercises

27. The measure of an exterior angle of a regular polygon is 45°. How many sides does the polygon have?

28. The length of a side of a regular decagon is 20. Find its perimeter.

29. As the number of sides of a regular polygon increases, what happens to the measure of an interior angle? What happens to the measure of an exterior angle?

30. Is there a regular polygon whose interior angles measure 147°? Explain.

▶▶ Challenge Exercise

31. Draw a regular pentagon. Extend the sides until they intersect and form a five-pointed star. Find the measure of the angle at each point of the star.

Computer Application   Finding Angle Measures

Find the measure of the angles in a regular polygon given the number of sides.

Command

```
 10 PRINT "HOW MANY SIDES DOES THE
        REGULAR POLYGON HAVE?"
 20 INPUT S
 30 LET A = 180 * (S − 2) / S
 40 IF S = 3 THEN 160
 50 IF S = 4 THEN 180
 60 IF S = 5 THEN 200
 70 IF S = 6 THEN 220
 80 IF S = 7 THEN 240
 90 IF S = 8 THEN 260
100 IF S = 9 THEN 280
110 IF S = 10 THEN 300
120 IF S = 11 THEN 320
130 IF S = 12 THEN 340
140 PRINT "A REGULAR   "; S; "-GON
        HAS ANGLES THAT MEASURE   "; A
150 GOTO 350
160 PRINT "AN EQUILATERAL
        TRIANGLE HAS ANGLES THAT
        MEASURE   "; A
170 GOTO 350
180 PRINT "A SQUARE HAS ANGLES THAT
        MEASURE   "; A
190 GOTO 350
200 PRINT "A REGULAR PENTAGON HAS
        ANGLES THAT MEASURE   "; A
210 GOTO 350
220 PRINT "A REGULAR HEXAGON HAS
        ANGLES THAT MEASURE   "; A
230 GOTO 350
240 PRINT "A REGULAR HEPTAGON HAS
        ANGLES THAT MEASURE   "; A
250 GOTO 350
260 PRINT "A REGULAR OCTAGON HAS
        ANGLES THAT MEASURE   "; A
270 GOTO 350
280 PRINT "A REGULAR NONAGON HAS
        ANGLES THAT MEASURE   "; A
290 GOTO 350
300 PRINT "A REGULAR DECAGON HAS
        ANGLES THAT MEASURE   "; A
310 GOTO 350
320 PRINT "A REGULAR UNDECAGON HAS
        ANGLES THAT MEASURE   "; A
330 GOTO 350
340 PRINT "A REGULAR DODECAGON HAS
        ANGLES THAT MEASURE   "; A
350 END
```

Comments

20 The computer accepts the input from the user.

30 The computer assigns the measure of the angle to the variable A.

40–130 The computer is sent to the indicated line if it satisfies the given conditions.

140–340 The computer prints the name of the regular polygon along with its angle measures.

Find the measure of each angle for the following regular polygons.

1. 13-gon   2. 20-gon   3. 37-gon   4. 99-gon   5. 150-gon

Chapter Review

1 **Which figures are polygons? Tell why the others are not.**

1.
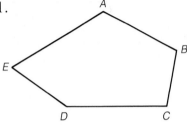

2.
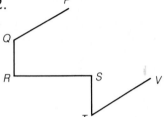

3.
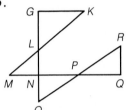

4.
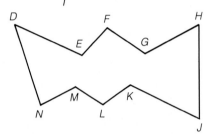

Classify each polygon by the number of sides.

5.
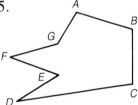

6.

7.
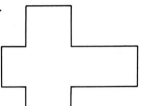

Classify each polygon as convex or concave.

8.
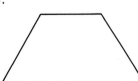

9.
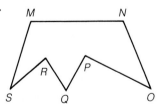

10.
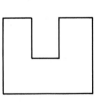

2 11. Find the number of diagonals of a 45-gon.

3 12. Find the sum of the angle measures of a 20-gon.

△13. The measures of the exterior angles of a hexagon are x, $2x$, $2x$, $2x$, $3x$, and $5x$. Solve for x and find the measure of each exterior angle.

14. Draw an isosceles right triangle. Find its circumcenter.

 15. Draw a scalene right triangle. Find its centroid.

16. Pentagon *ABCDE* ~ pentagon *GKLMN*. Find *GN* and *LK*.

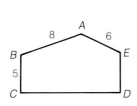

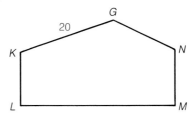

 17. Find the measure of each interior angle of a regular 30-gon.

18. Find the measure of each exterior angle of a regular 18-gon.

Chapter Test

Which figures are polygons? Tell why the others are not.

1.

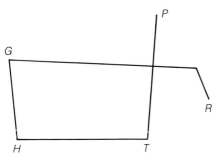

2.

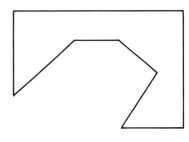

3.

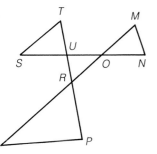

4.

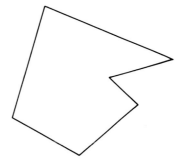

Classify each polygon by the number of sides.

5.

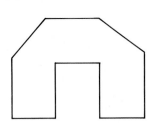

6.

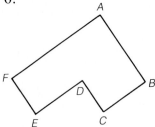

7.

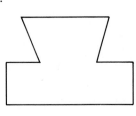

Classify each polygon as convex or concave.

8.

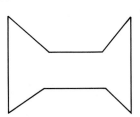

9.

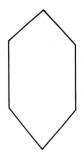

10.

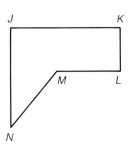

11. Find the number of diagonals of a 25-gon.

12. Find the sum of the angle measures of a 40-gon.

▲13. The measures of the exterior angles of a pentagon are x, $2x$, $3x$, $4x$, and $5x$. Solve for x and find the measure of each exterior angle.

14. Draw an acute isosceles triangle. Find its circumcenter.

15. Draw an obtuse isosceles triangle. Find its centroid.

16. Quadrilateral $DEFG \sim$ quadrilateral $PQRS$. Find PS and QR.

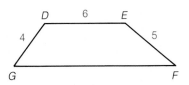

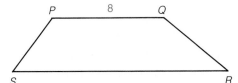

17. Find the measure of each interior angle of a regular 18-gon.

18. Find the measure of each exterior angle of a regular 24-gon.

Skills Review   Ratio and Proportion

Name each ratio two other ways.

1. 8 to 10

2. $\dfrac{5}{4}$

3. 6 to 5

4. 2:5

5. 3 to 100

6. 5:7

7. $\dfrac{2}{13}$

8. 8:3

9. 1:1,000

10. 9 to 1

11. $\dfrac{2}{3}$

12. $\dfrac{3}{4}$

Determine whether each proportion is true or false.

13. $\dfrac{2}{3} = \dfrac{3}{5}$

14. $\dfrac{5}{8} = \dfrac{8}{5}$

15. $\dfrac{5}{6} = \dfrac{15}{18}$

16. $\dfrac{2}{3} = \dfrac{5}{7}$

17. $\dfrac{3}{6} = \dfrac{2}{4}$

18. $\dfrac{2}{3} = \dfrac{8}{12}$

19. $\dfrac{9}{11} = \dfrac{4}{5}$

20. $\dfrac{2}{7} = \dfrac{4}{14}$

21. $\dfrac{7}{10} = \dfrac{6}{9}$

22. $\dfrac{2}{13} = \dfrac{3}{16}$

23. $\dfrac{12}{16} = \dfrac{6}{8}$

24. $\dfrac{5}{4} = \dfrac{25}{15}$

Solve. Find what x represents.

25. $\dfrac{3}{5} = \dfrac{6}{x}$

26. $\dfrac{3}{4} = \dfrac{x}{12}$

27. $\dfrac{5}{4} = \dfrac{x}{20}$

28. $\dfrac{2}{3} = \dfrac{x}{12}$

29. $\dfrac{3}{7} = \dfrac{6}{x}$

30. $\dfrac{7}{8} = \dfrac{14}{x}$

31. $\dfrac{5}{4} = \dfrac{10}{x}$

32. $\dfrac{2}{9} = \dfrac{x}{36}$

33. $\dfrac{1}{2} = \dfrac{x}{7}$

34. $\dfrac{3}{4} = \dfrac{5}{x}$

35. $\dfrac{3}{10} = \dfrac{x}{5}$

36. $\dfrac{5}{6} = \dfrac{x}{8}$

37. $\dfrac{6}{13} = \dfrac{x}{78}$

38. $\dfrac{3}{1} = \dfrac{15}{x}$

39. $\dfrac{3}{100} = \dfrac{x}{350}$

40. $\dfrac{12}{18} = \dfrac{x}{72}$

41. $\dfrac{5}{6} = \dfrac{x}{12}$

42. $\dfrac{2}{7} = \dfrac{x}{14}$

43. $\dfrac{2}{9} = \dfrac{4}{x}$

44. $\dfrac{2}{7} = \dfrac{6}{x}$

12
Area of Polygons

1   Polygonal Regions

After finishing Section 1, you should be able to
▲   *triangulate a polygonal region.*
▲▲ *apply area postulates to problems involving areas of polygonal regions.*

▲ Triangulations

A triangle is made up of three segments. A
triangular region includes the triangle and all of
the points in the interior.

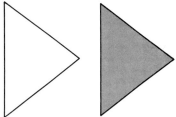

Triangle   Triangular Region

DEFINITION

A triangle together with its interior is called a *triangular region*.

Polygonal regions are made up of triangular regions.

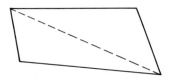 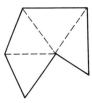

DEFINITION

A **polygonal region** is formed by coplanar triangular regions that
have no interior points in common.

A polygonal region can be divided into triangular regions
(triangulated). This can usually be done in more than one way.

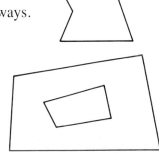

Example   1. Triangulate this polygonal region in two ways.

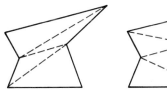

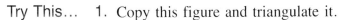

Try This...   1. Copy this figure and triangulate it.

▲▲ Some Area Postulates

We shall begin with the following assumption.

POSTULATE   *The Area Postulate*
   14   For every polygonal region, there corresponds a positive number
              called its *area*. The number is determined for any given unit.

For the area of a polygonal region *ABCD*, we shall write "area *ABCD*."

Comparing the areas of these regions is easier if we triangulate them:

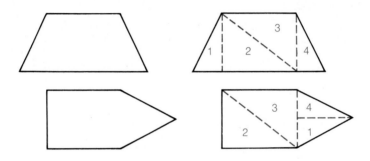

Because corresponding triangles appear to be congruent, it seems
reasonable to conclude that the polygonal regions have the same
area. Our reasoning suggests the following postulates.

POSTULATE   Congruent triangular regions have the same area.
   15

POSTULATE   The area of a triangulated polygonal region is the sum of the areas
   16   of its triangular regions.

Example   2. *ABCE* is a rectangle and area △ *ACE* = 12. Find area *ABCD*.

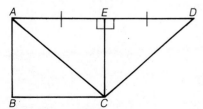

Because *ABCE* is a rectangle, △ *ABC* ≅ △ *CEA*.
By SAS, △ *AEC* ≅ △ *DEC*.

By Postulate 15,
area △ *ABC* = area △ *AEC* = area △ *DEC* = 12.

By Postulate 16,
area *ABCD* = 12 + 12 + 12 = 36.

Try This...   2. In the figure, area △ *ADC* = 4.
Find area △ *ABC*.

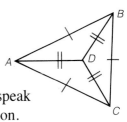

"Area" refers to a region. For convenience, however, we will speak of the area of a triangle instead of the area of a triangular region. We will do the same for the areas of other polygonal regions.

Exercises

▲   **Copy each figure and then triangulate the region.**

1. 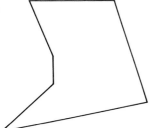   2. 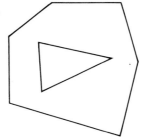   3.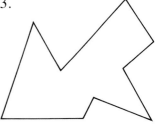

▲▲ **Find the area of each polygon.**

4. *ABCD* is a square. Area △ *AED* = 7. Find the area of *ABCD*.

5. *ABCDE* is a regular pentagon. Area △ *DFC* = 3. Find the area of *ABCDE*.

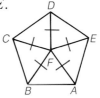

6. *ABCDEF* is a regular hexagon. Area of *ABCO* = 7. Find the area of *ABCDEF*.

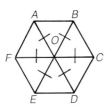

7. All the triangles in this figure are congruent. Area of *BDFH* = 10, and area △ *ABH* = 7. Find the area of *ABCDEFGH*.

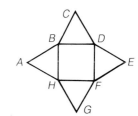

2 | Area of a Rectangle

After finishing Section 2, you should be able to
▲ *find the area of a rectangle.*
▲▲ *solve problems involving areas of rectangles.*

▲ Finding the Area of a Rectangle

We usually use a square region as a **unit of area**. If the side of
the square is 1 centimeter in length, then the unit is called
1 square centimeter, abbreviated cm^2.

1 cm^2

Examples
1. How many square centimeters
   are contained in this rectangle?

   There are three rows of
   4 square centimeters.

   The area of the rectangle
   is 12 cm^2.

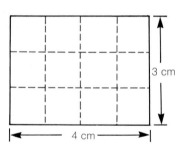

3 cm

4 cm

2. How many square centimeters are contained in this rectangle?

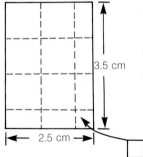

3.5 cm

2.5 cm

By counting the squares or parts of squares, we find

6 square centimeters $= 6 \quad cm^2$
5 half-square centimeters $= 5\frac{1}{2}\text{-}cm^2 = 2.5 \quad cm^2$
1 quarter-square centimeter $= 1\frac{1}{4}\text{-}cm^2 = \underline{0.25 \, cm^2}$
Area of rectangle $= 8.75 \, cm^2$

We can also say that there are $3\frac{1}{2}$ rows of 2.5 cm^2,
and $3.5 \times 2.5 = 8.75$.

These examples suggest that instead of counting squares we can
also find the area of a rectangle by multiplying the lengths of two
adjacent sides.

POSTULATE **17** The area of a rectangle is the product of the lengths of two adjacent sides.

Because we usually call the longest side the **length** and the other the **width,** we write:

$$\text{Area} = \ell \cdot w$$

We write A for "Area."

Because a square is a rectangle whose length and width are the same, we have the following theorem.

THEOREM **12.1** The area of a square is the square of the length of a side.

Examples   Find the area of each rectangle.

3.

$$A = \ell \cdot w$$
$$A = 5 \times 3$$
$$= 15\,\text{m}^2$$

4.

$$A = s^2$$
$$A = (17.5)^2$$
$$= 306.25\,\text{m}^2$$

Try This...   Find the area of each rectangle.

1.

2.

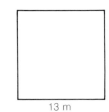

▲▲ Solving Area Problems

Examples ▲5. Find the missing length and width. Identify the unit.

$$A = 100 \text{ m}^2$$

with x on the left side and $4x$ on the bottom.

$$A = 4x \cdot x$$
$$100 = 4x^2$$
$$25 = x^2$$
$$\sqrt{25} = x$$
$$5 = x$$

Thus, $\ell = 4 \cdot 5 = 20$ m and $w = 5$ m.

6. Find the area of the shaded region.
   The area of each square is 4 cm^2.

$$A_{\substack{shaded \\ region}} = A_{rectangle} - A_{4\ squares}$$
$$= (12 \times 6) - (4 \times 4)$$
$$= 72 - 16$$
$$= 56 \text{ cm}^2$$

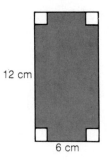

12 cm

6 cm

Try This... ▲3. Find the missing length and width. Identify the unit.

$$A = 108 \text{ cm}^2$$

with x on the left side and $3x$ on the bottom.

4. Find the area of the shaded region.

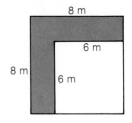

8 m

6 m

8 m

6 m

6 m

Exercises

▲ **Find the area of each rectangle or square.**

1. $\ell = 7$ km and $w = 14$ km
2. $\ell = 13$ km and $w = 8$ km
3. $\ell = 7$ cm and $w = 1.5$ cm
4. $\ell = 2.6$ cm and $w = 5$ cm
5. $s = 1.5$ cm
6. $s = 7\sqrt{2}$ m

▲▲ **Find the missing length or width. Identify the unit.**

7. $A = 78$ m^2, $\ell = 6$ m
8. $A = 21.6$ cm^2, $w = 2.7$ cm
9. $A = 169$ km^2 (square)
10. $A = 5\sqrt{6}$ cm^2, $w = \sqrt{3}$ cm
11. $A = 441$ km^2 (square)
12. $A = 0.09$ m^2 (square)

Find the area of each figure. All angles are right angles.

13.

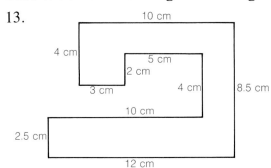

14.

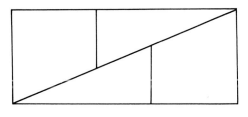

15. *ABCD* and *EFGH* are squares.
Find the area of the shaded region.

16. A 4.5 m by 6 m kitchen floor will be covered
with square vinyl tiles that are 30 cm on a side.
How many tiles will be needed?

17. A roofer is installing shingles on a rectangular roof that is
15 m by 18 m. A bundle of shingles will cover 93 m^2. How
many whole bundles will be needed for the job?

▶◀ Activity

If you take a square, cut it up and rearrange the pieces, does the area change?
(Try it and see.)

Draw a square 8 in. by 8 in. and then draw the lines as shown. Cut out the four
pieces and rearrange them to form a rectangle.

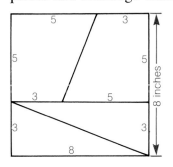

What is the area of the square?
What is the area of the rectangle?

▶ Extension Exercises

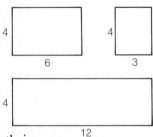

18. Find the area of each rectangle. What happens to the area of a rectangle if the width is constant and the length is halved? Doubled? Tripled?

19. What happens to the area of a rectangle if the length is constant and the width is halved? Doubled? Tripled?

20. A farmer has 220 m of fence available to enclose a rectangular area for his goat. What is the area of the largest rectangular region that he can enclose?

▶▶ Challenge Exercise

21. Draw several rectangles with the same length but different widths. Compare the ratio of the areas of two rectangles with the ratio of their widths. Compare other pairs of rectangles. What can you conclude? Explain how you know.

▶◀ Activity

The *golden rectangle*, discovered by the Greeks in the fifth century B.C., was thought to be one of the most beautifully proportioned geometric forms. The golden rectangle can be found in many art forms, including Greek temples and art masterpieces.

CONSTRUCTION OF A GOLDEN RECTANGLE

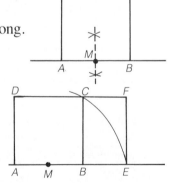

1. Construct square *ABCD* with sides several inches long.

2. Bisect $\overline{AB}$ and label this midpoint *M*.

3. Using *MC* as radius, draw an arc with *M* as the center. Extend the arc to intersect $\overleftrightarrow{AB}$ at *E*.

4. Construct $\overrightarrow{EF} \perp \overline{AE}$. Extend $\overline{DC}$ to meet $\overrightarrow{EF}$.

Quadrilateral *AEFD* is a golden rectangle. Measure the length and width of *AEFD*. Divide the length by the width to find the ratio. Your answer is the *golden ratio*.

Find the ratio of the length and width of quadrilateral *BEFC*. What can you conclude about *BEFC*?

3   Area of a Triangle

After finishing Section 3, you should be able to
▲   *find the area of a triangle.*
▲▲ *solve problems involving areas of triangles.*

▲ Finding the Area of a Triangle

A right triangle is "half" of a rectangle. Therefore, its area is half
the area of the rectangle.

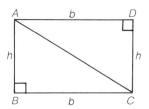

$$\triangle ABC \cong \triangle CDA \qquad \text{(SAS)}$$
$$\text{area } \triangle ABC = \text{area } \triangle CDA \qquad \text{(Postulate 15)}$$
$$\text{area } \triangle ABC = \tfrac{1}{2} \cdot \text{area } ABCD$$
$$= \tfrac{1}{2} \cdot b \cdot h$$

Any side of a triangle may be chosen as a **base.** For a chosen
base, a corresponding altitude can be found.

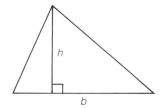 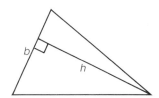 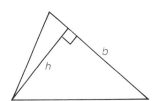

The area formula for right triangles also holds for other triangles.

THEOREM 12.2	The area of a triangle is one-half the product of a base and the corresponding altitude. Area $= \tfrac{1}{2} bh$	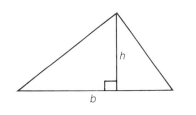

Examples   Find the area of each triangle.

1.

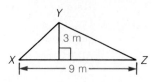

Area $\triangle XYZ = \frac{1}{2} \times 9 \times 3$
$= 13.5 \, \text{m}^2$

2.

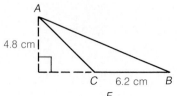

Area $\triangle ABC = \frac{1}{2} \times 6.2 \times 4.8$
$= 14.88 \, \text{cm}^2$

3.

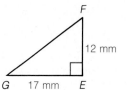

Area $\triangle GEF = \frac{1}{2} \times 17 \times 12$
$= 102 \, \text{mm}^2$

Try This...   Find the area of each triangle.

1.

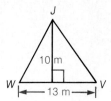

2.

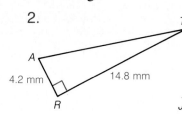

3.

Example   4. Area $\triangle DEF = 144 \, \text{m}^2$. What is
the length of the base of $\triangle DEF$?

Area $\triangle DEF = \frac{1}{2} bh$
$144 = \frac{1}{2} \cdot b \cdot 16$
$144 = 8b$
$18 = b$

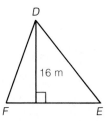

The corresponding base is $\overline{FE}$ and $FE = 18$ m.

Try This...   4. Area $\triangle ABC = 18 \, \text{cm}^2$ and $\overline{AB}$ is the
base of $\triangle ABC$. What is the altitude?

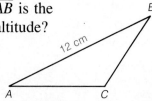

▲▲ Solving Problems

Example   5. Find the area of this equilateral triangle.

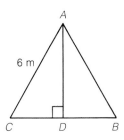

Because △ ABC is equilateral, altitude $\overline{AD}$ bisects $\overline{CB}$. Hence, $CD = 3$ m. By the Pythagorean Theorem,

$$3^2 + AD^2 = 6^2$$
$$AD^2 = 6^2 - 3^2$$
$$AD = 3\sqrt{3}\,\text{m}$$

$$\text{Area} \triangle ABC = \tfrac{1}{2} \times 6 \times 3\sqrt{3}$$
$$= 9\sqrt{3}\,\text{m}^2$$

Try This...   5. Find the area of △ DEF.

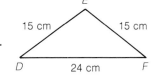

The following theorem is attributed to Hero, a mathematician who lived in Alexandria during the first century A.D. The theorem is known as Hero's Formula.

THEOREM **12.3**	The area of a triangle whose sides measure a, b, and c is $\sqrt{s(s - a)(s - b)(s - c)}$, where $s = \tfrac{1}{2}(a + b + c)$.

Example   6. Find the area of △ ABC.

$$s = \tfrac{1}{2}(4 + 5 + 6)$$
$$= 7.5\ \text{m}$$

$$\text{Area} \triangle ABC = \sqrt{7.5(7.5 - 4)(7.5 - 5)(7.5 - 6)}$$
$$= \sqrt{7.5 \times 3.5 \times 2.5 \times 1.5}$$
$$\approx \sqrt{98.44}$$
$$\approx 9.92\ \text{m}^2$$

Try This...   6. Find the area of △ NOP.

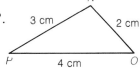

Exercises

▲ **Find the area of each triangle.**

1.

5 m

15 m

2.

7 cm

8 cm

3.

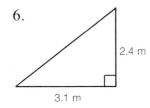

2√5 cm

4√5 cm

4.

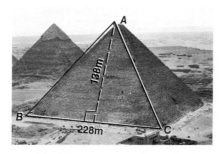

7.3 mm

8.9 mm

5.

4.5 m

6 m

6.

2.4 m

3.1 m

7.

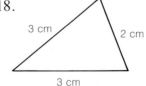

8.

Find the missing base or altitude for a triangle with the given measures.

9. $A = 72 \, \text{m}^2, h = 12 \, \text{m}$

10. $A = 48.4 \, \text{cm}^2, h = 4 \, \text{cm}$

11. $A = 15 \, \text{cm}^2, b = 2.5 \, \text{cm}$

12. $A = 7.2 \, \text{m}^2, b = 0.6 \, \text{m}$

13. $b = h, A = 18 \, \text{m}^2$

14. $b = h, A = 72 \, \text{cm}^2$

▲▲ 15. Find the area of an equilateral triangle whose sides are each 12 cm long.

16. Find the area of an equilateral triangle whose sides are each 14 cm long.

Use Hero's Formula to find the area of each triangle.

17.

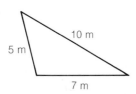

10 m

5 m

7 m

18.

3 cm

2 cm

3 cm

▶ Extension Exercises

Find the area of the shaded region.

19.

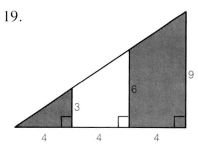

20. $\triangle ABC \sim \triangle DEF. GH = 8$,
$AD = 2, DC = 3$, and $CF = 4$.

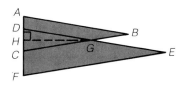

21. A parallelogram and a triangle have the same area. Their bases have the same measure. How are their altitudes related?

22. Derive a formula for the area of an equilateral triangle whose side has measure n.

23. Draw a square. Then construct a triangle whose area is equal to the area of the square. What are the dimensions of the triangle in relation to the square?

24. Draw a kite. The diagonals are 8 cm and 14 cm and are perpendicular bisectors of each other. Find the area of the kite.

▶▶ Challenge Exercises

25. Draw several triangles with congruent bases but different altitudes. Compare the ratio of the areas of two triangles with the ratio of their altitudes. Compare other pairs of triangles. What can you conclude? Explain how you know.

26. A median of a triangle divides the triangle into two triangular regions. What can you conclude about the areas of these two triangular regions? Explain how you know.

27. Compare the ratio of the areas of two similar triangles with the ratio of the corresponding altitudes. Explain how you know.

28. Medians $\overline{AF}, \overline{BD}$, and $\overline{CE}$ are concurrent at G, and determine six triangles. Compare the areas of these six triangles.

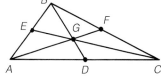

4 Area of a Parallelogram

After finishing Section 4, you should be able to
▲ *find the area of a parallelogram.*
▲▲ *solve problems involving areas of parallelograms.*

▲ Finding the Area of a Parallelogram

Any side of a parallelogram may be a **base**. Any segment that is perpendicular to the lines containing the base and the opposite side is a corresponding **altitude**.

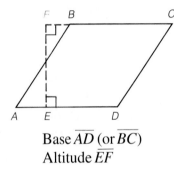

Base $\overline{AD}$ (or $\overline{BC}$)
Altitude $\overline{EF}$

Base $\overline{AB}$ (or $\overline{DC}$)
Altitude $\overline{GH}$

As with triangles, the base (b) and the altitude or height (h) refer to the lengths of these segments.

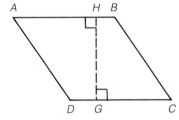

$$\text{Area } \square ABCD = \text{Area } \triangle ABD + \text{Area } \triangle CDB$$
$$= \tfrac{1}{2}bh \qquad + \tfrac{1}{2}bh$$
$$= \qquad bh$$

THEOREM 12.4	The area of a parallelogram is the product of a base and the corresponding altitude.
	$$\text{Area} = bh$$

Theorem 12.4 is also true for a rhombus because a rhombus is a parallelogram whose sides have the same length.

Here is another way to find the area of a rhombus.

THEOREM **12.5** The area of a rhombus is one-half the product of the lengths of its diagonals.

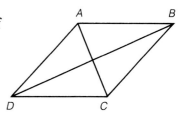

$$\text{Area} = \tfrac{1}{2} \cdot AC \cdot BD$$

Examples Find the area of each parallelogram.

1.

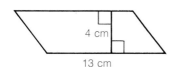

2.

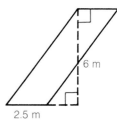

$$A = bh = 13 \times 4$$
$$= 52 \text{ cm}^2$$

$$A = 2.5 \times 6 = 15 \text{ m}^2$$

Try This... Find the area of each parallelogram.

1.

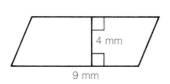

2.

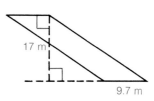

Example 3. Use the lengths of the diagonals to find the area of rhombus *ABCD*. *AC* = 12 cm and *BD* = 7 cm.

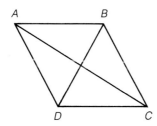

$$\text{Area } \square ABCD = \tfrac{1}{2} \cdot AC \cdot BD$$
$$= \tfrac{1}{2} \times 12 \times 7$$
$$= 42 \text{ cm}^2$$

Try This... 3. Use the lengths of the diagonals of rhombus *DEFG* to find its area. *DF* = 3.2 m and *GE* = 8 m.

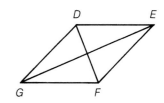

▲▲ Solving Problems

Example   4. Find the altitude of the rhombus.

$$A = bh$$
$$52.7 = 8.5\,h$$
$$\frac{52.7}{8.5} = h$$
$$6.2\,\text{cm} = h$$

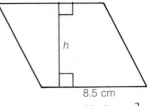

8.5 cm

Area = 52.7 cm^2

Try This...   4. Find the base of the parallelogram.

$A = 81$ dm^2

$h = 6$ dm

Example   5. Find the area of ▱$ABCD$.

Because △AEB is a 30°−60° right triangle,
$BE = \frac{1}{2}AB = \frac{1}{2} \times 6 = 3$ m.
$A = 8 \times 3 = 24$ m^2

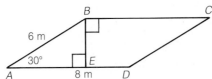

6 m   30°   B   E   C

A   8 m   D

Try This...   5. Find the area of ▱$MNOP$.

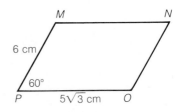

M   N

6 cm

60°

P   5√3 cm   O

Exercises

▲ **Find the area of each parallelogram from the given measures.**

1. $b = 7$ m, $h = 13$ m
2. $b = 8$ m, $h = 14$ m
3. $b = 1.2$ cm, $h = 5$ cm
4. $b = 7.3$ cm, $h = 3$ cm
5. $b = 70$ mm, $h = 58$ mm
6. $b = 120$ mm, $h = 70$ mm
7. $b = 2.5$ km, $h = 3.5$ km
8. $b = 5.25$ m, $h = 7.75$ m
9. $b = 5\sqrt{3}$ cm, $h = \sqrt{6}$ cm
10. $b = \sqrt{5}$ cm, $h = 2\sqrt{5}$ cm

Find the area of each rhombus.

11. $AC = 7\,\text{cm}, BD = 4.2\,\text{cm}$

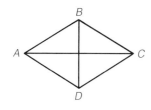

12. $LJ = 3\,\text{m}$
$HK = 5.2\,\text{m}$

▲▲ **Find the missing base or altitude of each parallelogram.**

13. $A = 2.25\,\text{m}^2, b = 1.5\,\text{m}$

14. $A = 120\,\text{mm}^2, h = 24\,\text{mm}$

15. $A = 175\,\text{cm}^2, h = 15\,\text{cm}$

16. $A = 5\sqrt{3}\,\text{m}^2, b = 5\sqrt{3}\,\text{m}$

Find the area of each parallelogram.

17.

18. $AE = ED = 6\,\text{cm}$

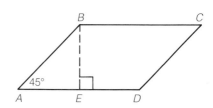

Find the area of the shaded region.

19. *ABCD* is a rectangle and
$DE = EC = BC$. *DEGF* and
ECJH are parallelograms.

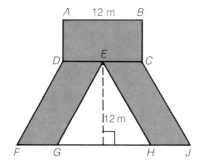

20. *ABCD* and *EFGH* are
parallelograms.

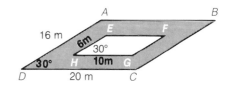

5 Area of a Trapezoid

After finishing Section 5, you should be able to
▲ *find the area of a trapezoid.*
▲▲ *solve problems involving areas of trapezoids.*

▲ Finding the Area of a Trapezoid

Every trapezoid can be divided into two triangles.

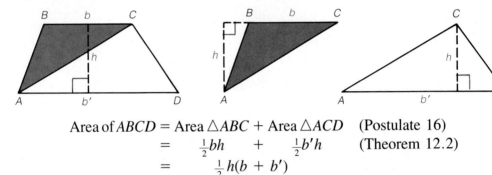

$$\begin{aligned}
\text{Area of } ABCD &= \text{Area } \triangle ABC + \text{Area } \triangle ACD && \text{(Postulate 16)} \\
&= \tfrac{1}{2}bh \quad + \quad \tfrac{1}{2}b'h && \text{(Theorem 12.2)} \\
&= \tfrac{1}{2}h(b + b')
\end{aligned}$$

THEOREM 12.6	The area of a trapezoid is one-half the product of the sum of its bases and the corresponding altitude.

$$A = \tfrac{1}{2}h(b + b')$$

Examples Find the area of each trapezoid.

1. $\text{Area of } ABCD = \tfrac{1}{2} \times 5 \times (12 + 16)$
    $= \tfrac{1}{2} \times 5 \times 28$
    $= 70 \text{ cm}^2$

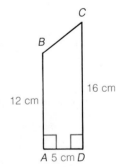

2. $\text{Area of } GHLK = \tfrac{1}{2}h(b + b')$
    $= \tfrac{1}{2} \times 4 \times (9 + 13)$
    $= \tfrac{1}{2} \times 4 \times 22$
    $= 44 \text{ m}^2$

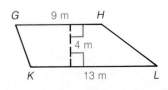

Try This...   Find the area of each trapezoid.

1.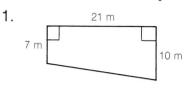

2.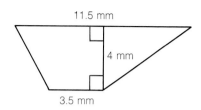

▲▲ Solving Problems

Example   3. The area of trapezoid *ABCE* is 104 m². *ABDE* is a square and
AE = 8 m. Find *AB* and *EC*.

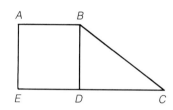

Because *ABDE* is a square, *AB* = 8 m and $\overline{AE}$ is
an altitude.

$$\text{Thus, the area of } ABCE = \tfrac{1}{2} AE(AB + EC)$$
$$104 = \tfrac{1}{2} \times 8(8 + EC)$$
$$104 = 32 + 4EC$$
$$18 = EC$$

Hence, *AB* = 8 m and *EC* = 18 m.

Try This...   3. The area of trapezoid *ABCD* is
234 cm². The altitude is 12 cm and
one base is twice as long as the
other base. Find *AB* and *DC*.

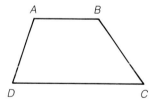

Example   4. In trapezoid *ABCD*, *m* ∠*CDA* = 60°, *BC* = 8 m, *CD* = 6 m,
and *AD* = 12 m. Find the area of *ABCD*.

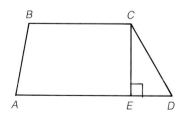

△*CED* is a 30°−60° right triangle.
Thus, *CE* = $\tfrac{6}{2}\sqrt{3}$ = $3\sqrt{3}$ m
Area of *ABCD* = $\tfrac{1}{2} \times 3\sqrt{3}(12 + 8)$
= $30\sqrt{3}$ m²

Try This...   4. In trapezoid *MNQP*, *m* ∠*MPQ* = 60°,
MN = 21 cm, *MP* = 8 cm, and
PQ = 18 cm. Find the area of *MNQP*.

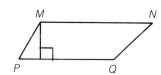

Exercises

▲ **Find the area of each trapezoid.**

1.

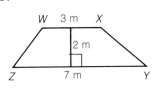

2.

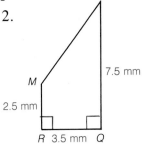

3.

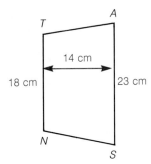

4.

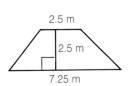

5.

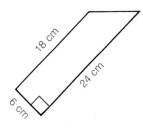

6.

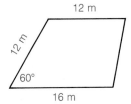

7.

8.

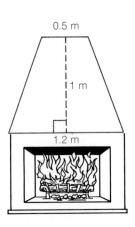

▲▲ **Find the missing base or altitude.**

9.

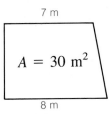

10.

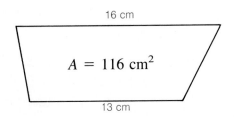

11.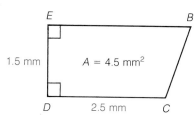

12.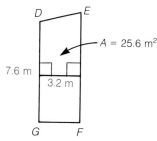

13. In trapezoid $ABCD$, $AB = 12$ m, $AD = 10$ m, $BC = 14$ m, and $m \angle ABC = 60°$. Find the area of $ABCD$.

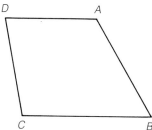

14. In isosceles trapezoid $RSTU$, $m \angle RUT = 45°$, $RS = 8$ m, and $UT = 16$ m. Find the area of $RSTU$.

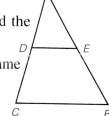

▶ Extension Exercises

15. D and E are midpoints of $\overline{AC}$ and $\overline{AB}$, respectively. Find the ratio of the areas of $\triangle ADE$ and trapezoid $CDEB$.

16. Draw a trapezoid, and then draw a rectangle with the same area as the trapezoid.

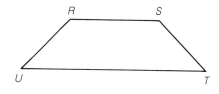

▶▶ Challenge Exercises

In 1876, while serving as a member of the United States House of Representatives, future President James A. Garfield published an original proof of the Pythagorean Theorem by comparing the area of a trapezoid (like the one shown below) with the areas of the three triangles.

17. Find the area of the trapezoid.

18. What is the measure of $\overline{EB}$?

19. What is the measure of $\angle AEB$?

20. Find the sum of the areas of the three triangles and compare it with the area of the trapezoid. Explain how this shows that the Pythagorean Theorem is true.

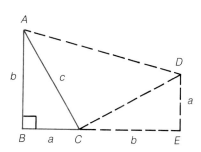

6 | Area of a Regular Polygon

After finishing Section 6, you should be able to
▲ *apply the formula for the area of a regular polygon.*

We shall begin with a definition.

DEFINITION

A perpendicular segment from center O to any side of the regular polygon is called an *apothem* (ap'-ə-thĕm´) of the regular polygon.

A segment from center O to any vertex is called a *radius* of the regular polygon.

$\overline{OA}$ is an **apothem**.
$\overline{OB}$ is a **radius**.

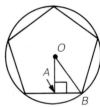

1. Draw a circle. Use a protractor and straightedge to draw a regular pentagon. s = length of each side and a = length of each apothem. Find the perimeter of the pentagon.

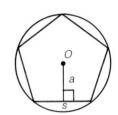

2. Connect center O to each vertex. How many triangles are formed by pentagon *ABCDE*? Why are these triangles congruent? Express the area of each triangle in terms of a and s.

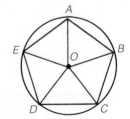

What is the area of pentagon *ABCDE*? Express the area in terms of the perimeter ($p = 5s$) and the length of the apothem, a.

> **THEOREM 12.7** The area of a regular polygon is one-half the product of its perimeter and the length of an apothem.
>
> $$\text{Area} = \tfrac{1}{2}ap$$

Examples 1. Find the area of this regular hexagon.

$$p = 6 \times 8 = 48 \text{ cm}$$
$$A = \tfrac{1}{2} \times 4\sqrt{3} \times 48$$
$$= 96\sqrt{3} \text{ cm}^2$$

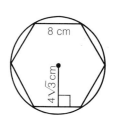

2. Find the area of this regular pentagon.

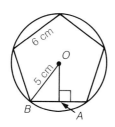

Thus,

$$OA^2 = OB^2 - BA^2$$
$$= 25 - 9$$
$$= 16$$
$$OA = 4$$
$$A = \tfrac{1}{2} \times 4 \times 30$$
$$= 60 \text{ cm}^2$$

Try This... Find the area of these regular polygons.

1.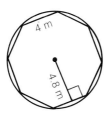

2.

Exercises

▲ **Find the area of each regular polygon.**

1.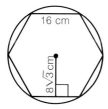

2.

3.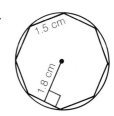

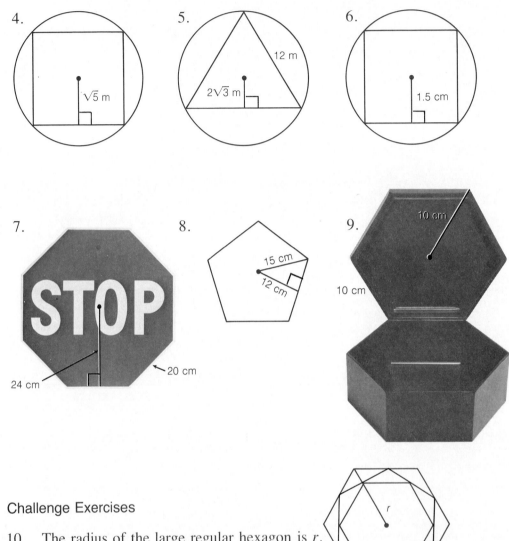

4. $\sqrt{5}$ m

5. 12 m $2\sqrt{3}$ m

6. 1.5 cm

7. 24 cm 20 cm

8. 15 cm 12 cm

9. 10 cm 10 cm

▶▶ Challenge Exercises

10. The radius of the large regular hexagon is r. Find the area of each of the three hexagons in terms of r.

11. Consider two regular polygons with the same number of sides. Set up a proportion between the areas of the two polygons and the measures of a side of each polygon.

12. Consider two regular polygons with the same number of sides. Set up a proportion between the areas of the two polygons and the measures of their apothems.

Consumer Application   Estimating Amounts of Paint

Many people decide to do their own painting rather than to contract
the job with a professional painter. To estimate the amount of paint
to buy, follow these rules:

> Find the area of the surface to be painted.

> Double the area if painting a light color over a dark color.

> Estimate the amount of paint if 1 gallon covers about 400 ft² and 1 quart covers about 100 ft².

Example   Estimate the amount of paint needed for this room:

Den: 16 ft × 18 ft
ceiling: 9 ft
2 doors: 7 ft × 3 ft
2 windows: 4 ft × 4 ft
paint: dark color over light color

First find the area of the surface to be painted.

$(16 + 18 + 16 + 18) \times 9 = 612$ Multiply the room's perimeter by the ceiling's
height to give you the area of all four walls.

$16 \times 18 = 288$ Multiply to find the area of the ceiling.

$612 + 288 = 900$ Add to find the total area.

$(7 \times 3) \times 2 = 42$
$(4 \times 4) \times 2 = 32$ Multiply to find the area of the doors
and windows.

$900 - (42 + 32) = 826$ Subtract the area of the doors and windows
from the total area to find the area to be painted.
(Note: We do not double the area because
we are not painting a light over a dark color.)

$826 \div 400 = 2\,r\,26$ Divide to find how many gallons and quarts
of paint are needed.

About 2 gallons and 1 quart of paint are needed.

Estimate the amount of paint needed for each room.

1. Living room: 17 ft × 20 ft
ceiling: 10 ft
2 doors: 7 ft × 4 ft
1 window: 4 ft × 8 ft
paint: light over dark

2. Bathroom: 8 ft × 8 ft
ceiling: 8 ft
1 door: 7 ft × 3 ft
1 window: 2 ft × 3 ft
paint: same color

3. Kitchen: 10 ft × 12 ft
ceiling: 8 ft
2 doors: 7 ft × 4 ft
2 windows: 3 ft × 4 ft
paint: dark over light

Chapter Review

1 1. *ABCDEF* is a regular hexagon.
Area △*AGF* = 13.
Find the area of the hexagon.

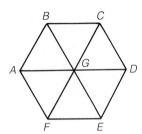

2 2. Find the width of a rectangle if
$A = 4.5$ m^2 and $\ell = 2.5$ m.

3. Find the area of the shaded region.

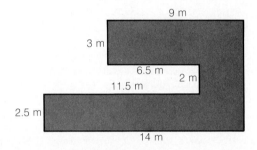

4. Three sides of a shower will be tiled with square tiles that are
10 cm on a side. The width of the wall behind the tub is
1.5 m. The width of the wall at each end of the tub is 70 cm.
The height of the walls to be tiled is 2 m. How many tiles are
needed?

3 **Find the area of each triangle.**

5.

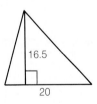

6.

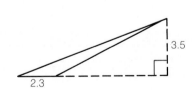

7.

8.

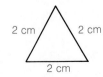

4 **Find the area of each parallelogram.**

9.

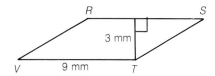

10.

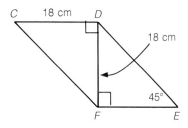

11. Find the base of □*GHJK*.
    Area = 48.75 mm².

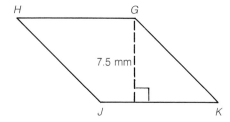

12. *ABCD* and *WXYZ* are parallelograms.
    Find the area of the shaded region.

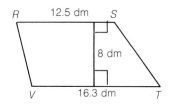

5 **Find the area of each trapezoid.**

13.

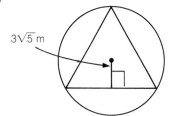

14.

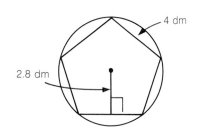

15. The area of a trapezoid is 9 m². The bases are $2\sqrt{3}$ m and $4\sqrt{3}$ m. Find the altitude.

6 **Find the area of each regular polygon.**

16.

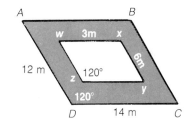

17.

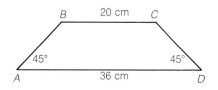

Chapter Test

1. All triangles in the figure are congruent. The area of each small square is 4 cm². Find the area of the figure.

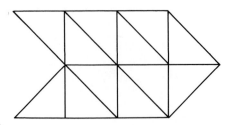

2. Find the length of a rectangle if $A = 3.6$ cm² and $w = 0.4$ cm.

3. Find the area of the shaded region.

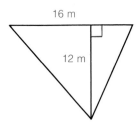
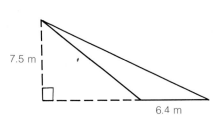

4. A kitchen floor measuring 4 m by 6 m will be tiled with square tiles that are 30 cm on a side. How many tiles are needed?

Find the area of each triangle.

5.

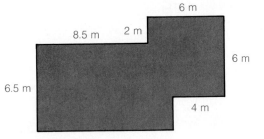

7.5 m

6.4 m

6.

16 m

12 m

7.

5 cm   5 cm

6 cm

8.

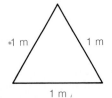

1 m   1 m

1 m

Find the area of each parallelogram.

9.

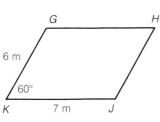

10.

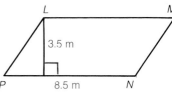

11. Area $\square WXYZ = 5,040$ mm².
    Find the base.

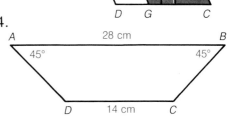

12. *ABCD* and *EFGD* are parallelograms.
    $\overline{AE} \cong \overline{ED}$ and $DG = \frac{1}{3}DC$. Find the area
    of the shaded region.

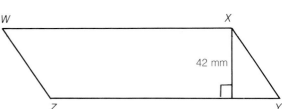

Find the area of each trapezoid.

13.

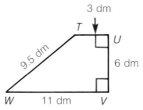

14.

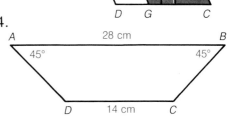

15. The area of a trapezoid is 16 m². The bases are $3\sqrt{2}$ m and
    $5\sqrt{2}$ m. Find the altitude.

Find the area of each regular polygon.

16.

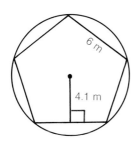

17.

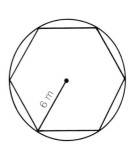

Skills Review — Multiplying and Dividing Fractions

Multiply and simplify.

1. $\dfrac{1}{5} \times \dfrac{1}{3}$

2. $\dfrac{2}{7} \times \dfrac{1}{4}$

3. $5 \times \dfrac{3}{8}$

4. $\dfrac{1}{5} \times \dfrac{5}{9}$

5. $\dfrac{2}{3} \times 8$

6. $\dfrac{3}{10} \times \dfrac{7}{8}$

7. $9 \times \dfrac{5}{11}$

8. $\dfrac{1}{2} \times \dfrac{5}{6}$

9. $\dfrac{3}{6} \times \dfrac{1}{3}$

10. $\dfrac{4}{7} \times \dfrac{7}{4}$

11. $30 \times \dfrac{1}{5}$

12. $\dfrac{5}{8} \times 64$

13. $\dfrac{15}{6} \times \dfrac{8}{5}$

14. $\dfrac{11}{9} \times \dfrac{3}{22}$

15. $\dfrac{3}{16} \times \dfrac{12}{13}$

16. $\dfrac{7}{2} \times \dfrac{7}{21}$

17. $3 \times 4\dfrac{1}{2}$

18. $3\dfrac{2}{3} \times \dfrac{1}{11}$

19. $5\dfrac{1}{3} \times \dfrac{3}{8}$

20. $2\dfrac{1}{2} \times \dfrac{5}{2}$

21. $1\dfrac{3}{5} \times \dfrac{5}{8}$

22. $1\dfrac{1}{3} \times \dfrac{1}{4}$

23. $4\dfrac{1}{2} \times \dfrac{3}{4}$

24. $6\dfrac{1}{5} \times 10$

Divide and simplify.

25. $\dfrac{1}{3} \div \dfrac{1}{6}$

26. $\dfrac{1}{2} \div \dfrac{1}{8}$

27. $\dfrac{5}{12} \div \dfrac{5}{12}$

28. $\dfrac{3}{8} \div 3$

29. $12 \div \dfrac{1}{6}$

30. $\dfrac{1}{10} \div \dfrac{3}{5}$

31. $\dfrac{2}{9} \div \dfrac{9}{2}$

32. $\dfrac{5}{9} \div 8$

33. $\dfrac{22}{7} \div \dfrac{11}{14}$

34. $10 \div \dfrac{5}{7}$

35. $\dfrac{6}{5} \div \dfrac{1}{6}$

36. $\dfrac{7}{8} \div \dfrac{3}{2}$

37. $1\dfrac{1}{2} \div 4$

38. $7 \div 3\dfrac{1}{2}$

39. $2\dfrac{3}{5} \div \dfrac{1}{3}$

40. $\dfrac{3}{4} \div \dfrac{1}{6}$

41. $8\dfrac{1}{2} \div 3\dfrac{1}{4}$

42. $13 \div 3\dfrac{1}{4}$

43. $100 \div 33\dfrac{1}{3}$

44. $5\dfrac{1}{4} \div 21$

45. $6\dfrac{2}{5} \div 4$

46. $3\dfrac{5}{6} \div \dfrac{3}{4}$

47. $2\dfrac{1}{2} \div 7\dfrac{6}{7}$

48. $\dfrac{1}{2} \div 3\dfrac{2}{3}$

Cumulative Review: Chapters 9–12

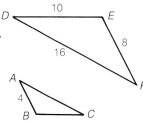

9–1   1.   Solve the proportion. Find what y represents.

$$\frac{25}{y} = \frac{75}{12}$$

9–2   2. $\triangle ABC \sim \triangle DEF$. Find AC and BC.

9–3   3.   In $\triangle XYZ$, $\angle XRS \cong \angle XZY$, $XZ = 8$,
           $RZ = 5$, and $ZY = 14$. Find RS.

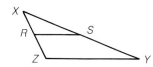

9–4   4.   In $\triangle JKL$, $\overset{\leftrightarrow}{MN} \parallel \overline{JL}$, $LN = 30$, $LK = 45$,
           and $MK = 6$. Find KJ.

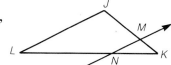

9–5   5. $\dfrac{DC}{CB} = \dfrac{CE}{CA}$.

           What can you conclude?

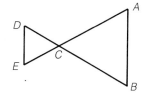

6.   *P* is the midpoint of
    $\overline{TS}$, *Q* is the midpoint of $\overline{XZ}$,
    $\angle X \cong \angle S$, and $\angle T \cong \angle Z$.

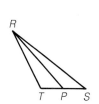
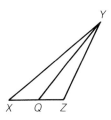

    What can you conclude about $\dfrac{RS}{XY}$ and $\dfrac{PS}{XQ}$? Explain how you know.

10–1   7.   Find the geometric mean of 6 and 8.

8. $MN = 35$ and $MQ = 14$. Find PQ.

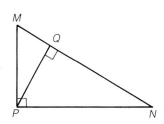

10–2

9. Find c.

10. Find a.

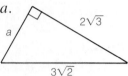

10–3

11. Can 6, 13, and 14 be the lengths of the sides of a right triangle?

12. Can 15, 20, and 25 be the lengths of the sides of a right triangle?

10–4

Find the missing lengths in each triangle.

13.

14.

11–1

Classify each polygon by the number of sides and tell whether it is convex or concave.

15.

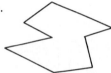

16.

11–2

17. Find the number of diagonals in a dodecagon.

18. Find the perimeter of the shaded region. All angles are right angles.

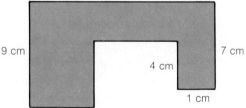

11–3

19. Find the sum of the angle measures of a convex hexagon.

11–4

20. Draw a scalene triangle and find its circumcenter.

21. Draw an obtuse isosceles triangle and find its centroid.

11–5

22. Hexagon $ABCDEF$ ~ hexagon $GHJKLM$. Find HJ and LM.

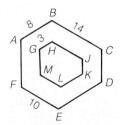

11–6 23. Find the measure of each interior angle of a regular dodecagon.

12–2 24. Find the area of the shaded region.

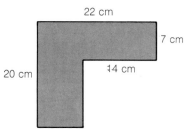
22 cm
7 cm
20 cm
14 cm

25. Find the length of a rectangle if $A = 18.75 \text{ m}^2$ and $w = 2.5 \text{ m}$.

26. A bundle of shingles covers 2.5 m^2 of roof. Find the total area of the roof and the number of bundles of shingles needed to cover the roof.

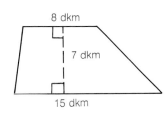
8.5 m
6 m
6 m

12–3
12–4

Find the area of each figure.

12–5 27.

25
9.5
13.25

28.

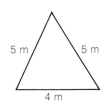
5 m
5 m
4 m

29.

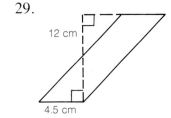
12 cm
4.5 cm

30.

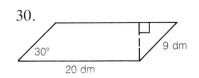
30°
9 dm
20 dm

31.

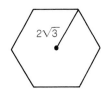
8 dkm
7 dkm
15 dkm

12–5 32. The area of a trapezoid is 168 m^2. The altitude is 7 m and one base is $\frac{5}{7}$ as long as the other base. Find the length of each base.

12–6 33. Find the area of this regular hexagon.

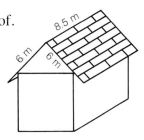
$2\sqrt{3}$

13
Circles

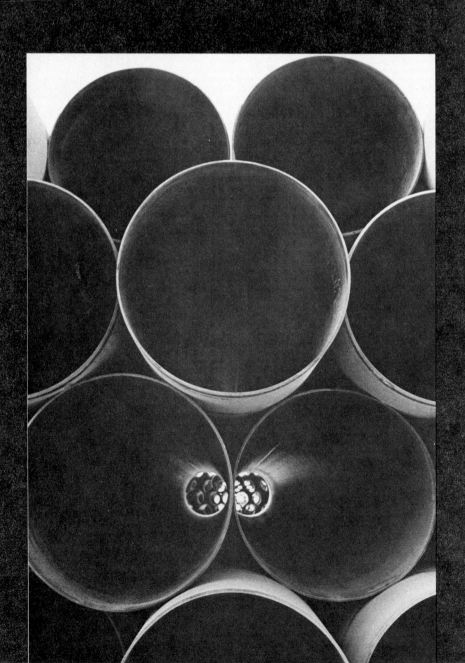

1   Circles and Chords

After finishing Section 1, you should be able to
▲   *identify radii, diameters, and chords of circles.*
▲▲   *solve problems involving radii and diameters.*

▲   Some Basic Definitions

A circle is a familiar figure.

DEFINITION

A **circle** is a set of all points in a plane a given distance (r) from a given point (O) in the plane. Point O is called the *center* of the circle.

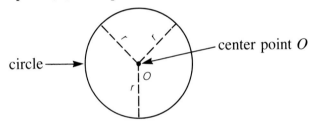

We will refer to this circle as $\odot O$ because O is the center. Here are some important segments associated with circles.

Term	Definition	Picture
Radius	A segment whose endpoints are the center of the circle and a point on the circle. The length of this segment is also called the radius.	
Chord	A segment with both endpoints on the circle.	
Diameter	A chord containing the center of the circle. The length of this segment is also called the diameter.	

Example   1. The center of this circle is *O*. Identify
all radii, chords, and diameters shown.

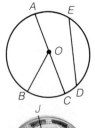

Radii: $\overline{OA}, \overline{OB}, \overline{OC}$
Chords: $\overline{DE}$ and $\overline{AC}$
Diameters: $\overline{AC}$

Try This...   1. Identify all radii, diameters, and
chords shown in this photograph.

▲▲ Radii and Diameters

1.   Draw a circle with a radius of 3 cm.

2.   Draw several diameters and radii.

3.   Measure the diameters and the radii. Compare their lengths.

THEOREM 13.1	All radii of a circle are congruent.
THEOREM 13.2	A diameter of a circle is twice the length of a radius of the circle. $$d = 2r$$

Examples   2. In ⊙*O*, *D-O-T* and *DT* = 16. Find *OK* and *OQ*.

Because $\overline{DT}$ is a diameter, its length is
twice that of a radius. Hence, *OK* = 8
and *OQ* = 8.

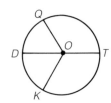

3. The length of a radius is 9.5. Find the length
of a diameter of the same circle.

$$d = 2r$$
$$= 2 \times 9.5 = 19$$

Try This... 2. The length of a diameter is 17. Find the length of a radius of the same circle.

3. The length of a radius is 4.6. Find the length of a diameter of the same circle.

Exercises

▲ **Identify all radii, chords, and diameters in each circle.**

1.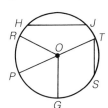

2.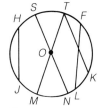

▲▲ **For each diameter, find the length of the radius.**

3. 82.6
4. 75.4 cm
5. $4\frac{3}{4}$

6. 21 mm
7. 0.243
8. 0.056 m

For each radius, find the length of a diameter.

9. 8.7
10. $4\frac{1}{8}$
11. 0.08

12. 4.5 m
13. 1.9 cm
14. 1.1 cm

▶ Extension Exercises

15. $\overline{AB}$ and $\overline{CD}$ are diameters. What must be true of figure *ABCD*? Explain how you know.

16. $\overline{OG}$ and $\overline{OT}$ are radii. What can you conclude about $\angle OGT$ and $\angle OTG$? Explain how you know.

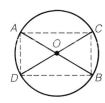

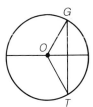

▶▶ Challenge Exercises

17. Explain why a diameter is the longest chord of a circle. (*Hint:* Consider the circle shown and use the triangle inequality.)

18. Write a definition for the interior of a circle.

2	More About Chords

After finishing Section 2, you should be able to
▲ *find the length of a chord given the radius and distance from the center.*
▲▲ *find the distance of a chord from the center given its length and the radius.*
▲▲ *find the radius of a circle given the length of a chord and its distance from the center.*
♠♠ *find the center of a circle.*

▲ Finding the Length of a Chord

Chords of circles have some special properties.

1. Draw a circle and several chords. Draw a perpendicular from the center of the circle to each chord. Where does the perpendicular intersect each chord?

2. Draw a circle and several chords. Draw a radius containing the midpoint of each chord. What kind of angle is formed by the intersection of the radius and the chord?

THEOREM 13.3	If a radius of a circle is perpendicular to a chord, then it bisects the chord.

The converse of this theorem is also true.

THEOREM 13.4	If a radius of a circle bisects a chord, then it is perpendicular to the chord.

Examples 1. $\overline{OM} \perp \overline{AB}$ and $AM = 3$. Find AB.

Because $\overline{OM} \perp \overline{AB}$, M is the midpoint of $\overline{AB}$ by Theorem 13.3. Thus, $AB = 2AM = 2 \times 3 = 6$.

2. Find the length of chord $\overline{AB}$.

By the Pythagorean Theorem,
$AM^2 + 4^2 = 5^2$. So, $AM = 3$.
Because M is a midpoint, $AB = 6$.

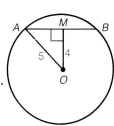

Try This...   Find the length of chord $\overline{AB}$.

1.

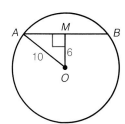

2.

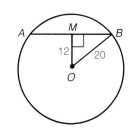

▲▲ Finding a Chord's Distance from the Center

A chord's distance from the center of a circle depends on the
length of the chord and the radius of the circle.

Example   3. Find the distance of chord $\overline{AB}$ from
the center of the circle.

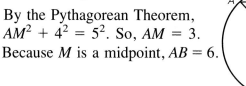

The distance from $\overline{AB}$ to the center is
OM, the length of the perpendicular
from $\overline{AB}$ to O.

This means $\triangle AMO$ is a right triangle.

So, we have $OM^2 + 12^2 = 13^2$
$$OM^2 = 13^2 - 12^2 = 25$$
$$OM = 5$$

The distance from chord $\overline{AB}$ to the center O is 5.

Try This...   3. Find the distance from chord $\overline{RT}$ to
the center of the circle.

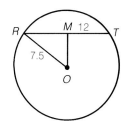

Finding the Radius of a Circle

If we know the length of a chord and its distance from the center
of a circle, we can find the radius.

Example 4. The length of chord $\overline{CD}$ is 24, and its distance from O is 9.
Find the radius of $\odot O$.

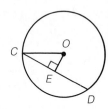

Because $\overline{OE} \perp \overline{CD}$, $\triangle OEC$ is a right triangle. We also know $CE = 12$.

So, $OC^2 = 9^2 + 12^2$
$= 225$

and $OC = 15$.

The radius of the circle is 15.

Try This... 4. The length of chord $\overline{XY}$ is 20, and its
distance from O is 7.5. Find the radius
of $\odot O$.

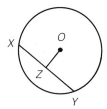

 Finding the Center of a Circle

Because there is only one perpendicular to a chord at its midpoint, we
have the following corollary.

COROLLARY **13.5**	The perpendicular bisector of a chord of a circle contains the center of the circle.

Example 5. Find the center of this circle.

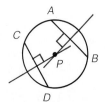

Draw any two chords $\overline{AB}$ and $\overline{CD}$. Draw the
perpendicular bisector of each chord. Because
the center of the circle lies on both bisectors,
it is the point at which they meet, P.

Try This... 5. Trace around a coin. Then use chords to find the center of the circle.

Exercises

▲ **Find the length of each chord.**

1.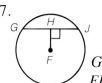

2.

3.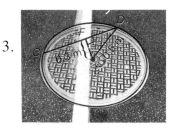

▲▲ **Find the distance of each chord from the center of the circle.**

4.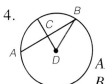

$AB = 2.4$
$BD = 1.3$

5.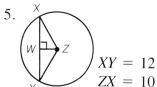

$XY = 12$
$ZX = 10$

6.

▲
▲▲ **Find the radius of each circle.**

7.

$GJ = 32$
$FH = 12$

8.

$AC = 3.2$
$DB = 1.2$

9.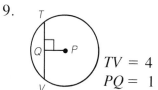

$TV = 4$
$PQ = 1$

▲▲
▲▲ 10. Trace around a half-dollar. Draw the perpendicular bisectors of two chords to locate the center of the circle. Test the accuracy of your drawing with a compass.

11. Repeat Exercise 10 by tracing around a can.

▶ **Extension Exercises**

12. Explain how a carpenter can find the center of a circular piece of wood using only a carpenter's square.

13. An engineer needs to find the radius of a circular railroad curve from these measurements: $AB = 200$ m, $CD = 40$ m, and $\overline{CD}$ is the perpendicular bisector of $\overline{AB}$. What is the radius of the circle that contains $\overset{\frown}{ADB}$?

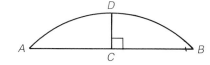

14. The diameter of a circle is 26 cm. A chord is perpendicular to a radius at a point 8 cm from its outer point. What is the length of the chord?

15. If a chord is the same length as a radius of a circle, what is the distance of the chord from the center of the circle?

16. A diameter of a circle bisects one of two parallel chords. Where does it intersect the other chord? Explain how you know.

17. O is the center of a circle, $\overline{AB}$ is a chord, C is on the circle, and $\overleftrightarrow{OC} \perp \overleftrightarrow{AB}$. What can you conclude about $\overline{AC}$ and $\overline{CB}$? Explain how you know.

18. $\overline{AB} \cong \overline{BC}$. What must be true of the bisector of $\angle ABC$? Explain how you know.

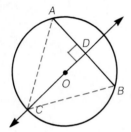

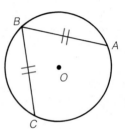

▶▶ Challenge Exercise

19. Explain why every three non-collinear points are on some circle.

▶◀ Activity

Trace a jar lid or other circle and cut it out. Fold the circle upon itself and crease. Open the circle and fold upon itself again to create a different crease. Open the circle.

What is the point of intersection of these two creases?

| **3** | Congruent Circles |

After finishing Section 3, you should be able to
▲ *solve problems involving chords and radii*
of congruent circles.

All circles have the same shape. Their size
depends on their radii.

DEFINITION

Congruent circles are circles with
congruent radii.

We write: $\odot A \cong \odot C$.

1. Draw two congruent circles, O_1 and O_2. In O_1 draw a
    chord $\overline{AB}$. In O_2 draw a chord $\overline{PQ}$ such that $\overline{AB} \cong \overline{PQ}$.
    Find the distances from O_1 to $\overline{AB}$ and from O_2 to $\overline{PQ}$.

2. In O_1 draw a chord $\overline{DF}$ such that $\overline{DF} \cong \overline{AB}$. Find the
    distance from O_1 to $\overline{DF}$.

3. What can you conclude about the distance from the center
    to congruent chords?

| THEOREM **13.6** | If chords of a circle (or congruent circles) are congruent, then they are equidistant from the center(s). |

The converse of Theorem 13.6 is also true.

| THEOREM **13.7** | If chords of a circle (or congruent circles) are equidistant from the center(s), then the chords are congruent. |

Examples 1. $\overline{AB} \cong \overline{CD}$, $\odot O \cong \odot P$, and $OM = 4$. Find PN.

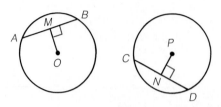

By Theorem 13.6, congruent chords of congruent circles are equidistant from the center. So, $OM = PN = 4$.

2. $RS = 11$. Find PT.

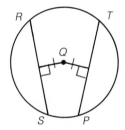

By Theorem 13.7, chords of a circle are congruent if they are equidistant from the center. So, $RS = PT = 11$.

Try This... 1. $AB = 9$. Find CD.

2. $\odot P \cong \odot K$, $\overline{MN} \cong \overline{JL}$, and $PQ = 3.4$. Find KH.

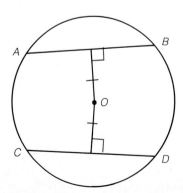

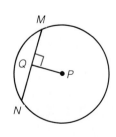

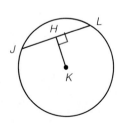

Example **▲3.** Find *AB* and *CD*.

By Theorem 13.7, chords of a circle are congruent if they are equidistant from the center. Thus,

$$3x - 2 = x + 6$$
$$2x = 8$$
$$x = 4$$

Hence, *AB* = *CD* = 10.

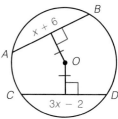

Try This... **▲3.** $\overline{AB} \cong \overline{CD}$. Find *OE* and *OF*.

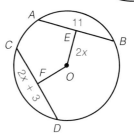

Exercises

▲ **Find each length.**

1. $\odot P \cong \odot T$, $\overline{QS} \cong \overline{VX}$, and $PR = 9$. Find *TW*.

2. $\odot A \cong \odot G$, $\overline{BD} \cong \overline{ML}$, and $GN = 3.15$. Find *AC*.

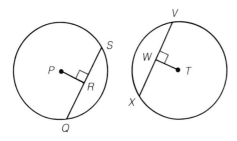

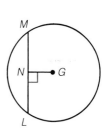

3. $EF = 23.5$. Find *BD*.

4. $JS = 9\frac{1}{4}$. Find *KR*.

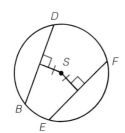

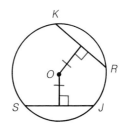

For each pair of circles, find the lengths of the other segments.

5. $HG = 10, AC = 8$, and
   $\triangle FCB \cong \triangle GJH$.

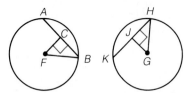

6. $DL = 12, MJ = 9$, and
   $\triangle KLE \cong \triangle JMF$.

7. $SP = 10, MN = 24$, and
   $\triangle PSR \cong \triangle QNM$.

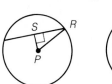

8. $AD = 20, HG = 16$, and
   $\triangle EGF \cong \triangle DBA$.

Find the length of each chord and its distance from the center.

▲9.

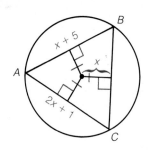

▲10.

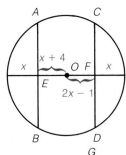

Use the figure for Exercises 11–12.
Assume G-O-H and $\overline{AB} \cong \overline{DC}$.

11. $OE = 8, OD = 12$. Find OF.

12. $OA = 20, \overline{OG}$ bisects $\angle AOB$ and
    $m \angle AOB = 120°$. Find EG.

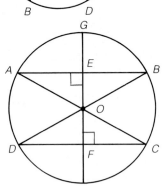

▶ Extension Exercises

13. Consider *all* the chords of a circle that are the same length.
    Describe the set of midpoints of these chords.

14. Chords $\overline{AB}$, $\overline{BC}$, and $\overline{CA}$ are equidistant from the center of the circle. What kind of triangle is $\triangle ABC$? Explain how you know.

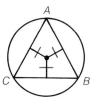

15. Suppose that $\odot O \cong \odot P$, and corresponding chords are equidistant from their centers. How are $\triangle ABC$ and $\triangle DEF$ related? Explain how you know.

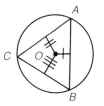 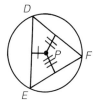

16. The front view of the color television tube shows the shape of the fluorescent screen that produces the image on a television screen. It is designed so that $\overline{AB}$ and $\overline{CD}$ are equidistant from the center of the tube, $\overline{AB} \parallel \overline{CD}$, and $\overline{BC}$ is a diameter. Explain why $\overline{AB} \cong \overline{CD}$ and $\overline{AC} \cong \overline{BD}$.

▶▶ Challenge Exercises

17. In $\odot O$, $\overline{AB} \cong \overline{CD}$. Explain why $\overline{PB} \cong \overline{PD}$.

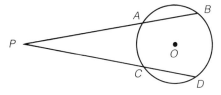

18. $\overline{AB} \cong \overline{CD}$, and $\overline{EF}$ is a diameter. Explain why $\angle AGE \cong \angle DGE$.

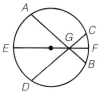

▶◀ Activity

Draw a circle with a radius of 10 cm and cut it out. Label the center M. Fold the circle so that the circle's edge falls on M. Unfold the paper. Make more folds in the same manner. Describe the pattern made by the folds.

4   Angles and Arcs

After finishing Section 4, you should be able to
▲   *identify minor arcs, major arcs, and semicircles.*
▲▲   *find the degree measure of an arc.*
▲▲▲   *solve problems involving the degree measure of an arc.*

▲ Arcs

A rainbow is an example of a circular arc.
Arcs are related to *central angles*.

___

DEFINITION
___

A **central angle** is an angle whose vertex is the center of a circle.

∠*AOB* is a central angle.

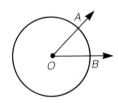

Some special types of arcs are defined in the chart.

___

Minor Arc	Major Arc	Semicircle
		$\overline{AB}$ is a diameter.
Minor arc $\overset{\frown}{AB}$	Major arc $\overset{\frown}{ACB}$	$\overset{\frown}{ACB}$ or $\overset{\frown}{ADB}$

___

Example   1. $\overline{AC}$ and $\overline{BD}$ are diameters of ⊙*O*. Name the minor and major arcs and semicircles.

Minor arcs: $\overset{\frown}{AB}$, $\overset{\frown}{BC}$, $\overset{\frown}{CD}$, and $\overset{\frown}{DA}$

Major arcs: $\overset{\frown}{ADB}$ (or $\overset{\frown}{ACB}$), $\overset{\frown}{BAC}$ (or $\overset{\frown}{BDC}$), $\overset{\frown}{DCA}$ (or $\overset{\frown}{DBA}$), and $\overset{\frown}{DAC}$ (or $\overset{\frown}{DBC}$).

Semicircles: $\overset{\frown}{DAB}$, $\overset{\frown}{DCB}$, $\overset{\frown}{ABC}$, and $\overset{\frown}{ADC}$.

Try This...   1. $\overline{DE}$ is a diameter of $\odot O$. Name the minor
           and major arcs and semicircles.

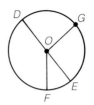

▲▲ Degree Measure of Arcs

For any arc $\overset{\frown}{ACB}$, the degree measure $m\overset{\frown}{ACB}$ is the same as
that of the measure of a central angle as defined in the table.

Minor arc	Semicircle	Major arc
$m\overset{\frown}{ACB} = m\angle AOB$ or $m\overset{\frown}{AB} = m\angle AOB$ $m\overset{\frown}{AB} < 180°$	$m\overset{\frown}{ACB} = 180°$	$m\overset{\frown}{ACB} = 360° - m\angle AOB$ $m\overset{\frown}{ACB} > 180°$

Examples   2. Find $m\overset{\frown}{AB}$.

$m\overset{\frown}{AB} = 42°$ because $m\angle AOB = 42°$.

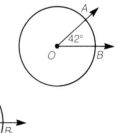

3. Find $m\overset{\frown}{ADB}$.

$m\overset{\frown}{ADB} = 360 - m\angle AOB$
$\qquad = 360 - 118$
$\qquad = 242°$

Try This...   2. Find $m\overset{\frown}{RS}$.   3.   Find $m\overset{\frown}{PRQ}$.

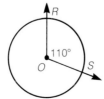

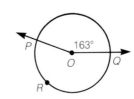

Using Degree Measures

1. Draw a circle with two adjacent central angles.
2. Measure ∠ *AOB* and ∠ *BOC*.
3. Find $m\widehat{AB}$ and $m\widehat{BC}$.
4. Find $m\widehat{ABC}$.

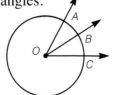

POSTULATE
18

The Arc Addition Postulate
If *C* is on $\widehat{AB}$, then $m\widehat{AC} + m\widehat{CB} = m\widehat{AB}$.

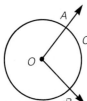

Example   4. $m\widehat{RS} = 24°$ and $m\widehat{ST} = 130°$.
Find $m\widehat{RST}$ and $m\widehat{RXT}$.

$$m\widehat{RST} = m\widehat{RS} + m\widehat{ST} \qquad m\widehat{RXT} = 360 - m\widehat{RST}$$
$$= 24 + 130 \qquad\qquad\quad = 360 - 154$$
$$= 154° \qquad\qquad\qquad\quad = 206°$$

Try This...   4. $m\widehat{AB} = 37°$ and $m\widehat{BC} = 80°$.
Find $m\widehat{ABC}$ and $m\widehat{ADC}$.

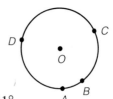

Example   5. $\overline{TP}$ and $\overline{GH}$ are diameters and $m\widehat{GP} = 81°$.
Find $m \angle TOH$, $m\widehat{TH}$, and $m\widehat{TG}$.

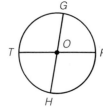

$m\widehat{GP} = 81°$. This means $m \angle GOP = 81°$. The Vertical Angle
Theorem tells us that $m \angle TOH$ is also $81°$. Thus, $m\widehat{TH} = 81°$.
$\overline{GH}$ is a diameter, so $m\widehat{HTG} = 180°$. Thus,

$$m\widehat{TG} = 180 - m\widehat{TH}$$
$$= 180 - 81$$
$$= 99°$$

Try This... 5. $\overline{AB}$ and $\overline{CD}$ are diameters and $m\overarc{CB} = 24°$.
Find $m \angle AOD$, $m\overarc{AD}$, and $m\overarc{DB}$.

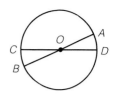

Exercises

▲ **Name the minor and major arcs and semicircles.**

1. X-O-Z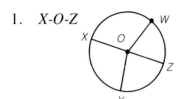

2. H-O-F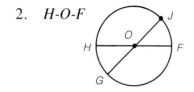

▲▲ **Find the degree measure of the indicated arc.**

3. $m\overarc{AB} =$ _____

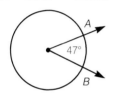

4. $m\overarc{CD} =$ _____

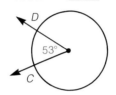

5. $m\overarc{PRQ} =$ _____

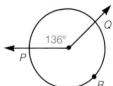

6. $m\overarc{KML} =$ _____

7. $\overline{ST}$ is a diameter.
$m\overarc{TUS} =$ _____

8. $m\overarc{BCA} =$ _____

▲▲▲ 9. $m\overarc{AB} = 37°$ and $m\overarc{BC} = 140°$.
Find $m\overarc{ABC}$ and $m\overarc{ADC}$.

10. $m\overarc{EF} = 72°$ and $m\overarc{FG} = 150°$.
Find $m\overarc{EFG}$ and $m\overarc{EHG}$.

11. $\overline{RT}$ and $\overline{SU}$ are diameters, and $m\overset{\frown}{RU} = 125°$. Find $m\angle ROU$, $m\overset{\frown}{RS}$, and $m\overset{\frown}{TS}$.

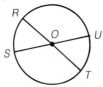

12. $\overline{AB}$ is a diameter, $m\overset{\frown}{AD} = 40°$. Find $m\overset{\frown}{ACD}$ and $m\overset{\frown}{DB}$.

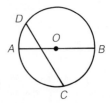

▶ Extension Exercises

13. A carriage wheel has 12 spokes that are equally spaced. Find the degree measure of each of the arcs formed by adjacent spokes.

14. A sand dollar is a sea animal with a circular body. On its back is a pattern of five equally-spaced lines. Find the degree measure of each of the central angles and each of the arcs in the pattern.

In ⊙O, $\overline{CE}$ is a diameter, D-O-F, $\overline{OF}$ bisects ∠BOC, and AE = BC = EO = 1.

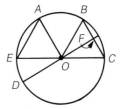

15. Find $m\overset{\frown}{AE}$, $m\overset{\frown}{ED}$, $m\overset{\frown}{DAB}$, and BF.

16. Find $m\overset{\frown}{AB}$, $m\angle BOF$, $m\overset{\frown}{ABC}$, and OF.

How many degrees does the hour hand of a clock pass through in the given time?

17. from 12:05 P.M. to 12:10 P.M.

18. from 10:10 A.M. to 1:15 P.M.

How many degrees does the minute hand of a clock pass through in the given time?

19. from 12 noon to 12 midnight

20. from 6 P.M. to 9 A.M.

21. from 4 P.M. to 3 P.M.

5	Congruent Arcs

After finishing Section 5, you should be able to
▲ *identify congruent arcs.*
▲▲ *apply theorems involving congruent arcs and chords.*

▲ Defining Congruent Arcs

Congruent arcs refer to arcs of the same circle or congruent circles.

DEFINITION

Congruent arcs must be arcs of the same circle (or congruent circles) that have the same degree measure.

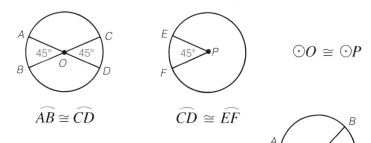

$$\overarc{AB} \cong \overarc{CD} \qquad \overarc{CD} \cong \overarc{EF} \qquad \odot O \cong \odot P$$

Example 1. $\overline{AC}$ and $\overline{DB}$ are diameters of $\odot O$. Identify all congruent arcs.

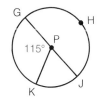

∠ *AOB* ≅ ∠ *DOC* and ∠ *AOD* ≅ ∠ *BOC* by the Vertical Angle Theorem, Hence, corresponding arcs have the same degree measure, and $\overarc{AB} \cong \overarc{DC}$, $\overarc{AD} \cong \overarc{BC}$, $\overarc{DAB} \cong \overarc{DCB}$,

$\overarc{ABC} \cong \overarc{ADC}$, $\overarc{ACB} \cong \overarc{DBC}$, and $\overarc{BDC} \cong \overarc{ABD}$.

Try This... 1. $\odot O \cong \odot P$, and $\overline{DE}$ and $\overline{GJ}$ are diameters. Identify all congruent arcs.

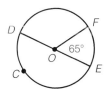

▲▲ Congruent Arcs and Chords

1. Draw ⊙O and diameters $\overline{AB}$ and $\overline{CD}$.
    Identify congruent minor arcs.

2. Draw chords $\overline{AC}$, $\overline{CB}$, $\overline{BD}$, and $\overline{AD}$.
    Compare their lengths.

THEOREM 13.8	If two arcs of a circle (or congruent circles) are congruent, then their chords are congruent.

The converse of this theorem is also true.

THEOREM 13.9	If two chords of a circle (or congruent circles) are congruent, then their arcs are congruent.

Example   2. Identify the congruent arcs.

Because $\angle C \cong \angle B$, $\triangle ABC$ is isosceles,
and $\overline{AC} \cong \overline{AB}$. By Theorem 13.9, $\overset{\frown}{AC} \cong \overset{\frown}{AB}$.

Try This...   2. Suppose $\triangle ABC$ in Example 2 is an equilateral triangle.
Identify the congruent arcs.

Example   3. ⊙$O \cong$ ⊙P

$m\overset{\frown}{AB} = 70°$ $m\overset{\frown}{FE} = 125°$

$m\overset{\frown}{BC} = 125°$ $m\overset{\frown}{DF} = 70°$

$m\overset{\frown}{CA} = 165°$ $m\overset{\frown}{DE} = 165°$

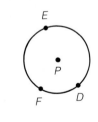

Identify all congruent chords and diameters.

By Theorem 13.8, $\overline{AB} \cong \overline{DF}$, $\overline{BC} \cong \overline{FE}$, and $\overline{AC} \cong \overline{DE}$. No
chord is a diameter because no arc is a semicircle.

Try This...   3. $\overline{XY}$ and $\overline{RS}$ are diameters
of congruent circles and
$m\overset{\frown}{XZ} = m\overset{\frown}{TS}$. Identify two
pairs of congruent chords.

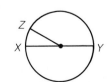
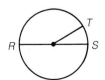

Exercises

▲ **Identify two pairs of congruent minor arcs and two pairs of congruent major arcs. All circles are congruent.**

1.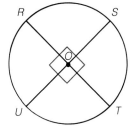

2. $\overline{AE}$ is a diameter. $\overline{FG}$ is a diameter.

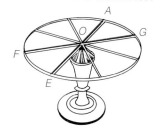

3. $\overline{AD}$ and $\overline{NK}$ are diameters.

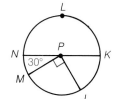 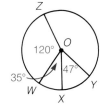

4. $\overline{SU}$ is a diameter.

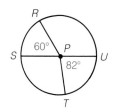

▲▲ **Identify all congruent arcs.**

5. $\overline{AB} \cong \overline{CD}$
6. $\overline{GE} \cong \overline{EF}$
7. $\overline{MP} \cong \overline{NQ}$
8. $\overline{RT}$ and $\overline{US}$ are diameters.

 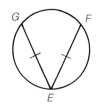 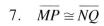 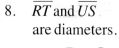

Identify all congruent chords and diameters in each pair of congruent circles.

9.

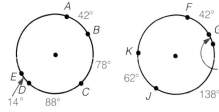

10.

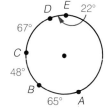 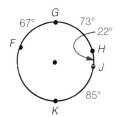

► Extension Exercises

11. $\overset{\frown}{AB} \cong \overset{\frown}{BC}$ and $\overset{\frown}{AD} \cong \overset{\frown}{CD}$.
Explain why $\triangle ABD \cong \triangle CBD$.

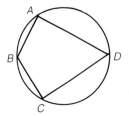

12. $\overline{MN}$ and $\overline{PQ}$ are equidistant from the center of the circle. Explain why $\overset{\frown}{MN} \cong \overset{\frown}{PQ}$.

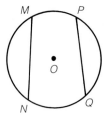

Activity

Draw a circle with a 3-inch radius and cut it out. Fold the circle in half. Fold again as shown. Fold again. Unfold the circle and draw chords between the adjacent endpoints created by the folds. What figure have you drawn?

 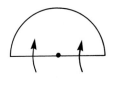

Cut out another circle with a 3-inch radius. Fold the circle in half. Then fold the two sides so that they meet in the middle. Unfold the circle and draw chords between the adjacent endpoints. What figure have you drawn?

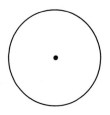 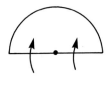

Try creating other polygons in the same manner.

6 | Inscribed Polygons

After finishing Section 6, you should be able to
▲ *draw regular polygons by inscribing them in a circle.*

△*ABC* is inscribed in the circle.
We can also say that the circle is
circumscribed about △*ABC*.

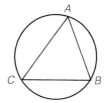

DEFINITION

A polygon is **inscribed** in a circle whenever every vertex of the
polygon lies on the circle. The circle is said to be **circumscribed**
about the polygon.

Some regular polygons can be drawn by inscribing them
in a circle.

Example   1. Inscribe a regular hexagon in a circle.

Step 1

Draw a circle with radius *r*.

Step 2

Choose a point *A* on the circle. Use a
compass opening equal to *r* and mark
off arcs around the circle.

Step 3

Connect these points on the circle to
obtain a regular hexagon.

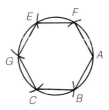

Try This…   1. Draw a circle and use a compass to inscribe an equilateral triangle.
(*Hint:* First find the points for a hexagon).

Example   2. Inscribe a regular pentagon in a circle.

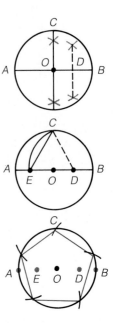

Step 1

Draw a circle and a diameter $\overline{AB}$.
Draw the perpendicular to $\overline{AB}$ at
center O.
Find the midpoint, D, of $\overline{OB}$.

Step 2

Place the compass point at D. Use a
compass opening CD and draw $\overset{\frown}{CE}$.

Step 3

Choose a point on the circle. Use
compass opening CE and mark off
arcs around the circle. Connect these
points to obtain a regular pentagon.

Try This... 2. Draw a circle and use a compass to inscribe a regular
decagon. (*Hint:* First find the points for a pentagon.)

Exercises

▲ **Draw a circle and use a compass to inscribe each polygon.**

1. Square   2. Regular octagon

3. Regular hexagon   4. Regular dodecagon (12 sides)

5. Regular pentagon   6. Regular decagon

▶ Extension Exercise

7. Draw three circles and inscribe an acute, a right, and an
   obtuse triangle. Which triangle has a diameter for one side?
   Which triangle intersects every diameter of the circle? Which
   triangle is contained in the interior of a semicircle?

▶▶ Challenge Exercise

8. Draw several circles and inscribe some quadrilaterals. Try to
   discover a relationship between the four angles of an inscribed
   quadrilateral.

7	Circumference of a Circle

After finishing Section 7, you should be able to
▲ *solve problems involving the circumference of a circle.*

We know that the distance around a polygon is its **perimeter (p)**.
The distance around a circle is its **circumference**. We can
use perimeters of inscribed regular polygons to approximate
the circumference of a circle.

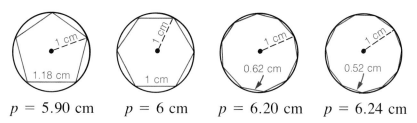

$p = 5.90$ cm $p = 6$ cm $p = 6.20$ cm $p = 6.24$ cm

As the number of sides of the inscribed polygons increases, the perimeters
approach a number called their *limit*. We can find perimeters as
close as we want to this limit.

DEFINITION
_____

The **circumference of a circle** is the limit of the perimeters of all
inscribed regular polygons.

In all circles, the ratio of the circumference to the diameter is the same.

1. One way to find the circumference of a coin is to roll
    it along a flat surface, and then measure the distance.
    Use a ruler to measure the circumference and diameter of
    three coins. Then find the ratio $\frac{\text{circumference}}{\text{diameter}}$ for each.

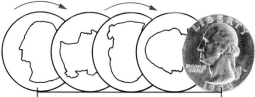

2. Using a measuring tape (or string), find the circumference
    and diameter of a can. Then find the ratio $\frac{\text{circumference}}{\text{diameter}}$.

THEOREM
13.10

For all circles, the ratio $\frac{\text{circumference}}{\text{diameter}}$ is the same number.

We use the Greek letter, π (pī), to represent this number.

$$\pi = \frac{c}{d} = \frac{\text{circumference}}{\text{diameter}} \quad \text{or } c = \pi d$$

π is an irrational number. It is approximately 3.1415926535. A rational number approximation that is often used for π is 3.14. With calculations involving π, we can either express the answer in terms of π, or use the approximation, 3.14.

Example   1. Find the circumference of the circle.

$$c = \pi d$$
$$= \pi \times 4$$
$$= 4\pi \text{ cm}$$

$d = 4$ cm

Try This...   1. Find the circumference of a circle whose diameter is 7.5 m.

Example   2. Find the circumference of a circle whose radius is 10 m. Use 3.14 for π.

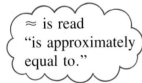
≈ is read "is approximately equal to."

$$c = \pi d$$
$$= \pi \cdot 2r \quad (d = 2r)$$
$$\approx 3.14 \times 2 \times 10$$
$$\approx 62.8 \text{ m}$$

10 m

Try This...   2. Find the circumference of a circle whose radius is 15 cm. Use 3.14 for π.

Example   3. A flagpole has a circumference of 30 cm. Find its diameter. Use 3.14 for π.

$$\pi d = c$$
$$d = \frac{c}{\pi}$$
$$d \approx \frac{30}{3.14} \approx 9.6 \text{ cm}$$

Try This...   3. The circumference of a tree is 76 cm. Find its diameter. Use 3.14 for π.

Example 4. The sides of a square are 10 cm. Find the circumference of the circumscribed circle.

Because the diagonal of the square contains the center of the circle, it is a diameter.

By the Pythagorean Theorem,

$$d^2 = 10^2 + 10^2 = 200$$

Thus, $d = 10\sqrt{2}$ and $c = \pi \times 10\sqrt{2}$, or $10\sqrt{2}\pi$ cm.

Try This... 4. A rectangle 40 cm by 30 cm is inscribed in a circle. Find the diameter and the circumference of the circle.

Exercises

▲ **Find the circumference of each circle. Express your answer in terms of π.**

1.

$d = 12$ m

2.

$r = 9.5$ m

3.

$d = 0.5$ km

4.

14 m

14 m

5.

24 cm

7 cm

6.

2 m

7. $d = 75$ cm

8. $r = 0.75$ m

9. $r = 0.86$ m

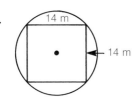

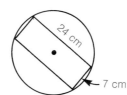

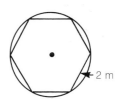

▶ Extension Exercises

Use 3.14 for π.

10. The girth (circumference) of a tree is 63 cm. Find its diameter.

11. The circumference of a pipe is 42 cm. Find its diameter.

12. The radius of a circle is doubled. How does the circumference change?

13. The diameter of a circle is halved. How does the circumference change?

14. The diameter of a wheel is 45 cm. How far does a wheel travel in 100 revolutions?

15. The radius of a wheel is 30 cm. How far does a wheel travel in 100 revolutions?

16. Suppose that the Earth travels in a nearly circular orbit around the sun. The average distance from the sun is about 150,000,000 km. Find the distance the Earth travels in one orbit around the sun.

17. Find the length of a circular orbit of a satellite if the satellite is 800 km above the surface of the earth. (The radius of the Earth is approximately 6,400 km.)

18. The circumference of a circle is 40π cm. Find the perimeter of an inscribed regular hexagon.

19. Imagine a steel band wrapped around the equator of the Earth. A 10-meter piece is added to the band. How does this affect its radius? Suppose the space between the band and the equator is equidistant around the sphere. Could you slip a piece of paper under the band, crawl under the band, or walk under the band?

▶▶ Challenge Exercise

20. Here is a formula for calculating the distance that a bicycle travels in one revolution of the pedals.

$$D = \pi \cdot d \cdot \frac{a}{b} \quad \text{where} \quad d = \text{diameter of the wheel (in cm)}$$

a = number of teeth on the pedal sprocket

b = number of teeth on the rear sprocket.

$d = 70$ cm, $a = 52$, and $b = 18$. Find D.

8	Area of a Circle

After finishing Section 8, you should be able to
▲   *find the area of a circle, given the radius or diameter.*
▲▲   *solve problems involving the area of a circle.*

▲   Area of a Circle

The areas of inscribed regular polygons can be used to
approximate the area of a circle. As the number of sides
of the inscribed polygons increases, the areas approach
a number called their *limit*. We can find numbers
as close to this limit as we want.

DEFINITION

The **area of a circle** is the limit of the areas of all inscribed regular
polygons.

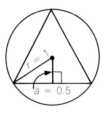   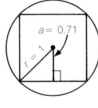   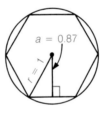   

$A_3 = 1.3$ $A_4 = 2$ $A_6 = 2.6$ $A_{12} = 3.0$

Recall that the area of a regular polygon of n sides is

$$A_n = \tfrac{1}{2}ap$$

where a is the length of the apothem and p is the perimeter.

The drawings above suggest the following:

As n, the number of sides, increases,

$\quad A_n = \tfrac{1}{2}ap$ approaches $A_\odot$, (area of the circle)

$\qquad a$ approaches r,

$\qquad p$ approaches $c = 2\pi r$,

and thus, $A_n = \tfrac{1}{2}ap$ approaches $\tfrac{1}{2} \cdot r \cdot 2 \cdot \pi r$, or πr^2.

THEOREM   The area of a circle with radius r is πr^2.
13.11

Examples
1. Find the area of a circle with a radius of 6 cm.

$$A = \pi r^2 = \pi \cdot 6^2 = 36\pi \text{ cm}^2$$

2. Find the area of a circle with a diameter of 4.8 m.

Because $r = \dfrac{d}{2}$, we have $r = \dfrac{4.8}{2} = 2.4$ m.

Thus, $A = \pi(2.4)^2 = 5.76\pi \text{ m}^2$.

3. Find the area (to the nearest meter) of a circle with a radius of 7.2 m. Use 3.14 for π.

$$A = \pi r^2 = \pi \cdot (7.2)^2 \approx 3.14 \times 51.84 \approx 163 \text{ m}^2.$$

Try This...   Find the area of each circle.

1. $r = 8$ cm
2. $d = 0.14$ m
3. $r = 2.8$ km. Use 3.14 for π.

▲▲ Applying the Area Formula for a Circle

Example
4. The area of a circular mobile home park is 70,650 m². Find the radius to the nearest tenth of a meter. Use 3.14 for π.

$$\pi r^2 = A$$

$$r^2 = \frac{A}{\pi}$$

$$r^2 \approx \frac{70,650}{3.14}$$

$$r^2 \approx 22,500$$

$$r \approx 150 \text{ m to the nearest meter.}$$

Try This...   4. The area of the top of a snare drum is 5,025 cm². Find its radius to the nearest centimeter. Use 3.14 for π.

Example   5. Find the area of the shaded region to the nearest tenth of a centimeter. Use 3.14 for π.

The area of the shaded region is the area of the circle minus the area of the rectangle.

$$A_\odot - A_\square$$

Diagonal $\overline{DB}$ is a diameter. So, by the Pythagorean Theorem,
$$DB^2 = 4^2 + 3^2 = 25$$

Thus, $DB = 5$ cm and the radius is 2.5 cm.

Now, $A_{shaded\,region} = \dfrac{25}{4}\pi - (4 \times 3)$
$$\approx 19.6 - 12 \text{ or } 7.6 \text{ cm}^2$$

Try This...   5. Find the area of the shaded region to the nearest tenth of a centimeter. The centers are O and P, and the radius of the smaller circle is 4 cm. Use 3.14 for π.

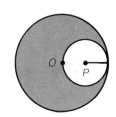

Exercises

▲ **Find the area of the circle from the radius.**
Express your answer in terms of π.

1.   14 m   2.   5.7 cm   3. $3\sqrt{2}$ mm

4.   0.3 m   5.   15 cm   6. $5\sqrt{3}$ mm

7.   10 km (Use 3.14 for π.)   8.   3 dm (Use 3.14 for π.)

Find the area of the circle from the diameter.
Express your answer in terms of π.

9.   24 cm   10.   18 cm   11.   1.2 m   12.   3 cm

▲▲ **Find the radius and diameter of each circle from the area.**
Use 3.14 for π.

13. $A = 380 \text{ cm}^2$ 14. $A = 410 \text{ cm}^2$ 15. $A = 7 \text{ m}^2$ 16. $A = 45 \text{ dm}^2$

Find the area of the shaded region. Use 3.14 for π.

17.

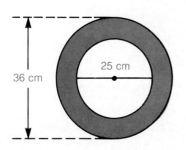

25 cm

36 cm

18.

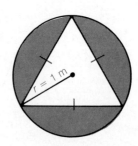

$r = 1$ m

19. All radii are 1 m.

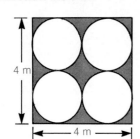

4 m

4 m

20. All diameters are $\frac{2}{3}$ m.

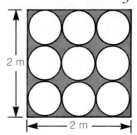

2 m

2 m

▶ Extension Exercises

Find the circumference of the circle from the area.

21. $A = 16\pi\,m^2$ 22. $A = 6.5\pi\,dm^2$ 23. $A = 1.21\pi\,cm^2$ 24. $A = \pi\,cm^2$

Find the area of the circle from the circumference.

25. 12π cm   26. 25π cm

27. A glass company charges $0.20 per square decimeter of glass for circular windows, and $0.10 per decimeter for the circular cutting. What will they charge for these three windows if the diameter of each window is 9 dm?

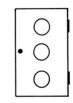

28. A circular table top made of oak weighs 2.5 grams per square centimeter of surface. If the top weighs no more than 20 kilograms, what is the maximum diameter of the table top?

Consumer Application   Preparing a Budget

A budget is a plan for managing money. Most budgets are done
on a monthly basis, and they can be displayed in a circle graph.

Example   The Wong family budgets a percentage of their net
monthly salary for each of the following items:

Food	25%	Housing	30%
Clothing	10%	Transportation	12%
Utilities	8%	Miscellaneous	15%

The Wong's net monthly salary is $1,225.00.
Make a circle graph to show the Wong's monthly budget.

Multiply each percentage by the monthly salary to find
the amount of money budgeted per item.

Food $0.25 \times \$1,225 = \$306.25$ Housing $0.30 \times \$1,225 = \$367.50$
Clothing $0.10 \times \$1,225 = \$122.50$ Transportation $0.12 \times \$1,225 = \$147.00$
Utilities $0.08 \times \$1,225 = \$ 98.00$ Miscellaneous $0.15 \times \$1,225 = \$183.75$

Multiply each percentage by 360° to find the size of each
section in the circle. Round the answer to the nearest degree.

Food $0.25 \times 360° = 90°$ Housing $0.30 \times 360° = 108°$
Clothing $0.10 \times 360° = 36°$ Transportation $0.12 \times 360° = 43.2°$ or $43°$
Utilities $0.08 \times 360° = 28.8°$ or $29°$ Miscellaneous $0.15 \times 360° = 54°$

Draw a circle and divide it into sections with
the above sections. Label each section.

Make a circle graph to show the monthly budget for each of the following.

1. | | |
    |---|---|
    | Food | 30% |
    | Clothing | 10% |
    | Utilities | 5% |
    | Housing | 35% |
    | Transportation | 10% |
    | Miscellaneous | 10% |
    | Monthly Salary | $1,300.00 |

2. | | |
    |---|---|
    | Housing and Utilities | 30% |
    | Food | 25% |
    | Savings | 12% |
    | Clothing | 8% |
    | Personal Expenses | 15% |
    | Other Debts | 10% |
    | Monthly Salary | $1,100.00 |

3. Make a circle graph to show your own monthly budget.

Chapter Review

1 **Use ⊙O for Exercises 1-2.**

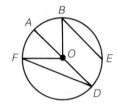

   1. Identify all radii, chords, and diameters.
   2. *AD* = 72. Find *OF*.

2 **Use ⊙A for Exercises 3-5.**

   3. If *AD* = 39 and *AB* = 15, what is *CD*?
   4. If *CD* = $2\sqrt{3}$ and *AB* = 1, what is *AD*?
   5. If *CD* = 24 and *AD* = 13, what is *AB*?

3   6. $\overline{PQ} \cong \overline{KL}$, ⊙O ≅ ⊙G, and *ON* = 12.
       Find *GH*.

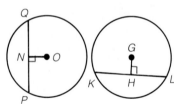

▲7. ⊙O ≅ ⊙P. *QR* = *x* + 7, *ST* = 2*x* + 4, and
     OM = *PN* = *x*. Find the length of each
     chord and its distance from the center.

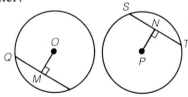

Use ⊙K for Exercises 8–11.

4 *A-K-B* and *C-K-D*, and *m∠AKD* = **72°.**

   8. Name the minor and major arcs and semicircles.

   9. Find *m* ∠ *AKC*.

  10. Find *m$\overset{\frown}{BC}$*.

  11. Find *m$\overset{\frown}{DCB}$*.

12. Identify all congruent arcs. $\overline{AD} \cong \overline{BC}$.

 13. Draw a circle and inscribe a regular hexagon in it.

 14. Find the circumference of ⊙O.

15. The girth of an oak tree is 3.5 times the girth of a sycamore. Compare their diameters.

16. Find the area of a circle with diameter $2\sqrt{3}$ cm. Express your answer in terms of π.

17. Find the area of the shaded region. Use 3.14 for π. Diameter $AB = 10$ cm and diameter $AC = 12$ cm.

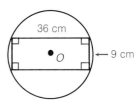

Chapter Test

Use ⊙O for Exercises 1-2.

1. Identify all radii, chords, and diameters in ⊙O.

2. $AD = 12.6$ cm. Find OC.

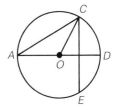

Use ⊙P for Exercises 3–4.

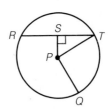

3. If $SP = 10$ and $TP = 26$, what is RT?

4. If $PQ = 30$ and $TR = 48$, what is PS?

5. If $PS = 24$ and $RT = 14$, what is PQ?

6. $GT = 13$. Find QR.

▲7.   ⊙O ≅ ⊙P. $RT = 2x + 3$, $MN = x + 10$, and $OS = PQ = x$.
Find the length of each chord and its distance from the center.

   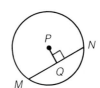

C-O-F and D-O-E, and $m\widehat{CD} = 52°$.

8. Name the minor and major arcs and semicircles.

9. Find $m \angle EOF$.

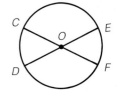

10. Find $m\widehat{CE}$.

11. Find $m\widehat{DCF}$.

12. $\overline{BD}$ is a diameter. Name four pairs of congruent arcs in ⊙O.

13. Draw a circle and inscribe a square in it.

14. Find the circumference of a circle with a radius of 7.5 m.

15. A pipe has a circumference of 78.5 cm. Find its diameter. Use 3.14 for π.

16. Find the area of a circle with a diameter of $4\sqrt{5}$ cm. Express your answer in terms of π.

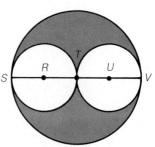

17. Find the area of the shaded region. Use 3.14 for π.

Diameter $SV = 24$ mm
Diameter $ST = 12$ mm

Skills Review   Adding and Subtracting Fractions

Add and simplify.

1. $\dfrac{3}{5} + \dfrac{2}{5}$ 2. $\dfrac{6}{10} + \dfrac{3}{10}$ 3. $\dfrac{1}{9} + \dfrac{3}{9}$ 4. $\dfrac{11}{12} + \dfrac{13}{12}$

5. $\dfrac{4}{7} + \dfrac{5}{7}$ 6. $\dfrac{4}{5} + \dfrac{11}{5}$ 7. $\dfrac{7}{3} + \dfrac{9}{3}$ 8. $\dfrac{7}{4} + \dfrac{1}{4}$

9. $\dfrac{2}{3} + \dfrac{1}{5}$ 10. $\dfrac{1}{4} + \dfrac{2}{5}$ 11. $\dfrac{3}{8} + \dfrac{1}{3}$ 12. $\dfrac{3}{10} + \dfrac{2}{3}$

13. $\dfrac{3}{4} + \dfrac{5}{6}$ 14. $\dfrac{5}{8} + \dfrac{5}{6}$ 15. $\dfrac{1}{8} + \dfrac{5}{12}$ 16. $\dfrac{2}{10} + \dfrac{5}{100}$

17. $11\dfrac{2}{3} + 9$ 18. $6\dfrac{1}{2} + 5\dfrac{1}{4}$ 19. $3\dfrac{1}{6} + 7\dfrac{1}{8}$ 20. $11\dfrac{7}{10} + 4\dfrac{3}{10}$

21. $12 + 4\dfrac{5}{9}$ 22. $8\dfrac{2}{3} + 3\dfrac{2}{3}$ 23. $9\dfrac{1}{2} + 9$ 24. $15\dfrac{4}{5} + 7\dfrac{1}{3}$

25. $2\dfrac{2}{3} + 3\dfrac{5}{6} + 4\dfrac{1}{2}$ 26. $2\dfrac{1}{5} + 1\dfrac{3}{4} + 8\dfrac{1}{2}$ 27. $6\dfrac{1}{10} + 4\dfrac{2}{4} + 5\dfrac{3}{4}$

Subtract and simplify.

28. $\dfrac{5}{8} - \dfrac{1}{8}$ 29. $\dfrac{7}{12} - \dfrac{1}{12}$ 30. $\dfrac{4}{5} - \dfrac{1}{2}$ 31. $\dfrac{1}{3} - \dfrac{1}{4}$

32. $\dfrac{9}{10} - \dfrac{3}{5}$ 33. $\dfrac{5}{6} - \dfrac{7}{9}$ 34. $\dfrac{3}{10} - \dfrac{1}{100}$ 35. $\dfrac{5}{7} - \dfrac{1}{2}$

36. $2\dfrac{7}{8} - \dfrac{5}{8}$ 37. $3\dfrac{9}{10} - \dfrac{3}{10}$ 38. $4\dfrac{3}{8} - 2\dfrac{1}{6}$ 39. $5\dfrac{8}{9} - 3\dfrac{5}{6}$

40. $10\dfrac{3}{4} - 6$ 41. $12\dfrac{2}{3} - 7$ 42. $15\dfrac{1}{2} - 10\dfrac{1}{3}$ 43. $20\dfrac{5}{9} - 9\dfrac{1}{4}$

44. $8 - 2\dfrac{1}{4}$ 45. $30 - 4\dfrac{7}{10}$ 46. $12\dfrac{1}{2} - 8\dfrac{3}{5}$ 47. $7\dfrac{1}{8} - 5\dfrac{1}{6}$

48. $10\dfrac{2}{7} - 5\dfrac{3}{7}$ 49. $7\dfrac{1}{5} - 3\dfrac{4}{5}$ 50. $13\dfrac{2}{3} - 10\dfrac{7}{8}$ 51. $18\dfrac{3}{5} - 7\dfrac{2}{3}$

14
Tangents
and Secants

1 | Tangents

After finishing Section 1, you should be able to
▲ *solve problems involving tangents.*
▲▲ *construct a tangent to a circle.*

▲ Using Tangents

DEFINITION

A line, coplanar with a circle, is **tangent** to the circle whenever it intersects the circle in exactly one point.

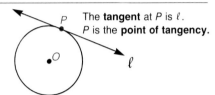

The **tangent** at *P* is ℓ.
P is the **point of tangency.**

1. Draw ⊙*O* and choose a point *P* on the circle.
2. Draw a line perpendicular to $\overline{OP}$ at *P*. The line intersects the circle in how many points?
3. Draw several other lines containing *P* that are not perpendicular to $\overline{OP}$. They intersect the circle in how many points?

THEOREM **14.1** A line is tangent to ⊙*O* at a point *P* whenever the line is perpendicular to the radius $\overline{OP}$ at *P*.

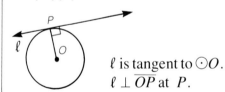

ℓ is tangent to ⊙*O*.
ℓ ⊥ $\overline{OP}$ at *P*.

ℓ is *not* tangent to ⊙*O*.
ℓ $\not\perp$ $\overline{OP}$ at *P*.

Example 1. $\overline{AB}$ is tangent to ⊙*O* at *B*, $\overline{OB} = 6$, and $OA = 10$. Find *AB*.

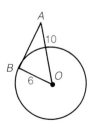

By Theorem 14.1, ∠ *ABO* is a right angle. Thus, △ *AOB* is a right triangle. By the Pythagorean Theorem,

$$6^2 + AB^2 = 10^2$$
$$AB^2 = 10^2 - 6^2$$
$$AB^2 = 64$$
and $$AB = 8$$

In Example 1, $\overline{AB}$ is a **tangent segment.**

Try This...   1. $\overline{DE}$ is tangent to $\odot O$ at D, $OD = 5$,
and $DE = 12$. Find OE.

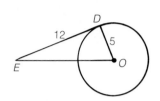

From Theorem 14.1 and the Hypotenuse-Leg Theorem,
we have the following corollary.

COROLLARY **14.2**   The tangent segments from a
point to a circle are congruent.

$$\overline{AP} \cong \overline{BP}$$

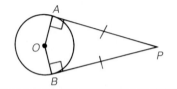

Example   2. $\overline{DE}$ and $\overline{DF}$ are tangent segments. $m \angle D = \frac{1}{2} m \angle DEF$.
Find the measures of the angles of $\triangle DEF$.

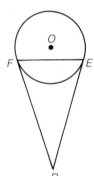

By Corollary 14.2, $\overline{DE} \cong \overline{DF}$. So, $\triangle DEF$ is isosceles and
$\angle DEF \cong \angle DFE$. By the Angle Sum Theorem,

$$m \angle D + m \angle DEF + m \angle DFE = 180°.$$

Substituting, we have

$$\frac{1}{2}m \angle DEF + m \angle DEF + m \angle DEF = 180$$
$$2\tfrac{1}{2} \cdot m \angle DEF = 180$$
$$m \angle DEF = 72°.$$

Thus, $m \angle DFE = 72°$ and $m \angle D = 36°$.

Try This...   ▲2. $\overline{PR}$ and $\overline{PS}$ are tangent segments.
$m \angle P = x$ and $m \angle PRS = 2x + 5$.
Find $m \angle P$.

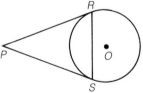

Example   3. $\overline{PA}$, $\overline{PB}$, and $\overline{PC}$ are tangent segments.
If $PA = 12$, what is PC?

By Corollary 14.2, $\overline{PA} \cong \overline{PB}$,
and $\overline{PB} \cong \overline{PC}$.

So, $\overline{PA} \cong \overline{PC}$ and $PC = 12$.

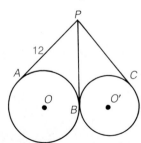

In Example 3, $\odot O$ and $\odot O'$ are tangent to each other.

Try This... 3. $\overline{RU}$ is tangent to the circles at R and U.
$\overline{ST}$ is tangent to the circles at S and T.
If $WS = 6$ and $WU = 4$, what is RU?

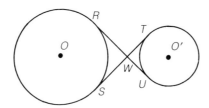

▲▲ Constructing a Tangent to a Circle

Example 4. Use a straightedge and compass to construct tangents to ⊙O from point P.

Step 1
Bisect $\overline{OP}$.

Step 2
Draw the circle with center A and radius OA.

Step 3
Draw segments $\overline{BP}$ and $\overline{CP}$ that are tangent to ⊙O at B and C.

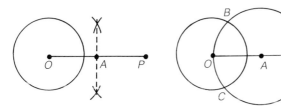

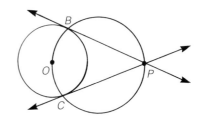

Try This... 4. Draw a circle and a point P outside the circle.
Construct tangents from P to the circle.

DEFINITION

Two coplanar **circles are tangent** to each other whenever they are tangent to the same line at the same point.

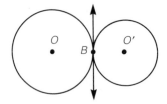
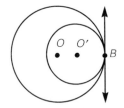

Externally tangent circles   *Internally tangent circles*

Exercises

▲ **Use the figure for Exercises 1–8. $\overline{PQ}$ is tangent to $\odot O$ at Q.**

1. $PQ = 12$ and $OP = 15$. Find OQ.
2. $OQ = 12$ and $OP = 20$. Find PQ.
3. $OQ = 0.9$ and $OP = 1.5$. Find PQ.
4. Diameter of $\odot O$ is 1 and $OP = 1.3$. Find PQ.
5. Diameter of $\odot O$ is 20 and $PQ = 24$. Find PS.
6. $OQ = QS = 1$. Find OP.
7. $PS = 80$ and the diameter of $\odot O$ is 100. Find PQ.
8. $PQ = OQ + 6$, $PS = OQ + 2$, and $OP = 12$. Find OQ and PQ.

Use the figure for Exercises 9–12.
$\overline{PA}$ and $\overline{PB}$ are tangent segments.

▲9. $AB = x$, $PA = 2x + 3$, and $PB = x + 28$. Find AB.
▲10. $m \angle BAP = 2x + 3$ and $m \angle ABP = x + 38$. Find $m \angle APB$.
11. $m \angle APB = 35°$. Find $m \angle AOB$.
12. $m \angle AOB = 136°$. Find $m \angle BAP$.

In the watch gears, $\odot O$ and $\odot O'$ are tangent at A. $\overline{BD}$ and $\overline{CE}$ are tangent segments.

13. If $BA = AC$ and $EC = 9$, what is DB?
14. If $BC = 12$ and $CE = 6.5$, what is DB?

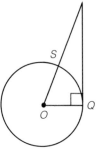

▶▶ Challenge Exercises

$\overline{PA}$ and $\overline{PB}$ are tangent to $\odot O$ at A and B.

15. How are $\angle BPA$ and $\angle AOB$ related? Explain how you know.

16. How are $\triangle OAP$ and $\triangle OBP$ related? Explain how you know.

17. Name two isosceles triangles.

18. Find three angles that are congruent to $\angle AOP$. Explain how you know.

19. How are $\triangle OAQ$ and $\triangle OBQ$ related? Explain how you know.

20. The Sears Tower in Chicago is about 440 m tall. Suppose that you are standing on the top of the tower. If the radius of the earth is 6,400 km, what is the distance of your line of sight to the horizon?

▶◀ Activity

Can you draw a circle with a ruler? Follow the procedure below and watch your results.

Mark a point on a sheet of paper. Place one edge of a ruler along the point, and then draw a line along the opposite edge of the ruler.

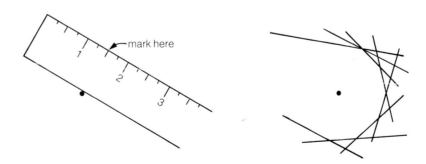

mark here

Repeat this step many times. What do you see happening?

2	Inscribed and Circumscribed Circles

After finishing Section 2, you should be able to
▲ *construct incircles and circumcircles.*

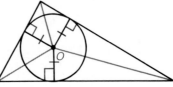

Recall that the angle bisectors of a triangle are concurrent in a point called the *incenter*.

Because the incenter is equidistant from the sides, it is the center of a circle tangent to all three sides of the triangle. This circle is called the *incircle* and it is inscribed in the triangle.

_____ DEFINITION _____

A **circle is inscribed in a polygon** whenever every side of the polygon is tangent to the circle.

We also know that the perpendicular bisectors of the sides of the triangle are concurrent at a point called the *circumcenter*.

Because the circumcenter is equidistant from the vertices of the triangle, it is the center of a circle containing all three vertices of the triangle. This circle is called the *circumcircle*.

_____ DEFINITION _____

A **circle is circumscribed about a polygon** whenever the circle contains every vertex of the polygon.

1. Draw a ⊙O and draw a regular hexagon as in Example 3, page 333.

2. Construct the perpendicular bisectors of each side of the hexagon.

3. Construct the angle bisectors of each angle of the hexagon.

4. How are all of these lines related?

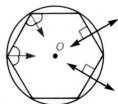

The drawing exercise suggests the following theorem.

> THEOREM 14.3   The angle bisectors and the perpendicular bisectors of any regular polygon are concurrent in a point that is equidistant from the sides and from the vertices of the polygon.

DEFINITION

For any regular polygon, the point of concurrency of the angle bisectors and the perpendicular bisectors is the **center** of the polygon.

Because the center of a regular polygon is equidistant from the vertices and from the sides, we can think of it as both the circumcenter and the incenter of the polygon. In other words, we can think of it as the center of both the circumcircle and the incircle.

Example   1. Construct the incircle and circumcircle of a regular pentagon.

Draw two perpendicular bisectors to find O that is both incenter and circumcenter. Place the compass point on O with opening OF for the radius to draw the incircle. Use OA as radius to draw the circumcircle.

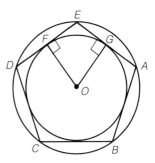

Try This...   1. Construct the incircle and circumcircle of a square.

Exercises

▲ **For each polygon, construct the incircle and circumcircle.**

1. Acute triangle	2. Obtuse triangle
3. Right triangle	4. Equilateral triangle
5. Isosceles triangle	6. Regular hexagon
7. Regular octagon	8. Regular pentagon

▶ Extension Exercises

9. A circle is inscribed in quadrilateral *DEFG*. *DH* = 7, *EJ* = 6, *FK* = 8, and *GL* = 10. Find the perimeter of *DEFG*.

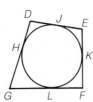

10. A circle is inscribed in △*ABC*. *AE* = 5, *BF* = 4, and *CD* = 8. Find the perimeter of △*ABC*.

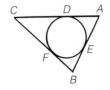

11. ⊙*O* is inscribed in isosceles triangle *ABC* with $\overline{AC} \cong \overline{BC}$. *CE* = 6 and *BF* = 9. Find the perimeter of △ *ABC*.

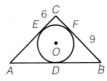

▶▶ Challenge Exercises

12. Equilateral triangle *ABC* is tangent to the inscribed circle at *D*, *E*, and *F*. *AE* = 5. What is the perimeter of △*ABC*? Explain how you know.

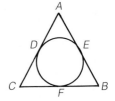

13. Square *ABCD* is tangent to the inscribed circle at *E*, *F*, *G*, and *H*. Explain why *E*, *F*, *G*, and *H* are midpoints of the sides.

14. △ *DEF* in Exercise 12 is what kind of triangle? Explain how you know.

15. Quadrilaterals that can be inscribed in a circle are called *cyclic* quadrilaterals. Try to discover a relationship involving the angles of a quadrilateral that can be used to distinguish cyclic quadrilaterals from noncyclic quadrilaterals.

16. Devise a method for constructing a circle so that it is tangent to a given line and is also tangent to a given circle. Is this always possible?

3 | Inscribed Angles

After finishing Section 3, you should be able to
▲ *identify inscribed angles and their intercepted arcs.*
▲▲ *apply theorems about inscribed angles to solve problems.*

▲ Defining Inscribed Angles

In Chapter 13, we studied inscribed polygons. Two sides of an
inscribed polygon determine an **inscribed angle**.

DEFINITION

An **inscribed angle** is an angle whose vertex is on the circle and
whose sides each intersect the circle in one other point.

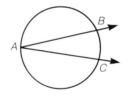

∠ *BAC* **intercepts** $\overarc{BC}$.
∠ *BAC* is **inscribed in** $\overarc{BAC}$.

Example   1. Identify each inscribed angle and its intercepted arc.

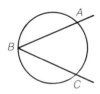 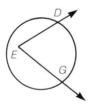 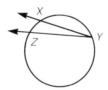 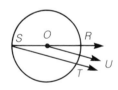

The inscribed angles are: ∠ *ABC*, which intercepts $\overarc{AC}$,
∠ *XYZ*, which intercepts $\overarc{XZ}$,
and   ∠ *RST*, which intercepts $\overarc{RT}$.

Try This...   1. Identify each inscribed angle and its intercepted arc.

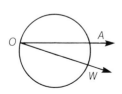 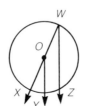 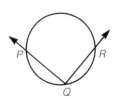

▲▲ Measures of Inscribed Angles

The measures of inscribed angles are related to the measures of their intercepted arcs.

1. Draw a circle and mark off an arc, $\overset{\frown}{AB}$ with measure 90°.

2. Choose points C, D, and E on the major arc and draw inscribed angles $\angle ACB$, $\angle ADB$, and $\angle AEB$. Measure the inscribed angles and compare them with $m\overset{\frown}{AB}$.

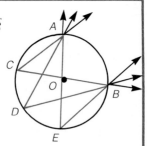

3. Draw another circle and mark off any arc, $\overset{\frown}{XY}$.

4. Choose points R, S, and T on one arc and draw inscribed angles $\angle XRY$, $\angle XSY$, and $\angle XTY$. Compare the measures of these angles with $m\overset{\frown}{XY}$.

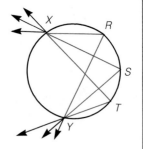

THEOREM
14.4

The measure of an inscribed angle is one-half the measure of its intercepted arc.

$$m \angle ABC = \tfrac{1}{2}\, m\overset{\frown}{AC}$$

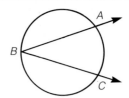

Examples
2. $m\overset{\frown}{AC} = 120°$. Find $m \angle ABC$.

$$m \angle ABC = \frac{1}{2} \times 120 = 60°$$

3. $m \angle DEF = 30°$. Find $m\overset{\frown}{DF}$.

$$m\overset{\frown}{DF} = 60°$$

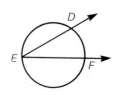

4. $m\widehat{SPQ} = 220°$. Find $m \angle P$ and $m \angle R$.

$$m \angle P = \frac{1}{2} (360 - 220) = 70°$$

$$m \angle R = \frac{1}{2} \times 220 = 110°$$

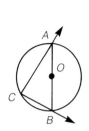

5. $\overline{AB}$ is a diameter. Find $m \angle C$.

$$m \angle C = \frac{1}{2} \times 180 = 90°$$

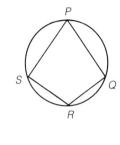

Try This... 2. $\overline{DE}$ is a diameter.
Find $m \angle A$, $m \angle B$, and
$m \angle C$.

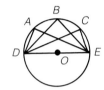

3. $m\widehat{AB} = m\widehat{BC} = 60°$.
Find $m \angle ADB$, $m \angle ADC$,
and $m \angle BEC$.

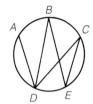

These examples suggest the following corollaries.

COROLLARY **14.5** An inscribed angle is a right angle whenever its intercepted arc is a semicircle.

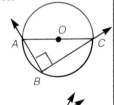

COROLLARY **14.6** Inscribed angles intercept the same arc or congruent arcs whenever the angles are congruent.

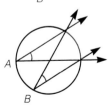

Example 6. $\overline{AC} \parallel \overline{BD}$ and $m\widehat{CD} = 94°$. Find $m\widehat{AB}$.

Because $\overline{AC} \parallel \overline{BD}$, alternate interior angles $\angle CAD \cong \angle BDA$.

By Corollary 14.6, $m\widehat{CD} = m\widehat{AB} = 94°$.

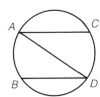

Example   ▲7. $m \angle ABD = y + 30$ and $m \angle ACD = 2y - 6$.
Find $m\widehat{AD}$.

By Corollary 14.6, $m \angle ABD = m \angle ACD$.
Thus, $y + 30 = 2y - 6$
$$y = 36$$

and $m \angle ABD = m \angle ACD = 66°$. Hence, $m\widehat{AD} = 132°$.

Try This...   4. $m\widehat{DF} = 124°$.
Find $m\widehat{DE}$.

5. $\overline{RS} \parallel \overline{UT}$, $m\widehat{RU} = 56°$, and
$m\widehat{RS} = 68°$. Find $m \angle RUT$.

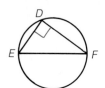

Exercises

▲   **Identify each inscribed angle and its intercepted arc.**

1.

2.

3.
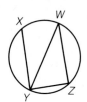

4.

▲▲ **Solve these problems.**

5. $m\widehat{AB} = 136°$.
Find $m \angle ACB$.

6. $m \angle DEF = 17°$.
Find $m\widehat{DF}$.

7. $\overline{XY}$ and $\overline{WZ}$ are
perpendicular
diameters.
Find $m \angle XWZ$.

8. $\overline{PQ}$ is a diameter.
Find $m \angle PRQ$.

9. $m \angle MNP = 70°$, $m \angle QMN = 94°$, and $m\widehat{QP} = 85°$. Find $m \angle MQP$ and $m \angle QPN$.

10. $m \angle C = 90°$, $m\widehat{AD} = 80°$, and $m\widehat{BC} = 125°$. Find $m \angle A$, $m \angle B$, and $m \angle D$.

Use ⊙O for Exercises 11–22. $m \angle P = 24°$, $m \angle Q = 18°$, and $\overline{TR}$ is a diameter. Find these measures.

11. $m\widehat{ST}$
12. $m\widehat{QR}$
13. $m \angle SUR$
14. $m\widehat{TQ}$
15. $m \angle PSQ$
16. $m \angle TRS$

Suppose that $m\widehat{TS} = 40°$, $m\widehat{QR} = 78°$, and $\overline{TR}$ is a diameter. Find these measures in ⊙O.

17. $m \angle QSR$
18. $m \angle P$
19. $m \angle TUQ$
20. $m\widehat{SR}$
21. $m \angle Q$
22. $m \angle PSQ$

▶▶ Challenge Exercises

23. $\triangle ABC$ is equilateral. Find the sum $m \angle D + m \angle E + m \angle F$.

24. Explain how a carpenter's square can be used to check whether a semicircle has been cut in a board.

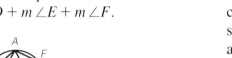

25. $\overline{AB} \parallel \overline{CD}$. How are arcs $\widehat{AC}$ and $\widehat{BD}$ related? Explain how you know.

26. Explain why the opposite angles of a *cyclic* quadrilateral are always supplementary. (See Exercise 15, Section 14–2.)

27. Draw a chord $\overline{AB}$ on a circle and a second chord $\overline{CB}$ such that $m \angle ABC = 45°$. Measure $\angle AOC$. Repeat for several other circles and chords. In each case, what is the measure of $\angle AOC$? Explain how you know.

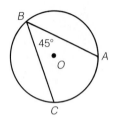

28. $\overline{AB}$ represents the crossbar of a goal post. A football player wishes to kick a ball through the posts. Explain why it is mathematically possible to kick the goal from any point on the circle without changing the difficulty of the angle.

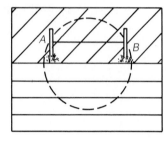

►◄ Activity

A *regular polyhedron* is a three-dimensional figure whose faces are regular polygons. The *icosahedron* is a regular polyhedron formed by equilateral triangles. It has 20 faces.

One way to construct an icosahedron is from circles circumscribed about equilateral triangles.

1. Draw 20 identical circles on stiff paper.

2. Inscribe an equilateral triangle in each circle, and then cut out each circle.

3. Fold each circle along the sides of the triangle so that each circle has three folded flaps.

4. Paste or tape five circles together by joining their flaps to form one corner. Paste five more circles together to form another corner.

5. Connect the remaining ten circles together in a strip.

6. Connect the flaps of the strip between the two corner sections to complete the icosahedron.

4 | Secants and Angles

After finishing Section 4, you should be able to

▲ *solve problems involving a secant angle with an interior vertex.*

▲▲ *solve problems involving a secant angle with an exterior vertex.*

DEFINITION

A **secant** is a line that intersects a circle in two points.

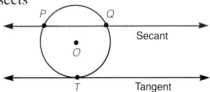

The angles below are formed by secants. They are called *secant angles*. Note that central angles and inscribed angles are special kinds of secant angles.

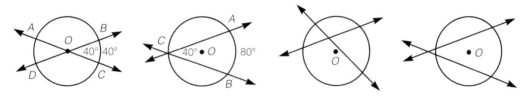

DEFINITION

A **secant angle** is an angle determined by two secants such that each side of the angle intersects the circle in at least one point other than the vertex.

▲ Secant Angles with Interior Vertices

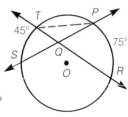

Example   1. $m\widehat{PR} = 75°$ and $m\widehat{TS} = 45°$. Find $m \angle PQR$.

Draw $\overline{TP}$. By Theorem 14.4, $m \angle PTR = \frac{1}{2} \times 75°$
and $m \angle TPS = \frac{1}{2} \times 45°$

By Corollary 7.14, $m \angle PQR = m \angle PTR + m \angle TPS$
$$= \left(\frac{1}{2} \times 75\right) + \left(\frac{1}{2} \times 45\right)$$
$$= \frac{1}{2}(75 + 45)$$
$$= \frac{1}{2} \times 120 = 60°$$

> | THEOREM 14.7 | If a secant angle has its vertex in the interior of a circle, then its measure is one-half the sum of the measures of the arcs intercepted by the angle and its vertical angle. |

Example   2. $m\widehat{DE} = 52°$ and $m\widehat{GF} = 136°$.

Find $m\angle GHF$.

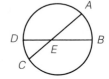

$$m\angle GHF = \tfrac{1}{2}(m\widehat{DE} + m\widehat{GF})$$
$$= \tfrac{1}{2}(52 + 136)$$
$$= 94°$$

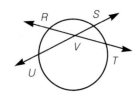

Try This...   1. $m\widehat{AB} = 46°$ and $m\widehat{CD} = 32°$. Find $m\angle AEB$.

Examples   3. $m\angle RVU = 40°$ and $m\widehat{ST} = 32°$. Find $m\widehat{RU}$.

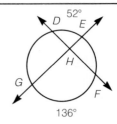

$$m\angle RVU = \tfrac{1}{2}(m\widehat{ST} + m\widehat{RU})$$
$$= \tfrac{1}{2}(32 + m\widehat{RU})$$
$$2m\angle RVU = 32 + m\widehat{RU}$$
$$80 - 32 = m\widehat{RU}$$
$$m\widehat{RU} = 48°$$

▲4. Find $m\angle WVZ$.

Because the measures of the arcs total 360°, we can solve for x.

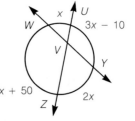

$$x + (3x - 10) + 2x + (2x + 50) = 360$$
$$8x + 40 = 360$$
$$x = 40$$

Because $x = 40$, $m\widehat{WZ} = 130°$ and $m\widehat{UY} = 110°$.

Thus, $m\angle WVZ = \tfrac{1}{2}(130 + 110)$
$$= 120°$$

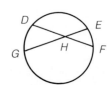

Try This...   2. $m\angle DHE = 142°$ and $m\widehat{GF} = 174°$.

Find $m\widehat{DE}$.

Try This... **▲3.** $m\overset{\frown}{AB} = x$, $m\overset{\frown}{DC} = x + 10$,
$m\overset{\frown}{BC} = 2x + 40$, and
$m\overset{\frown}{AD} = 3x - 5$. Find $m \angle DEC$.

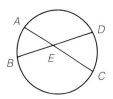

▲▲ Secant Angles with Exterior Vertices

The measure of a secant angle whose vertex is in the exterior of a
circle is also related to the measures of the intercepted arcs.

Example 5. $m\overset{\frown}{AE} = 75°$ and $m\overset{\frown}{BD} = 21°$. Find $m \angle C$.

Draw $\overline{BE}$. By Theorem 14.4,
$m \angle ABE = \frac{1}{2} \times 75°$, and
$m \angle BED = \frac{1}{2} \times 21°$.

By Corollary 7.14,
$m \angle ABE = m \angle C + m \angle BED$,
or $m \angle C = m \angle ABE - m \angle BED$
$= (\frac{1}{2} \times 75) - (\frac{1}{2} \times 21)$
$= \frac{1}{2}(75 - 21)$
$= \frac{1}{2} \times 54 = 27°$

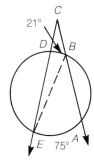

THEOREM 14.8	If a secant angle has its vertex in the exterior of a circle, then its measure is one-half the difference of the measures of the intercepted arcs.

Example 6. $m\overset{\frown}{MN} = 42°$ and $m\overset{\frown}{PQ} = 16°$. Find $m \angle R$.

By Theorem 14.8,
$m \angle R = \frac{1}{2}(m\overset{\frown}{MN} - m\overset{\frown}{PQ})$
$= \frac{1}{2}(42 - 16)$
$= 13°$

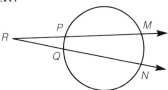

Try This... 4. $m\overset{\frown}{AC} = 37°$ and $m\overset{\frown}{BD} = 128°$.
Find $m \angle E$.

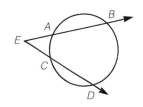

Examples   7. $m \angle T = 43°$ and $m\widehat{WX} = 120°$. Find $m\widehat{ZY}$.

$$m \angle T = \tfrac{1}{2}(m\widehat{WX} - m\widehat{ZY})$$
$$43 = \tfrac{1}{2}(120 - m\widehat{ZY})$$
$$120 - 86 = m\widehat{ZY}$$
$$m\widehat{ZY} = 34°$$

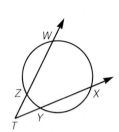

▲8. $m \angle D = 66°$, $m\widehat{GE} = x$, and
$m\widehat{FH} = 3x + 10$. Find $m\widehat{GE}$ and $m\widehat{FH}$.

$$66 = \tfrac{1}{2}(3x + 10 - x)$$
$$= \tfrac{1}{2}(2x + 10)$$
$$= x + 5$$
$$x = 61$$

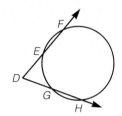

Thus, $m\widehat{GE} = 61°$ and $m\widehat{FH} = 193°$.

Try This...   5. $m \angle H = 83°$ and
$m\widehat{GJ} = 29°$. Find $m\widehat{FK}$.

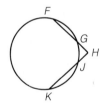

▲6. $m \angle D = 38°$, $m\widehat{LN} = y$,
and $m\widehat{KP} = 2y + 26$.
Find $m\widehat{LN}$ and $m\widehat{KP}$.

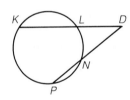

Exercises

▲ **Use the figure for Exercises 1–6.**

1. $m\widehat{PQ} = 82°$ and $m\widehat{SR} = 58°$. Find $m \angle PTQ$.

2. $m\widehat{PQ} = 96°$ and $m\widehat{SR} = 46°$. Find $m \angle STR$.

3. $m\widehat{PS} = 133°$ and $m\widehat{QR} = 118°$. Find $m \angle PTS$.

4. $m\widehat{PS} = 110°$ and $m\widehat{QR} = 103°$. Find $m \angle QTR$.

5. $m\widehat{PQ} = m\widehat{SR}$ and $m \angle PTQ = 73°$. Find $m\widehat{PQ}$ and $m\widehat{SR}$.

▲6. $m\widehat{PQ} = 3x + 16$, and $m\widehat{SR} = x + 10$, and $m \angle STR = 67°$.
Find $m\widehat{PQ}$ and $m\widehat{SR}$.

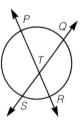

▲▲ Use the figure for Exercises 7–12.

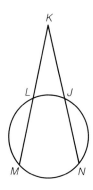

7. $m\widehat{MN} = 63°$ and $m\widehat{LJ} = 27°$. Find $m \angle K$.

8. $m\widehat{MN} = 57°$ and $m\widehat{LJ} = 29°$. Find $m \angle K$.

9. $m \angle K = 17°$ and $m\widehat{LJ} = 33°$. Find $m\widehat{MN}$.

10. $m \angle K = 23°$ and $m\widehat{MN} = 72°$. Find $m\widehat{LJ}$.

▲11. $m \angle K = 22°$, $m\widehat{LJ} = x + 10$, and $m\widehat{MN} = 2x + 6$.
Find $m\widehat{LJ}$ and $m\widehat{MN}$.

▲12. $m\widehat{LJ} = y$, $m\widehat{MN} = 2y$, $m\widehat{LM} = 108°$, and $m\widehat{JN} = 143°$.
Find $m \angle K$.

Use the figure for Exercises 13–16.

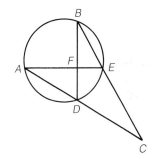

13. $m \angle C = 15°$ and $m \angle AFB = 56°$.
Find $m\widehat{AB}$ and $m\widehat{DE}$.

14. $m \angle C = 22°$ and $m \angle AFB = 70°$.
Find $m\widehat{AB}$ and $m\widehat{DE}$.

15. $m \angle A = 16°$ and $m \angle ADB = 31°$.
Find $m \angle C$ and $m \angle AFB$.

16. $m \angle B = 11°$ and $m \angle BEA = 39°$.
Find $m \angle C$ and $m \angle AFB$.

▶ Extension Exercises

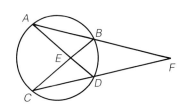

17. Name each pair of
similar triangles.
Explain how you know.

▲18. $m\widehat{AC} = 2x$ and $m\widehat{BD} = x$.
What kind of triangles
are $\triangle ADF$ and $\triangle CBF$?
Explain how you know.

5	Secants and Tangents

After finishing Section 5, you should be able to

▲ *solve problems involving a secant-tangent angle with vertex on the circle.*

▲▲ *solve problems involving a secant-tangent angle with an exterior vertex.*

▲ *solve problems involving a tangent-tangent angle.*

There are three kinds of angles involving secants and tangents of circles.

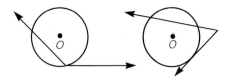

Secant-tangent angles

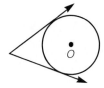

Tangent-tangent angle

▲ Secant-Tangent Angle with Vertex on the Circle

1. Draw ⊙O and two perpendicular diameters, $\overline{AC}$ and $\overline{BD}$. Then draw a tangent $\overrightarrow{BE}$ at B and rays $\overrightarrow{BC}$ and $\overrightarrow{BA}$.

2. Compare $m\widehat{CAB}$ and $m \angle CBE$. $\angle CBE$ intercepts $\widehat{CAB}$.

3. Compare $m\widehat{DAB}$ and $m \angle DBE$. $\angle DBE$ intercepts $\widehat{DAB}$.

4. Compare $m\widehat{AB}$ and $m \angle ABE$. $\angle ABE$ intercepts $\widehat{AB}$.

5. What can you conclude about the measures of secant-tangent angles and their intercepted arcs?

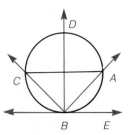

THEOREM 14.9	If a secant-tangent angle has its vertex on the circle, then its measure is one-half the measure of the intercepted arc.

Examples $\overleftrightarrow{EF}$ is tangent to $\odot O$ at E.

1. $m\widehat{DE} = 170°$. Find $m \angle DEF$.

$$m \angle DEF = \tfrac{1}{2}m\widehat{DE}$$

$$= \tfrac{1}{2} \times 170$$

$$= 85°$$

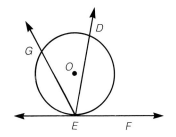

2. $m\widehat{GE} = 133°$. Find $m \angle GEF$.

$$m \angle GEF = \tfrac{1}{2}m\widehat{GDE}$$

$$= \tfrac{1}{2}(360 - m\widehat{GE})$$

$$= \tfrac{1}{2}(360 - 133)$$

$$= \tfrac{1}{2} \times 227$$

$$= 113.5°$$

Try This... $\overleftrightarrow{EB}$ is tangent to $\odot O$ at B.

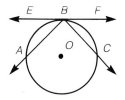

1. $m\widehat{AB} = 84°$ Find $m \angle ABE$.

2. $m\widehat{AB} = 75°$ and $m \angle ABC = 90°$.
   Find $m\widehat{BC}$.

3. $m \angle EBA = m \angle FBC$ and $m \angle ABC = 90°$.
   Find $m\widehat{AB}$ and $m\widehat{BC}$.

▲▲ Secant-Tangent Angles with Exterior Vertex

Suppose that $\overrightarrow{EA}$ is fixed and $\overrightarrow{EB}$ moves so that $m \angle E$ increases.
Eventually the secant-secant angle ($\angle E$) becomes a secant-tangent angle.

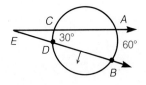   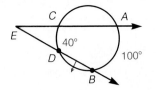   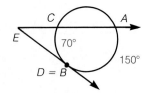

$m \angle E = \frac{1}{2}(60° - 30°)$ $m \angle E = \frac{1}{2}(100° - 40°)$ $m \angle E = \frac{1}{2}(150° - 70°)$

THEOREM 14.10	If a secant-tangent angle has its vertex in the exterior of the circle, then its measure is one-half the difference of the measures of the intercepted arcs.

Examples   3. $m\widehat{AD} = 166°$ and $m\widehat{BD} = 86°$. Find $m \angle C$.

$m \angle C = \frac{1}{2}(166 - 86) = 40°$

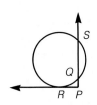

4. $m \angle P = 90°$ and $m\widehat{QR} = 25°$. Find $m\widehat{SR}$.

$$m \angle P = \frac{1}{2}(m\widehat{SR} - 25)$$
$$2 \times 90 + 25 = m\widehat{SR}$$
$$m\widehat{SR} = 205°$$

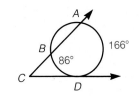

Try This...   4. $m\widehat{GJ} = 130°$, $m\widehat{JK} = 40°$,
$m\widehat{JN} = 38°$, and $m\widehat{JP} = 118°$.
Find $m \angle L$, $m \angle M$, and $m\widehat{GP}$.

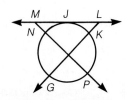

Tangent-Tangent Angles

Suppose that $\overrightarrow{DB}$ is fixed and $\overrightarrow{DA}$ moves so that $m\angle D$ increases. Eventually, the secant-tangent angle ($\angle D$) becomes a tangent-tangent angle.

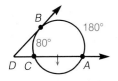 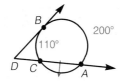 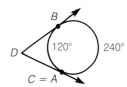

$m\angle D = \frac{1}{2}(180° - 80°)$ $\qquad$ $m\angle D = \frac{1}{2}(200° - 110°)$ $\quad$ $m\angle D = \frac{1}{2}(240° - 120°)$

THEOREM 14.11	The measure of a tangent-tangent angle is one-half the difference of the measures of the intercepted arcs.

Examples 5. $m\widehat{AC} = 135°$. Find $m\widehat{ADC}$ and $m\angle B$.

$$m\angle ADC = 360 - m\widehat{AC}$$
$$= 360 - 135$$
$$= 225°$$
$$m\angle B = \frac{1}{2}(225 - 135)$$
$$= 45°$$

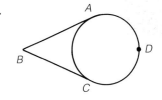

Try This... 5. $m\widehat{QSR} = 210°$. Find $m\angle P$.

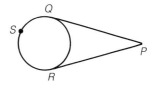

Exercises

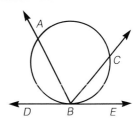

▲ **Use the figure for Exercises 1–6.**

1. $m\widehat{CB} = 82°$. Find $m\angle CBE$.

2. $m\widehat{ACB} = 236°$. Find $m\angle ABE$.

3. $m\widehat{CAB} = 275°$. Find $m\angle CBD$.

4. $m\angle ABD = 78°$. Find $m\widehat{ACB}$.

▲5. $m\angle ABD = 2y - 1$, $m\angle ABC = 2y + 6$, and $m\angle CBE = y$. Find $m\widehat{AB}$.

▲6. $m\widehat{AB} = 2x + 2$, $m\widehat{AC} = 2x + 6$, and $m\widehat{CB} = x + 2$. Find $m\angle CBE$.

▲▲ **Use the figure for Exercises 7–12.**

7. $m\widehat{MP} = 170°$ and $m\widehat{RP} = 100°$. Find $m\angle MQP$.

8. $m\widehat{NP} = 73°$ and $m\widehat{SP} = 35°$. Find $m\angle NQP$.

9. $m\widehat{TR} = 61°$ and $m\widehat{TM} = 89°$. Find $m\angle TQM$.

10. $m\angle TQN = 47°$ and $m\widehat{TS} = 99°$. Find $m\widehat{TMN}$.

▲11. $m\widehat{TM} = 2x + 4$, $m\widehat{TR} = x$, and $m\angle TQM = 28°$. Find $m\widehat{TM}$ and $m\widehat{TR}$.

▲12. $m\angle MQN = 34°$, $m\angle NQP = 28°$, $m\widehat{RP} = y$, and $m\widehat{MP} = 2y + 20$. Find $m\widehat{RP}$ and $m\widehat{MP}$.

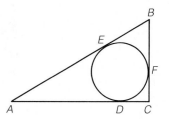

▲▲ ⊙*O* **is inscribed in** △*ABC*.

13. $m\widehat{EFD} = 220°$ and $m\widehat{ED} = 140°$. Find $m\angle A$.

14. $m\widehat{DF} = 95°$ and $m\widehat{DEF} = 265°$. Find $m\angle C$.

15. $m\widehat{EF} = 125°$. Find $m\angle B$.

16. $m\widehat{ED} = m\widehat{EF}$. What kind of triangle is △*ABC*?

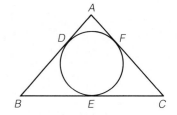

▶▶ Challenge Exercises

17. $m\widehat{ED} = m\widehat{EF}$. What kind of triangle is △*ABC*? Explain how you know.

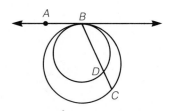

18. Two circles are internally tangent at *B*, and *B-D-C*. Compare $m\widehat{BD}$ and $m\widehat{BC}$. What can you conclude? Explain how you know.

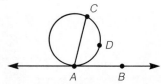

19. $\overrightarrow{AB}$ is a tangent, $\overline{AC}$ is a secant, and *D* is the midpoint of $\widehat{AC}$. Compare the distance from *D* to $\overline{AC}$ and from *D* to $\overleftrightarrow{AB}$. Repeat for another secant $\overline{AE}$. Explain how you know.

6 | Cross Products and Segment Lengths

After finishing Section 6, you should be able to
▲ *apply a theorem about products of lengths of chord segments.*
▲▲ *apply a theorem about products of lengths of secant and tangent segments.*

▲ Cross Products of Chord Lengths

Two intersecting chords determine similar triangles. In this circle, chords $\overline{AD}$ and $\overline{CB}$ intersect each other. If we connect the endpoints of the chords, we have $\triangle AEC$ and $\triangle BED$.

$$\angle 1 \cong \angle 2 \qquad \text{Both angles intercept } \overset{\frown}{AB}.$$
$$\angle 3 \cong \angle 4 \qquad \text{Both angles intercept } \overset{\frown}{CD}.$$

Thus, $\triangle AEC \sim \triangle BED$ by the AA Similarity Theorem. By definition of similar triangles, the sides are proportional.

Thus,
$$\frac{AE}{EB} = \frac{CE}{ED} = \frac{AC}{BD}$$

From the first two ratios, we get the cross product
$$AE \cdot ED = CE \cdot EB$$

THEOREM **14.12**   If two chords, $\overline{AD}$ and $\overline{BC}$, intersect at E in the interior of a circle, then
$$AE \cdot ED = CE \cdot EB.$$

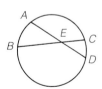

Example   1. $AE = 6$, $BE = 3$, and $CE = 9$. Find ED.

$$6 \cdot ED = 3 \cdot 9$$
$$ED = \frac{27}{6} = \frac{9}{2}$$

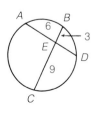

Example   2. $\overline{PQ}$ is a diameter, $\overline{RS} \perp \overline{PQ}$, $PT = 2$, and $TQ = 6$. Find RT and TS.

Because diameter $\overline{PQ}$ is perpendicular to $\overline{RS}$, $RT = TS$.

Thus, $RT^2 = 2 \cdot 6$
$RT = TS = \sqrt{12} = 2\sqrt{3}$

Try This...   1. $ZV = 3$, $XV = 2.5$, $WV = 6$. Find YV.

2. $\overline{DE}$ is a diameter, $\overline{FG} \perp \overline{DE}$, $DH = 3$, $FH = 3.5$. Find HE and HG.

▲▲ Cross Products of a Secant and Tangent

Consider two secants that intersect in the exterior of a circle. By connecting the points where they intersect the circle, we have $\triangle CDA$ and $\triangle CBE$.

$\angle 1 \cong \angle 2$ Both angles intercept $\overset{\frown}{BD}$.
$\angle C \cong \angle C$

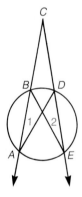

Thus, $\triangle CDA \sim \triangle CBE$ by the AA Similarity Theorem. By definition of similar triangles, the sides are proportional.

So, $\dfrac{AC}{EC} = \dfrac{DC}{BC} = \dfrac{AD}{EB}$

From the first two ratios, we get the cross product
$AC \cdot BC = EC \cdot DC$

THEOREM 14.13	If two secants intersect in a point C in the exterior of a circle and intersect the circle in points A, B, D, and E, then $AC \cdot BC = EC \cdot DC$.	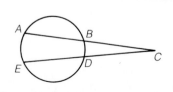

Example   3. $KJ = 4$, $JH = 6$, and $GH = 5$.
             Find FH.

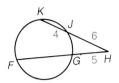

$KH = KJ + JH = 4 + 6 = 10.$
Thus, $10 \cdot 6 = FH \cdot 5$, and $FH = 12$.

Try This...   3. $PR = 36$, $QR = 4$, and $RS = 6$.
                Find RT.

Suppose that $\overline{CA}$ is fixed and $\overline{CE}$ moves so that
points D and E approach each other:

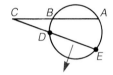   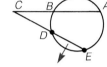   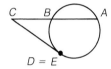

$AC \cdot BC = EC \cdot DC$ $AC \cdot BC = EC \cdot DC$ $AC \cdot BC = DC \cdot DC = DC^2$

THEOREM **14.14**	If a secant and a tangent intersect in a point C in the exterior of the circle, the secant intersects the circle in points B and A, and the tangent intersects the circle in a point D, then $AC \cdot BC = DC^2$.

Examples   4. $PT = 12$ and $TS = 4$. Find RS.

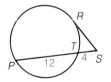

$PS = 12 + 4 = 16.$
$16 \cdot 4 = RS^2$
$\quad RS = 8$

5. $\odot O$ is tangent to $\odot P$ at D. $BC = 5$,
   $AC = 16$, and $CE = 8$. Find CF and CD.

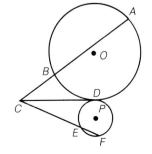

$AC \cdot BC = CD^2 = FC \cdot EC$
$16 \cdot 5 = 8 \cdot FC$
$\quad FC = 10$
$\quad CD = \sqrt{80} = 4\sqrt{5}$

Try This...   4. $HG = 2.5$ and $FG = 1.25$. Find EG.

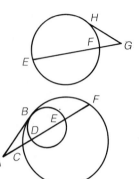

5. The circles are internally tangent at B.
$FA = 20$, $AC = 4$, and $DA = 6$.
Find EA and AB.

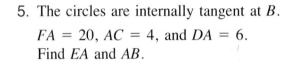

Exercises

▲ **Use the figure for Exercises 1–6.**

1. $AE = 7$, $EB = 8$, and $CE = 4$. Find DE.

2. $AE = 10$, $DE = 15$, and $CE = 8$. Find EB.

3. $AE = EB$, $CE = 4$, and $DE = 9$. Find AB.

4. $AE = EB$, $DC = 15$, and $DE = 12$. Find AE.

5. $AE = 1.5$, $EB = 2$, and $CE = 1$. Find CD.

6. $DE = 3$, $CE = 0.5$, and $AE = 0.6$. Find EB.

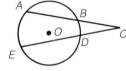

▲▲ **Use $\odot O$ for Exercises 7–9.**

7. $AC = 18$, $BC = 8$, and $EC = 16$. Find DC.

8. $ED = 3$, $DC = 5$, and $BC = 4$. Find AC.

9. $BC = 15$, $AB = 12$, and $CD = 18$. Find CE.

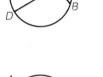

Use $\odot P$ for Exercises 10–12.

10. $BD = 9$ and $BC = 4$. Find BA.

11. $BC = 6$ and $BD = 11$. Find BA.

12. $BA = 2\sqrt{21}$ and $BC = 7$. Find BD.

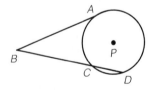

13. The circles are tangent at T.
$RS = 12$, $SP = 12$, and $PX = 8$.
Find XY.

14. The circles are tangent at J.
$EF = 6$, $FH = 3$, and $GH = 2$.
Find HJ and DG.

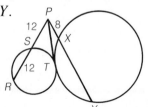

Calculator Application   Finding Cross Products

Use a calculator to find the missing lengths.
Round your answer to the nearest hundredth.

Example $AE = \sqrt{5}$, $EB = \sqrt{8}$, and $CE = \sqrt{7}$.
                 Find ED.

$$AE \cdot EB = CE \cdot ED$$
$$\sqrt{5} \cdot \sqrt{8} = \sqrt{7} \cdot ED$$
$$\frac{\sqrt{5} \cdot \sqrt{8}}{\sqrt{7}} = ED$$

Enter: 5 $\boxed{\sqrt{}}$ $\boxed{\times}$ 8 $\boxed{\sqrt{}}$ $\boxed{=}$ $\boxed{\div}$ 7 $\boxed{\sqrt{}}$ $\boxed{=}$

Display: 2.3904571

$ED = 2.39$

1. Find MN.

2. Find RS.

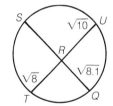

3. Find WY.

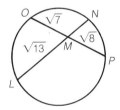

4. Find GH.

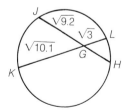

5. Find JK.

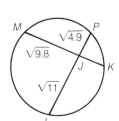

6. Find TV.

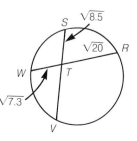

Chapter Review

1 $\overline{AB}$ **and** $\overline{AC}$ **are tangent segments.**

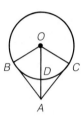

1. The diameter of $\odot O$ is 10 and $AD = 8$. Find AB.

2. $OB = 4.5$ and $AD = 3$. Find the perimeter of quadrilateral $OBAC$.

2 3. Construct the incircle and circumcircle for an acute triangle.

3 4. Name an inscribed angle and its intercepted arc.

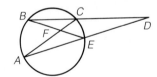

5. $\overline{CD}$ is a diameter, $m\widehat{BD} = 50°$, and $m\widehat{DE} = 96°$. Find $m\angle BCD$ and $m\widehat{BC}$.

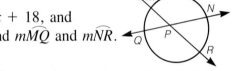

4 **6.** $m\widehat{MQ} = x$, $m\widehat{NR} = x + 18$, and $m\angle MPQ = 53°$. Find $m\widehat{MQ}$ and $m\widehat{NR}$.

7. $m\widehat{DH} = 3 \cdot m\widehat{EG}$, $m\widehat{DE} = 120°$, and $m\widehat{GH} = 152°$. Find $m\angle F$.

8. $m\angle A = 18°$ and $m\angle ACB = 34°$. Find $m\angle D$ and $m\angle AFB$.

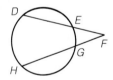

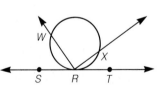

5 **9.** $\overline{ST}$ is tangent to the circle at R. $m\angle WRS = x$, $m\angle WRX = x + 35$, and $m\angle XRT = 2x - 75$. Find $m\widehat{XR}$.

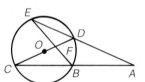

10. $\overrightarrow{BA}$ is tangent to the circle at A. $m\widehat{AC} = 80°$ and $m\widehat{CD} = 105°$. Find $m\angle B$.

11. The circle is inscribed in $\triangle ABC$. $m\widehat{DEF} = 270°$ and $m\widehat{DE} = m\widehat{EF}$. Find $m\angle A$.

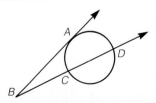

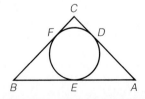

6 12. $AE = 0.6$, $EB = 1.5$, and $DE = 0.9$. Find EC.

13. $WU = 18$, $WZ = 30$, and $ZV = 10$. Find VX.

14. $RS = 2\sqrt{3}$ and $PR = 6$. Find QR.

15. $\overline{PR}$ is tangent to $\odot O$ and $\odot O'$ at R and Q, $\odot O$ is tangent to $\odot O'$ at S, $OR = 2 \cdot O'Q$, $PQ = 5\sqrt{2}$, and $PT = 5$. Find OS.

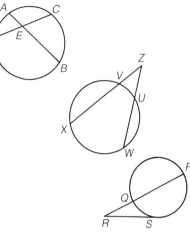

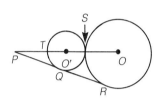

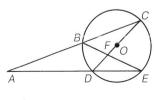

Chapter Test

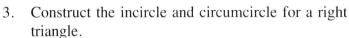

$\overline{AB}$ **and** $\overline{AC}$ **are tangent to** $\odot O$ **at** B **and** C.

1. $OC = 7.5$ and $OA = 15$. Find AB.

2. $m\widehat{BC} = 150°$. Find $m\angle A$.

3. Construct the incircle and circumcircle for a right triangle.

4. Name an inscribed angle and its intercepted arc.

5. $\overline{CD}$ is a diameter, $m\widehat{BD} = 48°$, and $m\widehat{DE} = 88°$. Find $m\angle A$ and $m\angle BFC$.

6. $\overline{CD}$ is a diameter, $m\widehat{AC} = 30°$, and $m\widehat{CB} = 86°$. Find $m\angle AEC$.

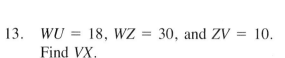

7. $m\widehat{JK} = 2m\widehat{LM}$, $m\widehat{KL} = 95°$, and $m\widehat{JM} = 130°$. Find $m \angle N$.

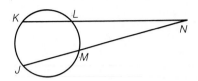

8. $m \angle W = 22°$ and $m \angle RSW = 46°$. Find $m \angle T$ and $m \angle SXU$.

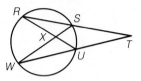

9. AD is tangent to the circle at A. $m\widehat{BA} = m\widehat{CA}$, and $m \angle CAD = 52°$. Find $m \angle BAD$.

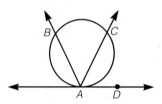

10. $\overrightarrow{AB}$ is tangent to $\odot O$ at B, $\overline{DC}$ is a diameter, and $m\widehat{DB} = 110°$. Find $m \angle A$.

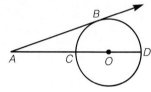

11. The circle is inscribed in $\triangle RST$, $m\widehat{XZ} = 125°$, and $m\widehat{XZ} = m\widehat{YZ}$. Find $m \angle T$.

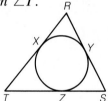

12. $\overline{AB}$ is a diameter, $OE = EB = 0.5$, and $\overline{AB} \perp \overline{CD}$. Find CE and ED.

13. $KL = 5$, $LM = 3$, and $\overline{PN} \cong \overline{NM}$. Find PM.

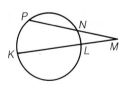

14. $\overline{AB}$ is tangent to the circle at B, $AB = 14$, and $AC = 10$. Find AD.

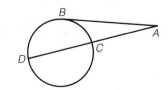

15. Two circles are tangent to $\overline{AB}$ at B, $\overline{AE}$ is tangent to the inner circle at D, $AE = 9$, and $AC = 4$. Find AD.

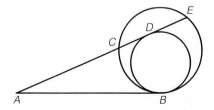

Skills Review   Expressions and Equations

Evaluate each expression for $a = 3$ and $b = -2$.

1. $a + b$

2. ab

3. $a - b$

4. $a + 3b$

5. $-5ab$

6. $4a + 5b$

7. $6 \times a \times a$

8. $-2a - 10b$

9. $11ab$

10. $\dfrac{b}{a}$

11. $\dfrac{2a}{b}$

12. $\dfrac{2b}{a} \times -3$

Solve.

13. $x + 8 = 11$

14. $x + 3 = 1$

15. $5 + x = -3$

16. $x + 25 = 63$

17. $28 + x = 20$

18. $x + 16 = -10$

19. $x - 9 = 5$

20. $x - 11 = -7$

21. $x - 10 = 20$

22. $x - 12 = -24$

23. $x - 13 = -48$

24. $x - 34 = 97$

25. $x + \dfrac{5}{8} = 1$

26. $x - \dfrac{1}{4} = \dfrac{3}{4}$

27. $x - 1 = \dfrac{1}{2}$

Solve.

28. $4x = 24$

29. $8x = 72$

30. $-5x = 45$

31. $3x = -18$

32. $9x = -27$

33. $-11x = -22$

34. $\dfrac{x}{3} = 10$

35. $\dfrac{x}{5} = -3$

36. $\dfrac{x}{8} = -8$

37. $\dfrac{x}{-2} = 7$

38. $\dfrac{x}{4} = -30$

39. $\dfrac{x}{-3} = -7$

40. $2x + 4 = 10$

41. $4x - 3 = 21$

42. $5x + 8 = -12$

15
Coordinate
Geometry

1   Points and Coordinates

After finishing Section 1, you should be able to
▲   *plot points associated with ordered pairs.*
▲▲   *find the coordinates of a point on a graph.*

▲ Plotting Points

The ideas of perpendicular axes and ordered pairs of coordinates allow us to think of a plane as an infinite sheet of graph paper.

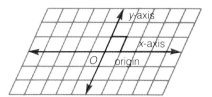

The **x-axis** and the **y-axis** are perpendicular and intersect in a point, *O*, the *origin*. The origin has coordinates (0, 0). The *x*-axis and the *y*-axis determine the **x-y plane**. Point *A* has coordinates (4,3). The first number, 4, is the **x-coordinate** and the second number, 3, is the **y-coordinate**. The *x*-coordinate tells the distance right (positive) or left (negative) from the vertical axis. The *y*-coordinate tells the distance up (positive) or down (negative) from the horizontal axis.

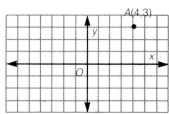

We use the notation *P* (*a*,*b*) to denote the point *P* with coordinates (*a*,*b*). Each point in the plane can be thought of as the **graph** of an ordered pair of numbers.

A city map suggests a coordinate plane. The location of any building can be described by its cross streets. For example, we can locate Pennsylvania Station by its address, the corner of 34th Street and Seventh Avenue. The street and avenue numbers represent the *x*- and *y*-coordinates, respectively.

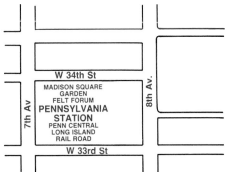

Example 1. Plot the points A $(-2, 3)$, B $(3, -5)$, and C $(-3, -3)$.

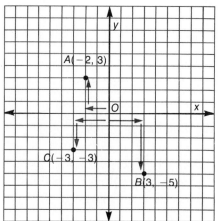

The x-coordinate, -2, is negative. We move 2 units left of the vertical axis. The y-coordinate, 3, is positive. We move 3 units up from the horizontal axis. The graphs of B $(3, -5)$ and C $(-3, -3)$ are shown.

Try This... Use graph paper. Draw and label an x-axis and a y-axis. Plot these points.

1. $M(4, 2)$ 2. $P(5, 4)$ 3. $D(-3, 5)$

4. $R(-2, -6)$ 5. $K(3, -1)$ 6. $W(-3, -5)$

When one coordinate is 0, the point is on one of the axes.

Example 2. Plot the points $A(0, -4)$ and $B(3, 0)$.

The x-coordinate, 0, tells us to move 0 units right or left from the vertical axis. The y-coordinate, -4, tells us to move 4 units down from the horizontal axis. The point $A(0, -4)$ is on the y-axis. The point $B(3, 0)$ is on the x-axis.

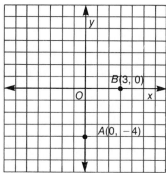

Try This... Plot the following points.

7. $H(0, 6)$ 8. $S(-4, 0)$ 9. $T(0, 0)$ 10. $G(0, -2)$

▲▲ Finding Coordinates

Example   3. Find the coordinates of points E and S.

Point E is 2 units to the left from the vertical
axis and 4 units down from the horizontal axis.
Its coordinates are $(-2, -4)$.

The coordinates of point S are $(5, -3)$.

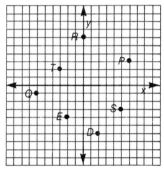

Try This... 11. Find the coordinates of points T, Q, R, P,
and D in the graph of Example 3.

Exercises

▲ **Use graph paper. Draw and label an *x*-axis and a *y*-axis. Plot these points.**

1. $N(5, 2)$ 2. $T(6, 4)$

3. $P(-3, 1)$ 4. $L(-4, 2)$

5. $C(2, -3)$ 6. $A(3, -5)$

7. $Q(-2, -4)$ 8. $W(-7, -5)$

9. $H(0, 6)$ 10. $S(0, -4)$

11. $J(6, 0)$ 12. $M(-5, 0)$

▲▲ **Find the coordinates of points *A, B, C, D*, and *E*.**

13.   14.

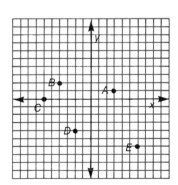

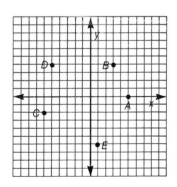

▶ Extension Exercises

Use graph paper. Plot a point that satisfies each of the following conditions.

15. The x-coordinate is 3 greater than the y-coordinate.

16. The x-coordinate and the y-coordinate are the same.

17. The x-coordinate is the inverse of the y-coordinate.

18. The product of the coordinates is -24.

19. The x-coordinate is the square of the y-coordinate.

20. The sum of the coordinates is 12.

▶▶ Challenge Exercises

21. Graph 12 points such that the sum of the coordinates of each point is 8. What do you observe?

22. Graph 12 points such that the difference between the coordinates of each point is 2. What do you observe?

▶◀ Activity

Draw and label an x-axis and a y-axis on graph paper. Plot each point and then connect the points to create a geometric figure. What kind of figure do you get?

Figure A	$(-3, -1)$	$(1, -1)$	$(1, 3)$	$(-3, 3)$
Figure B	$(2, 1)$	$(6, 3)$	$(6, 0)$	$(2, -2)$
Figure C	$(-3, -2)$	$(6, -2)$	$(5, 1)$	$(-2, 1)$
Figure D	$(-1, -1)$	$(1, 1)$	$(5, -3)$	$(3, -5)$
Figure E	$(-5, -1)$	$(-6, -1)$	$(-7, -2)$	$(-7, -3)$
	$(-6, -4)$	$(-5, -4)$	$(-4, -3)$	$(-4, -2)$

2	The Distance Formula

After finishing Section 2, you should be able to
▲ *find the distance between any two points in the coordinate plane using the Distance Formula.*
▲▲ *solve problems using the Distance Formula.*

▲ Calculating Distance

In Chapter 2, we found the distance between two points on a line by using absolute value. This method works on any horizontal or vertical line.

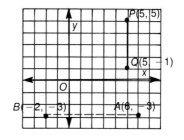

Example 1. Find PQ.

PQ is the absolute value of the difference of the y-coordinates.

$PQ = |5 - 1| = |4| = 4$

Try This... 1. Find AB in the drawing above.

There is also a method for finding distances on lines that are neither vertical nor horizontal.

1. Use graph paper. Graph points $A(4, 5)$ and $B(1, 1)$.
2. Draw the vertical line that contains point A and the horizontal line that contains B. Label their intersection C. What kind of triangle is $\triangle ABC$?
3. Find AC and BC.
4. Use the Pythagorean Theorem. Find AB.

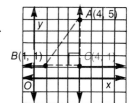

The following formula can be used to find the distance between any two points.

THEOREM
15.1

The Distance Formula

The distance between any two points $A(x_1, y_1)$ and $B(x_2, y_2)$ is given by the formula

$$d = \sqrt{(x_2 - x_1)^2 + (y_2 - y_1)^2}$$

Examples   2. Find the distance between $P(7, 8)$ and $Q(-5, 3)$.

Use $(7, 8)$ for (x_1, y_1) and $(-5, 3)$ for (x_2, y_2).

$$\begin{aligned} d &= \sqrt{(x_2 - x_1)^2 + (y_2 - y_1)^2} \\ &= \sqrt{(-5 - 7)^2 + (3 - 8)^2} \qquad \text{Substituting for } x_1, x_2, \\ &= \sqrt{(-12)^2 + (-5)^2} \qquad\qquad\quad y_1, \text{ and } y_2 \\ &= \sqrt{144} + 25 \\ &= \sqrt{169} \end{aligned}$$

Thus, $PQ = 13$.

3. Find the distance between $G(-2, 5)$ and $K(3, 7)$.

Use $(-2, 5)$ for (x_1, y_1) and $(3, 7)$ for (x_2, y_2).

$$\begin{aligned} d &= \sqrt{(x_2 - x_1)^2 + (y_2 - y_1)^2} \\ &= \sqrt{[3 - (-2)]^2 + (7 - 5)^2} \qquad \text{Substituting} \\ &= \sqrt{(5)^2 + (2)^2} \\ &= \sqrt{25 + 4} = \sqrt{29} \end{aligned}$$

When we are using the distance formula, the order of the points is not important. We must, however, subtract the coordinates in the same order.

Try This...   Find the distance between each pair of points.

2. $(3, 2)$ and $(-1, -1)$ 3. $(5, 9)$ and $(1, -6)$

▲▲ Solving Problems

The distance formula can be used to help solve problems.

Example   4. Find the perimeter of a triangle with vertices $A(1, 2)$, $B(4, 6)$, and $C(6, 3)$.

First we find AB, BC, and AC using the distance formula.
$$AC = \sqrt{(6 - 1)^2 + (3 - 2)^2}$$
$$= \sqrt{(5)^2 + (1)^2}$$
$$= \sqrt{26}$$

$$AB = \sqrt{(1 - 4)^2 + (2 - 6)^2}$$
$$= \sqrt{(-3)^2 + (-4)^2}$$
$$= \sqrt{9 + 16}$$
$$= \sqrt{25}$$
$$= 5$$

$$BC = \sqrt{(6 - 4)^2 + (3 - 6)^2}$$
$$= \sqrt{(2)^2 + (-3)^2}$$
$$= \sqrt{4 + 9}$$
$$= \sqrt{13}$$

The perimeter is $AC + AB + BC$ or $\sqrt{26} + 5 + \sqrt{13}$.

Try This...   4. Find the perimeter of a triangle with vertices $P(4, 2)$, $Q(5, 3)$, and $R(1, 9)$.

Exercises

▲   **Find the distance between each pair of points.**

1. $(6, 1)$ and $(9, 5)$
2. $(1, 10)$ and $(7, 2)$
3. $(-5, -2)$ and $(1, -5)$
4. $(-2, 1)$ and $(2, 4)$
5. $(3, -4)$ and $(0, -7)$
6. $(-5, 9)$ and $(1, -6)$

7. $(2, 2)$ and $(7, 3)$ 8. $(-3, 0)$ and $(0, 8)$

9. $(-2, -6)$ and $(-3, 8)$ 10. $(0, 3)$ and $(-8, 6)$

11. $(3, 7)$ and $(-1, -2)$ ▲12. $(x, -3)$ and $(2x, 5)$

▲13. $(5, 2y)$ and $(-3, y)$ ▲14. $(4, y)$ and $(-x, y)$

▲15. $(a - b, a + b)$ and $(a + b, b - a)$

Solve these problems.

16. Find the perimeter of a triangle with vertices $P(5, 6), Q(-1, -2)$, and $R(6, -3)$.

17. Find the perimeter of a triangle with vertices $A(-2, 7), B(-3, 9)$, and $C(2, 6)$.

18. Find the lengths of the diagonals of a quadrilateral with vertices $X(3, 7), Y(-1, -2), Z(-5, 1)$, and $W(-2, 9)$.

19. Find the lengths of the diagonals of a quadrilateral with vertices $R(2, 9), S(-2, -3), T(-6, 2)$, and $V(-3, 10)$.

▶ Extension Exercises

20. A triangle has vertices $A(3, 4), B(4, -1)$, and $C(-1, -2)$. Explain why the triangle is isosceles.

21. A quadrilateral has vertices $M(2, 1), N(7, 3), Q(8, 7)$, and $P(3, 5)$. Explain why it is a parallelogram. (*Hint:* Show that the opposite sides are congruent.)

22. A triangle has vertices $G(5, 6), K(1, 3)$, and $L(4, -1)$. Explain why it is a right triangle. (*Hint:* Use the converse of the Pythagorean Theorem.)

▶▶ Challenge Exercise

23. Suppose $PQ = 10$. P has coordinates $(1, 6)$ and Q has coordinates $(0, y)$. Find all possible y-coordinates of Q.

3	Slope

After finishing Section 3, you should be able to
▲   *find the slope of a line that contains a given pair of points.*
▲▲ *find the slope, if possible, of a horizontal or vertical line.*

▲   Slope of a Line

Segments in a coordinate plane can slant in different directions and at different angles.

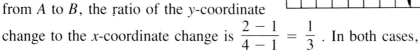

Segments AB and PQ in the figure appear to have the same slant. As we move from P to Q, the change in the y-coordinate is $4 - 2 = 2$. The change in the x-coordinate is $(-1) - (-7) = 6$.

The ratio of the y-coordinate change to the x-coordinate change is the ratio $\dfrac{2}{6}$, or $\dfrac{1}{3}$. Similarly, as we move from A to B, the ratio of the y-coordinate change to the x-coordinate change is $\dfrac{2 - 1}{4 - 1} = \dfrac{1}{3}$. In both cases, the ratio is the same. This ratio is the **slope** of the segment.

DEFINITION

For points $P_1(x_1, y_1)$ and $P_2(x_2, y_2)$, if P_1P_2 is a nonvertical segment, then the ratio $\dfrac{y_2 - y_1}{x_2 - x_1}$ is the **slope** of P_1P_2.

Example   1. Consider the points $P(2, 3)$ and $Q(1, 1)$. Find the slope of PQ.

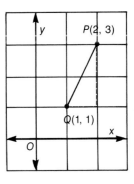

$$\text{The slope } m = \frac{y_2 - y_1}{x_2 - x_1}$$

$$= \frac{\text{change in } y}{\text{change in } x}$$

$$= \frac{3 - 1}{2 - 1} = \frac{2}{1} \text{ or } 2$$

Note that if the points $P(2, 3)$ and $Q(1, 1)$ are considered in the opposite order, the change in both x and y is negative. Thus, we get the same slope:

$$m = \frac{1 - 3}{1 - 2} = \frac{-2}{-1} = 2$$

When we are computing slope, the order of the points does not matter as long as we use the same order when we subtract. The slope of segment $\overline{PQ}$ is the same as the slope of segment $\overline{QP}$.

Try This... Find the slopes of the segments with these endpoints.

1. $(2, 4)$ and $(5, 6)$ 2. $(3, 7)$ and $(6, 8)$

Segments slanting upward from left to right have positive slopes. Segments slanting downward from left to right have negative slopes.

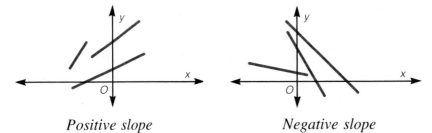

Positive slope *Negative slope*

It seems sensible that any two segments on a line have the same slope. The following theorem guarantees that this is true.

Slope $\overline{PQ}$ = Slope $\overline{AB}$

THEOREM If ℓ is any nonvertical line, then all segments on ℓ have the same
15.2 slope.

___ DEFINITION

The slope of any nonvertical line ℓ is the slope of any segment on ℓ.

Example 2. Plot the points $A(2, 1)$ and $B(5, -3)$.
Draw $\overleftrightarrow{AB}$ and find its slope.

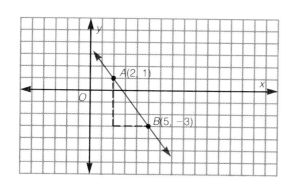

Slope $\overleftrightarrow{AB} = \dfrac{y_2 - y_1}{x_2 - x_1}$

$= \dfrac{1 - (-3)}{2 - 5}$

$= \dfrac{4}{-3}$ or $-\dfrac{4}{3}$

Try This... Use graph paper. Draw the line that contains each pair of points. Then find its slope.

3. $G(1, 4)$ and $K(5, -2)$ 4. $M(-2, 3)$ and $N(2, -3)$

▲▲ Slopes of Horizontal and Vertical Lines

What are the slopes of horizontal and vertical lines?

Examples 3. Find the slope of the line that contains points $L(-3, 2)$ and $G(4, 2)$.

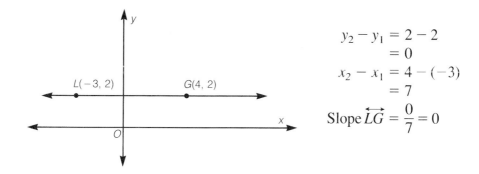

$y_2 - y_1 = 2 - 2$
$\qquad = 0$
$x_2 - x_1 = 4 - (-3)$
$\qquad = 7$
Slope $\overleftrightarrow{LG} = \dfrac{0}{7} = 0$

Any two points on a horizontal line have the same y-coordinate.
Because the change in y is 0, the slope of a horizontal line is 0.

4. Find the slope of the line that contains points $N(-3, 3)$ and $F(-3, -2)$.

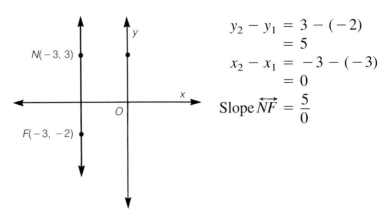

$$y_2 - y_1 = 3 - (-2)$$
$$= 5$$
$$x_2 - x_1 = -3 - (-3)$$
$$= 0$$
$$\text{Slope } \overleftrightarrow{NF} = \frac{5}{0}$$

Because we do not define division by 0, this line has no slope.

THEOREM 15.3 A horizontal line has slope 0.
A vertical line has no slope.

Try This... Find the slope (if possible) of the line that contains the given pair of points.

5. $D(5, 7)$ and $F(-3, 7)$ 6. $T(-4, 8)$ and $K(-4, 10)$

Exercises

▲ **Find the slope of the line that contains the given pair of points.**

1. $(6, 0)$ and $(7, 9)$ 2. $(5, 0)$ and $(6, 2)$
3. $(0, 9)$ and $(-3, 6)$ 4. $(-2, 1)$ and $(-4, 5)$
5. $(0, 0)$ and $(-6, -9)$ 6. $(0, 0)$ and $(-8, -12)$
7. $(4, -2)$ and $(8, -3)$ 8. $(5, -3)$ and $(9, -4)$

9. $(-3, -6)$ and $(-7, -4)$ 10. $(-2, -5)$ and $(-8, -6)$

11. $\left(\frac{1}{2}, \frac{1}{4}\right)$ and $\left(\frac{1}{4}, \frac{3}{4}\right)$ 12. $\left(\frac{1}{4}, \frac{1}{8}\right)$ and $\left(\frac{3}{4}, \frac{1}{2}\right)$

13. $\left(\frac{1}{8}, \frac{1}{2}\right)$ and $\left(\frac{3}{8}, \frac{1}{4}\right)$ 14. $\left(\frac{1}{3}, -\frac{1}{5}\right)$ and $\left(\frac{2}{3}, \frac{1}{10}\right)$

▲▲ **Find the slope (if possible) of the line that contains the given pair of points.**

15. $(8, 9)$ and $(-4, 9)$ 16. $(2, 4)$ and $(2, -6)$

17. $(-2, 6)$ and $(-2, 21)$ 18. $(0, 11)$ and $(5, 11)$

19. $(4, -10)$ and $(18, -10)$ 20. $(-5, -4)$ and $(16, -4)$

21. $(3, 6)$ and $(3, -11)$ 22. $(-11, 9)$ and $(16, 9)$

▶ Extension Exercises

The slope of a line and the coordinates of two points on the line are given. Find the missing coordinate.

23. $m = 2$, $A(4, 3)$ and $B(x, 7)$

24. $m = -3$, $C(2, y)$ and $D(6, 4)$

25. $m = \frac{2}{3}$, $E(9, y)$ and $F(-6, 3)$

▶▶ Challenge Exercises

26. Three nonvertical lines, each containing the origin, have slopes 5, -2, and n. What is the y-coordinate of the point on each line if the x-coordinate is 1?

27. A line contains $P(0, 0)$ and $Q(4, 6)$. Find the coordinates of point $R(a, b)$ such that P-Q-R and $QR = 8\sqrt{13}$.

28. If p and q are not zero, find the slope of the line containing $A\left(p, \frac{p}{q}\right)$ and $B\left(q, \frac{q}{p}\right)$

4   Lines and Equations

After finishing Section 4, you should be able to

▲   *write the Point-Slope Equation of a line, given the slope of the line and a point on the line.*

▲▲   *find the slope and y-intercept of a line, given the Slope-Intercept Equation of the line.*

▲   The Point-Slope Equation

We can use equations to describe lines. Consider a line that contains the point (3, 2) and has slope 3. Suppose (x, y) is any other point on the line. Because the slope is 3, we know

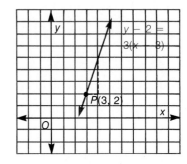

$$\frac{y - 2}{x - 3} = 3$$

When $x = 3$, this equation is meaningless. However, if we multiply both sides by $(x - 3)$, we have $y - 2 = 3(x - 3)$.

This equation is satisfied by every point on the line.

THEOREM   *The Point-Slope Equation*

15.4   A nonvertical line ℓ that contains point $A(x_1, y_1)$ and has slope m has an equation

$$y - y_1 = m(x - x_1)$$

Example   1. Write an equation for the line that contains the point (1, 4) and has slope 4.

$$
\begin{aligned}
y - y_1 &= m(x - x_1) \\
y - 4 &= 4(x - 1) &&\text{Substituting} \\
y - 4 &= 4x - 4 \\
y &= 4x &&\text{Simplifying}
\end{aligned}
$$

Try This...   Write an equation for the line that contains the given point and has the given slope.

1. $P(2, 3), m = 3$ 2. $P(0, -6), m = -\dfrac{1}{2}$

▲▲ The Slope-Intercept Equation

Any nonvertical line must intercept the y-axis.

DEFINITION

> The y-coordinate of the point of intersection of a line and the y-axis is the **y-intercept**.

If we know the slope and y-intercept of a line, we can write an equation for the line. Suppose a line has slope 3 and intersects the y-axis at $P(0, -4)$. From the point-slope equation, we have

$$y - (-4) = 3(x - 0)$$
$$y + 4 = 3x$$
$$y = 3x - 4$$

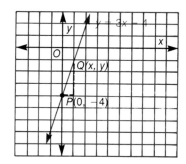

This is the slope-intercept equation for the line.

THEOREM *The Slope-Intercept Equation*

15.5 A nonvertical line with slope m and y-intercept b has an equation

$$y = mx + b$$

Examples 2. Find the slope and y-intercept of the line with equation
$y = 4x - \dfrac{1}{5}$.

We can read the numbers directly from the slope-intercept equation:

$$y = 4x - \frac{1}{5}$$

slope = 4   y-intercept = $-\dfrac{1}{5}$

3. Find the slope and y-intercept of the line with equation $2x - 4y - 8 = 0$.

First, we solve for y:

$$2x - 4y - 8 = 0$$
$$-4y = -2x + 8$$
$$-\frac{1}{4}(-4y) = -\frac{1}{4}(-2x + 8)$$
$$y = \frac{1}{2}x - 2$$

Then, from the equation we see that the slope is $\frac{1}{2}$ and the y-intercept is -2.

Try This...   Find the slope and y-intercept of the line described by each equation.

3. $y = -5x + 16$

4. $y = -3$

5. $-2x + 3y - 8 = 0$

6. $3x - 6y - 11 = 0$

Exercises

▲   **Write an equation for the line that contains point A and has slope m.**

1. $A(2, 5)$ and $m = 5$

2. $A(3, 4)$ and $m = 4$

3. $A(-3, 1)$ and $m = 2$

4. $A(-2, 3)$ and $m = 3$

5. $A(-2, -3)$ and $m = 7$

6. $A(-4, -2)$ and $m = 6$

7. $A(-1, 2)$ and $m = -2$

8. $A(-2, 3)$ and $m = -3$

9. $A(-3, 0)$ and $m = -3$

10. $A(-4, 0)$ and $m = -5$

11. $A(0, 5)$ and $m = -1$

12. $A(0, 4)$ and $m = -2$

13. $A(5, 6)$ and $m = 0$

14. $A(-2, 3)$ and $m = 0$

15. $A(4, 3)$ and $m = \frac{3}{4}$

16. $A(3, 5)$ and $m = \frac{3}{4}$

17. $A(5, 6)$ and $m = -\frac{2}{3}$

18. $A(2, 7)$ and $m = -\frac{5}{6}$

▲▲ **Find the slope and *y*-intercept of the line described by each equation.**

19. $y = 8x + 3$ 20. $y = 9x + 2$ 21. $y = -5x + 4$

22. $y = -4x + 7$ 23. $y = -6x - 9$ 24. $y = -8x - 12$

25. $y = \dfrac{2}{3}x + 8$ 26. $y = \dfrac{3}{5}x + 10$ 27. $3x - 4y - 14 = 0$

28. $2x - 5y - 10 = 0$ 29. $5x - 8y + 15 = 0$ 30. $4x - 3y + 18 = 0$

31. $y = 11$ 32. $y = -4$ 33. $y = 0$

▶ Extension Exercises

Write an equation for the line that contains each pair of points. (*Hint:* First find the slope.)

34. $(2, 3)$ and $(-6, 1)$ 35. $(12, 16)$ and $(1, 5)$

36. $(4, 2)$ and $(0, 4)$ 37. $(0, 0)$ and $(4, 6)$

Write an equation for the horizontal line that contains the given point.

38. $(4, 6)$ 39. $(7, 18)$

40. $(-8, 21)$ 41. $(-2, 16)$

▶◀ Activity

Draw and label an *x*-axis and a *y*-axis on graph paper. Starting from (0, 6), draw segments in the order shown. What kind of figure did you draw? (Read across the page.)

Start   (0, 6) (−4, −4)   (6, 0)   (−4, 4)
(0, −6)   (4, 4)   (−6, 0)   (4, −4)   (0, 6)   End

How many lines of symmetry can you find? How many other geometric figures can you find in the drawing?

| 5 | Parallel and Perpendicular Lines |

After finishing Section 5, you should be able to
▲   *use equations to determine whether two lines are parallel.*
▲▲ *use equations to determine whether two lines are perpendicular.*

▲   Parallel Lines

The equations of lines can help us determine whether the lines are parallel.

1. Use graph paper. Graph each of these equations using the same set of axes.

| $y = 2x$ | $y = 2x + 1$ | $y = 2x + 2$ |
| $y = 2x - 1$ | $y = 2x - 2$ | $y = 2x + 4$ |

2. Describe these lines.

| THEOREM 15.6 | Two nonvertical lines are parallel whenever they have the same slope. |

Examples   1. Determine whether the graphs of $y = -2x + 5$ and $4y = -12x + 20$ are parallel.

The slope-intercept form of $4y = -12x + 20$ is the slope-intercept equation $\qquad y = -3x + 5$.

The slopes are different, so the lines are not parallel.

2. Tell whether the graphs of $3y = 9x + 24$ and $2y - 6x = -4$ are parallel.

The slope-intercept equations are $y = 3x + 8$ and $y = 3x - 2$. The slopes are the same, so the lines are parallel.

Try This... Use the equations to determine whether the lines in each pair are parallel.

1. $x + 8 = y$
    $y - x = -5$

2. $2x + 8 = 6y$
    $4x - y = -17$

▲▲ Perpendicular Lines

We can use the equations of lines to determine whether the lines are perpendicular.

1. Use graph paper. Draw a line that has slope 2 and contains the point $P(-1, 3)$.

2. On the same x-y plane, draw a line that has slope $-\dfrac{1}{2}$ and contains P.

3. Use graph paper. Draw a line ℓ that contains point $A(3, 5)$ and has slope $\dfrac{3}{4}$.

4. At A, draw the line ℓ_1 perpendicular to ℓ. What is the slope of ℓ_1?

5. What can you conclude about the slopes of perpendicular lines?

THEOREM 15.7	Two nonvertical lines ℓ and ℓ_1 are perpendicular whenever the product of their slopes is -1.

Example 3. Determine whether the graphs of $y = \dfrac{2}{3}x + 6$ and $4y + 6x - 18 = 0$ are perpendicular.

We find the slope-intercept equation of the second line:

$$y = -\frac{3}{2}x + \frac{9}{2}$$

The product of the slopes is -1:

$$\left(\frac{2}{3}\right)\left(-\frac{3}{2}\right) = -1$$

Thus, the lines are perpendicular.

Try This...   Use the equations to determine whether the lines in each pair are
               perpendicular.

3. $2y - x = 3$ 4. $3y = 2x + 10$
     $y + 2x = 8$ $2y = 3x - 8$

Exercises

▲   **Use the equations to determine whether the lines in each
     pair are parallel.**

1. $x + 4 = y$ 2. $3x - 9 = y$ 3. $y + 4 = 4x$
     $y - x = -3$ $y - 3x = 10$ $2x - y = -6$

4. $y + 10 = -3x$ 5. $y = 5x + 7$ 6. $y = -4x - 8$
     $-5x + y = 6$ $2y + 10x = -4$ $2y + 8x = 3$

7. $3y - 9x - 7 = 0$ 8. $4y - 10x - 8 = 0$ 9. $5y - 7x - 6 = 0$

     $y - 3x = 0$ $y = -\dfrac{5}{2}x + 7$ $y = \dfrac{7}{5}x + 11$

▲▲   **Use the equations to determine whether the lines in
     each pair are perpendicular.**

10. $x + 5 = y$ 11. $3x - 5 = y$ 12. $4x + 5y = 7$

     $y + x = -2$ $\dfrac{1}{3}x + y = -2$ $4x + 5y = 8$

13. $3x + 7y = 9$ 14. $3x - 8y - 7 = 0$ 15. $5x + 9y = 17$
     $7x - 3y = 12$ $3y + 5 = 8x$ $9x + 5y + 8 = 0$

▶◀ Activity

Draw and label an x-axis and a y-axis on graph paper.
Draw segments between the points listed here.

$(-2,7) \rightarrow (2, 7); (2, 7) \rightarrow (2, 3); (2, 3) \rightarrow (-2, 3);$
$(-2, 3) \rightarrow (-2, 7); (-2, 3) \rightarrow (-4, 0); (2, 3) \rightarrow (4, 0);$
$(-4, 0) \rightarrow (4, 0); (-4, 0) \rightarrow (-2, -3); (4, 0) \rightarrow (2, 3);$
$(4, 0) \rightarrow (6, -3); (-4, 0) \rightarrow (-6, -3); (6, -3) \rightarrow (-6, -3)$

Cut out the figure and fold along the segments to form
a space figure. Use two copies of this figure to form
a pyramid.

6 | The Midpoint Theorem

After finishing Section 6, you should be able to
▲ *find the coordinates of the midpoint of a segment.*
▲▲ *solve problems involving the Midpoint Theorem.*

▲ Coordinates of Midpoints

We can describe the midpoint of a segment in terms of the coordinates of its endpoints.

1. Use graph paper. Graph the segments with these endpoints:

$A(6, 4)$ and $B(8, -6)$ $P(0, 5)$ and $Q(4, 3)$
$H(10, 3)$ and $F(6, 7)$ $K(8, 2)$ and $M(-6, 10)$

2. Find the coordinates of the midpoint of each segment.

3. Do you observe a relationship between the coordinates of the endpoints and midpoint of a segment?

THEOREM
15.8

The Midpoint Theorem

The coordinates of the midpoint M of a segment with endpoints $A(x_1, y_1)$ and $B(x_2, y_2)$ are

$$\frac{x_1 + x_2}{2}, \frac{y_1 + y_2}{2}$$

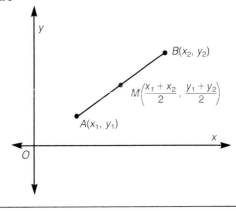

Example   1. Find the coordinates of the midpoint of $\overline{PQ}$ if the coordinates of the endpoints are $P(5, 7)$ and $Q(9, -3)$.

We can substitute the coordinates of P and Q for (x_1, y_1) and (x_2, y_2) in the midpoint formula. Then the coordinates of the midpoint are

$$\left(\frac{x_1 + x_2}{2}, \frac{y_1 + y_2}{2}\right) = \left(\frac{5 + 9}{2}, \frac{7 + (-3)}{2}\right)$$

$$= \left(\frac{14}{2}, \frac{4}{2}\right) = (7, 2)$$

Thus, the coordinates of the midpoint of $\overline{PQ}$ are (7, 2).

Try This... Given the coordinates of P and Q, find the coordinates of the midpoint of $\overline{PQ}$.

1. $P(5, 10)$ and $Q(7, -2)$ 2. $P(6, -12)$ and $Q(-8, 2)$

▲▲ Solving Problems

We can use the Midpoint Theorem to solve problems.

Example 2. Consider $\overline{AB}$. The coordinates of A are (5, 8) and the coordinates of the midpoint M are (−2, 3). Find the coordinates of B.

Suppose the coordinates of B are (x, y). Then we substitute in the midpoint formula:

$$-2 = \frac{x_1 + x_2}{2} \quad 3 = \frac{y_1 + y_2}{2}$$

$$-2 = \frac{5 + x}{2} \quad 3 = \frac{8 + y}{2}$$

$$-4 = 5 + x \quad 6 = 8 + y$$

$$-9 = x \quad \quad -2 = y$$

The coordinates of B are (−9, −2).

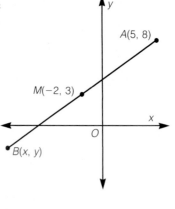

Try This... 3. Consider $\overline{PQ}$. The coordinates of P are (7, 2) and the coordinates of the midpoint M are (−6, 4). Find the coordinates of Q.

Example 3. Suppose $\triangle ABC$ has vertices $A(6, 2)$, $B(-4, 6)$, and $C(-6, -4)$. Find the length of the median from A to $\overline{BC}$.

Suppose M, the midpoint of $\overline{BC}$, has coordinates (x, y).

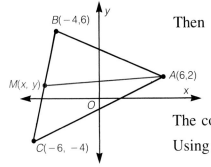

Then $\quad x = \dfrac{-4 + (-6)}{2} \quad$ and $\quad y = \dfrac{6 + (-4)}{2}$

$$= \frac{-10}{2} \qquad\qquad = \frac{2}{2}$$

$$= -5 \qquad\qquad\quad = 1$$

The coordinates of M are $(-5, 1)$.

Using the Distance Formula, we then find AM.

$$AM = \sqrt{(-5 - 6)^2 + (1 - 2)^2}$$
$$= \sqrt{(-11)^2 + (-1)^2}$$
$$= \sqrt{121 + 1}$$
$$= \sqrt{122}$$

Try This... 4. Consider $\triangle ABC$ in Example 3. Find the length of the median from B to $\overline{AC}$.

Exercises

▲ **Given the coordinates of P and Q, find the coordinates of the midpoint of $\overline{PQ}$.**

1. $P(2, 5), Q(6, 3)$
2. $P(8, 2), Q(6, 10)$
3. $P(5, 4), Q(-3, 6)$
4. $P(7, 5), Q(3, 3)$
5. $P(0, 2), Q(6, 3)$
6. $P(0, 5), Q(8, 2)$
7. $P(9, 10), Q(-6, -4)$
8. $P(17, 12), Q(-8, -5)$
9. $P(-8, -5), Q(-7, -6)$
10. $P(0, 9), Q(-11, 0)$
11. $P(0, -8), Q(-6, 0)$
12. $P(a, 6), Q(5a, 9)$
13. $P(s, t), Q(6s, 9t)$
14. $P(6x, 3), Q(-2x, -4)$

▲▲ **Given the coordinates of the midpoint and one endpoint of $\overline{PQ}$, find the coordinates of the other endpoint.**

15. $M(-1, 5), P(3, 8)$ 16. $M(1, 6), P(4, 7)$
17. Suppose $\triangle PQR$ has vertices $P(8, 4)$, $Q(-4, 10)$, and $R(-8, -6)$.
    a.   Find the length of the median from P to $\overline{QR}$.
    b.   Find the length of the median from Q to $\overline{PR}$.

Computer Application   Finding the Slope of a Segment

Find the slope of a segment using the coordinates of the endpoints.

Command

```
10 PRINT "TYPE IN THE
   COORDINATES OF THE FIRST
   POINT."
20 INPUT A, B
30 PRINT "TYPE IN THE
   COORDINATES OF THE SECOND
   POINT."
40 INPUT C, D
50 IF C - A = 0 THEN 100
60 LET M = (D - B) / (C - A)
70 IF M > 0 THEN 120
80 IF M < 0 THEN 140
90 IF M = 0 THEN 160
100 PRINT "THE SEGMENT IS
    VERTICAL AND HAS NO SLOPE."
110 GOTO 170
120 PRINT "THE SEGMENT HAS A
    POSITIVE SLOPE OF   "; M
130 GOTO 170
140 PRINT "THE SEGMENT HAS A
    NEGATIVE SLOPE OF   "; M
150 GOTO 170
160 PRINT "THE SEGMENT IS
    HORIZONTAL AND HAS A SLOPE
    OF   "; M
170 END
```

Comments

20 AND 40 The computer accepts input from the user.

50 The computer proceeds to line 100 if the divisor is zero, because division by zero is undefined.

60 The computer assigns the value of the slope to the variable M.

70-90 The computer is sent to the indicated line if it satisfies the given conditions.

100-160 The computer prints the value of the slope for the segment.

Use the above program to find the slope of a segment with the following endpoints.

1. $(2,3),(4,5)$ 2. $(4,0),(0,6)$ 3. $(-1,-4),(-1,5)$ 4. $(5,7),(-2,1)$
5. $(-2,1),(-4,3)$ 6. $(1,-8),(-7,-8)$ 7. $(9,9),(-5,3)$ 8. $(-5,9),(-5,-3)$
9. Write and run a program in BASIC that will find the slope and y-intercept of an equation $ax + by + c = 0$.

Chapter Review

 Use graph paper. Draw and label an *x*-axis and a *y*-axis. Plot these points.

1. $G(-3, -5)$
2. $E(0, 6)$
3. $O(-1, 4)$

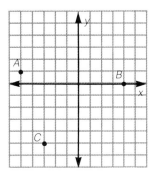

4–6. Find the coordinates of points A, B, and C.

 7. Find the distance between $P(-2, 3)$ and $Q(8, 0)$.

3 8. Find the slope of the line containing $R(4, 2)$ and $S(3, 4)$.

Find the slopes (if possible) for the lines that contain these points.

9. $G(7, 8)$ and $K(-5, 8)$
10. $H(4, 9)$ and $T(4, -6)$

4 ▲ 11. Write an equation for the line that contains point $P(3, 4)$ and has slope 2.

12. Find the slope and y-intercept of the line $y = 5x - 2$.

5 13. Write an equation for the line that contains point $R(2, 3)$ and is parallel to the line $y = 4x - 2$.

14. Write an equation for the line that contains the point $T(1, 4)$ and is perpendicular to the line $x + 4 = y$.

6 15. Find the coordinates of the midpoint of $\overline{PQ}$ where the endpoints are $P(3, 7)$ and $Q(7, -4)$.

Chapter Test

Use graph paper. Draw and label an *x*-axis and a *y*-axis. Plot these points.

1. $F(-5, -2)$ 2. $U(3,0)$ 3. $N(-2,6)$

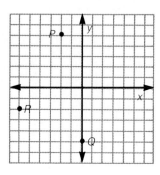

4–6.   Find the coordinates
of points P, Q, and R.

7.   Find the distance between $K(5, -3)$ and $M(9,2)$.

8.   Find the slope of the line containing $G(5,1)$ and $R(2,3)$.

Find the slopes (if possible) of the lines containing these points:

9. $G(9,7)$ and $P(9,3)$ 10. $R(6, -3)$ and $S(10, -3)$

11.   Write an equation for a line that contains point $S(2, 3)$ and has slope 3.

12.   Find the slope and y-intercept of the line $y = -2x + 5$.

13.   Write an equation for the line that contains point $B(3,2)$ and is parallel to the line $y = 5x + 3$.

14.   Write an equation for the line that contains point $S(2,3)$ and is perpendicular to the line $x - 5 = y$.

15.   Find the coordinates of the midpoint of AB where the endpoints are $A(2,9)$ and $B(6, -5)$.

Skills Review　　　　Positive and Negative Numbers

Compare. Use > or <.

1.　−3 and 4
2.　−1 and 6
3.　5 and −3
4.　0 and −2
5.　5 and 0
6.　−9 and 0
7.　−12 and −2
8.　−5 and −8
9.　−3 and −40
10.　3 and −3
11.　3 and 8
12.　−13 and 13

Add.

13.　−7 + 5
14.　−3 + (−9)
15.　−4 + 11
16.　6 + (−6)
17.　−10 + 2
18.　−4 + 7
19.　100 + (−25)
20.　−60 + (−56)
21.　−88 + 22
22.　−48 + (−12)
23.　−73 + (−108)
24.　47 + (−802)

Subtract.

25.　−5 − 3
26.　−4 − (−5)
27.　−2 − 9
28.　−9 − 5
29.　−6 − 7
30.　−6 − (−9)
31.　2 − 100
32.　10 − (−15)
33.　−2 − 100
34.　−18 − 18
35.　15 − 75
36.　−149 − (−149)

Multiply.

37.　−6 × (−8)
38.　−12 × 5
39.　−9 × (−4)
40.　−10 × 13
41.　8 × (−8)
42.　5 × (−22)
43.　−12 × (−9)
44.　−14 × (−20)
45.　−100 × 3
46.　45 × (−11)
47.　−13 × 185
48.　−59 × (−36)

Divide.

49.　−36 ÷ 12
50.　−72 ÷ (−9)
51.　48 ÷ (−16)
52.　300 ÷ (−10)
53.　−200 ÷ (−25)
54.　−100 ÷ 2
55.　−130 ÷ 13
56.　−99 ÷ (−11)
57.　108 ÷ −12
58.　−328 ÷ 4
59.　−555 ÷ (−5)
60.　486 ÷ −6

16
Transformations

| 1 | Reflections |

After finishing Section 1, you should be able to
▲ *find the reflection of a figure across a line.*
▲▲ *locate the line of reflection, given a figure and its reflection.*

▲ Reflections Across a Line

1. Draw △*ABC* on a thin sheet of paper.

2. Fold the paper and trace the triangle on the opposite side of the fold. Label the corresponding vertices *A'*, *B'*, and *C'*.

3. Draw $\overline{AA'}$, $\overline{BB'}$, and $\overline{CC'}$. How is the fold line ℓ related to each of these segments?

4. Find the midpoints of $\overline{BC}$ and $\overline{B'C'}$. Call them *D* and *D'*, respectively. How is the line ℓ related to $\overline{DD'}$?

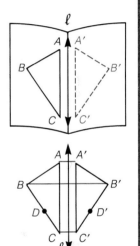

Pairs of points *A* and *A'*, *B* and *B'*, and *C* and *C'* are *reflections* of each other across the line ℓ. We also say that △*ABC* and △*A'B'C'* are reflections of each other across the line ℓ.

DEFINITION

Given a line ℓ in a plane, any two points *A* and *A'* in the plane are **reflections** (or **images**) of each other across ℓ whenever ℓ is the perpendicular bisector of $\overline{AA'}$. The **line of reflection** is ℓ.

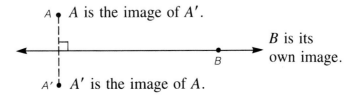

A is the image of *A'*.

B is its own image.

A' is the image of *A*.

Example   1. Find the reflection (image) of points D, E, F, G, and H across line m.

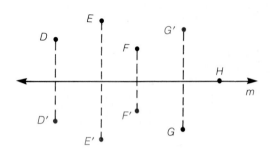

Draw a perpendicular from D to line m, and extend to D' so that D and D' are equidistant from line m.

In the same way we can find E', F', and G'. Point H is its own image (reflection).

Try This...   1. Draw a line and three points A, B, and C not on the line. Find the reflection of each point across the line.

Any line in the plane determines a matching of every point in the plane with its reflection (image). If the point is on the line, it is its own image.

Example   2. Find the reflection of $\triangle ABC$ across line m.

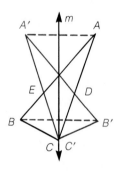

Find the images of A and B. C is its own image because it is on line m.

Note that points D and E of $\triangle ABC$ are images of each other.

$\triangle A'B'C'$ is the reflection of $\triangle ABC$.

Try This...   2. Copy $\triangle ABC$ and line m. Then find the reflection of $\triangle ABC$ across line m.

Example   3. Find the reflection of this curve across line p.

One way to find the image of the curve is to fold the paper along line p and trace the curve.

A second method is described here. Choose several points on the curve. From each point, draw a segment perpendicular to line p.

Extend the segment and locate the image of each point on the curve.

Then connect the image points to draw an approximate image of the curve.

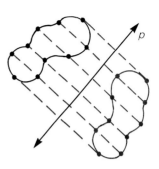

Try This...   3. Draw a curve and a line on a sheet of paper. Find the reflection of the curve by folding and tracing.

▲▲ Drawing a Line of Reflection

If two figures are reflections of each other, we can use the definition on page 475 to find the line of reflection.

Example   4. $\triangle ABC$ is a reflection of $\triangle A'B'C'$. Find the line of reflection. Assume that A and A', B and B', and C and C' are corresponding points.

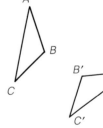

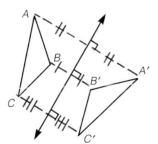

The line of reflection bisects every segment joining corresponding points. Thus, we need to draw only two segments and join their midpoints to find the line of reflection.

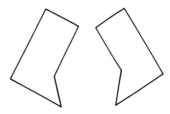

Try This...   4. Trace these figures and find the line of reflection.

Sometimes we can determine whether two figures are reflections of each other by looking for their line of reflection.

Examples   Which pairs of figures are reflections of each other?

5.

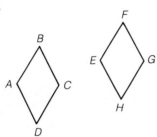
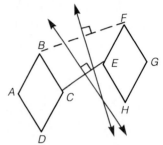

These figures are *not* reflections of each other.
The perpendicular bisectors of $\overline{BF}$ and $\overline{CE}$ are not the same line.

6.

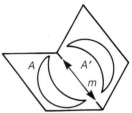

Figure *A* folds onto figure *A′*. Thus, the fold line *m* is the line
of reflection.

Try This…   Trace these figures and determine whether they are reflections of each
other.

5.

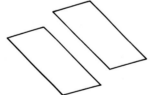

6.

Exercises

▲   **Copy each line and set of points. Then find the reflections
of these points across line *m*.**

1.

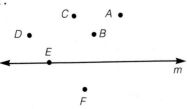

2.

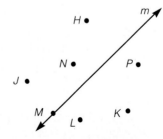

3. Name the reflections of points A, B, C, D, and E across line m.

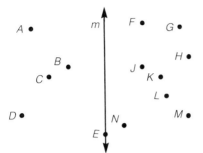

4. Name the reflections of points K, L, M, N, and P across line m.

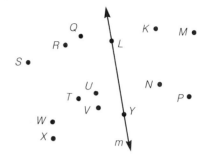

Copy each figure and find its reflection across line p.

5.

6.

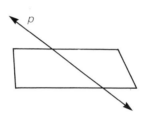

7.

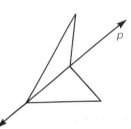

Copy each figure. Find its reflection across line ℓ by folding and tracing.

8.

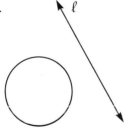

9.

10.

▲▲ **Copy each pair of figures. Find the line of reflection (if it exists).**

11.

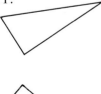

12.

13.

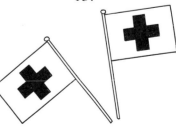

2 Properties of Line Reflections

After finishing Section 2, you should be able to
▲ *recognize properties of line reflections and apply them in solving problems.*

When a figure is reflected across a line, a number of properties of that figure do not change. We say that the properties are "preserved."

1. Draw a line *m* and three collinear points *A, B,* and *C* on a sheet of paper. Find the reflection of each point across line *m*. What do you observe about *A′, B′,* and *C′*?

2. Compare distances *AB* and *A′B′*, and *BC* and *B′C′*.

3. Draw a point *D* not on $\overleftrightarrow{AC}$, and find its reflection. Compare *m* ∠*ACD* and *m* ∠*A′C′D′*. Find some other pairs of angles with the same measures.

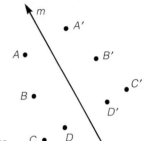

The reflection of a figure has several properties that are identical to those of the original figure. We will state one of these properties as a postulate. This postulate can be used to explain the other properties that we list as theorems.

POSTULATE
19
The reflection of a set of collinear points across a line is also a set of collinear points. (Reflections preserve collinearity.)

The following theorems state that line reflections preserve distance and angle measure.

THEOREMS
16.1

16.2

If *A′* and *B′* are the reflections of *A* and *B* across a line, then *AB* = *A′B′*.

If ∠*A′B′C′* is the reflection of ∠*ABC* across a line, then *m* ∠*ABC* = *m* ∠*A′B′C′*.

Example   1. $\triangle RST$ is the reflection of $\triangle R'S'T'$ across line m. Name the congruent segments and angles.

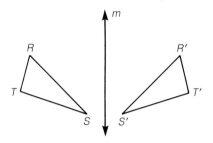

Sides	Angles
$RS = R'S'$	$m\angle RST = m\angle R'S'T'$
$ST = S'T'$	$m\angle STR = m\angle S'T'R'$
$TR = T'R'$	$m\angle TRS = m\angle T'R'S'$

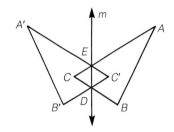

Try This...   1. $\triangle ABC$ is a reflection of $\triangle A'B'C'$ across line m. Name the congruent segments and angles.

COROLLARY   A triangle and its reflection across a line are congruent.

16.3

If we count from 1 to 12 on a clock, we move in a clockwise direction. In the reflection however, we move in a counterclockwise direction as we count from 1 to 12.

Line reflections change the **orientation** of a figure. This means that if a sequence of points in a figure is ordered in a particular direction, then the sequence of image points has a reverse (or opposite) order. An example is from clockwise to counterclockwise.

Examples   Determine whether the figures in each pair have the same or a reverse orientation.

2.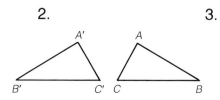

3.

4.

Reverse orientation	Same orientation	Reverse orientation

Try This... Determine whether the figures in each pair have the same or a reverse orientation.

2.   3.

Exercises

▲ △*ABC* **is the reflection of** △*DCB* **across line** *m*. **State a theorem or postulate to support the statements in Exercises 1–8.**

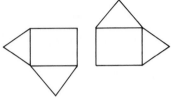

1. $CE = BE$

2. $\angle CAE \cong \angle BDE$

3. $\triangle ABC \cong \triangle DCB$

4. $CF = BF$

5. If *A-E-B*, then *D-E-C*.

6. If *A-G-C*, then *D-H-B*.

7. △*CFE* and △*BFE* are right triangles.

8. If △*ACE* is a right triangle, then △*DBE* is a right triangle.

Determine whether the figures in each pair have the same or a reverse orientation.

9. 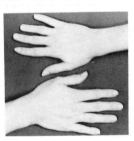   10.    11.

12.

13. $\overline{BC}$ is perpendicular to *p*. Explain how to find the reflection of *B* across line *p* using only a straightedge. *A′* is the reflection of *A*.

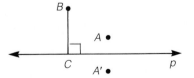

3 Translations

After finishing Section 3, you should be able to
▲ *find a translation image of a figure.*
▲▲ *recognize and apply properties of translations.*

▲ Translation of a Figure

A car passing by you is a simple example of a translation, a movement along a line from one position to another.

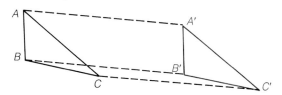

1. Draw △*ABC* on a sheet of paper.

2. Choose a point *A'*, 4 cm from *A*. Draw $\overline{AA'}$.

3. Draw $\overline{BB'}$ and $\overline{CC'}$, each 4 cm long and in the same direction as $\overrightarrow{AA'}$.

4. Draw △*A'B'C'*. What do you observe?

△*A'B'C'* is a *translation image* of △*ABC*. Under this translation, every point *P* in the plane has an image *P'*, where $PP' = AA'$, and $\overrightarrow{PP'}$ is in the same direction as $\overrightarrow{AA'}$.

DEFINITION

Given distance XY and direction $\overrightarrow{XY}$ (from X to Y) in a plane, the **translation image** of any point P is a point P' such that $PP' = XY$, and $\overrightarrow{PP'}$ is in the same direction as $\overrightarrow{XY}$.

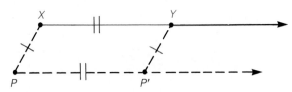

Example   1. Find the image of $\triangle DEF$ under the translation $\overrightarrow{XY}$.

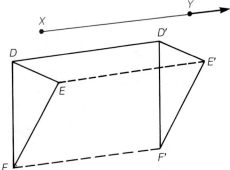

Choose points D', E', and F' so that
$$XY = DD' = EE' = FF'$$
and
$\overline{DD'}$, $\overline{EE'}$, and $\overline{FF'}$ are in the same direction as $\overrightarrow{XY}$.

Connecting the image points, we find that $\triangle D'E'F'$ is the image of $\triangle DEF$.

Try This...   1. Copy and find the image of $\triangle KLM$ under the translation $\overrightarrow{XY}$.

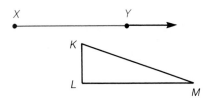

▲▲ Properties of Translations

Translations are related to line reflections.

$\triangle ABC$ is reflected across line m to $\triangle A'B'C'$.

$\triangle A'B'C'$ is reflected across line n to $\triangle A''B''C''$.

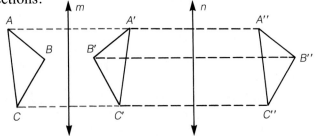

One line reflection followed by another line reflection is called the *composite* of two line reflections. $\triangle A''B''C''$ is the image of $\triangle ABC$ under the composite of two line reflections across m and n.

Note that $\triangle A''B''C''$ is also the image of $\triangle ABC$ under the translation $\overrightarrow{AA''}$.

| THEOREM 16.4 | A translation is the composite of two line reflections across parallel lines. |

Example   2. The translation from $\triangle ABC$ to $\triangle A''B''C''$ is the composite of which two successive line reflections?

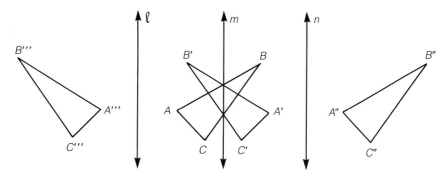

$\triangle ABC$ is reflected across line m to $\triangle A'B'C'$. Then $\triangle A'B'C'$ is reflected across line n to $\triangle A''B''C''$.

Try This...   2. In the drawing above, the translation from $\triangle A'B'C'$ to $\triangle A'''B'''C'''$ is the composite of which two successive line reflections?

Because a translation is the same as the composite of two line reflections, we can state the following theorems.

| THEOREM 16.5 | Translations preserve collinearity of points. |

THEOREMS   Translations preserve distance.
16.6

16.7   Translations preserve
angle measure.

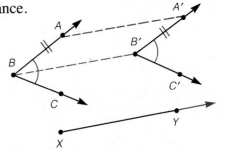

Because one reflection changes the orientation, two successive
reflections preserve the orientation of the original figure.

THEOREM   Translations preserve the orientation of a figure.
16.8

Examples $\odot O'$ is the translation image of $\odot O$.
Which theorem justifies each statement?

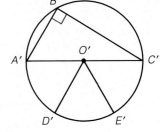

3. $\odot O \cong \odot O'$
Radii are congruent by Theorem 16.6.

4. $m\overarc{ED} = m\overarc{E'D'}$

Central angle measures are equal by Theorem 16.7.
Hence, the arcs have the same measure.

5. A, O, and C are collinear.

Because $m \angle A'B'C' = 90°, \overline{A'C'}$ is a diameter. Hence, A', O',
and C' are collinear, and by Theorem 16.5, A, O, and C are
collinear.

Try This...   Use $\odot O$ and $\odot O'$ from Examples 3–5. Which theorem justifies
each statement?

3. $\triangle ABC \cong \triangle A'B'C'$

4. $m\overarc{AE} = m\overarc{A'E'}$

5. The orientation of $\triangle ABC$ is the same as the orientation of
$\triangle A'B'C'$.

Exercises

▲ **Copy each figure and find its image under the given translation.**

1.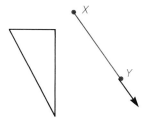

2.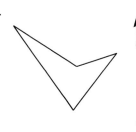

3.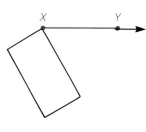

4.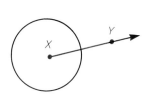

5.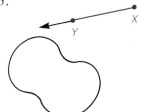

6.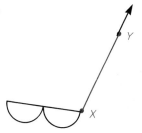

Which illustrations are examples of translations?

7. Airplane taxiing

8. Car on track

9. Windmill blades

10. Door closing

▲▲ **Identify the composite of line reflections that matches the given translation.**

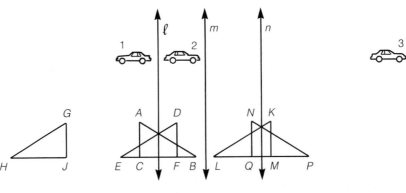

11. Car 2 to Car 3

12. Car 3 to Car 2

13. △ABC to △GHJ

14. △ABC to △NPQ

Identify the theorem(s) used to explain each statement.

15. The translation image of a circle is a circle congruent to the original circle.

16. If A, B, and C are points on a line, then their translation images are three collinear points.

17. The translation image of a right triangle is a right triangle.

18. If the order of the vertices of a triangle is clockwise, then the order of the image points A', B', and C' under a translation is also clockwise.

▶ Extension Exercises

19. Refer to the figures in Exercises 11–14. Describe the relationships between the distance of a translation and the distance between the parallel reflection lines associated with the translation.

20. What two transformations are illustrated by locking a door bolt?

4	Rotations

After finishing Section 4, you should be able to
▲ *find a rotation image of a figure.*
▲▲ *recognize and apply properties of rotations.*

▲ Rotation of a Figure

The waterwheel is a simple example of a
rotation about a center point.

1. Draw △ *ABC*.
   Choose a point *O* and draw
   three concentric circles with
   center *O* and radii *OA*, *OB*,
   and *OC*.

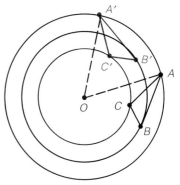

2. Choose a 60° angle, and
   find points *A′*, *B′*, and *C′* on
   the three circles (moving
   counterclockwise) such that
   $m\angle A'OA = m\angle B'OB = m\angle C'OC = 60°$.

3. Draw △ *A′B′C′*. It is a *rotation image* of △ *ABC*.

DEFINITION

α is the Greek letter "alpha."

Given a point *O*, and an angle measure α, the **rotation image** of
any point *P* (not *O*) is a point *P′* on a circle with center *O* and radius
OP, such that $m\widehat{PP'} = α$.

The point *O* is the **center of
rotation**. It is its own image.

α is the **angle of rotation**.

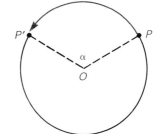

If α is positive, the rotation is counterclockwise.
If α is negative, the rotation is clockwise.

Example   1. Find the image of △ *DEF* under a rotation of 180° about point *O*.

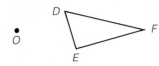

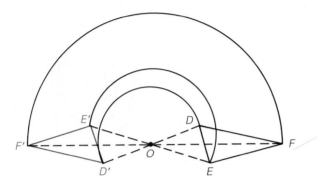

Try This...   1. Copy and find the image of △ *RST* under a rotation of 120° about point *O*.

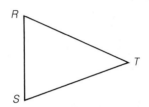

The center of rotation may be anywhere in the plane.

Example   2. Find the image of each figure under a rotation of 75° about point *O*.

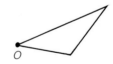

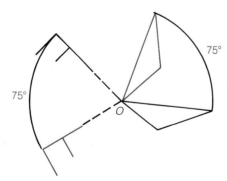

Try This...   2. Copy rectangle *ABCD* and find its image under a rotation of 90° about point *O*.

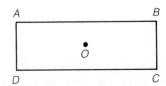

▲▲ Properties Of Rotations

Like translations, rotations are related to line reflections.

$\triangle ABC$ is reflected across line m to $\triangle A'B'C'$.

$\triangle A'B'C'$ is reflected across line n to $\triangle A''B''C''$.

$\triangle A''B''C''$ is the image of $\triangle ABC$ under the composite of two line reflections across intersecting lines m and n.

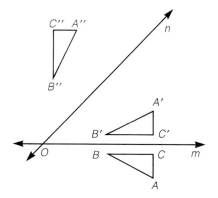

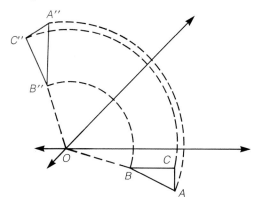

Note that $\triangle A''B''C''$ is also the image of $\triangle ABC$ under a rotation about point O.

THEOREM 16.9	A rotation is the composite of two line reflections across intersecting lines.

Because any rotation is the same as the composite of two reflections, we can state the following theorems.

THEOREMS

16.10	Rotations preserve collinearity of points.
16.11	Rotations preserve distance.
16.12	Rotations preserve angle measure.

$\angle D'A'C'$ is the rotation image of $\angle DAC$.

Thus, if A-B-C, then A'-B'-C';

$AD = A'D'$;

and $m \angle DAC = m \angle D'A'C'$.

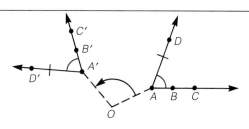

Because two successive reflections preserve the orientation of a figure, we have the following theorem.

THEOREM   Rotations preserve the orientation of a figure.
16.13

Examples   △ $A'B'C'$ is the rotation image of a triangle, △ ABC. O is the center of a rotation of 180°. Which theorems explain each statement?

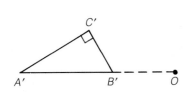

3. $m \angle ACB = 90°$
   By Theorem 16.12, angle measure is preserved, and $m \angle A'C'B' = 90°$.

4. $OB = OB'$
   O is its own image. Thus, by Theorem 16.11, distance is preserved and $OB = OB'$.

5. △ $A'B'C' \cong$ △ ABC
   By Theorems 16.11 and 16.12, corresponding angles and sides are congruent.

Try This...   ▱$A'B'C'D'$ is the rotation image of ▱$ABCD$. Point O is the center of a rotation of 90°. Which theorem explains each statement?

3. $\overline{AC} \cong \overline{A'C'}$
4. $\overline{AB} \parallel \overline{DC}$
5. $OB' = OB$
6. $m \angle D'E'C' = m \angle DEC$

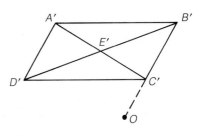

Exercises

▲   **Sketch the image of each figure under the given rotation about point O.**

1.

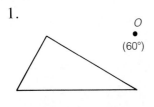

2.

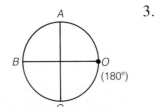

3.

4.

5.

6.

▲▲ **Identify the definition or theorem that explains each statement.**

7. If A' and B' are rotation images of A and B about point O, then $m \angle A'OA = m \angle B'OB$.

8. The rotation image of an equilateral triangle is an equilateral triangle.

9. If A, B, and C are collinear, then the rotation images A', B', and C' are also collinear points.

10. # ONE WAY

   cannot be the rotation image of

   # YAW ƎNO

▶ Extension Exercises

The figure on the right is a rotation image of the other figure. Find the center of rotation.

11.

12.

13.

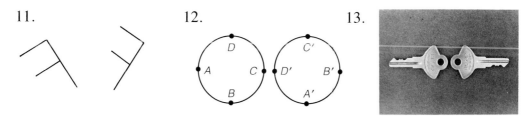

14. Try to determine a relationship between the measures of the angle of rotation and the angle formed by the intersecting lines of reflection associated with a rotation.

▶◀ Activity

Many computer graphics are created by transformations of a simple figure. Figure 1 is created by rotating a square 60°, six successive times. Figure 2 is created by translating a diamond ten successive times.

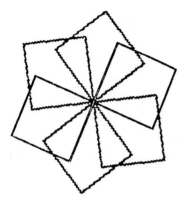

Figure 1

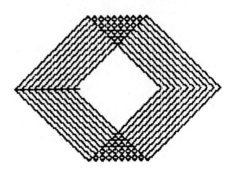

Figure 2

Determine what figure is being transformed to create each of the following figures. Then determine the transformation used for each one.

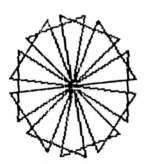

Create your own designs. Draw a square and rotate it 45°, eight successive times. Draw an equilateral triangle and translate it nine successive times.

5·	Symmetry

After finishing Section 5, you should be able to

▲ *determine whether a figure is symmetric with respect to a line, and find lines of symmetry.*

▲▲ *determine whether a figure has rotational or point symmetry, and find the point of symmetry.*

▲ Line Symmetry

The easiest way to understand line symmetry is to draw a figure that is symmetric with respect to a line.

1. Draw a line $\overleftrightarrow{AD}$ and three segments to form a quadrilateral *ABCD*. Find the reflection of points *B* and *C* across $\overleftrightarrow{AD}$.

   The hexagon *ABCDC'B'* is *symmetric with respect to line* $\overleftrightarrow{AD}$.

   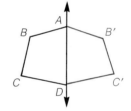

2. Draw a line *p* and a curve as shown. Make a fold at line *p* and trace the curve.

   The complete curve is *symmetric with respect to line p*.

DEFINITION

A set of points is symmetric with respect to a line *m* whenever the reflection of every point in the set across line *m* is also a point in the set.

Examples   Which figures have line symmetry? Find all lines of symmetry.

1.

One line of symmetry

2.

No line of symmetry

3. Three lines of symmetry.

 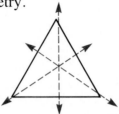

Try This... Which figures have line symmetry? Find all lines of symmetry.

1.   2.    3.

▲▲ Rotational Symmetry/Point Symmetry

A propeller looks the same if we rotate it 120° or 240°.

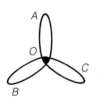 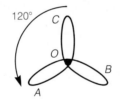 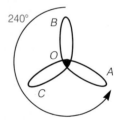

We say that the propeller has *rotational symmetry*. The image of each blade under the rotation is also a blade.

DEFINITION
_____

A set of points has rotational symmetry whenever for some rotation between 0° and 360° about a point O, the image of every point in the set is also a point in the set.

Examples Which figures have rotational symmetry? Find the point of symmetry.

4.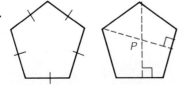

Rotational symmetry about P for rotations of 72°, 144°, 216°, and 288°.

5. 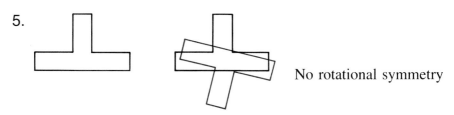 No rotational symmetry

If a figure has rotational symmetry for a 180° rotation about a point, we say that it has *point symmetry*.

DEFINITION

A set of points has point symmetry whenever there is some point O such that for a 180° rotation about O, the image of every point in the set is also a point in the set.

Examples Which figures have point symmetry? Find the point(s) of symmetry.

6.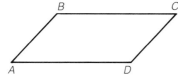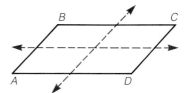

$\square ABCD$ has point symmetry.

7.   No point symmetry

Try This... Which figures have rotational symmetry? Which have point symmetry? Find all points of symmetry.

4.    5.    6.

Exercises

▲ **Which figures have line symmetry? Describe the lines of symmetry.**

1. 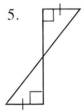 2. 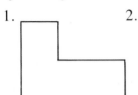 3. 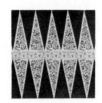 4.

▲▲ **Which figures have point symmetry? Which figures have rotational symmetry? Describe all points of symmetry.**

5.  6. 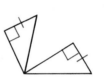 7.  8.

▶ Extension Exercises

9. Determine whether each capital letter of the alphabet has line symmetry, point symmetry, or rotational symmetry.

Copy the design and shade additional squares so that the design has the indicated symmetry.

10. Line symmetry   11. Point symmetry

Define each figure using the concept of symmetry.

12. Isosceles triangle   13. Parallelogram   14. Square

15. Why is it impossible for a triangle to have exactly two lines of symmetry?

Draw as many different kinds of quadrilaterals as possible with the indicated lines of symmetry.

16. None   17. Exactly one   18. Exactly two   19. Exactly three

▶▶ Challenge Exercises

Construct figures (other than quadrilaterals) that have these properties.

20. A line of symmetry, but no point symmetry   21. Four lines of symmetry

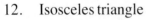

▶◀ **Activity**

You can make symmetric designs of your own by folding and cutting as shown here.

Start with an $8\frac{1}{2}$-inch by 11-inch sheet of paper.

1. Fold the paper in half along $\overline{AB}$.

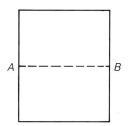

2. Locate C, the center of $\overline{AB}$.

3. Mark $60°$ angles from C. Align $\overline{AC}$ along $\overline{CE}$ and fold. Align $\overline{CB}$ to meet $\overline{CD}$, folding in the opposite direction of the previous fold.

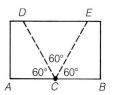

4. Fold the paper along $\overline{CF}$.

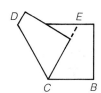

5. Turn the paper over and cut along $\overline{AG}$.

6. Cut out geometric shapes. Unfold the paper and find the lines of symmetry.

Computer Application   Rotating Geometric Figures

Logo is a computer language that can be used to draw geometric shapes on a computer screen. A small triangle shape, called the "turtle," moves across the screen following certain commands.

FD 30	Draws a segment forward 30 units.
BK 30	Draws a segment backward 30 units.
RT 30	Turns the "turtle" 30° to the right (clockwise).
LT 30	Turns the "turtle" 30° to the left (counterclockwise).
RCIRCLE 30	Draws a circle with radius of 30 units to the right.
LCIRCLE 30	Draws a circle with radius of 30 units to the left.
RARC 30 90	Draws an arc to the right with radius 30 and through 90°.
LARC 30 180	Draws an arc to the left with radius 30 and through 180°.
PU FD 30	Brings the pen up and moves the "turtle" 30 units without drawing.
PD	Brings the pen down into drawing position.
HT	Hides the "turtle."
ST	Shows the "turtle."
CS	Clears the screen.
REPEAT 30	Repeats a command 30 times.

Draw a geometric figure and rotate the figure 45° clockwise.

Command	**Comments**
TO SQUARE	TO SQUARE defines the procedure.
REPEAT 4 [FD 20 RT 90]	This program draws a square by repeating one side
END	4 times.
TO ROTATESQUARE	Calls upon the SQUARE procedure.
REPEAT 2 [RT 45 SQUARE]	Draws a square and then draws a
END	second square rotated 45° from the
	original position.

Write and run programs to draw and to rotate each of the following figures.

1. square, 30°   2. rectangle, 45°   3. equilateral triangle, 60°

4. semicircle, 180°   5. pentagon, 36°   6. hexagon, 30°

Chapter Review

1 **Copy each figure and find its reflection across line *m*.**

1.

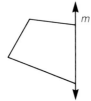

2.

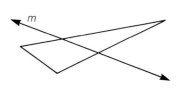

Copy these figures and determine if each pair has a line of reflection. Find the line of reflection if it exists.

3.

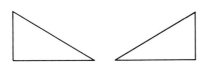

4.

2 **△*A′C′D′* is the reflection of △*ACD* across line *p*.**

5.   Explain why ∠*ABE* ≅ ∠*A′BE*.

6.   How are $\overline{C'B}$ and $\overline{CB}$ related? Why?

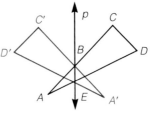

Determine whether the figures in each pair have the same or a reverse orientation.

7.

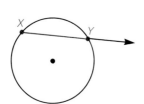

8.

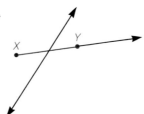

3 **Copy each figure and find its image under the given translation.**

9.

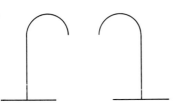

10.

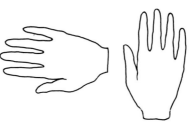

11. Why is the translation image of an isosceles triangle also an isosceles triangle?

12. Name three properties that are preserved under a translation.

Copy each figure and find its image under the given rotation about point *O*.

13.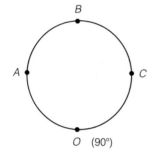

14.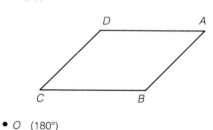

15. If *A′* is the rotation image of *A* about a point *P*, how are $\overline{A'P}$ and $\overline{AP}$ related? Why?

16. △*ABC* is the rotation image of △*A′B′C′*. If the order of vertices *A*, *B*, and *C* is counterclockwise, what is the order of vertices *A′*, *B′*, and *C′*? Why?

Determine whether each figure has line symmetry. Describe all lines of symmetry.

17.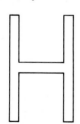

18.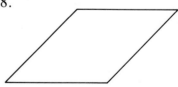

Which figures have point symmetry? Which have rotational symmetry? Describe all points of symmetry.

19.

20.

Chapter Test

Copy each figure and find its reflection across line _m_.

1.

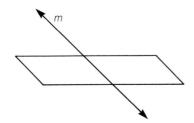

2.

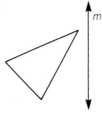

Copy these figures and determine if each pair has a line of reflection. Find the line of reflection if it exists.

3.

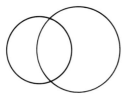

4.

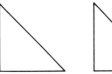

△_ECD_ is the reflection of △_ADC_ across line _m_.

5.   What type of triangle is △_DBC_? Why?

6.   Identify the reflection of △_CBE_ across line _m_.

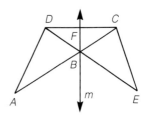

Determine whether the figures in each pair have the same or a reverse orientation.

7.

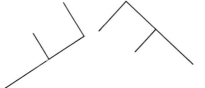

8.

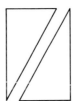

Copy each figure and find its image under the given translation.

9.

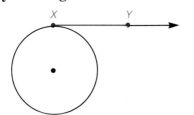

10.

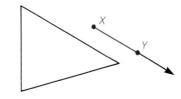

11. Explain why the translation image of two perpendicular lines is also two perpendicular lines.

12. The translation images of ℓ, m, and p are ℓ', m', and p'. If $\ell \parallel m$, does it necessarily follow that $\ell' \parallel m'$? Why?

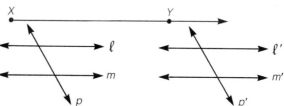

Copy each figure and find its image under the given rotation about point *O*.

13. $O(90°)$

14.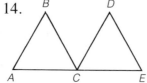

 $O(120°)$

15. If *A* is the rotational image of itself, what else do we know about *A*?

16. Is a 180° rotation about a point *P* the same as a line reflection across a line containing *P*? Make a drawing to support your answer.

Determine whether each figure has rotational symmetry. Does either have point symmetry?

17.

18.

19.

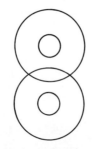

20.

Skills Review   Graphing Ordered Pairs

Graph each ordered pair.

1. (1,2)   2. (7,7)   3. (2,−3)   4. (0,3)

5. (−4,0)   6. (−5,1)   7. (0,0)   8. (2,−4)

9. (6,1)   10. (−3,−3)   11. (−10,10)   12. (4,9)

13. (−8,−3)   14. (7,0)   15. (0,10)   16. (8,8)

Find an ordered pair for each point.

17. A   18. B

19. C   20. D

21. E   22. F

23. G   24. H

25. I   26. J

27. K   28. L

29. M   30. N

31. O   32. P

33. Q   34. R

35. S   36. T

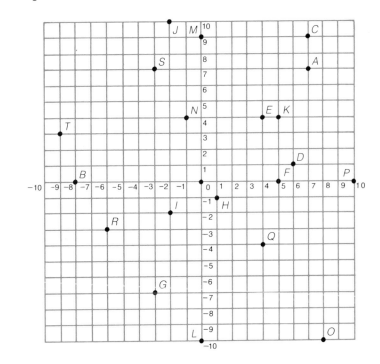

17
Space Figures

1   Prisms

After finishing Section 1, you should be able to
▲   *identify faces, edges, and vertices of polyhedrons.*
▲▲   *identify different types of prisms and their parts.*
▲▲   *sketch prisms.*

▲ Polyhedrons

The three-dimensional counterpart of a polygon is
a **polyhedron**. A polyhedron is made up of
polygonal regions, or **faces.** The sides and
vertices of each face are **edges** and
vertices (singular **vertex**), respectively.

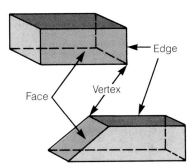

DEFINITION

A **polyhedron** consists of a finite number of polygonal
regions such that
1. each edge of a region is an edge of exactly one other region, and
2. if two regions intersect, then their intersection is a vertex
   or an edge.

Example   1. Name the faces, edges, and vertices of this polyhedron.

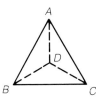

Faces: △ABC, △ADC, △ADB, and △BDC

Edges: $\overline{AB}$, $\overline{AC}$, $\overline{AD}$, $\overline{BD}$, $\overline{BC}$, and $\overline{DC}$

Vertices: A, B, C, and D

Try This. . .   1. Name the faces, edges, and vertices
of this polyhedron.

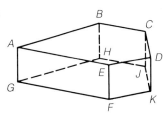

▲▲ Prisms

A **prism** is a special type of polyhedron. Two faces of a prism, or **bases,** are congruent polygonal regions. They lie in parallel planes.

The other faces are **lateral faces.** The intersection of two lateral faces is a **lateral edge.**

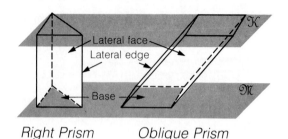

Right Prism   *Oblique Prism*

The bases of a prism are bounded by parallelograms. If the parallelograms are rectangles, the prism is a **right prism.** Otherwise, the prism is an **oblique prism.**

Prisms are classified by their bases.

Type of Prism	Right	Oblique
Triangular		
Quadrangular		
Pentagonal		

Examples   Classify each prism and name the bases, the lateral faces, and the lateral edges.

2.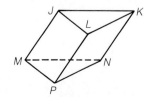

Oblique triangular prism
Bases: △*JKL* and △*MNP*
Lateral faces: ▱ *JLPM,* ▱ *JKNM,* and ▱ *LKNP*
Lateral edges: $\overline{LP}$, $\overline{JM}$, and $\overline{KN}$

3. 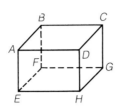 Right quadrangular prism
Bases: ABCD and *EFGH*
Lateral faces: ADHE, DCGH,
BCGF, and *ABFE*
Lateral edges: $\overline{AE}$, $\overline{DH}$, $\overline{CG}$,
and $\overline{BF}$

Note that all faces are rectangular regions and that any pair of
opposite faces could be called bases of this prism. When
the bases are rectangular, the figure is a **rectangular prism.**
A right rectangular prism whose edges are all congruent is a **cube.**

Try This. . . Classify each prism and name the bases, the
lateral faces, and the lateral edges.

2. 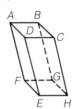   3.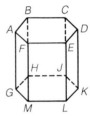

 Sketching Prisms

When sketching a prism, remember that the lateral edges are
congruent and parallel to each other.

Example   4. Sketch a right pentagonal prism.

Step 1

Draw a pentagon.

Step 2

Draw two congruent segments
perpendicular to the front edge of the
base. From the other vertices, draw
segments that are congruent and
parallel to these segments. Hidden
edges are drawn as dashed lines.

Step 3

Connect the endpoints of these lateral
edges to obtain the second base.

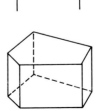

Example

5. Sketch an oblique triangular prism.

Step 1

Draw a triangle.

Step 2

From the vertices of the base, draw three parallel and congruent segments (not perpendicular to the front edge of the triangle).

Step 3

Connect the endpoints of these lateral edges to obtain the second base.

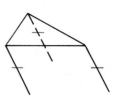

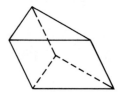

Try This. . .

4. Sketch a right quadrangular prism.

5. Sketch an oblique hexagonal prism.

Exercises

▲ **Name each face, edge, and vertex.**

1.
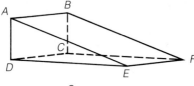

2.
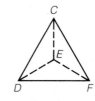

3.
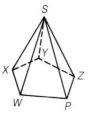

4.
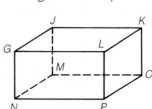

▲▲ **Classify each prism and name the bases, the lateral faces, and the lateral edges.**

5.
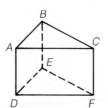

6.
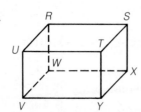

7.
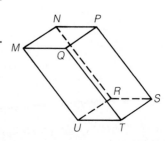

8. 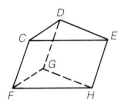   9. 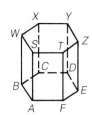   10.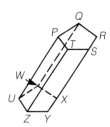

▲▲ **Sketch each figure.**

11. Right rectangular prism
12. Right triangular prism
13. Oblique pentagonal prism
14. Oblique hexagonal prism
15. Right hexagonal prism
16. Cube

▶ **Extension Exercises**

17. Copy and complete this table.

Type of Prism	Faces	Lateral Faces	Edges	Lateral Edges	Vertices
Triangular					6
Quadrangular	6				
Pentagonal					
Hexagonal					
Octagonal	10			8	

Determine whether each statement is always true, sometimes true, or always false.

18. The lateral faces of a right prism are rectangular regions.
19. A prism has twice as many vertices as lateral faces.
20. The bases of a prism are bounded by congruent polygons.
21. The lateral faces of a prism are bounded by parallelograms.
22. The lateral edges of a prism are congruent and parallel.
23. The bases of a prism are bounded by regular polygons.
24. The ratio of the number of edges to the number of vertices in a prism is 3:2.
25. A prism has the same number of lateral edges and lateral faces.

2	Volumes of Prisms and Cylinders

After finishing Section 2, you should be able to

▲ *find volumes of prisms.*

▲▲ *find volumes of circular cylinders.*

▲ The Volume of a Prism

We shall begin with an assumption.

POSTULATE
20
For every polyhedron, there corresponds a positive number called its *volume*.

When we speak of the volume of a polyhedron we will mean the polyhedron and its interior, sometimes called a *polyhedral solid*.

We agree that a cube, whose edges are all a length of 1 centimeter, has a volume of 1. We use such a cube as a unit of volume. The cube on the right has a volume of 1 cubic centimeter, abbreviated 1 cm³.

1 cm
1 cm
1 cm
1 cm³

Example   1. How many cubic centimeters are contained in this right rectangular prism?

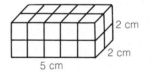

2 cm
2 cm
5 cm

There are 5×2 or 10 cm^3 in each layer.

Because there are two layers, the prism contains 10×2, or 20 cm^3.

Example 1 suggests the following assumption.

POSTULATE
21
The volume of a right rectangular prism is the product of its base area and its height. $V = Bh$

Example   2. Find the volume of this right rectangular prism.

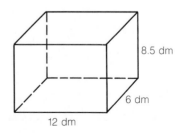

8.5 dm
6 dm
12 dm

Volume = Base area × height

$V = Bh$

$V = \ell w \cdot h$

$V = 12 \times 6 \times 8.5$

$V = 612 \text{ dm}^3$

Try This. . . 1. Find the volume of this right rectangular prism.

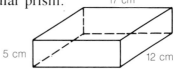

To find volumes of other types of prisms we need to consider the idea of a cross section.

DEFINITION

A **cross section of a polyhedral solid** is the intersection of a plane and the polyhedral solid.

The intersection of plane $\mathcal{M}$ and the prism is the triangular region ABC.

Triangular region ABC is a cross section.

The Italian mathematician Bonaventura Cavalieri (1598–1647) was the first to recognize the special relationship between the cross sections and the volumes of two solids.

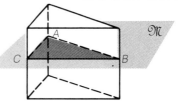

POSTULATE
22

Cavalieri's Principle

Suppose that S_1 and S_2 are two prisms of the same height and $\mathcal{M}$ is a plane containing their bases. If any plane, parallel to $\mathcal{M}$ and intersecting either S_1 or S_2 also intersects the other solid, and if the resulting cross sections have the same area, then S_1 and S_2 have the same volume.

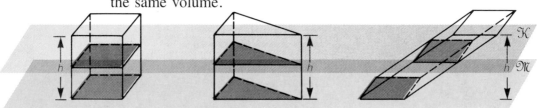

Base Area of S_1 = Base Area of S_2

Suppose three prisms with bases in plane $\mathcal{M}$ have the same base area and the same height. Then every plane parallel to plane $\mathcal{M}$ will intersect all or none of the prisms. It can be shown that every cross section of a prism is congruent to its base. Because the bases have the same area, all cross sections will have the same area. Cavalieri's Principle tells us that all three prisms have the same volume.

By Cavalieri's Principle, we can state the following theorem.

THEOREM
17.1

The volume of any prism is the product of its base area B and its height h.

$$V = Bh$$

Example 3. Find the volume of this right prism.

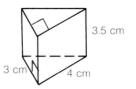

$$V = Bh$$

$$V = \frac{3 \times 4}{2} \times 3.5$$

$$V = 21 \text{ cm}^3$$

Try This. . . 2. Find the volume of this right prism.

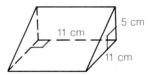

▲▲ The Volume of a Circular Cylinder

Like prisms, circular cylinders have bases that lie in parallel planes.
The bases are congruent circular regions.

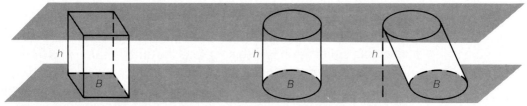

Suppose the cylinders and the prism shown have the same base
area and the same height. It can be shown that every cross
section of a cylinder parallel to its base has the same area as the
base. By Cavalieri's Principle, each cylinder has the same volume
as the prism. Because the volume of the prism is Bh, we have the
following theorem.

THEOREM
17.2   The volume of a cylinder is the product of its base area, B,
and its height h.
$$V = Bh$$

Examples 4. Find the volume of this right
circular cylinder.

$$V = Bh$$
$$V = \pi r^2 h$$
$$V = \pi \times 4^2 \times 12$$
$$V = 192\pi \text{ cm}^3$$

5. If cylinder *A* holds 1 liter, how many liters does cylinder *B* hold?

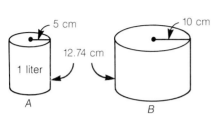

$$V_A = \pi r^2 h = \pi \times 5^2 \times 12.74 \approx 1{,}000 \text{ cm}^3$$
$$V_B = \pi r^2 h = \pi \times 10^2 \times 12.74 \approx 4{,}000 \text{ cm}^3$$

Thus, cylinder *B* holds 4 liters.

Note that if the height is the same and the radius is doubled, then the volume is quadrupled.

$$V_A = \pi h r^2 \quad \text{and} \quad V_B = \pi h (2r)^2 = 4\pi h r^2$$

Exercises

▲ **Find the volume of each prism.**

1.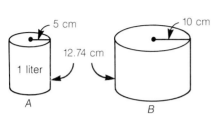

2.

3.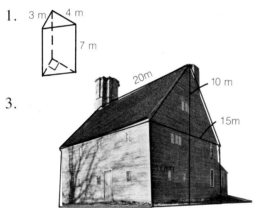

4.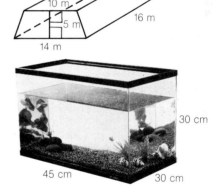

5. How many cubic meters of concrete are needed for a sidewalk 1.2 m wide, 30 m long, and 0.1 m thick?

6. During a snowstorm, 5 cm of snow fell. At the end of the storm, how many liters of snow covered a lawn that is 32 m by 18 m?
($1\text{m}^3 = 1{,}000$ liters.)

▲▲ **Find the volume of each cylinder.**

7.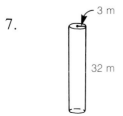

8.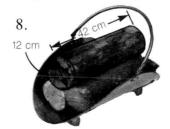

9.

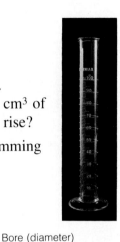

Solve the following. Use 3.14 for π.

10. A graduated cylinder is a device for measuring liquids. Suppose a cylinder has an inside radius of 4 cm. If 10 cm³ of liquid is poured into it, how much will the water level rise?

11. Find the quantity of water needed to fill a circular swimming pool that is 7 m in diameter and 1.5 m deep. (1 m³ = 1,000 liters.)

▶ Extension Exercises

12. The piston in an automobile engine moves up and down in a cylinder, as shown in the figure. When it moves up, it displaces a certain volume of gas mixture. Find the volume displaced in this cylinder.

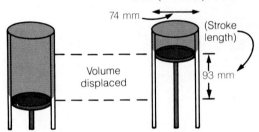

Bore (diameter)

74 mm

(Stroke length)

Volume displaced

93 mm

13. An engine with four cylinders has a combined gas displacement of 1,600 cm³. The bore of each cylinder is 74 mm. What is the stroke length?

14. An eight-cylinder engine has a combined displacement of 5 liters. The stroke length of each cylinder is 103 mm. What is the bore?

15. How does the volume change when the diameter of a cylinder is doubled? Halved?

16. A rock is submerged in a rectangular tank that is 25 cm by 40 cm. The rock raises the water level by 2 cm. What is its volume?

▶▶ Challenge Exercise

17. A can is packed securely in a box as shown. Find the ratio of the volume of the can to the volume of the box. (Ignore the thickness of the box and the can.

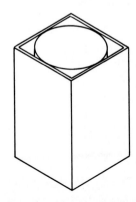

| **3** | Areas of Prisms and Cylinders |

After finishing Section 3, you should be able to
▲   *find the area of a prism.*
▲▲ *find the area of a right circular cylinder.*

▲   The Area of a Prism

The **area of a prism** is the sum of the areas of all of its faces.
The sum of the areas of the lateral faces is the
lateral area. We shall need the following definitions.

DEFINITIONS

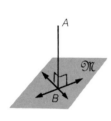

A segment (or line) $\overline{AB}$ **is perpendicular to a**
plane $\mathfrak{M}$ at point B whenever it is perpendicular
to two lines in plane $\mathfrak{M}$.

An **altitude of a prism** (or cylinder)
is any segment perpendicular to
and joining the planes of both bases.

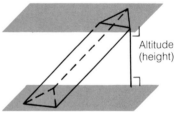

Altitude
(height)

The length of an altitude is the
height of the prism.

In a right prism, any lateral edge is an altitude.

Example   1. Find the lateral area of this right triangular prism.

Because this is a right prism, the lateral faces are rectangular regions, and
$AD = CE = BF = 5$ cm.

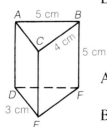

Thus,
Lateral Area = Area $ACED$ + Area $CBFE$ + Area $ABFD$
$= (3 \times 5) + (4 \times 5) + (5 \times 5)$
$= \quad 15 \quad + \quad 20 \quad + \quad 25$
$= 60$ cm²

Also, Lateral Area = $(3 \times 5) + (4 \times 5) + (5 \times 5)$
$= (3 + 4 + 5) \times 5$ Removing a factor of 5
But, $(3 + 4 + 5)$ is the perimeter of $\triangle ABC$ and 5 is the
height of the prism. This suggests the following theorem.

> THEOREM **17.3**   The lateral area of a right prism is the product of the perimeter p of a base and the height h of the prism.
>
> $$\text{Lateral Area} = ph$$

Example   2. Find the lateral area of this right rectangular prism.

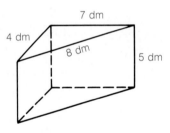

Because the bases are rectangular regions, the perimeter is

$$2(2 + 5) = 14 \text{ m}$$

Thus, Lateral Area $= 14 \times 3 = 42 \text{ m}^2$.

Try This. . .   Find the lateral area of these right prisms.

1.

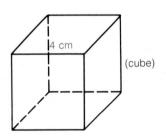

4 cm

(cube)

2.

7 dm

4 dm

8 dm

5 dm

Example   3. Find the total area of this right triangular prism. All the edges are 10 cm. Use the formula: Area of an equilateral triangle $= \frac{s^2}{4}\sqrt{3}$

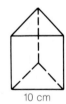

10 cm

$$\text{Lateral Area} = ph$$
$$= 30 \times 10 = 300 \text{ cm}^2$$

$$\text{Base Area} = \frac{s^2}{4}\sqrt{3} = \frac{(10)^2}{4}\sqrt{3} = 25\sqrt{3} \text{ cm}^2$$

$$\text{Total Area} = 300 + 2 \times 25\sqrt{3}$$
$$= (300 + 50\sqrt{3}) \text{ cm}^2$$

Try This. . .   3. Find the total area of this right trapezoidal prism. (*Hint:* The area of a trapezoid is $\frac{1}{2}h(b + b')$.)

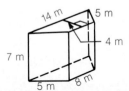

14 m   5 m

4 m

7 m

5 m   8 m

▲▲ The Area of a Right Circular Cylinder

Suppose we remove the label from a can.
The label is a rectangular region.
The width is the height of the cylinder.
The length is the circumference of the
circular base. The lateral area of the can
is the same as the area of the label,
$2\pi r \cdot h$.

THEOREM **17.4** | The lateral surface of a right circular cylinder with radius r and height h is $2\pi rh$.

Example | 4. Find the total area of this cylinder.

Lateral Area = circumference × height

$$= \qquad 2\pi r \qquad \times \qquad h$$

$$= 2 \times \pi \times 4 \times 12$$

$$= 96\pi$$

4 cm

12 cm

Base Area = πr^2

$$= \pi \times 4^2$$

$$= 16\pi$$

Total Area = $96\pi + 2 \times 16\pi = 128\pi$ cm²

Try This. . . 4. Find the total area of
this cylinder.

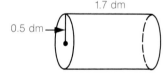

1.7 dm

0.5 dm

Example | 5. Find the total area of a cylinder that has a circumference of
6π cm and a height twice the diameter of the base.

Because circumference = $\pi d = 6\pi$, the diameter of the bases
is 6 cm. Hence, the height is 2 × 6, or 12 cm.

Total Area = $6\pi \times 12 + 2 \times \pi \times 3^2$

$$= \qquad 72\pi \qquad + \qquad 18\pi$$

$$= 90\pi \text{ cm}^2$$

Try This. . . 5. Find the total area of a cylinder that has a height of 14 dm
and a diameter half the height of the cylinder.

Exercises

▲ **Find the lateral area and the total area of each right prism.**

1.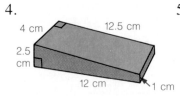

2.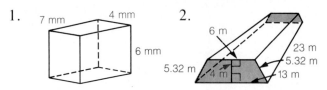

3.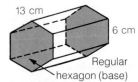
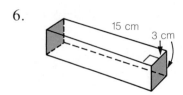
Regular
hexagon (base)

4.

5.

6.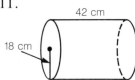

7. A room with a ceiling 2.5 m high has floor dimensions of 3.7 m by 4.3 m. If a liter of paint covers 10 m², how many liters are needed to paint the walls?

8. How much wrapping paper is needed to cover a box (a right rectangular prism) whose dimensions are 16 cm by 12 cm by 35 cm?

▲▲ **Find the lateral area and the total area of each cylinder.**

9.

10.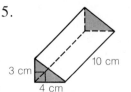

11.

12.

13.

14.

15. A cylindrical paint can has a diameter of 16 cm and a height of 21 cm. What is the area of the paper label needed to cover the side of the can?

16. A cement roller has a length of 3.5 m and a radius of 0.7 m. What is the area of road surface covered in one revolution of the roller?

4 | Volumes of Pyramids and Cones

After finishing Section 4, you should be able to
▲ *find the volume of a pyramid.*
▲▲ *find the volume of a cone.*

▲ The Volume of a Pyramid

We begin with polygonal region in a plane 𝔐
and any point *P* not in 𝔐. The polygonal region
in 𝔐, together with the set of all segments
connecting *P* to a point on the polygon, is called
a *pyramid*.

A **regular pyramid** is a pyramid whose base is à
regular polygon and whose lateral edges are congruent.

Pyramids are often classified by their bases.

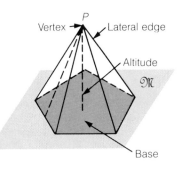

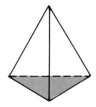
Triangular pyramid
(Tetrahedron)

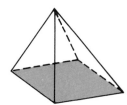
Regular quadrangular
pyramid

Regular hexagonal
pyramid

The next theorem results from the fact that any triangular prism
can be broken up into three pyramids of equal volume, as shown.

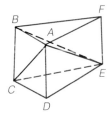 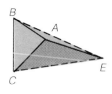 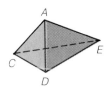 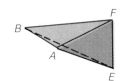

| THEOREM **17.5** | The volume of a triangular pyramid is one-third the product of its base area and its height. |

$$\dot{V} = \tfrac{1}{3}Bh$$

Any pyramid can be separated into triangular pyramids.

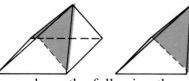

Therefore, we have the following theorem.

THEOREM
17.6
The volume of any pyramid is one-third the product of its base area and its height.

$$V = \tfrac{1}{3}Bh$$

Example   1. Find the volume of this pyramid.

$V = \tfrac{1}{3}Bh$

$= \tfrac{1}{3} \times 3 \times 5.5 \times 6$

$= 33 \text{ cm}^3$

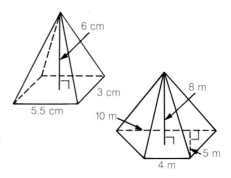

Try This. . .   1. Find the volume of this pyramid.

▲▲ The Volume of a Cone

Consider a circle in a plane $\mathfrak{M}$, and choose any point P not in $\mathfrak{M}$. The circular region in $\mathfrak{M}$, together with the set of all segments connecting P to a point on the circle, is called a *circular cone*.

It can be shown that if a pyramid and a cone have the same height and base area, then they have the same volume. Because the volume of a pyramid is $\tfrac{1}{3}Bh$, we have the following theorem.

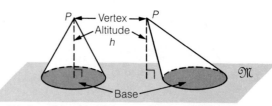

Right Circular Cone   Oblique Cone

THEOREM
17.7
The volume of a circular cone with base radius r is one-third the product of the base area and the height.

$$V = \tfrac{1}{3}Bh = \tfrac{1}{3}\pi r^2 h$$

Example   2. Find the volume of this cone.

$$V = \tfrac{1}{3}\pi r^2 h$$

$$= \tfrac{1}{3}\pi \times 3^2 \times 7$$

$$= 21\pi \text{ cm}^3$$

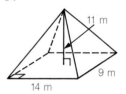

Try This. . .   2. Find the volume of this cone.

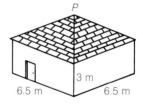

Exercises

▲ **Find the volume of each pyramid.**

1.

2.
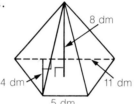

3.
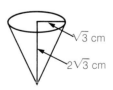

4. The distance from the vertex P of the building to the floor is 5.5 m. Find the total volume of the building.

5. The Great Pyramid in Egypt is approximately 137 m tall. The square base measures 225 m on each edge. Find the volume of the Pyramid.

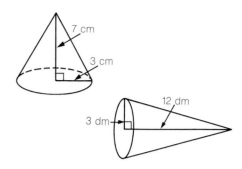

▲▲ **Find the volume of each cone.**

6.
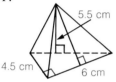

7.
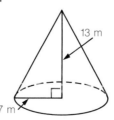

8.

▶▶ Challenge Exercise

9. A cube is broken up into six identical pyramids as shown. Each face of the cube is a base of a pyramid. An edge of the cube is 10 cm. What is the volume of a pyramid?

| 5 | Areas of Pyramids and Cones |

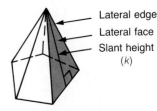

Lateral edge
Lateral face
Slant height
(k)

After finishing Section 5, you should be able to
▲ *find the area of a pyramid.*
▲▲ *find the area of a cone.*

▲ The Area of a Pyramid

Lateral faces of pyramids are triangular regions.
The **slant height** is the length of the perpendicular
from the vertex to an edge of the base.

Example 1. Find the area of this regular quadrangular pyramid.

Because the base is a square region, its area is 10×10, or 100 cm^2.

The lateral faces are congruent, and the slant height k
is the altitude of each face.

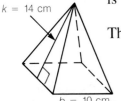

$k = 14$ cm

$b = 10$ cm

Thus, Lateral Area $= 4 \times \frac{1}{2} bk$

$$= 4 \times \frac{1}{2} \times 10 \times 14$$

$$= 280 \text{ cm}^2$$

Total Area $= 100 + 280 = 380 \text{ cm}^2$

Note that $4b$ is the perimeter of the base. Thus, the lateral
area is also $\frac{1}{2} kp$, where p is the perimeter.

THEOREM **17.8** For any regular pyramid, where k is the slant height and p
is the perimeter of the base,

$$\text{Total Area} = \text{Lateral Area} + \text{Base Area}$$
$$= \frac{1}{2} kp + B$$

Example 2. Find the area of this regular pyramid.

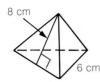

8 cm

6 cm

Because this is a regular pyramid, the base is bounded by an
equilateral triangle with sides 6 cm. Thus, its altitude is $3\sqrt{3}$,
and its area is $9\sqrt{3}$.

Lateral Area $= \frac{1}{2} kp = \frac{1}{2} \times 8 \times 18 = 72 \text{ cm}^2$

Total Area $= (72 + 9\sqrt{3}) \text{ cm}^2$

Try This. . . Find the area of each regular pyramid.

1.

10 cm

4 cm

2.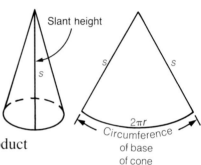

7√2 cm

4√2 cm

▲▲ The Area of a Cone

The length of a segment joining the vertex of a cone to the circle is called a *slant height*. If we cut along such a segment and "spread out" the lateral surface, we get a figure called a *sector* of a circle. The sector has radius *s* (slant height). The length of the arc of the sector is $2\pi r$ (circumference of the base of the cone).

Slant height

s

s

s

2πr
Circumference
of base
of cone

It can be shown that the area of a sector is $\frac{1}{2}$ the product of the radius and the arc length.

So, Lateral Area = Area of the sector

$= \frac{1}{2} \times$ radius $\times$ arc length

$= \frac{1}{2} \times s \times 2\pi r$

$= \pi s r$

THEOREM 17.9	For any right circular cone with base radius *r* and slant height *s*, the lateral area is πrs.

$$\text{Total Area} = \text{Lateral Area} + \text{Base Area}$$
$$= \pi rs + \pi r^2$$
$$= \pi r(s + r)$$

Example 3. Find the area of this right circular cone.

Lateral Area $= \pi rs$

$= \pi \times 8 \times 20$

$= 160\pi$ cm^2

Total Area $= \pi r(s + r)$

$= \pi \times 8(20 + 8)$

$= 224\pi$ cm^2

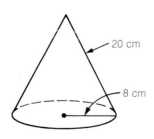

20 cm

8 cm

Try This. . . 3. Find the area of a right
circular cone with a radius
of 4 dm and slant height
15 dm.

►◄ Activity

A pyramid whose faces are all equilateral triangles is
called a *regular tetrahedron*. Make your own tetrahedron
by following these instructions.

1. Fold a rectangular-shaped paper in half
along $\overline{EF}$.

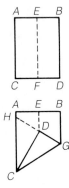

2. Place *D* on the crease and fold as shown. Leave
the paper folded. Extend $\overline{GD}$ to find point *H*.

3. Fold along $\overline{HDG}$ as shown.

4. Unfold the paper and cut out triangle *CGH*.

5. Place each vertex of the triangle at the center of the
opposite base. Crease and unfold.

6. Place each base of the triangle on the crease
parallel to it and fold.

7. Cut out the shaded area as shown.

8. Fold along the creases to produce a tetrahedron.
Paste or tape the faces in place.

Exercises

▲ **Find the area of each regular pyramid.**

1.

8 cm

4 cm

2.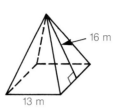

16 m

13 m

3.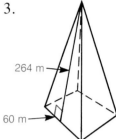

264 m

60 m

4. The cost of roofing is $6 per square meter. How much will it cost to roof this garage?

5. The Great Pyramid is approximately 137 m tall. The square base measures 225 m on each edge. Find the lateral area of the Pyramid.

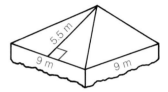

5.5 m

9 m

9 m

▲▲ **Find the area of each circular cone.**

6.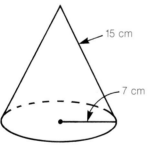

15 cm

7 cm

7.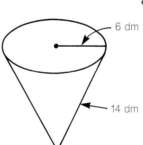

6 dm

14 dm

8.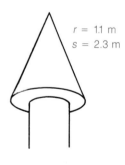

r = 1.1 m
s = 2.3 m

▶ Extension Exercises

9. A manufacturer plans to produce 500 tin funnels. Each funnel has a 7-cm radius and is 15 cm deep. Tin costs $5 per square meter. What is the cost per funnel for the tin?

10. A special metallic coating is applied to the lateral surface of a space capsule. The cost of materials is $3,700 for a capsule with a diameter of 2.5 m and an altitude of 2.5 m. What is the cost per square centimeter?

| **6** | Spheres |

After finishing Section 6, you should be able to
▲ *find the volume of a sphere.*
▲▲ *find the area of a sphere.*

▲ The Volume of a Sphere

A sphere is the three-dimensional counterpart of a circle.

DEFINITION

A **sphere** is the set of all points in space that are a given distance (the radius) from a given point (the center).

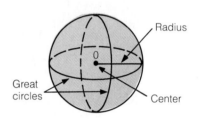

A plane that contains the center of the sphere divides the sphere into two **hemispheres** having the same volume. The intersection of such a plane with the sphere is a **great circle.**

Consider a cylinder, a cone, and a hemisphere, all with the same radius r. The cylinder and cone also have height r. We can inscribe the hemisphere in the cylinder and then inscribe the cone in the hemisphere.

We note that

Volume of cone $<$ Volume of hemisphere $<$ Volume of cylinder

or, $\quad \dfrac{1}{3}\pi r^3 <$ Volume of hemisphere $< \pi r^3$

Although we shall not demonstrate it here, it can be shown that the volume of the hemisphere is simply the average of the other two volumes. That is,

$$\text{Volume of hemisphere} = \frac{1}{2}\left(\frac{1}{3}\pi r^3 + \pi r^3\right) = \frac{2}{3}\pi r^3$$

Because the volume of a sphere is twice that of its hemisphere, we have the following theorem.

THEOREM
17.10

The volume of a sphere with radius r is $\frac{4}{3}\pi r^3$.

Example   1. Find the volume of a sphere with radius 6 m.

$$V = \frac{4}{3}\pi r^3$$
$$= \frac{4}{3} \times \pi \times 6^3$$
$$= 288\pi \text{ m}^3$$

Try This. . . 1. Find the volume of a sphere with radius 3 cm.

Example   2. The volume of a ball is 36π cm³. Find the dimensions of a box that is just large enough to hold the ball.

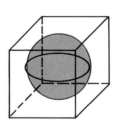

$$V = \frac{4}{3}\pi r^3 = 36\pi$$
$$r^3 = 27$$
$$r = 3 \text{ cm}$$

Thus, the diameter of the sphere is 6 cm and each edge of the box is 6 cm.

Try This. . . 2. The volume of a ball is 288π cm³. Find the dimensions of a box that is just large enough to hold the ball.

▲▲ The Area of a Sphere

Although no part of the surface of a sphere is "flat," the following intuitive argument assumes that very small parts of the surface of a sphere act like "flat" regions.

Imagine dividing the surface of a sphere into n small "polygons." Now join each vertex to the center of the sphere. Each of these slightly rounded "polygons" is now a base of a pyramid. All the pyramids have height r, the radius of the sphere.

The volume of each pyramid is $\frac{1}{3}Br$.

The volume of the sphere is the sum of the volumes of all of these pyramids.

Volume of sphere $= \frac{1}{3}B_1r + \frac{1}{3}B_2r + \ldots + \frac{1}{3}B_nr$

$$= \frac{1}{3}r(B_1 + B_2 + \ldots + B_n)$$

But $(B_1 + B_2 + \ldots + B_n)$ is the surface area of the sphere.

Thus,　Volume of sphere $= \frac{1}{3}r \times$ Area of sphere

$$\frac{4}{3}\pi r^3 = \frac{1}{3}r \times \text{Area of sphere}$$

and　　　Area of sphere $= 4\pi r^2$

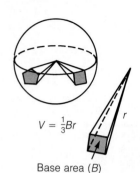

$V = \frac{1}{3}Br$

Base area (B)

This argument suggests the following theorem.

THEOREM
17.11　　The area of a sphere with radius r is $4\pi r^2$.

Example　3. Find the area of this sphere.

$A = 4\pi r^2$

$= 4 \times \pi \times 5^2$

$= 100\pi \text{ cm}^2$

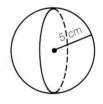

5 cm

Try This. . .　3. Find the area of a sphere with radius 8 dm.

Example　4. The area of a sphere is 64π cm². Find the radius and volume of the sphere.

$A = 4\pi r^2 = 64\pi$

Thus, $4r^2 = 64$

$r = 4$ cm

$V = \frac{4}{3}\pi r^3$

$= \frac{4}{3} \times \pi \times 64$

$= \frac{256}{3}\pi \approx 85.3\pi \text{ cm}^3$

Try This. . .　4. The area of a sphere is 36π m². Find the radius and volume of the sphere.

Exercises

 Find the volume and area of a sphere with the given radius.

1. 4 cm   2. 9 m   3. 1.5 m

4. 1.3 dm   5. 7 cm   6. 8.7 cm

7. 2.1 cm   8. 3.2 cm   9. 3.5 cm

10. 17 cm   11. 1,600 km   12. 6,400 km

▶ Extension Exercises

13. The volume of one sphere is twice the volume of another sphere. Compare their radii.

14. A can contains three tennis balls, each with radius r. The radius of the base of the container is also r. The height of the container is $6r$. Find the total volume of the tennis balls and the volume of the container. Compare the volumes.

15. d represents the diameter of a sphere. Express the volume of the sphere in terms of d.

16. A sphere with radius r is enclosed in a right circular cylinder with radius r and height $2r$. Compare the total area of the cylinder with the surface area of the sphere.

▶▶ Challenge Exercises

17. Find the volumes of spheres with radii of r, $2r$, and $\frac{1}{2}r$. How does a change in the radius affect the volume of a sphere?

18. Find the areas of spheres having radii of 1, 2, and 4. How does a change in the radius affect the area of a sphere?

19. How is the area of a sphere related to the area of a great circle of the sphere?

▶◀ Activity

Draw a 1-inch-by-1-inch square on heavy paper. Cut
the square out and use it as an outline.

Draw as many arrangements of five of these squares
as you can. Their corners must be lined up and
their edges must be touching as shown. Such arrangements
are called *pentominoes*. There are 12 different pentominoes.
Find all of them.

Cut out the 12 pentominoes. (If you have more than
12, you will find that you have duplicates.) How
many of the 12 pentominoes can be folded up into
an open box?

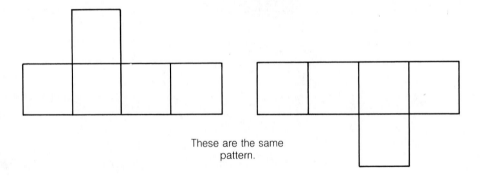

These are the same
pattern.

Now use the 1-inch square to create a pattern of six
connecting squares. How many patterns can you find that
can be folded into a cube?

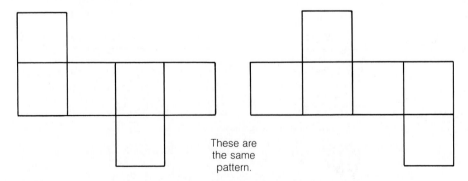

These are
the same
pattern.

Consumer Application   Finding Utility Costs

Utility costs are calculated by multiplying the cost of the unit
of measurement by the number of units used. The unit for water
is 1,000 gallons.

Example   The Pedersons filled their new rectangular pool with water. The pool
is 30 ft long, 15 ft wide, and 8 ft deep. If each unit of water cost 0.67,
about how much did it cost to fill the pool?

1 gallon is about 231 in^3.

$30 \times 12 = 360$
$15 \times 12 = 180$ Multiply to find the pool's measure
$8 \times 12 = 96$ in inches.

The pool is 360 in. long, 180 in. wide, and 96 in. deep.

$l \times w \times h$ = volume of a rectangular prism
$360 \times 180 \times 96 = 6,220,800$ Multiply to find the volume of the pool.

The volume of the pool is 6,220,800 in^3.

$6,220,800 \div 231 = 26,929.87$ Divide to find the number of gallons.
$26,929.87 \div 1,000 = 26.92987$ Divide to find number of units of water.
$26.92987 \approx 27$ Round to the nearest unit.
$27 \times 0.67 = 18.09$ Multiply to find the total cost of the water.

It cost the Pedersons about $18.09 to fill their pool.

Find the cost.

1. To fill a rectangular pool:
   40 ft long
   20 ft wide
   7 ft deep

   Cost per unit of water = $0.50.

2. To fill a square pool:
   20 ft long
   20 ft wide
   2 ft deep

   Cost per unit of water = $0.60.

3. To fill a circular pool:
   10 ft radius
   4 ft deep

   Cost per unit of water = $0.65.

4. To fill a circular pool:
   15 ft radius
   5 ft deep

   Cost per unit of water = $0.55.

Chapter Review

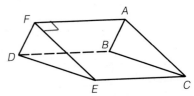

 1. Classify this prism and name the bases, the lateral faces, and the lateral edges.

2. Sketch a right rectangular prism.

Find the volume of each prism.

3.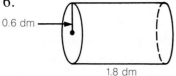

15 dm
6 dm
10 dm

4.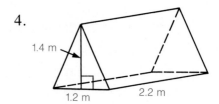

1.4 m
1.2 m   2.2 m

5. How many cubic meters of air are contained in a room that is 2.9 m by 7 m by 12 m?

Find the volume of each cylinder.

6.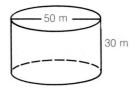

0.6 dm
1.8 dm

7.

50 m
30 m

8. A hot water pipe with diameter 1.2 cm extends 23 meters from a hot water tank. How many liters of hot water must be drawn out of the tank to fill the pipe?

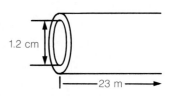

1.2 cm
23 m

9. Find the total area of this prism.

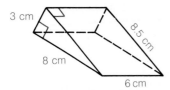

3 cm
8 cm
8.5 cm
6 cm

10. Find the lateral area of this cylinder.

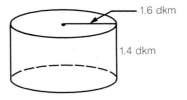

1.6 dkm
1.4 dkm

11. How much wrapping paper is needed to cover a box that is 18 cm by 10 cm by 8 cm?

12. How many square meters of tin are required for a cylindrical air duct 20 m long and 20 cm in diameter?

4 **Find the volume of each pyramid.**

13.

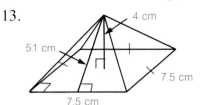

4 cm

5.1 cm

7.5 cm

7.5 cm

14.

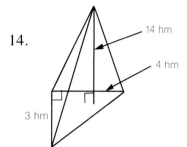

14 hm

4 hm

3 hm

Find the volume of each cone.

15.

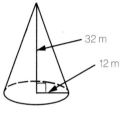

32 m

12 m

16.

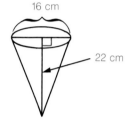

16 cm

22 cm

5 17. Find the area of the pyramid in Exercise 13.

18. Find the area of the cone in Exercise 15.

6 **Find the volume and area of a sphere with the given radius.**

19. $r = 20$ cm

20. $r = 4.1$ m

Chapter Test

1. Classify this prism and name the bases and three lateral edges.

2. Sketch a right triangular prism.

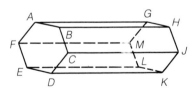

A

F

B

E

C

D

G

H

M

L

J

K

Find the volume of each prism.

3.

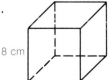

8 cm

4.

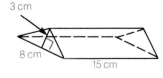

3 cm

8 cm

15 cm

5. How many cubic meters of water are needed to fill this swimming pool?

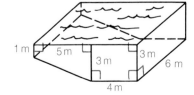

1 m

5 m

3 m

3 m

6 m

4 m

6. Find the volume of
   this cylinder.

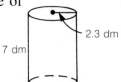

7. Compare the volumes of these cylinders.

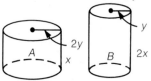

8. A hot water pipe with diameter 1.1 cm extends 17 m from a hot water tank. How many cubic centimeters of hot water must be drawn from the tank to fill the pipe?

9. Find the lateral area of
   this prism.

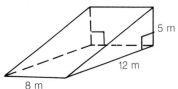

10. Find the total area of this cylinder.

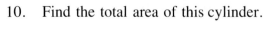

11. A room with a ceiling 3 m high has floor dimensions of 5 m by 6.2 m. If a liter of paint covers 10 m², how many liters are needed to paint the walls?

12. How many square meters of steel plate are required for a cylindrical tank 8 m long and 4 m in diameter?

13. Find the volume of
    the pyramid.

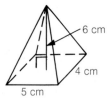

14. Find the volume of the cone.

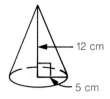

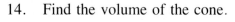

15. Find the area of the pyramid.

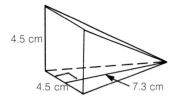

16. Find the lateral area of the funnel.

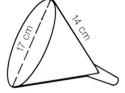

17. Find the volume and area of a sphere with a radius of 3 dm.

18. A sphere has radius r and a right circular cylinder has radius r and height $2r$. Compare their volumes.

Skills Review   Percent

Write each decimal as a percent.

1. 0.33   2. 0.97   3. 0.49   4. 0.64

5. 1.22   6. 2.58   7. 4.26   8. 7.08

9. 0.08   10. 0.05   11. 0.004   12. 0.002

Write each fraction as a percent.

13. $\dfrac{3}{5}$ 14. $\dfrac{8}{10}$ 15. $\dfrac{6}{25}$ 16. $\dfrac{3}{50}$

17. $\dfrac{3}{20}$ 18. $\dfrac{9}{100}$ 19. $\dfrac{9}{4}$ 20. $\dfrac{2}{25}$

21. $\dfrac{18}{30}$ 22. $\dfrac{3}{8}$ 23. $\dfrac{7}{16}$ 24. $\dfrac{5}{8}$

Solve.

25. 35% of 10 is what number?   26. 75% of 8 is what number?

27. 80% of 20 is what number?   28. What is $12\dfrac{1}{2}$ % of 16?

29. What is 25% of 40?   30. What is $33\dfrac{1}{3}$ % of 27?

31. What percent of 20 is 5?   32. What percent of 18 is 6?

33. What percent of 100 is 79?   34. 24 is what percent of 36?

35. 33 is what percent of 66?   36. 16 is what percent of 8?

37. 7 is 10% of what number?   38. 5 is 20% of what number?

39. 9 is $33\dfrac{1}{3}$ % of what number?   40. 4 is 100% of what number?

41. 5 is $12\dfrac{1}{2}$ % of what number?   42. 150 is 50% of what number?

18
Trigonometric Ratios

1   Similar Right Triangles

After finishing Section 1, you should be able to
▲   *find a missing side of similar right triangles using proportions.*
▲▲   *find the six trigonometric ratios for a right triangle.*

▲   Right Triangles

Trigonometry is concerned with right triangles. Because all right
angles are congruent, two right triangles are similar, by
Theorem 9.1, whenever an acute angle of one triangle is congruent
to an acute angle of the other triangle.

Example   1. Which right triangles are similar?

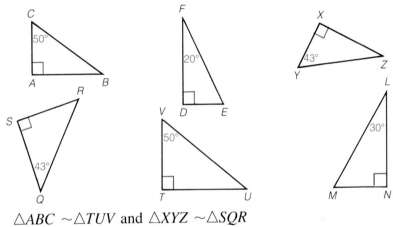

$$\triangle ABC \sim \triangle TUV \text{ and } \triangle XYZ \sim \triangle SQR$$

Try This. . .   1. Which right triangles are similar?

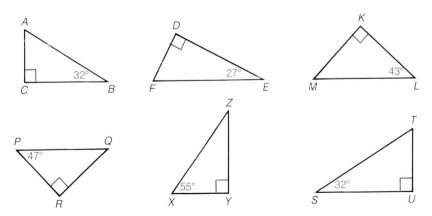

If two triangles are similar, their corresponding sides are proportional.

Example 2. $\triangle XYZ \sim \triangle ABC$. Find the length a.

Because $\triangle XYZ \sim \triangle ABC$,

$$\frac{a}{5} = \frac{16}{4}.$$

$$4a = 80$$

$$a = 20$$

Thus, $BC = 20$

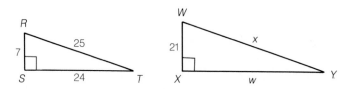

Try This. . . 2. $\triangle RST \sim WXY$. Find the length x.

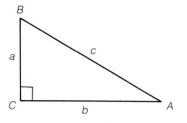

▲▲ Trigonometric Ratios

For any right triangle six ratios of pairs of sides are possible.

$$\frac{a}{c}, \quad \frac{b}{c}, \quad \frac{a}{b}, \quad \frac{b}{a}, \quad \frac{c}{a}, \quad \frac{c}{b}$$

These six ratios are called *trigonometric ratios*. Any right triangle similar to $\triangle ABC$ would have six trigonometric ratios equal to these.

Example 3. Find the trigonometric ratios for $\triangle PQR$. The six trigonometric ratios are

$$\frac{15}{39}, \quad \frac{36}{39}, \quad \frac{15}{36}, \quad \frac{36}{15}, \quad \frac{39}{15}, \quad \frac{39}{36}$$

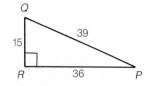

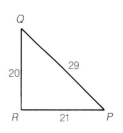

Try This. . .   3. Find the six trigonometric ratios for △*PQR*.

Exercises

▲ **Find the missing lengths.**

1. △*PQR* ~ △*XYZ*. Find *p*.

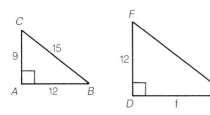

2. △*ABC* ~ △*PQR*. Find *a*.

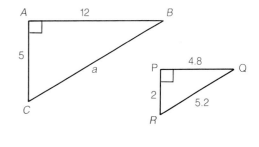

3. △*ABC* ~ △*DEF*. Find *f*.

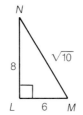

4. △*LMN* ~ △*HJK*. Find *h*.

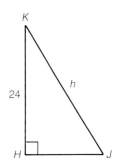

▲▲ **For each of the following, find the six trigonometric ratios.**

5.   6.   7.   8.

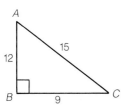

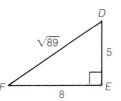

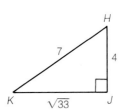

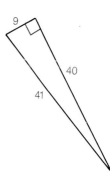

▶ Extension Exercises

Assume that the three sides of △RST are 12, 16, and 20.

9. If △DEF is similar to △RST, and the longest side of △DEF is 30, what are the lengths of the other two sides?

10. If △XYZ ~ △RST, and the shortest side of △XYZ is 6, what are the lengths of the other two sides?

11. △ABC ~ △PRQ. Find the length r.

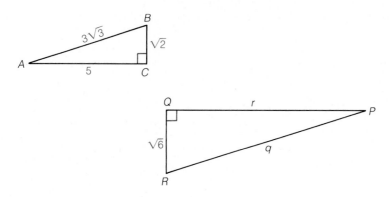

▶▶ Challenge Exercises

In Exercises 12–15, refer to the figure at the right.

12. Name the similar triangles in the figure.

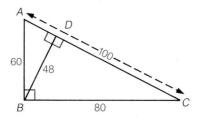

13. Which of these proportions are true?

$$\frac{AB}{BC} = \frac{AC}{DB}$$

$$\frac{AC}{AB} = \frac{BC}{BD}$$

$$\frac{BD}{BC} = \frac{AB}{BC}$$

14. Suppose that $\frac{AD}{AB} = \frac{AB}{AC}$. Find AD.

15. Suppose that $\frac{AD}{BD} = \frac{BD}{DC}$. Find DC.

2 Naming Trigonometric Ratios

After finishing Section 2, you should be able to
▲ *find the sine of an acute angle of a right triangle.*

▲ The Sine Ratio

We often associate a trigonometric ratio with one of the acute angles
of a right triangle. When we do this, we can name the ratio.

If we associate the ratio

$$\frac{a}{c} = \frac{\text{length of side opposite } \angle A}{\text{length of the hypotenuse}}$$

with $\angle A$, we call the ratio

the *sine* of $\angle A$, and we write

$$\sin A = \frac{a}{c}.$$

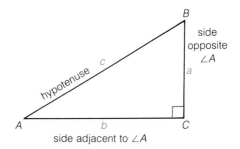

side adjacent to $\angle A$

DEFINITION

For any acute angle, $\angle A$, of a right triangle,

$$\mathbf{\sin A} = \frac{\text{length of side opposite } \angle A}{\text{length of the hypotenuse}}$$

Example   1. In $\triangle ABC$, find $\sin B$.

$$\sin B = \frac{\text{length of side opposite } \angle B}{\text{length of the hypotenuse}}$$

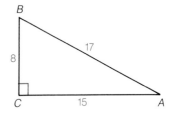

$$\sin B = \frac{15}{17}$$

Try This. . .   1. In $\triangle PQR$, find $\sin R$ and $\sin P$.

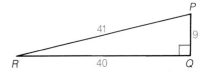

Example
2. Find the sine of the 30° angle in each triangle and compare the ratios.

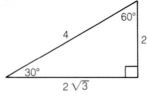
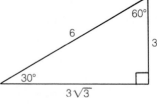

$$\sin 30° = \frac{1}{2} = 0.5 \qquad \sin 30° = \frac{2}{4} = 0.5 \qquad \sin 30° = \frac{3}{6} = 0.5$$

Because the triangles are similar, corresponding ratios are the same. Thus, the sine of 30° is the same number in any such triangle.

Try This. . .
2. Find the sine of the 60° angle in each triangle in Example 2, and compare the ratios.

Example
3. In △PQR, find sin R to four decimal places.

$$\sin R = \frac{20}{52} = 0.3846$$

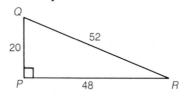

Try This. . .
3. In △PQR, find sin Q to four decimal places.

Exercises

▲ **In each of the following triangles, find the sine ratio for each acute angle.**

1.

2.

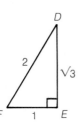

3.

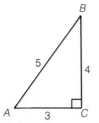

4.

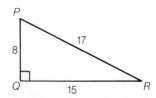

5.

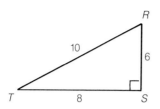

6.

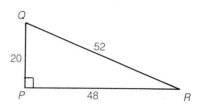

▲▲ **7–12. Find the sine of each acute angle in Exercises 1–6 to four decimal places.**

▶ Extension Exercises

Use a calculator for Exercises 13–14.

13. In $\triangle ABC$, find the sine of each acute angle to four decimal places.

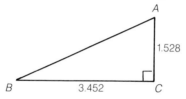

14. In $\triangle XYZ$, find the sine of each acute angle to four decimal places.

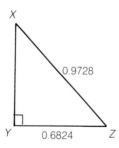

▶▶ Challenge Exercise

15. Use the sine ratio to find AD and DC.

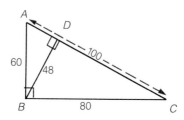

3 | The Cosine and Tangent Ratios

After finishing Section 3, you should be able to
▲ *find the cosine of an acute angle of a right triangle.*
▲▲ *find the tangent of an acute angle of a right triangle.*

▲ The Cosine Ratio

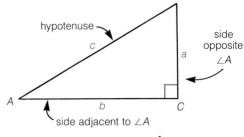

If we associate the ratio

$$\frac{b}{c} = \frac{\text{length of side adjacent to} \angle A}{\text{length of the hypotenuse}}$$

with $\angle A$, we call the ratio the *cosine* of $\angle A$, and we write $\cos A = \frac{b}{c}$.

DEFINITION

For any acute angle, $\angle A$, of a right triangle,

$$\mathbf{cos\ } A = \frac{\text{length of side adjacent to } \angle A}{\text{length of the hypotenuse}}$$

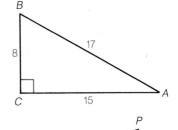

Example 1. In $\triangle ABC$, find $\cos B$.

$$\cos B = \frac{\text{length of side adjacent to } \angle B}{\text{length of the hypotenuse}}$$

$$\cos B = \frac{8}{17}$$

Try This. . . 1. In $\triangle PQR$, find $\cos R$ and $\cos P$.

Example 2. Find the cosine of the 30° angle in each triangle and compare the ratios.

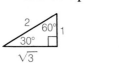 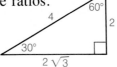 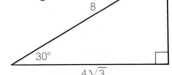

$$\cos 30° = \frac{\sqrt{3}}{2} \qquad \cos 30° = \frac{2\sqrt{3}}{4} = \frac{\sqrt{3}}{2} \qquad \cos 30° = \frac{4\sqrt{3}}{8} = \frac{\sqrt{3}}{2}$$

Because the triangles are similar, corresponding ratios are equal.
Thus, the cosine of 30° is the same number in any such triangle.

Try This. . . 2. Find the cosine of the 60° angle in each triangle in
Example 2, and compare the ratios.

Example 3. In △*DEF*, find cos *E* to four decimal places.

$$\cos E = \frac{36}{39} = 0.9231$$

Try This. . . 3. In △*DEF*, find cos *D* to four
decimal places.

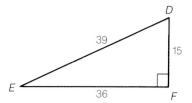

▲▲ The Tangent Ratio

If we associate the ratio

$$\frac{a}{b} = \frac{\text{length of side opposite } \angle A}{\text{length of side adjacent to } \angle A}$$

with ∠*A*, we call the ratio

the *tangent* of ∠*A*, and we write

$$\tan A = \frac{a}{b}.$$

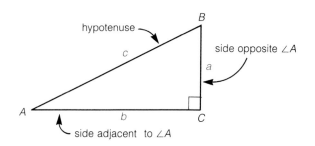

DEFINITION

For any acute angle, ∠*A*, of a right triangle,
$$\mathbf{\tan A} = \frac{\text{length of side opposite } \angle A}{\text{length of side adjacent to } \angle A}$$

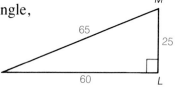

Example 4. In △*KLM*, find tan *K*.

$$\tan K = \frac{\text{length of side opposite } \angle K}{\text{length of side adjacent to } \angle K}$$

$$\tan K = \frac{25}{60}$$

Try This. . . 4. In △*RST*, find tan *R*.

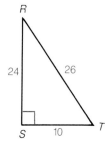

Example   5. Find the tangent of $\angle A$ for each triangle and compare the ratios.

$\angle ABC \sim \triangle ADE \sim \triangle AFG$ (by Theorem 9.1)

Thus, $\tan A = \dfrac{BC}{AC} = \dfrac{DE}{AE} = \dfrac{FG}{AG}$

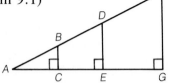

Try This. . .   5. Compare the tangent ratios for $\angle ABC$, $\angle ADE$, and $\angle AFG$ in the triangles in Example 5.

Exercises

▲ **In each of the following triangles, find the cosine ratio for each angle.**

1.

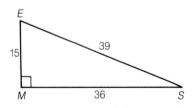

2.

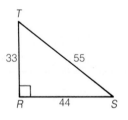

3.

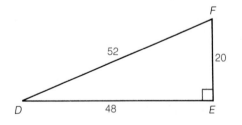

4.

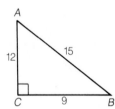

5.

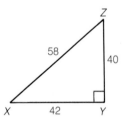

6.

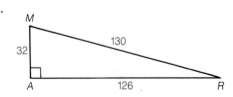

7–12. Find the cosine of each acute angle in Exercises 1–6 to four decimal places.

▲▲ In each of the following triangles, find the tangent ratio for each acute angle.

13.

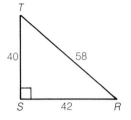

14.

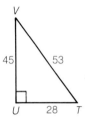

15.

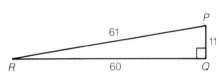

16.

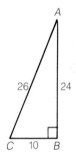

17.

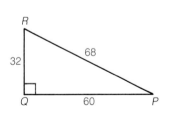

18.

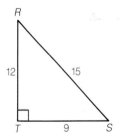

19–24. Find the tangent of each acute angle in Exercises 13–18 to four decimal places.

▶ Extension Exercises

Use a calculator to solve.
25. In $\triangle PQR$, find $\cos R$ to four
    decimal places.

26. In $\triangle ABC$ find $\tan B$ to four
    decimal places.

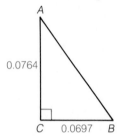

27. What type of triangle will have a tangent ratio of 1 for each
    acute angle?

28. What is the measure of an angle whose cosine and sine
    ratios are the same?

▶▶ Challenge Exercise

29. Using the triangle in Exercise 1, find $(\sin S)^2$, $(\cos S)^2$, and
    $(\sin S)^2 + (\cos S)^2$. Do this for several other triangles. What do
    you observe about the sum?

▶◀ Activity
Use the Trigonometric Table on page 565.

Draw a right triangle with an angle whose tangent is 0.4663.
What are the measures of the acute angles?

Draw a right triangle with an angle whose cosine is 0.1736. What
are the measures of the acute angles?

Draw a right triangle with an angle whose sine is 0.7071. What
are the measures of the acute angles?

4   Using a Trigonometric Table

After finishing Section 4, you should be able to
▲   *find trigonometric ratios using a table.*
▲▲   *find the measure of an angle, given its trigonometric ratio in a table.*

▲ Reading a Table

Trigonometric ratios have been computed for angle measures between 0° and 90°. A part of a table showing these approximate values is shown here. The complete Trigonometric Table is on page 565.

Degrees	Sin	Cos	Tan
56°	0.8290	0.5592	1.4826
57°	0.8387	0.5446	1.5399
58°	0.8480	0.5299	1.6003
59°	0.8572	0.5150	1.6643

Examples   1. Find sin 57°.

First find 57° in the Degrees column. Then find the entry in the Sin column opposite 57°. This is 0.8387, so sin 57° ≈ 0.8387.

2. Find cos 59°.

First find 59°. Then find the entry in the Cos column opposite 59°. This is 0.5150, so cos 59° ≈ 0.5150.

Try This. . . Use the table above to find these ratios.

1. sin 58°   2. cos 56°   3. tan 59°

▲▲ Finding Measures of Angles

Example   3. Suppose that cos A = 0.5592. Find $m\angle A$.

In the Cos column find the entry 0.5592. Find the entry in the Degrees column opposite 0.5592. This is 56°, so $m\angle A$ = 56°.

Try This. . . Use the table on page 551 to find each angle measure.

4. $\sin A = 0.8290$ 5. $\tan B = 1.6003$

Example 4. Suppose $\sin A = 0.8489$. Find $m\angle A$ to the nearest degree. In the Sin column the entry 0.8480 is closest to 0.8489, so $m\angle A = 58°$ to the nearest degree.

Try This. . . Use the table on page 551.

6. $\sin B = 0.8550$. Find $m\angle B$ to the nearest degree.

7. $\cos A = 0.5475$. Find $m\angle A$ to the nearest degree.

Exercises

▲ **Use the table on page 565 to find these trigonometric ratios.**

1. $\sin 38°$ 2. $\sin 47°$ 3. $\tan 56°$ 4. $\tan 84°$ 5. $\cos 9°$
6. $\cos 31°$ 7. $\sin 60°$ 8. $\sin 30°$ 9. $\tan 45°$ 10. $\tan 55°$
11. $\cos 1°$ 12. $\cos 89°$ 13. $\sin 71°$ 14. $\sin 45°$ 15. $\sin 15°$

▲▲ **Use the table on page 565 to find $m\angle A$.**

16. $\sin A = 0.2588$ 17. $\sin A = 0.9397$ 18. $\cos A = 0.8572$
19. $\cos A = 0.1564$ 20. $\tan A = 0.4877$ 21. $\tan A = 2.2460$
22. $\cos A = 0.7547$ 23. $\cos A = 0.9816$ 24. $\tan A = 9.5144$
25. $\tan A = 1.1918$ 26. $\sin A = 0.7193$ 27. $\sin A = 0.0872$

Use the table on page 565 to find $m\angle A$ to the nearest degree.

28. $\sin A = 0.1746$ 29. $\sin A = 0.8753$ 30. $\tan A = 2.9064$
31. $\tan A = 0.7824$ 32. $\cos A = 0.8749$ 33. $\cos A = 0.4234$
34. $\tan A = 9.5234$ 35. $\tan A = 2.8011$ 36. $\sin A = 0.9948$

▶ Extension Exercise

37. One degree is 60 minutes (60′). The trigonometric ratio of an angle measured in degrees and minutes can be approximated using the idea of proportion.

For example, $\sin 37°10'$ must lie between $\sin 37°$ and $38°$. It is reasonable to assume that $\sin 37°10'$ would be $\dfrac{10}{60}$ of the difference between $\sin 37°$ and $\sin 38°$. Find $\sin 37°10'$, $\sin 37°20'$, and $\sin 37°50'$.

5	Solving Triangle Problems

After finishing Section 5, you should be able to
▲   *solve problems using trigonometric ratios.*

▲   Problem Solving Using Trigonometric Ratios

Example   1. In right triangle ABC, $m\angle B = 61°$ and $c = 20$ cm.
Find b.

The sine ratio for $\angle B$ involves the opposite side
and the hypotenuse.

$$\sin B = \frac{b}{c}$$

$$\sin 61° = \frac{b}{20}$$

$$0.8746 \approx \frac{b}{20} \quad \text{Finding } \sin 61° \text{ in the Trigonometric Table}$$

$$20(0.8746) \approx b$$
$$17.492 \approx b$$

Thus, b is about 17.5 cm.

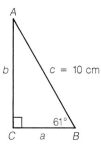

Try This. . .   1. In right triangle ABC, $m\angle A = 44°$ and
$c = 10$ cm. Find a.

Example   2. In right triangle DEF, $m\angle D = 25°$ and
$f = 18$ km. Find e.

$$\cos D = \frac{f}{e}$$

$$\cos 25° = \frac{18}{e}$$

$$0.9063 \approx \frac{18}{e} \quad \text{Finding } \cos 25° \text{ in the Trigonometric Table}$$

$$0.9063e \approx 18$$

$$e \approx \frac{18}{0.9063}$$

$$e \approx 19.8609$$

Thus, e is about 19.9 km.

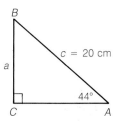

Try This. . . 2. In right triangle DEF, $D = 36°$ and $f = 30$ m. Find e.

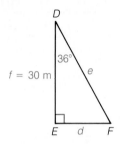

Real world problems involving angles can often be solved using a right-triangle diagram.

Examples 3. Look at a jetliner. The angle of elevation is 12°. The distance to the jetliner is 16 km. How high is the jetliner?

Call the height of the jetliner h.

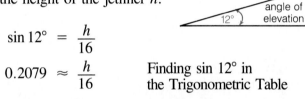

$$\sin 12° = \frac{h}{16}$$

$$0.2079 \approx \frac{h}{16} \qquad \text{Finding } \sin 12° \text{ in the Trigonometric Table}$$

$$16(0.2079) \approx h \qquad \text{Solving for } h.$$
$$3.3264 \approx h$$

The height of the jetliner is about 3.3 km.

4. A fire lookout tower is 43 m tall. The angle of depression from the top of the tower to a fire in the woods is 5°. How far away from the base of the tower is the fire?

Call the distance from the fire to the base of the tower d.

$$\tan 5° = \frac{43}{d}$$

$$0.0875 \approx \frac{43}{d} \qquad \text{Finding } \tan 5° \text{ in the Trigonometric Table.}$$

$$0.0875d \approx 43 \qquad \text{Multiplying by } d$$
$$d \approx 491.4286 \qquad \text{Solving for } d$$

The distance to the fire is about 491.4 m.

Try This. . . 3. A kite is flown with 180 m of string. The angle of elevation of the kite is 58°. How high is the kite?

Exercises

▲ **Solve the following triangle problems. Use the table on page 565.**

1. $m\angle B = 38°$ and $c = 37$ cm.
   Find b.

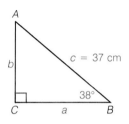

2. $m\angle B = 57°$ and $c = 24$ cm.
   Find b.

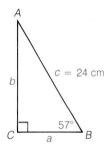

3. $m\angle D = 39°$ and $f = 42$ cm.
   Find e.

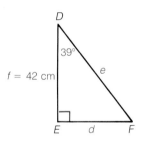

4. $m\angle D = 18°$ and $f = 16$ cm.
   Find e.

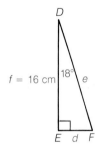

5. $k = 18$ cm and $g = 26$ cm.
   Find $m\angle K$ to the nearest degree.

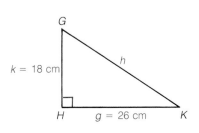

6. $k = 29$ cm and $g = 41$ cm.
   Find $m\angle K$ to the nearest degree.

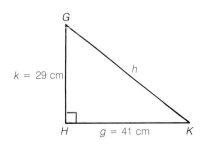

Solve the following problems. Draw a picture first.

7. The angle of elevation of an airplane is 9°. The distance to the plane is 21 km. How high is the plane?

8. A kite is flown with 210 m of string. The angle of elevation of the kite is 61°. How high is the kite?

9. The top of a lighthouse is 110 m above the level of the water. The angle of depression from the top of the lighthouse to a fishing boat is 18°. How far from the base of the lighthouse is the fishing boat?

10. An observation tower is 98 m tall. The angle of depression from the top of the tower to a historical marker is 23°. How far from the base of the tower is the marker?

11. A flagpole casts a shadow 4.6 m long. The angle of elevation of the sun is 49°. How high is the flagpole?

12. A water tower casts a shadow 23 m long. The angle of elevation of the sun is 52°. How tall is the water tower?

13. A pilot in a plane 3 km above the ground estimates the angle of depression to a runway is 51°. How far is the pilot from the runway?

14. A balloonist 1.4 km above the ground estimates the angle of depression to a highway intersection to be 37°. How far is the balloonist from the intersection?

15. Karen is walking to the Texas Commerce Tower, which she knows is 1,002 ft tall. The angle of elevation of the top of the building is 7°. How far does she have to walk?

16. A person atop a 20 ft wall needs to know the distance from the bottom of the wall to the edge of a stream. The angle of depression to the stream edge is 52°. How far is the stream from the wall?

▶ **Extension Exercises**

It can be shown that the area of a triangle equals one half the product of two adjacent sides times the sine of the angle between them. Use the formula, area of $\triangle ABC = \frac{1}{2}bc \sin A$, to find the area of the following triangles to the nearest tenth.

17. $\triangle ABC$ where $m\angle A = 50°$, $b = 12$, and $c = 8$.

18. $\triangle MNP$ where $m\angle N = 67°$, $m = 40$, and $p = 52$.

19. $\triangle XYZ$ where $m\angle Z = 12°$, $x = 18$, and $y = 18$.

20. $\triangle GHJ$ where $m\angle J = 24°$, $g = 6$, and $h = 6$.

Calculator Application   Solving Problems Using Ratios

A scientific calculator contains tables of trigonometric ratios.

Example
In right triangle PQR,
$m\angle P = 42°$ and $c = 25$ cm.
Find b. Round your answer
to the nearest tenth.

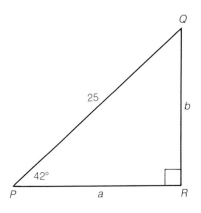

$$\sin P = \frac{b}{25}$$

$$\sin 42° = \frac{b}{25}$$

$$(\sin 42°)(25) = b$$

Enter: 42 $\boxed{\text{sin}}$ $\boxed{\text{x}}$ 25 $\boxed{=}$

Display: 16.72826516

$$b \approx 16.7 \text{ cm}$$

Find the missing lengths. Round your answer to the nearest tenth.

1. Find b.

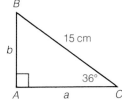

2. Find a.

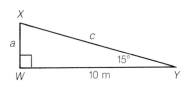

3. Find a and b.

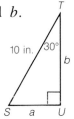

4. Find a and b.

5. Find a and b.

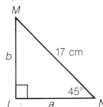

6. Find a.

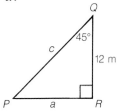

Chapter Review

 1. $\triangle ABC \sim \triangle DEF$. Find f.

2. Find the six trigonometric ratios.

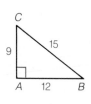

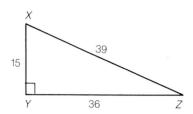

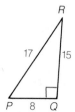

 3–5. In $\triangle XYZ$, find sin Z, cos Z, and tan Z to four decimal places.

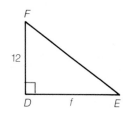

 Use the table on page 565 for Exercises 6–16.

6. Find sin 27°.   7. Find cos 65°.   8. Find tan 88°.

9. Sin A = 0.6947. Find $m \angle A$.   10. Cos B = 0.8572. Find $m \angle B$.

11. Tan X = 1.0000. Find $m \angle X$.

 12. In right triangle CLF, L is the right angle, $m \angle C = 46°$, and $l = 40$ cm. Find c.

13. In right triangle XYZ, Z is the right angle, $m \angle X = 23°$, and $z = 30$ cm. Find y.

14. In right triangle ABC, C is the right angle, $b = 70$ km and $a = 120$ km. Find $m \angle B$ to the nearest degree.

15. A kite is flown with 225 m of string. The angle of elevation of the kite is 56°. How high is the kite?

16. The top of the lighthouse is 120 m above the water level. The angle of depression from the top of the lighthouse to a motorboat is 20°. How far from the base of the lighthouse is the motorboat?

Chapter Test

1. $\triangle ABC \sim \triangle DEF$. Find f.

2. Find the six trigonometric ratios.

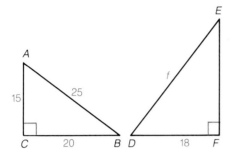

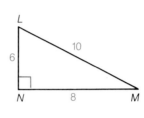

3–5. In $\triangle JKL$, find sin L, cos L, and tan L to four decimal places.

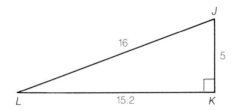

Use the table on page 565 for Exercises 6 –16.

6. Find sin 78°.　　7. Find cos 89°.　　8. Find tan 69°.

9. Sin A = 0.4384. Find $m\angle A$.　　10. Cos B = 0.1736. Find $m\angle B$.

11. Tan X = 0.1051. Find $m\angle X$.

12. In right triangle ABC, B is the right angle, $m\angle C$ = 48°, and c = 42 cm. Find a.

13. In right triangle DEF, F is the right angle, $m\angle D$ = 26°, and f = 32 cm. Find e.

14. In right triangle RST, T is the right angle, s = 60 km, and r = 110 km. Find $m\angle S$ to the nearest degree.

15. At a distance of 60 m from the front of a building, the angle of elevation of the top of the building is 27°. How tall is the building?

16. A pilot in a plane 4 km above the ground estimates the angle of depression to the runway to be 35°. How far is the pilot from the runway?

Skills Review	Statistics

Find the mean.

1. 16, 15, 21, 47, 49

2. 101, 102, 109, 97, 119, 99

3. 34, 36, 35, 34, 39, 38

4. 85, 61, 69, 78

5. $1.50, $1.32, $1.48, $1.38

6. $0.56, $0.60, $0.68, $0.48

7. 82, 84, 81, 80, 79

8. 130, 136, 200, 250, 180

Find the median.

9. 50, 21, 32, 18, 15

10. 110, 98, 108, 110, 103

11. 79, 80, 77, 78, 76

12. 110, 102, 120, 103, 120, 110, 107

13. 400, 350, 280, 380, 500

14. 80, 68, 48, 60, 77, 57

15. 1,054, 680, 982, 888

16. 2,410, 3,890, 2,300, 3,506

Find the mode.

17. 15, 13, 12, 11, 15, 16, 19

18. 16, 25, 25, 16, 17, 25

19. 98, 97, 96, 96, 95, 100, 94

20. 8, 8, 2, 9, 13, 8, 2, 9

21. 74, 62, 74, 88, 62, 79

22. 140, 139, 144, 138, 137, 139

23. 1,450, 1,451, 1,450, 1,452, 1,450

24. 2,400, 2,401, 2,399, 2,397, 2,401

Find the range.

25. 57, 61, 57, 58, 56

26. 48, 32, 46, 36, 36, 42

27. 1, 10, 2, 5, 7, 8

28. 33, 20, 42, 36, 36, 33

29. 140, 132, 132, 142, 136

30. 220, 199, 223, 218, 221

31. 1,560, 1,561, 1,574, 1,570

32. 5,000, 10,000, 15,000, 500

Cumulative Review   Chapters 13–18

13-2 1. If $AO = 3\sqrt{3}$ and $BO = 3$, find CD.

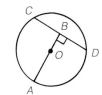

13-3 2. An equilateral triangle is inscribed in a circle with a radius of 1. If the perimeter of the triangle is 4.5, find the distance of each side from the center of the circle.

13-5 3. Identify all the congruent arcs. $\overline{AC} \cong \overline{BD}$.

13-7 4. The circumference of a pipe is 66 cm. Find the pipe's diameter to the nearest tenth.

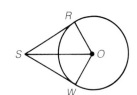

13-8 5. Find the area of the shaded region. Use 3.14 for π.

14-1 6. $\overline{RS}$ and $\overline{WS}$ are tangent segments. $OS = 13$ and $m\angle RSO = 30°$. Find OW and WS.

14-2 7. Draw an equilateral triangle. Inscribe a circle in it. Circumscribe a circle about it.

14-3 8. $\overline{VS}$ is a diameter, $m\widehat{RV} = 84°$, and $m\widehat{VU} = 106°$. Find $m\angle T$ and $m\angle RWS$.

14-4 9. $m\widehat{KM} = 60°$, $m\angle JKN = 45°$. Find $m\angle L$ and $m\angle KPM$.

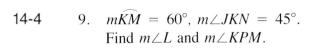

14-5 10. $\overrightarrow{CD}$ is tangent to the circle at D, $m\angle C = 44°$ and $m\widehat{BD} = 88°$. Find $m\widehat{AD}$.

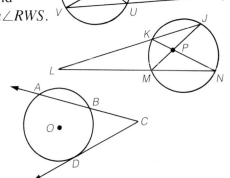

14-6   11. $AG = 3, BG = 3, GF = 10, CH = 4,$ and
$HD = 2$. Find EH.

15-2   12. Find the distance between $P(3, -2)$ and
$Q(-4, 3)$.

15-3   13. Find the slope of the line containing $T(4,2)$
and $V(6,4)$.

15-4   14. Find the slope and y-intercept of
$y + 3x + 2 = 0$.

15-5   15. Write an equation for the line that contains the
point $(1, -3)$ and is perpendicular to the line
$x - 2 = y$.

15-6   16. Find the coordinates of the midpoint of $\overline{PQ}$
if the coordinates of P and Q are $(2,7)$ and
$(-1,5)$, respectively.

16-1   17. Copy and find the reflection of the triangle
across m.

16-2   18. Determine whether each pair of figures has
the same or a reverse orientation.

a.   b.

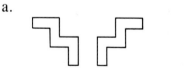

16-3   19. Find the image of $\angle ABC$ under the
translation $\overrightarrow{XY}$.

16-4   20. $\triangle D'E'F'$ is the rotation image of $\triangle DEF$.
O is the center of rotation of $180°$. Identify
all collinear points, congruent segments,
and congruent angles.

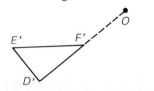

16-5   21.   Which figures have line symmetry?
Which figures have rotational symmetry?

a.   b.

17-2   **Find the volume of these figures.**

22.   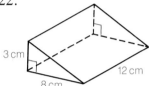   23.

17-3   24.   Find the total area of this prism.

25.   A cylindrical container has a radius of 7.5 cm and a height of 19 cm. Find the area of the paper label need to cover the lateral surface of the container.

17-4   26.   Find the volume of this cone.

17-6   27.   The diameter of a ball is 7 cm. Find its area and volume.

18-1   28. $\triangle RST \sim \triangle ABC$. Find the length c.

18-2   29.   In $\triangle RST$, find $\sin S$, $\cos S$, and $\tan S$ to four
18-3   decimal places.

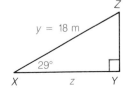

18-5   30.   In $\triangle XYZ$, $X = 29°$ and $y = 18$ m. Find z.

Table of Squares and Square Roots

Number n	Square n^2	Square root $\sqrt{n}$	Number n	Square n^2	Square root $\sqrt{n}$
1	1	1.000	51	2,601	7.141
2	4	1.414	52	2,704	7.211
3	9	1.732	53	2,809	7.280
4	16	2.000	54	2,916	7.348
5	25	2.236	55	3,025	7.416
6	36	2.449	56	3,136	7.483
7	49	2.646	57	3,249	7.550
8	64	2.828	58	3,364	7.616
9	81	3.000	59	3,481	7.681
10	100	3.162	60	3,600	7.746
11	121	3.317	61	3,721	7.810
12	144	3.464	62	3,844	7.874
13	169	3.606	63	3,969	7.937
14	196	3.742	64	4,096	8.000
15	225	3.873	65	4,225	8.062
16	256	4.000	66	4,356	8.124
17	289	4.123	67	4,489	8.185
18	324	4.243	68	4,624	8.246
19	361	4.359	69	4,761	8.307
20	400	4.472	70	4,900	8.367
21	441	4.583	71	5,041	8.426
22	484	4.690	72	5,184	8.485
23	529	4.796	73	5,329	8.544
24	576	4.899	74	5,476	8.602
25	625	5.000	75	5,625	8.660
26	676	5.099	76	5,776	8.718
27	729	5.196	77	5,929	8.775
28	784	5.292	78	6,084	8.832
29	841	5.385	79	6,241	8.888
30	900	5.477	80	6,400	8.944
31	961	5.568	81	6,561	9.000
32	1,024	5.657	82	6,724	9.055
33	1,089	5.745	83	6,889	9.110
34	1,156	5.831	84	7,056	9.165
35	1,225	5.916	85	7,225	9.220
36	1,296	6.000	86	7,396	9.274
37	1,369	6.083	87	7,569	9.327
38	1,444	6.164	88	7,744	9.381
39	1,521	6.245	89	7,921	9.434
40	1,600	6.325	90	8,100	9.487
41	1,681	6.403	91	8,281	9.539
42	1,764	6.481	92	8,464	9.592
43	1,849	6.557	93	8,649	9.644
44	1,936	6.633	94	8,836	9.695
45	2,025	6.708	95	9,025	9.747
46	2,116	6.782	96	9,216	9.798
47	2,209	6.856	97	9,409	9.849
48	2,304	6.928	98	9,604	9.899
49	2,401	7.000	99	9,801	9.950
50	2,500	7.071	100	10,000	10.000

Trigonometric Ratios

Degrees	Sin	Cos	Tan	Degrees	Sin	Cos	Tan
0°	0.0000	1.0000	0.0000				
1°	0.0175	0.9998	0.0175	46°	0.7193	0.6947	1.0355
2°	0.0349	0.9994	0.0349	47°	0.7314	0.6820	1.0724
3°	0.0523	0.9986	0.0524	48°	0.7431	0.6691	1.1106
4°	0.0698	0.9976	0.0699	49°	0.7547	0.6561	1.1504
5°	0.0872	0.9962	0.0875	50°	0.7660	0.6428	1.1918
6°	0.1045	0.9945	0.1051	51°	0.7771	0.6293	1.2349
7°	0.1219	0.9925	0.1228	52°	0.7880	0.6157	1.2799
8°	0.1392	0.9903	0.1405	53°	0.7986	0.6018	1.3270
9°	0.1564	0.9877	0.1584	54°	0.8090	0.5878	1.3764
10°	0.1736	0.9848	0.1763	55°	0.8192	0.5736	1.4281
11°	0.1908	0.9816	0.1944	56°	0.8290	0.5592	1.4826
12°	0.2079	0.9781	0.2126	57°	0.8387	0.5446	1.5399
13°	0.2250	0.9744	0.2309	58°	0.8480	0.5299	1.6003
14°	0.2419	0.9703	0.2493	59°	0.8572	0.5150	1.6643
15°	0.2588	0.9659	0.2679	60°	0.8660	0.5000	1.7321
16°	0.2756	0.9613	0.2867	61°	0.8746	0.4848	1.8040
17°	0.2924	0.9563	0.3057	62°	0.8829	0.4695	1.8807
18°	0.3090	0.9511	0.3249	63°	0.8910	0.4540	1.9626
19°	0.3256	0.9455	0.3443	64°	0.8988	0.4384	2.0503
20°	0.3420	0.9397	0.3640	65°	0.9063	0.4226	2.1445
21°	0.3584	0.9336	0.3839	66°	0.9135	0.4067	2.2460
22°	0.3746	0.9272	0.4040	67°	0.9205	0.3907	2.3559
23°	0.3907	0.9205	0.4245	68°	0.9272	0.3746	2.4751
24°	0.4067	0.9135	0.4452	69°	0.9336	0.3584	2.6051
25°	0.4226	0.9063	0.4663	70°	0.9397	0.3420	2.7475
26°	0.4384	0.8988	0.4877	71°	0.9455	0.3256	2.9042
27°	0.4540	0.8910	0.5095	72°	0.9511	0.3090	3.0777
28°	0.4695	0.8829	0.5317	73°	0.9563	0.2924	3.2709
29°	0.4848	0.8746	0.5543	74°	0.9613	0.2756	3.4874
30°	0.5000	0.8660	0.5774	75°	0.9659	0.2588	3.7321
31°	0.5150	0.8572	0.6009	76°	0.9703	0.2419	4.0108
32°	0.5299	0.8480	0.6249	77°	0.9744	0.2250	4.3315
33°	0.5446	0.8387	0.6494	78°	0.9781	0.2079	4.7046
34°	0.5592	0.8290	0.6745	79°	0.9816	0.1908	5.1446
35°	0.5736	0.8192	0.7002	80°	0.9848	0.1736	5.6713
36°	0.5878	0.8090	0.7265	81°	0.9877	0.1564	6.3138
37°	0.6018	0.7986	0.7536	82°	0.9903	0.1392	7.1154
38°	0.6157	0.7880	0.7813	83°	0.9925	0.1219	8.1443
39°	0.6293	0.7771	0.8098	84°	0.9945	0.1045	9.5144
40°	0.6428	0.7660	0.8391	85°	0.9962	0.0872	11.4301
41°	0.6561	0.7547	0.8693	86°	0.9976	0.0698	14.3007
42°	0.6691	0.7431	0.9004	87°	0.9986	0.0523	19.0811
43°	0.6820	0.7314	0.9325	88°	0.9994	0.0349	28.6363
44°	0.6947	0.7193	0.9657	89°	0.9998	0.0175	57.2900
45°	0.7071	0.7071	1.0000	90°	1.0000	0.0000	

Postulates

POSTULATE 1   Given any two points, there is exactly one line containing them. [p. 16]

POSTULATE 2   Given any three points, there is at least one plane containing them. Given any three noncollinear points, there is exactly one plane containing them. [p. 17]

POSTULATE 3   Any line contains at least two points. Any plane contains at least three noncollinear points. Space contains at least four noncoplanar points. [p. 17]

POSTULATE 4   If two points lie in a plane, then the line containing them is in the plane. [p. 20]

POSTULATE 5   If two planes intersect, then their intersection is a line. [p. 21]

POSTULATE 6   *The Distance Postulate*   To every pair of points, A and B, there corresponds a positive number, AB, called the distance between them. [p. 31]

POSTULATE 7   *The Ruler Postulate*   Every line has at least one coordinate system. [p. 33]

POSTULATE 8   *The Angle Measure Postulate*   To each angle there corresponds exactly one real number n, called its measure, such that $0° < n \le 180°$. [p. 48]

POSTULATE 9   *The Protractor Postulate*   Consider a ray $\overrightarrow{AB}$, and a real number n, such that $0° < n \le 180°$. If $n < 180°$, there is exactly one ray, $\overrightarrow{AC}$ or $\overrightarrow{AC'}$, on each side of $\overleftrightarrow{AB}$ such that $m\angle CAB = m\angle C'AB = n$. [p. 49]

POSTULATE 10   *The Angle Addition Postulate*   For any nonstraight angle $\angle ABC$, if D is a point in its interior, then $m\angle ABD + m\angle DBC = m\angle ABC$. For any straight angle $\angle ABC$, if D is a point not on $\angle ABC$, then $m\angle ABD + m\angle DBC = m\angle ABC$. [p. 52]

POSTULATE 11   *The SAS Postulate*   Two triangles are congruent if two sides and the included angle of one triangle are congruent to two sides and the included angle of the other triangle [p. 101]

POSTULATE 12 *The Parallel Postulate* Given a line ℓ and a point P not on ℓ, there is at most one line through P that is parallel to ℓ. [p. 199]

POSTULATE 13 *The AAA Similarity Postulate* For any two triangles, if the corresponding angles are congruent, then the triangles are similar. [p. 269]

POSTULATE 14 *The Area Postulate* For every polygonal region, there corresponds a positive number called its area. The number is determined for any given unit. [p. 342]

POSTULATE 15 Congruent triangular regions have the same area. [p. 342]

POSTULATE 16 The area of a triangulated polygonal region is the sum of the areas of its triangular regions. [p. 342]

POSTULATE 17 The area of a rectangle is the product of the lengths of two adjacent sides [p. 345]

POSTULATE 18 *The Arc Addition Postulate* If C is on $\overset{\frown}{AB}$, then $m\overset{\frown}{AC} + m\overset{\frown}{CB} = m\overset{\frown}{AB}$. [p. 390]

POSTULATE 19 The reflection of a set of collinear points across a line is also a set of collinear points. (Reflections preserve collinearity.) [p. 480]

POSTULATE 20 For every polyhedron, there corresponds a positive number called its volume. [p. 512]

POSTULATE 21 The volume of a right rectangular prism is the product of its base area and its height. [p. 512]

POSTULATE 22 *Cavalieri's Principle* Suppose that S_1 and S_2 are two prisms of the same height and that $\mathfrak{M}$ is a plane containing their bases. If any plane parallel to $\mathfrak{M}$, interesecting either S_1 or S_2 also intersects the other solid, and if the resulting cross sections have the same area, then S_1 and S_2 have the same volume. [p. 513]

Theorems and Corollaries

The Organization of Geometry

1.1   If two lines intersect, then they intersect in exactly one point. [p. 20]

1.2   If a line and a plane intersect and the line is not in the plane, then they intersect in a point. [p. 21]

1.3   If ℓ is a line and P is a point not on the line, then ℓ and P are contained in exactly one plane. [p. 21]

1.4   If two lines ℓ_1 and ℓ_2 intersect, then they are contained in exactly one plane. [p. 24]

Points and Angles

2.1   If the same real number is added to each coordinate of a coordinate system, then a new coordinate system is obtained. [p. 35]

2.2   If each coordinate of a coordinate system is multiplied by -1, then a new coordinate system is obtained. [p. 37]

2.3   *The Ruler Placement Theorem* If A and B are any points on a line, then there is a coordinate system in which the coordinate of A is the origin and the coordinate of B is a positive number. [p.37]

2.4   Every segment has exactly one midpoint. [p. 42]

2.5   If two angles are complementary, then they are acute angles. [p. 60]

2.6   If two angles form a linear pair, then they are supplementary. [p. 63]

2.7   If two angles form a linear pair and have the same measure, then each is a right angle. [p. 63]

Congruence and Angles

3.1   If two angles are congruent, then their supplements are congruent. [p. 75]

3.2   If two angles are congruent, then their complements are congruent. [p. 76]

3.3   *The Vertical Angle Theorem*   Vertical angles are congruent. [p. 78]

3.4   If two lines intersect to form one right angle, then they form four right angles. [p. 84]

3.5   If line ℓ is in a plane and A is any point on ℓ, then there is exactly one line in the plane that is perpendicular to ℓ at A. [p. 85]

Triangles and Congruence

4.1   *The SSS Theorem*   If three sides of one triangle are congruent to three sides of another triangle, then the triangles are congruent. [p. 102]

4.2   *The ASA Theorem*   If two angles and the included side of a triangle are congruent to two angles and the included side of another triangle, then the triangles are congruent. [p. 104]

Applying Congruent Triangles

5.1   *The Isosceles Triangle Theorem*   Two sides of a triangle are congruent whenever the angles opposite them are congruent. Two angles of a triangle are congruent whenever the sides opposite them are congruent. [p. 142]

COROLLARY   A triangle is equilateral whenever it is equiangular. [p. 145]
5.2

5.3   *The Perpendicular Bisector Theorem*   In a plane, a point is on the perpendicular bisector of a segment whenever it is equidistant from the endpoints of the segment. Any point on the perpendicular bisector of a segment is equidistant from the endpoints of the segment. [p. 148]

COROLLARY 5.4   In a plane, if points P and Q are equidistant from the endpoints of $\overline{XY}$, then $\overleftrightarrow{PQ}$ is the perpendicular bisector of $\overline{XY}$. [p. 150]

Triangles and Inequalities

6.1   If A, B, and C are any points and A-B-C, then $AC > AB$ and $AC > BC$. [p. 160]

6.2   If $\angle PQR$ is any angle and S is a point in the interior of $\angle PQR$, then $m\angle PQS < m\angle PQR$ and $m\angle SQR < m\angle PQR$. [p. 160]

6.3   *The Exterior Angle Theorem*   The measure of an exterior angle of a triangle is greater than the measure of either of its remote interior angles. [p. 161]

6.4   If one angle of a triangle is a right angle, then the other two angles are both acute. [p. 162]

6.5   If ℓ is any line and A is a point not on ℓ, then there is exactly one line containing A that is perpendicular to ℓ. [p. 162]

6.6   *The Opposite Parts Theorem*   In any $\triangle ABC$, if $CA > CB$, then $m\angle B > m\angle A$. [p. 164]

6.7   In any $\triangle ABC$, if $m\angle C > m\angle B$, then $AB > AC$. [p. 165]

COROLLARY 6.8   No two angles of a scalene triangle are congruent. [p. 166]

COROLLARY 6.9   In a right triangle, the hypotenuse is the longest side. [p. 166]

6.10   The sum of the lengths of any two sides of a triangle is greater than the length of the third side. [p. 168]

6.11   *The Derrick Theorem*   In $\triangle PQR$ and $\triangle P'Q'R'$, if $\overline{PQ} \cong \overline{P'Q'}$, $\overline{PR} \cong \overline{P'R'}$, and $m\angle P < m\angle P'$, then $RQ < R'Q'$. [p. 171]

6.12   In $\triangle PQR$ and $\triangle P'Q'R'$, if $\overline{PQ} \cong \overline{P'Q'}$, $\overline{PR} \cong \overline{P'R'}$, and $RQ < R'Q'$, then $m\angle P < m\angle P'$. [p. 172]

6.13   *The SAA Theorem*   If two angles and a non-included side of one triangle are congruent to two angles and a non-included side of another triangle, then the triangles are congruent. [p. 174]

6.14   *The HL Theorem*   If the hypotenuse and a leg of one right triangle are congruent to the hypotenuse and a leg of another right triangle, then the two right triangles are congruent. [p. 175]

6.15   *The Angle Bisector Theorem*   The bisector of an angle is the set of interior points equidistant from the sides of the angle. [p. 179]

6.16   The angle bisectors of a triangle are concurrent in a point that is equidistant from the sides of the triangle. [p. 180]

Parallel Lines

7.1   If two lines and a transversal form congruent alternate interior angles, then the lines are parallel. [p. 195]

COROLLARY
7.2   If two lines and a transversal form congruent corresponding angles, then the lines are parallel. [p. 195]

COROLLARY
7.3   If two lines are perpendicular to a transversal, then the two lines are parallel. [p. 195]

COROLLARY
7.4   If two lines and a transversal form supplementary interior angles on the same side of the transversal, then the lines are parallel. [p. 196]

7.5   If a transversal intersects two parallel lines, then the corresponding angles are congruent. [p. 200]

COROLLARY
7.6   If a transversal intersects two parallel lines, then the alternate interior angles are congruent. [p. 200]

COROLLARY
7.7   In a plane, if two lines are parallel to a third line, then the two lines are parallel to each other. [p. 200]

COROLLARY
7.8   In a plane, if a line intersects one of two parallel lines, then it intersects the other. [p. 201]

COROLLARY
7.9   If a transversal intersects two parallel lines, then the interior angles on the same side of the transversal are supplementary. [p. 201]

COROLLARY 7.10	If a transversal is perpendicular to one of two parallel lines, then it is perpendicular to the other. [p. 201]
7.11	*The Angle Sum Theorem* The sum of the measures of the angles of a triangle is 180°. [p. 204]
COROLLARY 7.12	If two angles of one triangle are congruent to two angles of another triangle, then the third angles are congruent. [p. 205]
COROLLARY 7.13	The acute angles of a right triangle are complementary. [p. 206]
COROLLARY 7.14	The measure of an exterior angle of a triangle is the sum of the measures of the two remote interior angles. [p. 206]

Quadrilaterals

8.1	The sum of the measures of the angles of a quadrilateral is 360°. [p. 217]
8.2	A diagonal of a parallelogram determines two congruent triangles. [p. 220]
COROLLARY 8.3	The opposite angles of a parallelogram are congruent. [p. 220]
COROLLARY 8.4	The opposite sides of a parallelogram are congruent. [p. 220]
COROLLARY 8.5	Consecutive angles of a parallelogram are supplementary. [p. 222]
COROLLARY 8.6	The diagonals of a parallelogram bisect each other. [p. 222]
8.7	Parallel lines are equidistant. [p. 223]
8.8	If the opposite angles of a quadrilateral are congruent, then the quadrilateral is a parallelogram. [p. 226]
8.9	If the opposite sides of a quadrilateral are congruent, then the quadrilateral is a parallelogram. [p. 226]

8.10   If the diagonals of a quadrilateral bisect each other, then the quadrilateral is a parallelogram. [p. 226]

8.11   If two sides of a quadrilateral are both parallel and congruent, then the quadrilateral is a parallelogram. [p. 227]

8.12   *The Triangle Midpoint Theorem*   The segment determined by the midpoints of two sides of a triangle is parallel to and is half as long as the third side. [p. 230]

8.13   If three or more parallel lines intercept congruent segments on one transversal, then they intercept congruent segments on every transversal. [p. 234]

8.14   A parallelogram is a rhombus whenever its diagonals are perpendicular. [p. 240]

8.15   A parallelogram is a rectangle whenever its diagonals are congruent. [p. 241]

8.16   A parallelogram is a square whenever its diagonals are perpendicular and congruent. [p. 241]

8.17   A median of a trapezoid is parallel to the bases. Its length is half the sum of the lengths of the two bases. [p. 246]

8.18   In an isosceles triangle, each pair of base angles is congruent. [p. 248]

8.19   The diagonals of an isosceles trapezoid are congruent. [p. 248]

Similarity

9.1   *The AA Similarity Theorem*   For any two triangles, if two pairs of corresponding angles are congruent, then the triangles are similar. [p. 270]

9.2   If a line is parallel to one side of a triangle and intersects the other sides at any point except a vertex, then a triangle similar to the given triangle is formed and the line divides the sides proportionally. [p. 274]

COROLLARY   For any $\triangle ABC$, if a line intersects $\overline{AB}$ and $\overline{AC}$ at D and E,
9.3   respectively, and $\overleftrightarrow{DE} \parallel \overleftrightarrow{BC}$, then $\frac{AB}{DB} = \frac{AC}{EC}$. [p. 274]

9.4   If a line divides two sides of a triangle into proportional segments, then the line is parallel to the third side. [p. 275]

9.5   *The SAS Similarity Theorem*   For any two triangles, if one pair of corresponding angles is congruent and the sides that include these angles are proportional, then the triangles are similar. [p. 277]

9.6   *The SSS Similarity Theorem*   For any two triangles, if all three pairs of corresponding sides are proportional, then the triangles are similar. [p. 278]

Using Similar Triangles

10.1   In a right triangle, the altitude to the hypotenuse forms two triangles, each similar to the right triangle and similar to each other. [p. 287]

COROLLARY   In a right triangle, the length of the altitude to the hypotenuse is
10.2   the geometric mean of the lengths of the segments on the hypotenuse. [p. 289]

COROLLARY   In a right triangle with the altitude to the hypotenuse, the length of
10.3   each leg is the geometric mean of the length of the hypotenuse and the length of the segment of the hypotenuse adjacent to the leg. [p. 289]

10.4   *The Pythagorean Theorem*   In a right triangle, the sum of the squares of the lengths of the two legs is equal to the square of the length of the hypotenuse. [p. 292]

10.5   *The Converse of the Pythagorean Theorem*   If the lengths of the sides of a triangle are a, b, and c, and $a^2 + b^2 = c^2$, then the triangle is a right triangle with right angle opposite the longest side, whose length is c. [p. 297]

10.6   *The 30°–60° Right Triangle Theorem*   For any 30°–60° right triangle, the hypotenuse is twice as long as the shorter leg and the longer leg is $\sqrt{3}$ times as long as the shorter leg. [p. 300]

10.7   *The Isosceles Right Triangle Theorem*   For any isosceles right triangle, the hypotenuse is $\sqrt{2}$ times as long as either leg. [p. 302]

Polygons

11.1   A polygon has *n* sides whenever it has *n* vertices. [p. 312]

11.2   For a polygon with *n* sides, the number of diagonals is $\frac{1}{2} n \cdot (n - 3)$. [p. 315]

11.3   The sum *S* of the angle measures of any convex polygon with *n* sides is given by the formula $S = (n - 2)180$. [p. 320]

11.4   For a convex polygon, the sum of the measures of the exterior angles, one at each vertex, is 360°. [p. 322]

11.5   The perpendicular bisectors of the sides of a triangle are concurrent at a point that is equidistant from the vertices of the triangle. [p. 325]

11.6   The medians of a triangle are concurrent in a point whose distance from each vertex is $\frac{2}{3}$ the length of the corresponding median. [p. 326]

11.7   The measure of an interior angle of a regular polygon with *n* sides is $\dfrac{(n - 2)\, 180}{n}$. [p. 332]

COROLLARY   The measure of each exterior angle of a regular polygon of *n* sides
11.8   is $\dfrac{360}{n}$. [p. 332]

Area of Polygons

12.1   The area of a square is the square of the length of a side $(A = s^2)$. [p. 345]

12.2   The area of a triangle is one-half the product of a base and the corresponding altitude $(A = \frac{1}{2} bh)$. [p. 349]

12.3   The area of a triangle whose sides measure *a*, *b*, and *c* is $\sqrt{s(s - a)(s - b)(s - c)}$ where $s = \frac{1}{2}(a + b + c)$. [p. 351]

12.4   The area of a parallelogram is the product of a base and the corresponding altitude $(A = bh)$. [p. 354]

12.5   The area of a rhombus is one-half the product of the lengths of its diagonals. [p. 355]

12.6   The area of a trapezoid is one-half the product of the sum of its bases and the corresponding altitude ($A = \frac{1}{2} h(b + b')$). [p. 358]

12.7   The area of a regular polygon is one-half the product of its perimeter and the length of an apothem ($A = \frac{1}{2} ap$). [p.363]

Circles

13.1   All radii of a circle are congruent. [p. 376]

13.2   A diameter of a circle is twice the length of a radius of the circle. ($d = 2r$). [p. 376]

13.3   If a radius of a circle is perpendicular to a chord, then it bisects the chord. [p. 378]

13.4   If a radius of a circle bisects a chord, then it is perpendicular to the chord. [p. 378]

COROLLARY   The perpendicular bisector of a chord of a circle contains the
13.5   center of the circle. [p. 380]

13.6   If chords of a circle (or congruent circles) are congruent, then they are equidistant from the center(s). [p. 383]

13.7   If chords of a circle (or congruent circles) are equidistant from the center(s), then the chords are congruent. [p. 383]

13.8   If two arcs of a circle (or congruent circles) are congruent, then their chords are congruent. [p. 394]

13.9   If two chords of a circle (or congruent circles) are congruent, then their arcs are congruent. [p. 394]

13.10   For all circles, the ratio $\dfrac{\text{circumference}}{\text{diameter}}$ is the same number. [p. 400]

13.11   The area of a circle with radius r is πr^2. [p. 403]

Tangents and Secants

14.1   A line is tangent to $\odot O$ at a point P whenever the line is perpendicular to the radius $\overline{OP}$ at P. [p. 413]

14.2   The tangent segments from a point to a circle are congruent. [p. 414]

14.3   The angle bisectors and perpendicular bisectors of any regular polygon are concurrent in a point that is equidistant from the sides and from the vertices of the polygon. [p. 419]

14.4   The measure of an inscribed angle is one-half the measure of its intercepted arc. [p. 422]

COROLLARY 14.5   An inscribed angle is a right angle if its intercepted arc is a semicircle. [p. 423]

COROLLARY 14.6   Inscribed angles intercept the same arc or congruent arcs whenever the angles are congruent. [p. 423]

14.7   If a secant angle has its vertex in the interior of a circle, then its measure is one-half the sum of the measures of the arcs intercepted by the angle and its vertical angle. [p. 428]

14.8   If a secant angle has its vertex in the exterior of a circle, then its measure is one-half the difference of the measures of the intercepted arcs. [p. 429]

14.9   If a secant-tangent angle has its vertex on the circle, then its measure is one-half the measure of the intercepted arc. [p. 433]

14.10   If a secant-tangent angle has its vertex in the exterior of the circle, then its measure is one-half the difference of the measures of the intercepted arcs. [p. 434]

14.11   The measure of a tangent-tangent angle is one-half the difference of the measures of the intercepted arcs. [p. 435]

14.12   If two chords, $\overline{AD}$ and $\overline{BC}$, intersect in E in the interior of a circle, then $AE \cdot ED = CE \cdot EB$. [p. 437]

14.13   If two secants intersect in a point C in the exterior of a circle and intersect the circle in points A, B and D, E, then $AC \cdot BC = EC \cdot DC$. [p. 438]

14.14   If a secant and a tangent intersect in a point C in the exterior of the circle, the secant intersects the circle in points B and A, and the tangent intersects the circle in a point D, then $AC \cdot BC = DC^2$. [p. 439]

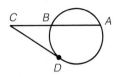

Coordinate Geometry

15.1   *The Distance Formula*   The distance between any two points $A(x_1, y_1)$ and $B(x_2, y_2)$ is given by the formula $d = \sqrt{(x_2 - x_1)^2 + (y_2 - y_1)^2}$. [p. 452]

15.2   If ℓ is any nonvertical line, then all segments on ℓ have the same slope. [p. 456]

15.3   A horizontal line has slope 0. A vertical line has no slope. [p. 458]

15.4   *The Point-Slope Equation*   A nonvertical line that contains point $A(x_1, y_1)$ and has slope m has an equation $y - y_1 = m(x - x_1)$. [p. 460]

15.6   Two nonvertical lines are parallel whenever they have the same slope. [p. 464]

15.7   Two nonvertical lines ℓ and ℓ_1 are perpendicular whenever the product of their slopes is -1. [p. 465]

15.8   *The Midpoint Theorem*   The coordinates of the midpoint M of a segment with endpoints $A(x_1, y_1)$ and $B(x_2, y_2)$ are $\left(\dfrac{x_1 + x_2}{2}, \dfrac{y_1 + y_2}{2}\right)$. [p. 467]

Transformations

16.1   If A' and B' are the reflections of A and B across a line, then $AB = A'B'$. [p. 480]

16.2   If $\angle A'B'C'$ is the reflection of $\angle ABC$ across line, then $m \angle ABC = m \angle A'B'C'$. [p. 480]

COROLLARY

16.3   A triangle and its reflection across a line are congruent. [p. 481]

16.4   A translation is the composite of two line reflections across parallel lines. [p. 485]

16.5   Translations preserve collinearity of points. [p. 485]

16.6   Translations preserve distance. [p. 486]

16.7   Translations preserve angle measure. [p. 486]

16.8   Translations preserve the orientation of a figure. [p. 486]

16.9   A rotation is the composite of two line reflections across intersecting lines. [p. 491]

16.10   Rotations preserve collinearity of points. [p. 491]

16.11   Rotations preserve distance. [p. 491]

16.12   Rotations preserve angle measure. [p. 491]

16.13   Rotations preserve the orientation of a figure. [p. 492]

Space Figures

17.1   The volume of any prism is the product of the base area B and its height h ($V = Bh$). [p. 513]

17.2   The volume of a cylinder is the product of its base area B and its height h ($V = Bh$). [p. 514)

17.3   The lateral area of a right prism is the product of the perimeter p of a base and the height h of the prism (Lateral Area $= ph$). [p. 518]

17.4   The lateral surface area of a right circular cylinder with radius r and height h is $2\pi rh$. (p. 519]

17.5   The volume of a triangular pyramid is one-third the product of its base area and its height ($V = \frac{1}{3} Bh$). [p. 521]

17.6   The volume of any pyramid is one third the product of its base area and its height ($V = \frac{1}{3} Bh$). [p. 522]

17.7   The volume of a circular cone with base radius r is one-third the product of the base area and the height. ($V = \frac{1}{3} Bh = \frac{1}{3} \pi r^2 h$) [p. 522]

17.8   For any regular pyramid, where k is the slant height and p is the perimeter of the base,

$$\text{Total Area} = \text{Lateral Area} + \text{Base Area}$$
$$= \frac{1}{2} kp + B \qquad \text{[p. 524]}$$

17.9   For any right circular cone with base radius r and slant height s, the lateral area is πrs.

$$\text{Total Area} = \text{Lateral Area} + \text{Base Area}$$
$$= \pi r(s + r) \qquad \text{[p. 525]}$$

17.10   The volume of a sphere with radius r is $\frac{4}{3} \pi r^3$. [p. 529]

17.11   The area of a sphere with radius r is $4\pi r^2$. [p. 530]

Glossary

For more precise and formal definitions, please refer to the text.

acute angle   An angle whose measure is less than 90°. (p. 50)

acute triangle   A triangle with only acute angles. (p. 96)

adjacent angles   Angles having a common side and interiors that do not intersect. (p. 62)

alternate interior angles $\angle 4$ and $\angle 6$ or $\angle 3$ and $\angle 5$ in the figure. (p. 194)

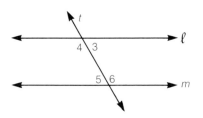

altitude of a figure   The height of the figure. (pp. 287, 354, 517)

angle   A figure consisting of two rays with a common endpoint. (p. 45)

apothem of a regular polygon   A segment from the center of a regular polygon perpendicular to any side. (p. 362)

arc   A curve that is part of a circle. (p. 388)

betweenness B is between A and C if A, B, and C are collinear and $AB + BC = AC$. (p. 40)

bisector of an angle   Given point D in the interior of $\angle ABC$, $\overrightarrow{BD}$ is the bisector of $\angle ABC$ if $m\angle ABD = m\angle DBC$. (p. 54)

bisector of a segment   Its midpoint. (p. 2)

center of a polygon   For any regular polygon, the point of concurrency of the angle bisectors and the perpendicular bisectors. (p. 419)

central angle   An angle whose vertex is the center of a circle. (p. 388)

centroid of a triangle   The point of concurrency of the medians. (p. 326)

chord of a circle   A segment with both endpoints on the circle. (p. 375)

circle   A set of all points in a plane a fixed distance (r) from a given point (O) in the plane. (p. 375)

circular cone   A circular region in plane $\mathcal{M}$ together with the set of all segments connecting a point P outside the plane to a point on the circle. (p. 522)

circumcenter of a triangle   The point of concurrency of the perpendicular bisectors of the sides. (p. 325)

circumcircle   A circle that contains all vertices of a polygon. (p. 418)

circumference of a circle   The distance around the circle. (p. 399)

circumscribed circle   A circle is circumscribed about a polygon if every vertex of the polygon lies on the circle. (pp. 397, 418)

collinear points   Points that are on the same line. (p. 15)

complementary angles   Angles whose measures total 90°. (p. 59)

concave polygon A polygon for which a line containing a side intersects the interior. (p. 313)

conclusion The "then" part of a conditional sentence. (p. 23)

conditional sentences "If-then" sentences. (p. 23)

concurrent lines Lines intersecting in a single point. (p. 180)

congruent figures Figures that have the same size and shape. (p. 73)

congruent triangles Triangles in which the vertices can be matched so that the corresponding sides and the corresponding angles are congruent. (p. 98)

converse of a conditional sentence A conditional sentence in which the antecedent and the consequent have been interchanged. (p. 24)

convex polygon A polygon for which no line containing a side intersects the interior. (p. 313)

coordinate of a point on a line A number that corresponds to the point. (p. 31)

coordinates of a point on a plane A pair of numbers that corresponds to the point. (p. 447)

coplanar points Points that are in the same plane. (p. 16)

corresponding angles $\angle 2$ and $\angle 6$, $\angle 3$ and $\angle 7$, $\angle 1$ and $\angle 5$, $\angle 4$ and $\angle 8$ in the figure. (p. 194)

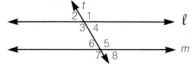

cosine ratio For any acute angle, $\angle A$, of a right triangle,
$$\cos A = \frac{\text{length of side adjacent to } \angle A}{\text{length of the hypotenuse}}.$$
(p. 546)

counterexample An example that disproves a statement. (p. 10)

cross section of a polyhedral solid The intersection of a plane and that figure. (p. 513)

cube A right rectangular prism whose edges are all congruent. (p. 509)

decagon A polygon with ten sides. (p. 312)

deductive reasoning Reasoning that allows us to reach a conclusion on the basis of assumptions. (p. 12)

degree A unit of angle measure. (p. 48)

diagonal of a quadrilateral A segment that joins two opposite vertices. (p. 216)

diagonal of a polygon A segment that joins any two nonconsecutive vertices. (p. 315)

diameter of a circle A chord containing the center of a circle or the length of such a chord. (p. 375)

dodecagon A polygon with twelve sides. (p. 312)

divider Tool for marking congruent segments. (p. 3)

edges of a polyhedron The sides of each face of the polyhedron. (p. 507)

equiangular triangle A triangle with all three angles congruent. (p. 96)

equilateral triangle A triangle with all three sides congruent. (p. 96)

exterior angle of a convex polygon An angle that forms a linear pair with an interior angle of the polygon. (p. 322)

faces of a polyhedron A polyhedron consists of polygonal regions. Each region is called a face. (p. 507)

geometric mean For any positive numbers p, q, and r, q is the geometric mean of p and r if $\dfrac{p}{q} = \dfrac{q}{r}$. (p. 288)

great circle A circle that is the intersection of a sphere and a plane that contains the center of the sphere. (p. 528)

hexagon A polygon with six sides. (p. 312)

hypotenuse The side opposite the right angle in a right triangle. (p. 166)

hypothesis The "if" part of a conditional sentence. (p. 23)

if-then sentence *See* conditional sentence.

incenter of a triangle The point of concurrency of the angle bisectors. (p. 180)

incircle A circle that is tangent to all the sides of a polygon. (p. 418)

inductive reasoning Reaching a conclusion on the basis of examples. (p. 10)

inscribed angle An angle whose vertex is on a circle and whose sides each intersect the circle in one other point. (p. 421)

inscribed circle A circle tangent to every side of a polygon. (p. 418)

inscribed polygon A polygon whose vertices all lie on a circle. (p. 397)

interior angles $\angle 3$, $\angle 4$, $\angle 5$, and $\angle 6$ in the figure. (p. 194)

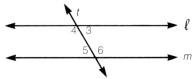

interior of an angle The shaded region in the figure. (p. 47)

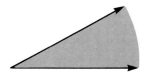

interior of a triangle The shaded region in the figure. (p. 135)

isosceles trapezoid A trapezoid with two congruent non-parallel sides. (p. 247)

isosceles triangle A triangle with at least two congruent sides. (p. 96)

kite A quadrilateral with two pairs of congruent consecutive sides. (p. 218)

lateral area of a prism The sum of the areas of the prism's lateral faces. (p. 517)

lateral edge of a prism The intersection of the two lateral faces. (p. 508)

lateral faces of a prism The faces that are not bases. (p. 508)

legs of a right triangle The perpendicular sides of it. (p. 175)

linear pair Adjacent angles whose noncommon sides are opposite rays. (p. 62)

locus A set that contains all the points that satisfy a given condition. (p. 149)

major arc An arc whose measure is greater than 180° but less than 360°. (p. 388)

mean proportional In a proportion $\frac{a}{b} = \frac{b}{c}$, b is the mean proportional between a and c. (p. 288)

median of a trapezoid The segment whose midpoints are the midpoints of the legs. (p. 245)

median of a triangle A segment from the vertex to the midpoint of the opposite side. (p. 9)

midpoint A point halfway between the endpoints of a line segment. (pp. 2, 42)

minor arc An arc whose measure is less than 180°. (p. 388)

n-gon A polygon with n sides. (p. 312)

nonagon A polygon with nine sides. (p. 312)

noncollinear points Points that are not all on the same line. (p. 15)

noncoplanar lines Lines that are not all in the same plane. (p. 190)

noncoplanar points Points that do not lie in the same plane. (p. 16)

oblique prism A prism in which the lateral faces are not all rectangular. (p. 508)

obtuse angle An angle whose measure is greater than 90° but less than 180°. (p. 50)

obtuse triangle A triangle with one obtuse angle. (p. 96)

octagon A polygon with eight sides. (p. 312)

opposite angles of a quadrilateral Angles in a quadrilateral that do not share a common side. (p. 215)

opposite rays $\overrightarrow{AB}$ and $\overrightarrow{CD}$ are opposite rays whenever $A = C$ and B-A-D. (p. 41)

opposite sides of a quadrilateral Sides of a quadrilateral that do not intersect. (p. 215)

opposite vertices of a quadrilateral *See* opposite angles of a quadrilateral.

origin A point with coordinate zero; also the point at which the x-axis and y-axis intersect. (pp. 31, 447)

orthocenter of a triangle The point of concurrency of the altitudes of a triangle. (p. 325)

overlapping triangles Triangles whose interiors overlap. (p. 135)

pantograph An instrument used to reduce or enlarge a drawing. (p. 281)

parallel lines Lines in the same plane that do not intersect. (p. 189)

parallelogram A quadrilateral with two pairs of parallel sides. (p. 218)

parallel segments Segments contained in parallel lines. (p. 189)

pentagon A polygon with five sides. (p. 312)

pentagonal prism A prism with a pentagonal base. (p. 508)

perimeter of a polygon The sum of the lengths of the sides, that is, the

distance around the polygon.
(pp. 317, 399)

perpendicular bisector of a segment
The line that is perpendicular to a
segment at its midpoint. (p. 148)

perpendicular lines Two lines that
intersect to form a right angle.
(p. 83)

perpendicular rays Rays contained in
perpendicular lines. (p. 84)

perpendicular segments Segments
contained in perpendicular lines.
(p. 84)

perpendicular to a plane A segment
(or line) AB is perpendicular to a
plane $\mathcal{K}$ at point B if it is perpendicular to two lines in plane $\mathcal{K}$. (p. 517)

point symmetry A set of points has
point symmetry if there is some point
O such that for a 180° rotation about
O, the image of every point in the set
is also a point in the set. (p. 497)

polygon A closed figure formed by
connecting three or more coplanar
points with segments. (p. 311)

polyhedron A three-dimensional closed
figure formed by polygonal regions.
(p. 507)

proportion A statement that two ratios
are equal. (p. 260)

pyramid A closed three-dimensional
figure whose base is a polygonal
region and whose lateral faces are
triangles. (p. 521)

Pythagorean triple Three positive
integers that can be the lengths of
the sides of a right triangle. (p. 295)

quadrilateral A polygon consisting of

four coplanar segments that intersect
only at their endpoints. (p. 215)

radius of a circle A segment whose endpoints are the center of the circle
and a point on the circle. (p. 375)

ratio The quotient $\frac{a}{b}$ of two numbers,
a and b. (p. 259)

ray The segment, $\overline{AB}$, together with the
set of all points X such that $A\text{-}B\text{-}X$.
(p. 41)

rectangle A parallelogram with four
right angles. (p. 218)

rectangular prism A prism with a
rectangular base. (p. 509)

reflections (images) Given a line ℓ in
a plane, any two points A and A'
in the plane are reflections (or
images) of each other across the line ℓ
if ℓ is the perpendicular bisector of
$\overline{AA'}$. (p. 475)

regular polygon A convex polygon that
is both equilateral and equiangular.
(p. 331)

regular pyramid A pyramid whose
base is a regular polygon and whose
lateral edges are congruent. (p. 521)

rhombus A parallelogram with four
congruent sides. (p. 218)

right angle An angle whose measure
is 90°. (p. 50)

right prism A prism whose lateral faces
are all rectangular. (p. 508)

right triangle A triangle with one right
angle. (p. 96)

rotation image For any point P, a point
P' on a circle with center O and
radius OP, such that $m\overset{\frown}{PP'} = \alpha$.
(p. 489)

scalene triangle   A triangle with no congruent sides. (p. 96)

secant   A line that intersects a circle in two points. (p. 427)

segment   A set of points containing two points and all the points between them. (p. 41)

semicircle   An arc whose measure is 180°. (p. 388)

similar figures   Figures with the same shape, but not necessarily the same size. (p. 264)

sine ratio   For any acute angle, $\angle A$, of a right triangle,
$$\sin A = \frac{\text{length of side opposite } \angle A}{\text{length of the hypotenuse}}.$$
(p. 543)

skew lines   Noncoplanar lines. (p. 190)

slant height of a cone   The length of a segment joining the vertex of a cone to the boundary of the base. (p. 525)

slant height of a pyramid   The length of the perpendicular from the vertex to an edge of the base. (p. 524)

slope   For points $P_1(x_1, y_1)$ and $P_2(x_2, y_2)$, if P_1P_2 is a nonvertical segment then the ratio $\frac{y_2 - y_1}{x_2 - x_1}$. (p. 455)

sphere   A set of all points in space that are a fixed distance from a given point. (p. 528)

square   A rectangle with four congruent sides. (p. 218)

straight angle   An angle in which the rays are opposite. (pp. 45, 50)

supplementary angles   Two angles whose measures total 180°. (p. 61)

symmetry   A set of points is symmetric with respect to a line m if the reflection of every point in the set across line m is also a point in the set. (p. 495)

tangent   A line, coplanar with a circle, that intersects the circle in exactly one point. (p. 413)

tangent circles   Coplanar circles that are tangent to the same line at the same point. (p. 416)

tangent ratio   For any acute angle, $\angle A$, of a right triangle,
$$\tan A = \frac{\text{length of side opposite } \angle A}{\text{length of side adjacent to } \angle A}.$$
(p. 547)

translation   A movement along a line from one position to another. (p. 484)

transversal   A line that intersects two or more coplanar lines in different points. (p. 194)

trapezoid   A quadrilateral with at least one pair of parallel sides. (p. 218)

triangle   A figure consisting of three segments joined at their endpoints. (p. 7)

triangle prism   A prism with a triangular base. (p. 508)

triangular region   A triangle together with its interior. (p. 341)

triangulate   To divide a polygonal region into triangular regions. (p. 341)

vertex of an angle   The point at which rays intersect. (p. 45)

vertex of a polygon   The point at which two sides intersect. (p. 311)

vertex of a polyhedron   The point at which three or more edges intersect. (p. 507)

vertical angles   Two non-straight angles whose sides form two pairs of opposite rays. (p. 78)

Index

Selected Answers

CHAPTER 1

Section 1-1

Try This. . .
1. The copy should be as long as the original.

Exercises
1, 3, 5. The copy should be as long as the original.

9. Each new segment should be about 6 cm long.

3. Each smaller segment should have the same length and be about 4 cm long.

7. Each new segment should be about 4 cm long.

11. Some possible answers are: edges of pieces of paper, edge of a ruler, and the edge of the chalk ledge.

Section 1-2

Try This. . .
1.

P T Q

Exercises
1, 3. A drawing triangle should snugly fit at the point where the segments meet.

7. The sides of the copy should measure 3 cm, 5 cm, and 4.5 cm.

3. The copy should fit precisely over $\triangle ABC$.

5. The copy should fit precisely over $\triangle PQR$.

9. The lines should be parallel.

Section 1-3

Try This. . .
1. The sum of the $\angle$ measures is 360°.

Exercises
1. The $\angle$s are the same size.

5. A rose that is not red, e.g., white or yellow.

9. Corn that is not yellow, e.g., white.

13. A $\triangle$ with two $\angle$s the same size but with opposite sides of different lengths.

3. A beet that is not red, e.g., yellow.

3. The largest $\angle$ is opposite the longest side and so on.

7. A squash that is not green e.g., yellow.

11. An even number greater than 4 that cannot be expressed as the sum of two odd prime numbers.

Section 1-4

Try This. . .
1. All squares are polygons.

Exercises
1. All elephants have hair.

5. The measures of the other two $\angle$s add up to 90°, or they are acute.

9. The measures of the $\angle$s of an octagon add up to 1,080°.

3. A pentagon can be divided into three $\triangle$. $3 \times 180° = 540°$.

3. $b = a$

7. The diagonals of a $\square$ bisect each other.

Section 1-5

Try This. . .
1. Points, line

5. Collinear: $A, B, C; A, G, J; A, F, E.$ Coplanar: $B, H, F, G; B, H, C, D; H, F, E, D.$ There are other possibilities.

Exercises
1. Points, line
5. Post. 1
9. Post. 3
13. Post. 2

3. Post. 1

3. Points, plane
7. Post. 2
11. Post. 3
15. Fifteen lines

17. $\overleftrightarrow{GK}$ and $\overleftrightarrow{FH}$ are the same.
19. The planes, $\mathcal{M}$ and $\mathcal{P}$ are the same.
21. Nose and wing tips of an airplane; one bird flying off a fence where others are sitting.
23. Corners of a pyramid; corners of a paper hat.
25. From each of the n points, $n - 1$ lines are determined. Altogether this gives $n(n - 1)$ lines. But this counts each line twice. Thus, there are $n(n - 1)/2$ lines determined.

Section 1-6

Try This. . .   1. Post. 5   3. Th. 1.1

Exercises   1. Post. 1   3. Th. 1.3
             5. Post. 5   7. Th. 1.1
             9. Post. 3   11. Post. 1
            13. Th. 1.1

Section 1-7

Try This. . .   1. If <u>it rains</u> (hypothesis), then <u>you will get wet</u> (conclusion).
3. If <u>two points are in a plane</u> (hypothesis), then <u>the line containing them is in the plane</u> (conclusion).

             5. If a figure has four sides, then it is a □.

Exercises   1. If <u>a number has three factors</u> (hypothesis), then <u>it is a composite number</u> (conclusion).
3. If <u>the grass is green</u> (hypothesis), then <u>there are no weeds</u> (conclusion).
             5. If $2x = 10$ (hypothesis), then $x = 5$ (conclusion).
7. If <u>Mary is wary</u> (hypothesis), then <u>Tim is slim</u> (conclusion).
             9. If <u>it rains</u> (hypothesis), then <u>it pours</u> (conclusion).
11. If a number is a composite number, then it has three factors.
           13. If there are no weeds, then the grass is green.
15. If $x = 5$, then $2x = 10$.
           17. If Tim is slim, then Mary is wary.
19. If it pours, then it rains.
           21. If you spare the rod, then you spoil the child.
23. If you use too much pepper, then you will ruin the sauce.
           25. If two lines ℓ_1 and ℓ_2 are contained in exactly one plane, then the two lines intersect. False; the lines could be parallel.

Chapter Review

            1. Check with ruler.
3. A drawing triangle should fit snugly where the line segments meet.
            5. A △which is not equilateral.
7. All trout have gills.
            9. Post. 2
11. Th. 1.1
          13. If <u>the rain falls</u> (hypothesis), then <u>the weeds grow</u> (conclusion). Converse: If the weeds grow, then the rain falls.

Skills Review

1. 3	3. 0	5. 2	7. 1	9. 16	11. 8
13. 5	15. 22	17. 30	19. 32	21. 44	23. 50
25. 66	27. 99	29. 101	31. 3	33. 8	35. 3
37. 18	39. 16	41. 75	43. 0	45. 55	47. 100
49. 125	51. 3	53. 1	55. 5	57. 20	59. 15
61. 20	63. 50	65. 100	67. 4,000	69. 3,300	

CHAPTER 2

Section 2-1

Try This. . .   1. $-2, -6, 5$, and 0, respectively   3. E 5. 9
             7. 5   9. 4   11. $12 = b$ or $b = -6$.

Exercises   1. $40°$ 3. $20°$
             5. $50°$ 7. 4
             9. -5 11. L

13. Q

15. Y

17. 5

19. 13

21. 12

23. $14°C$

25. $27°C$

27. 0 or 14

29. -11 or -1

31. The coordinates of A and C are 0.5 and 1.5, respectively.

33. The coordinates of B and D are 0 and 4, respectively.

35. The coordinates of B and C are -1 and 0, respectively.

Section 2-2

Try This. . .

1. The new coordinates are $-5, -3, 0,$ and 1, respectively. Distances in the new system are the same as the corresponding distances in the old system.

3. $77°K$

5.

Exercises

1. $223°K$

3. $87°C$

5.

7.

9.

11.

13.

15.

17. The coordinates of A and C are 7 and -1, respectively.

19. Possible answers are a scale and an auto speedometer.

Section 2-3

Try This. . .

1. $A\text{-}C\text{-}B$

3. $\overline{AB}, \overline{AC}, \overline{BC}, \overline{DC}, \overline{CE}, \overline{DE}, \overline{AE}, \overline{DB}$

5. $\overline{BD}$

7. 7

Exercises

1. $P-Q-R$

3. $P-Q-R$

5. $P-R-Q$

7. 23.8

9. 1.214

11. $\frac{3}{4}$

13. Segments: $\overline{AB}, \overline{BC}, \overline{AC}, \overline{DB}, \overline{BE}, \overline{DE}$; rays: $\overrightarrow{BD}$, $\overrightarrow{BE}, \overrightarrow{BA}, \overrightarrow{BC}, \overrightarrow{CA}, \overrightarrow{AC}$; opposite rays: $\overrightarrow{BA}$ and $\overrightarrow{BC}$.

15. $\overline{RS}$

17. 13

19. $11\frac{1}{2}$

21. 36.9

23. Four: $D, A, B, C; A, D, B, C; A, B, D, C; A, B, C, D$

25. 38 or -14

27. -29

29. If a and b are the coordinates of A and B, and m is the coordinate of M, the midpoint of $\overline{AB}$, then

$$m = \frac{a+b}{2}.$$

Section 2-4

Try This. . .

1. $\angle E, \angle DEF, \angle FED$

3. $\angle CBD, \angle DBC, \angle CAD, \angle DAC, \angle A, \angle B$

5. Vertex of each: T; sides of $\angle RTS$: $\overrightarrow{TR}, \overrightarrow{TS}$; sides of $\angle QTS$: $\overrightarrow{TQ}, \overrightarrow{TS}$

Exercises

1. $\angle B, \angle ABC, \angle CBA$; vertex: B; sides $\overrightarrow{BA}, \overrightarrow{BC}$

3. $\angle JKL, \angle LKJ$; vertex: K; sides: $\overrightarrow{KJ}, \overrightarrow{KL}$; $\angle JKM, \angle MKJ$; vertex: K; sides: $\overrightarrow{KJ}, \overrightarrow{KM}$; $\angle MKL, \angle LKM$; vertex: K; sides: $\overrightarrow{KM}, \overrightarrow{KL}$

5. $\angle N$, $\angle MNP$, $\angle PNM$; vertex: N; sides: $\overrightarrow{NM}$, $\overrightarrow{NP}$

7. $\angle XWY$, $\angle YWX$; vertex: W, sides: $\overrightarrow{WX}$, $\overrightarrow{WY}$; $\angle YWZ$, $\angle ZWY$; vertex: W; sides: $\overrightarrow{WY}$, $\overrightarrow{WZ}$; $\angle XWZ$, $\angle ZWX$; vertex: W; sides: $\overrightarrow{WX}$, $\overrightarrow{WZ}$

9. $\angle EDF$, $\angle FDE$; vertex: D; sides: $\overrightarrow{DE}$, $\overrightarrow{DF}$; $\angle FDG$, $\angle GDF$; vertex: D; sides: $\overrightarrow{DF}$, $\overrightarrow{DG}$; $\angle EDG$, $\angle GDE$; vertex: D; sides: $\overrightarrow{DE}$, $\overrightarrow{DG}$

11. Fifteen

Section 2-5

Try This...

1. $m\angle PQR = 60°$, $m\angle PQS = 105°$, $m\angle PQT = 150°$

3. $m\angle DEF = 151°$

5.

95°

7. Acute

9. Right

Exercises

1. 120°
5. 70°
9. 35°
13.

75°

3. 75°
7. 120°
11. 82°
15.

15°

17.

135°

19. Straight

21. Obtuse

Section 2-6

Try This...

1. $m\angle BFD$
5. $m\angle DEG = 45°$ and $\angle GEF = 135°$

3. $m\angle BFD$

Exercises

1. $m\angle AFE$
5. $m\angle ACD$
9. $m\angle MPL$
13. 45°
17. 132°

3. $m\angle AFE$
7. $m\angle GPK$
11. 66°
15. $m\angle DBC = m\angle ABD = 87°$

Section 2-7

Try This...

1. Check work against steps in Example 1.

3. Check work against steps in Example 2.

5.

60° — 2b

Exercises

1, 3, 5. Follow the steps of Example 2 and then the steps of Example 1.

7.

$a + b$

9.

$c - b$

11.

$2a$

13.

$\frac{1}{2} c$

15.

$2a - b$

Section 2-8

Try This. . .
1. $\angle JOK$ and $\angle KOL$; $\angle JOK$ and $\angle MON$; $\angle KOL$ and $\angle LOM$; $\angle LOM$ and $\angle MON$
3. 72°
5. 72° and 18°
7. a. 142°; b. 23°; c. 90°
9. $\angle 3$ and $\angle 4$ are adjacent and do form a linear pair.
11. $\angle 7$ and $\angle 8$ are not adjacent and do not form a linear pair.

Exercises
1. $\angle 2$ and $\angle 3$, $\angle 1$ and $\angle 4$
3. 68°
5. 5°
7. $90 - t$
9. n
11. $90 - x - y$
13. 60° and 30°
15. $\angle 1$ and $\angle 2$, $\angle 3$ and $\angle 4$, $\angle 2$ and $\angle 3$, $\angle 1$ and $\angle 4$
17. 61°
19. 37°
21. 106°
23. $180 - y$
25. $180 - a - b$
27. 81° and 99°
29. Adjacent and linear: $\angle ABD$ and $\angle DBC$, $\angle ABE$ and $\angle EBC$, $\angle ABF$ and $\angle FBC$; adjacent but not linear: $\angle ABD$ and $\angle ABF$, $\angle ABF$ and $\angle FBE$, $\angle FBE$ and $\angle EBC$, $\angle EBC$ and $\angle CBD$
31. Th. 2.6 and def. of supp. $\angle$s
33. Def. of linear pair Th. 2.6
35. Post. 10
37. $\angle AEB$, $\angle BEC$, $\angle CED$, $\angle BED$
39. $\angle AEB$ and $\angle BEC$, $\angle BEC$ and $\angle CED$
41. $m \angle AEB = m \angle CED$
43. $m \angle BCA$

Chapter Review

1. $-3, 5, 0$
3. 7, 5, 3
5. 203° K
7. $-4\frac{1}{2}$
9. $\angle EDF$, $\angle FDE$; vertex: D; sides: $\overrightarrow{DE}$, $\overrightarrow{DF}$; $\angle EBC$, $\angle DBC$, $\angle CBD$, $\angle CBE$; vertex: B; sides: $\overrightarrow{BE}$, $\overrightarrow{BC}$; $\angle EBA$, $\angle ABE$, $\angle DBA$, $\angle ABD$; vertex: B; sides: $\overrightarrow{BE}$, $\overrightarrow{BA}$; $\angle FDB$, $\angle BDF$, vertex: D, sides: $\overrightarrow{DF}$, $\overrightarrow{DB}$
11.

125°

13. $m \angle ABD = 42°$
$m \angle DBC = 84°$
15. $\angle 2$ and $\angle 3$, $\angle 1$ and $\angle 4$
17. 144° and 36°

Skills Review

1. 116
3. 939
5. 16.5
7. 8.36
9. 1,425
11. 1,041
13. $8.69
15. $14.42
17. 11,800
19. 10,870
21. 14.677
23. 3.587
25. 20,396
27. 1,695,301
29. 10.8909
31. 100.73
33. 1,078
35. 1,899
37. $186.50
39. 40.843

CHAPTER 3

Section 3-1

Try This. . .
1. $\neq$
3. $\neq$

Exercises
1. $\neq$
3. $\cong$
5. $\cong$
7. $\cong$
9. 48°
11. $\overline{TV}$
13. $\angle S$
15. "$m \angle ABC = m \angle STR$" means that $\angle ABC$ and $\angle STR$ have the same measure. "$\angle ABC \cong \angle STR$" means the two $\angle$s are the same.
17. 54°
19. 27°
21. Because the two $\angle$s are $\cong$ and supp., $2m \angle s = 180°$. Thus, $m \angle s = 90°$. Each $\angle$ measures 90°.

Section 3-2

Try This. . .
1. $m \angle 3 = 98°$, $m \angle 4 = 82°$

Exercises
1. $m \angle 2 = 142°$, $m \angle 3 = 38°$

3. $m \angle PQR = 32° = m \angle TQS$

3. $m \angle 1 = 107°$, $m \angle 2 = 26°$, $m \angle 3 = 107°$, $m \angle 4 = 47°$

5. $m \angle PQR = m \angle TQS = 135°$
9. $m \angle ABC = m \angle DBF = 85°$

7. $m \angle TQS = m \angle GQR = 22°$
11. Because $\angle 1$ and $\angle 2$ are vertical $\angle$s, $\angle 1 \cong \angle 2$. Because $\angle 3$ and $\angle 4$ are vertical $\angle$s, $\angle 3 \cong \angle 4$. Because $\angle 2 \cong \angle 3$, $\angle 1 \cong \angle 3$ and $\angle 1 \cong \angle 4$.

13. Both $\angle$s are $\cong$ by Vert. $\angle$ Th. Because both $\angle$s are $\cong$ and supp., $2\ m \angle$s $= 180°$. Thus, $m \angle$s $= 90°$. Each $\angle$ is a right $\angle$.

Section 3-3

Try This. . .
1. $\overleftrightarrow{DH} \perp \overleftrightarrow{KL}$, $\overleftrightarrow{GB} \not\perp \overleftrightarrow{MR}$, $\overleftrightarrow{AC} \perp \overleftrightarrow{XY}$

Exercises
1. $\not\perp$
5. $\perp$
9. $m \angle 1 = m \angle 2 = m \angle 3 = m \angle 4 = 90°$, $m \angle 6 = 47°$, $m \angle 5 = m \angle 7 = 133°$

3. $\perp$
7. $\not\perp$
11. Here are some of the possible answers.

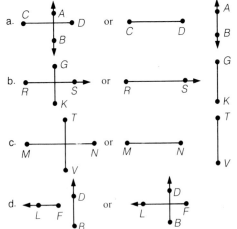

13. If two lines intersect, the adj. $\angle$s form a linear pair. Because the $\angle$s are $\cong$ and form a linear pair, they are right $\angle$s by Th. 2.7. The two lines are $\perp$ because they intersect to form a right $\angle$.

Section 3-4

Try This. . .
1. Check by measuring the $\angle$s formed. They should measure $90°$.

Exercises
1. Check by measuring the $\angle$s formed. They should measure $90°$.

3. Check by measuring the $\angle$s formed. They should measure $90°$.

Chapter Review

1. $\cong$
5. $\cong$
9. $m \angle 1 = 68°$, $m \angle 2 = 83°$, $m \angle 3 = 68°$, $m \angle 4 = 29°$
13. $\not\perp$

3. $\neq$
7. $\neq$
11. $\perp$

Skills Review

1. 26
13. $6.18
25. 44,012
37. 6,354

3. 39
15. $5.68
27. 36,835
39. $9.43

5. 1.5
17. 1,091
29. $1.86
41. $64.96

7. 1.9
19. 1,186
31. $80.20

9. 79
21. 2.661
33. 1.78

11. 276
23. 271.5
35. 3.21

CHAPTER 4

Section 4-1

Try This. . .
1. ∠A
3. ∠C
5. Equiangular, obtuse, right

Exercises
1. ∠Q
3. $\overline{QS}$
5. RS
7. Acute
9. Obtuse
11. Scalene
13. Isosceles
15. No two sides should have equal lengths. All ∠s should have measure less than 90°.
17. One ∠ should measure 90°. The two sides adjacent to it should have equal lengths.
19. Because an equilateral △ has all sides ≅, it has two sides ≅. By def., the △ is isosceles.

Section 4-2

Try This. . .
1. ∠A ≅ ∠D, ∠B ≅ ∠E, ∠C ≅ ∠F, $\overline{AB} \cong \overline{DE}$, $\overline{BC} \cong \overline{EF}$, $\overline{AC} \cong \overline{DF}$

Exercises
1. ∠A ≅ ∠R, ∠B ≅ ∠S, ∠C ≅ ∠T, $\overline{AB} \cong \overline{RS}$, $\overline{BC} \cong \overline{ST}$, $\overline{AC} \cong \overline{RT}$
3. ∠X ≅ ∠U, ∠Y ≅ ∠V, ∠Z ≅ ∠W, $\overline{XY} \cong \overline{UV}$, $\overline{YZ} \cong \overline{VW}$, $\overline{XZ} \cong \overline{UW}$
5. ∠A ≅ ∠A, ∠B ≅ ∠B, ∠C ≅ ∠C, $\overline{AB} \cong \overline{AB}$, $\overline{BC} \cong \overline{BC}$, $\overline{AC} \cong \overline{AC}$
7. ∠A and ∠F, ∠B and ∠E, ∠C and ∠D, $\overline{AC}$ and $\overline{DF}$, $\overline{AB}$ and $\overline{EF}$, $\overline{BC}$ and $\overline{DE}$
9. ∠M and ∠Q, ∠O and ∠S, ∠N and ∠P, $\overline{MN}$ and $\overline{PQ}$, $\overline{OM}$ and $\overline{SQ}$, $\overline{ON}$ and $\overline{SP}$
11. △ABC ≅ △ACB, △ABC ≅ △ABC, △ABC ≅ △BAC, △ABC ≅ △BCA, △ABC ≅ △CAB, △ABC ≅ △CBA

Section 4-3

Try This. . .
1. Pair *a*, pair *c*
3. Pair *b*

Exercises
1. ≇ by SAS
3. ≅ by SAS
5. ≅ by SAS
7. ≇ by SSS
9. ≅ by SSS
11. ≅ by SSS
13. ≅ by ASA
15. ≅ by ASA
17. ≅ by ASA
19. The addition of a rod forms two △, which are rigid. The SSS Th. assures that these △ cannot change shape.
21. By the SSS Th., the △ in the jungle gym are ≅.
23. Same reason as Exercise 19.
25. No. If a side and the ∠ opposite it and another ∠ of a △ are ≅ to a side and the ∠ opposite it and another ∠ of a second △, then the two △ are ≅. The theorem is true.

Section 4-4

Try This. . .
1. None
3. ASA Th.
5. SSS Th.
7. None
9. ∠A ≅ ∠D

Exercises
1. ASA Th.
3. SAS Post.
5. SAS Post. or SSS Th.
7. SSS Th.
9. SAS Post.
11. ASA Th.
13. ∠Q ≅ ∠T, ∠R ≅ ∠V
15. $\overline{QP} \cong \overline{TS}$

Section 4-5

Try This. . .
1. Because the door is in the middle of the building, $\overline{DB} \cong \overline{EB}$. Because $\overline{AB} \perp \overline{DE}$, ∠DBA ≅ ∠EBA. $\overline{BA} \cong \overline{BA}$. By SAS, △ABD ≅ △ABE.

Exercises
1. Because $\overline{PQ} \cong \overline{ST}$, $\overline{PR} \cong \overline{RS}$, and $\overline{RQ} \cong \overline{RT}$, then by SSS, △PQR ≅ △STR.
3. $\overline{AX} \cong \overline{XY}$ because the crossboards are equally spaced apart. $\overline{XB} \cong \overline{YZ}$ because the crossboards have the same length. ∠AXB ≅ ∠XYZ because the crossboards are perpendicular to the vertical boards. By SAS, △ABX ≅ △XZY.
5. $\overline{PR} \cong \overline{RT}$ and $\overline{QR} \cong \overline{RS}$ because R is the midpoint of both $\overline{PT}$ and $\overline{QS}$. By the Vertical Angle Th., ∠PRQ ≅ ∠SRT. By SAS, △PRQ ≅ △TRS.
7. Because L is the midpoint of $\overline{KM}$, $\overline{KL} \cong \overline{LM}$. Because $\overline{GL} \perp \overline{KM}$, ∠GLK ≅ ∠GLM. $\overline{GL} \cong \overline{GL}$. By SAS, △KLG ≅ △MLG.

9. Because B is the midpoint of $\overline{ED}$, $\overline{EB} \cong \overline{BD}$. $\overline{AE} \cong \overline{AB} \cong \overline{CB} \cong \overline{CD}$. By SSS, $\triangle AEB \cong \triangle CDB$.

13. $\overline{RT} \cong \overline{TS}$ because T is the midpoint of $\overline{RS}$. $\angle ATS \cong \angle PTS$ by Vert. $\angle$ Th. $\angle TRP$ is supp. to $\angle 3$ because they form a linear pair. Thus, $\angle TRP \cong \angle AST$ because they both are supp. to $\angle 3$. By ASA, $\triangle AST \cong \triangle PRT$.

17. $\overline{PQ} \cong \overline{QR}$ because Q is the midpoint of $\overline{PR}$. $\overline{TQ} \cong \overline{SQ}$ and $\overline{TP} \cong \overline{SR}$. By SSS, $\triangle TQP \cong \triangle SQR$.

11. $\overline{MK} \cong \overline{MK}$, $\overline{GK} \cong \overline{ML}$, and $\angle GKM \cong \angle LMK$. By SAS, $\triangle GKM \cong \triangle LMK$.

15. $\overline{FT} \cong \overline{FR}$, $\overline{ST} \cong \overline{SR}$, and $\overline{FS} \cong \overline{FS}$. By SSS, $\triangle FTS \cong \triangle FRS$.

19. $\angle 1$ and $\angle ABC$ and $\angle 2$ and $\angle DEF$ are supp. because they both form linear pairs. Because $\angle 1 \cong \angle 2$, $\angle ABC \cong \angle DEF$ by Th. 3.1. $\overline{AB} \cong \overline{DE}$ and $\overline{EF} \cong \overline{BC}$. By SAS, $\triangle ABC \cong \triangle DEF$.

Section 4-6

Try This...

1. $\angle RSQ \cong \angle TSQ$, R-Q-T, $\angle RSQ$ and $\angle TSQ$ are adjacent, $\angle RQS$ and $\angle TQS$ are adjacent.

3.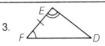

Exercises

1. $\overline{LC} \cong \overline{BT}$, $\overline{VC} \cong \overline{AT}$, $\overline{VL} \cong \overline{AB}$.

3. $\overline{GQ} \perp \overline{RP}$, R—Q—P, $\angle R \cong \angle P$, $\angle GQR$ and $\angle GQP$ are right $\angle$s, $\angle RGQ$ and $\angle PGQ$ are adjacent, $\angle RQG$ and $\angle PQG$ are adjacent.

5.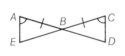

7.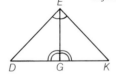

9.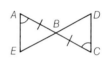

11.

13.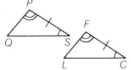

15.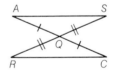

Chapter Review

1. Obtuse
5. Equilateral

9. $\cong$ by SAS
13. $\cong$ by SSS
17. SAS

3. Right
7. $\angle G \cong \angle P$, $\angle K \cong \angle T$, $\angle L \cong \angle L$, $\overline{GK} \cong \overline{PT}$, $\overline{KL} \cong \overline{TL}$, $\overline{GL} \cong \overline{PL}$
11. $\ncong$ by SSS
15. $\ncong$ by ASA
19. By the Vertical Angle Th., $\angle MSE \cong \angle LSB$. $\overline{MS} \cong \overline{LS}$ and $\overline{ES} \cong \overline{BS}$. By SAS, $\triangle MES \cong \triangle LBS$.

21.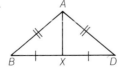

Skills Review

1. 252   3. 1,184   5. $8.73   7. $9.40   9. 1,800   11. 32,000
13. 64.68   15. 58,443   17. 260,748   19. 394,800   21. 7r1   23. 2r5
25. $4.45   27. $0.30   29. 709r2   31. 8,008   33. 71.5   35. 1.7
37. 2,319r8   39. 189r29   41. 97.1   43. 360   45. 38r74   47. 162r79

Cumulative Review: Chapters 1-4

1. A △ that is not isosceles, e.g. a △ whose sides measure 3, 4, and 5.

3. If the apple is red (antecedent), then it is ripe (consequent).

5. —5, 0 and 6

7. 9, 9, and 15

9.
```
    HD TK    F R MG CSPN
◄──┼┼┼┼┼┼┼┼┼┼┼┼┼┼┼┼┼┼──►
   -4 -2  0   2   4   6   8  10  12
```

11.
46°

13. 45° and 135°

15. $m \angle 1 = 86°$, $m \angle 2 = 66°$, $m \angle 3 = 28°$, $m \angle 4 = 66°$

17. Equilateral, scalene, isosceles

19. None

21. $\overline{GT} \cong \overline{RT}$, $\angle GTS \cong \angle RTS$, and $\overline{TS} \cong \overline{TS}$. By SAS, $\triangle SGT \cong \triangle SRT$.

CHAPTER 5

Section 5-1

Try This. . .

1. We know $\overline{RS} \cong \overline{RT}$, $\overline{SQ} \cong \overline{QT}$, and $\overline{RQ} \cong \overline{RQ}$. By SSS, $\triangle RSQ \cong \triangle RTQ$. We have these $\cong$ corr. parts: $\angle S \cong \angle T$, $\angle RQS \cong \angle RQT$, and $\angle SRQ \cong \angle TRQ$.

3. We know $\overline{RS} \cong \overline{RT}$. We know $\overline{SQ} \cong \overline{QT}$. We know $\overline{RQ} \cong \overline{RQ}$. By SSS, $\triangle SRQ \cong \triangle TRQ$. Thus, by corr. parts of $\cong$ ▵, $\angle RSQ \cong \angle RTQ$.

Exercises

1. We know $\overline{AB} \cong \overline{BC}$ and $\overline{ED} \cong \overline{DB}$. $\angle ABE \cong \angle CBD$ by Vert. ∠Th. By SAS, $\triangle ABE \cong \triangle CBD$. So, we have these $\cong$ corr. parts: $\overline{AE} \cong \overline{CD}$, $\angle BAE \cong \angle BCD$, and $\angle BEA \cong \angle BDC$.

3. We know $\overline{HK} \cong \overline{KJ}$ and $\overline{GK} \cong \overline{LK}$. Because $\overline{GK} \perp \overline{LJ}$, $\angle GKL \cong \angle GKJ$ because both are right ∠s. By SAS, $\triangle LKH \cong \triangle GKJ$. So, we have these $\cong$, corr., parts: $\angle G \cong \angle L$, $\angle LHK \cong \angle GJK$, and $\overline{LH} \cong \overline{GJ}$.

5. We know $\overline{AR} \cong \overline{AK}$, $\overline{RT} \cong \overline{KT}$, and $\overline{TA} \cong \overline{TA}$. By SSS, $\triangle TAR \cong \triangle TAK$. So, we have these $\cong$, corr. parts: $\angle TRA \cong \angle TKA$, $\angle TAR \cong \angle TAK$, and $\angle ATK \cong \angle ATR$.

7. We know $\angle K \cong \angle T$, $\angle KGP \cong \angle TPR$, and $\overline{KG} \cong \overline{TP}$. By ASA, $\triangle KGP \cong \triangle TPR$. By corr. parts of $\cong$ ▵, $\overline{GP} \cong \overline{PR}$. We know $G—P—R$. So, P is the midpoint of $\overline{GR}$.

9. The two halves of the kite are $\cong$ by SSS. So, $\angle 1$ and $\angle 2$ are $\cong$ as corr. parts of $\cong$ ▵.

11. He formed a pair of $\cong$ ▵. He was their common side. By sighting under his visor, he assured two $\cong$ ∠s. By standing straight, he assured two right ∠s. The ▵ formed were $\cong$ by ASA. So, $\overline{BS} \cong \overline{BQ}$ as corr. parts of $\cong$ ▵. So, BS was the river's width.

13. We know $\overline{PQ} \cong \overline{ST}$, $\angle P \cong \angle S$, and $\angle Q \cong \angle T$. By ASA, $\triangle QRP \cong \triangle TVS$. $\overline{PR} \cong \overline{SV}$ as corr. parts of $\cong$ ▵.

15. We know $\overline{PU} \cong \overline{PT}$ and $\angle 1 \cong \angle 2$. $\overline{PS} \cong \overline{PS}$. By SAS, $\triangle PSU \cong \triangle PST$. $\overline{US} \cong \overline{TS}$ as corr. parts of $\cong$ ▵.

17. We know $\overline{RH} \cong \overline{CM}$, $\overline{TH} \cong \overline{LM}$, and $\angle 1$ is supp. to $\angle 3$. $\angle 3$ is supp. to $\angle 2$ because they form a linear pair. So, $\angle 2 \cong \angle 1$ because they are supp. to the same $\angle$. By SAS, $\triangle CML \cong \triangle RHT$. $\overline{RT} \cong \overline{CL}$ as corr. parts of $\cong$ ▵.

Section 5-2

Try This. . .

1. $\triangle KNH$ and $\triangle KGL$

3. We know $\overline{TV} \cong \overline{SW}$, $\overline{RS} \cong \overline{QT}$, and $\angle RSW \cong \angle QTV$. By SAS, $\triangle SWR \cong \triangle TVQ$. So, we have these $\cong$, corr. parts: $\angle R \cong \angle Q$, $\angle W \cong \angle V$, and $\overline{WR} \cong \overline{VQ}$.

5. We know $\overline{RW} \cong \overline{QV}$, $\overline{WS} \cong \overline{VT}$, and $\overline{RT} \cong \overline{QS}$. $\overline{TS}$ is common to both $\overline{RS}$ and $\overline{QT}$. We can think of "adding" the common segment, $\overline{TS}$, to $\overline{RS}$ and $\overline{QT}$. This means $\overline{RS} \cong \overline{QT}$. By SSS, $\triangle RSW \cong \triangle QTV$. $\angle R \cong \angle Q$ as corr. parts of $\cong$ ▵.

Exercises

1. $\triangle GHK$ and $\triangle HGJ$

3. $\triangle PQR$ and $\triangle QST$

5. We know $\overline{PO} \cong \overline{RQ}$, $\overline{VP} \cong \overline{TR}$, and $\angle P \cong \angle R$. $\overline{OQ}$ is common to both $\overline{PQ}$ and $\overline{RO}$. We can think of "adding" the common segment, $\overline{OQ}$, to $\overline{PO}$ and $\overline{RQ}$. This means $\overline{PQ} \cong \overline{RO}$. By SAS, $\triangle PVQ \cong \triangle RTO$. So, we know $\overline{VQ} \cong \overline{TO}$, $\angle VQP \cong \angle TOR$, and $\angle PVQ \cong \angle RTO$ as corr. parts of $\cong$ ▵.

7. We know $\overline{RK} \cong \overline{LP}$, and $\angle KRL \cong \angle PLR$. $\overline{RL} \cong \overline{RL}$. By SAS, $\triangle KRL \cong \triangle PLR$. So, we know $\overline{KL} \cong \overline{PR}$, $\angle RKL \cong \angle LPR$, and $\angle KLR \cong \angle PRL$ as corr. parts of $\cong$ ▵.

9. We know $\overline{PS} \cong \overline{PT}$ and $\angle RTP \cong \angle QSP$. $\angle P \cong \angle P$. By ASA, $\triangle PTR \cong \triangle PSQ$. So, we know $\angle Q \cong \angle R$, $PR \cong \overline{PQ}$, and $\overline{TR} \cong \overline{SQ}$ as corr. parts of $\cong \triangle$.

11. We know $\angle N \cong \angle G$ and $\overline{NK} \cong \overline{GK}$. $\angle K \cong \angle K$. By ASA, $\triangle NKH \cong \triangle GKL$.

13. We know $\angle D \cong \angle K$, $\overline{DF} \cong \overline{KE}$, and $\angle DFS \cong \angle KES$. By ASA, $\triangle DFS \cong \triangle KES$. $\angle DSF \cong \angle KSE$ as corr. parts of $\cong \triangle$.

15. We know $\angle P \cong \angle T$, $\overline{PQ} \cong \overline{TS}$, and $\overline{PR} \cong \overline{TQ}$. By SAS, $\triangle PQR \cong \triangle TSQ$. $\angle QST \cong \angle RQP$ as corr. parts of $\cong \triangle$.

17. $\angle 1 \cong \angle 2 \cong \angle 3 \ldots$

Section 5-3

Try This. . .

1. $m \angle A = 73°$

3. 11

5. We know $\overline{AB} \cong \overline{CB}$. By the Isos. $\triangle$ Th., $\angle 1 \cong \angle 3$ and $\triangle ABC$ is isos. $\angle 1$ is supp. to $\angle 2$ and $\angle 3$ is supp. to $\angle 4$ because both pairs of angles form a linear pair. So, $\angle 2 \cong \angle 4$ by Th. 3.1.

Exercises

1. $m \angle Q = 70°$

3. $AC = 62$

5. 15

7. 5

9. 35

11. 1

13. We know $\overline{GR} \cong \overline{PR}$. By Isos. $\triangle$ Th., $\angle 2 \cong \angle 3$ and $\triangle GRP$ is isos. $\angle 2$ is supp. to $\angle 1$ and $\angle 3$ is supp. to $\angle 4$ because each pair of $\angle$s forms a linear pair. So, $\angle 1 \cong \angle 4$ by Th. 3.1.

15. We know $\overline{RS} \cong \overline{WS}$ and $\overline{RT} \cong \overline{WV}$. By Isos. $\triangle$Th., $\angle R \cong \angle W$. By SAS, $\triangle SRT \cong \triangle SWV$. $\overline{ST} \cong \overline{SV}$ as corr. parts of $\cong \triangle$. By Isos. $\triangle$ Th., $\angle STV \cong \angle SVT$ and $\triangle STV$ is isos.

17. We know $\overline{GR} \cong \overline{PR}$. By Isos. $\triangle$ Th., $\angle 2 \cong \angle 3$. $\angle 1$ is supp. to $\angle 2$ and $\angle 3$ is supp. to $\angle 4$ because each pair of angles forms a linear pair. So, $\angle 1 \cong \angle 4$ by Th. 3.1.

19. We know $\angle 1 \cong \angle 4$. $\angle 1 \cong \angle 2$ and $\angle 4 \cong \angle 3$ by Vert. $\angle$Th. $\angle 2 \cong \angle 3$ by substitution. So, $\overline{PK} \cong \overline{PT}$ by Isos. $\triangle$ Th. and $\triangle KPT$ is isos.

Section 5-4

Try This. . .

1. $DP = 6$, $FA = 10$

Exercises

1. 20

3. 17

5. 4

7. 2

9. 25

11. We know $\triangle XYZ$ is isos. with $\overline{XY} \cong \overline{XZ}$. We know Y and Z are endpoints of $\overline{YZ}$. Because $\overline{XY} \cong \overline{XZ}$, X is on the $\perp$ bisect. of $\overline{YZ}$ by Th. 5.3.

13. We know $\overline{RS} \cong \overline{ST}$ and $\overline{RV} \cong \overline{VT}$. By Isos. $\triangle$ Th., $\angle SRT \cong \angle STR$ and $\angle VRT \cong \angle VTR$. $\angle SRT + \angle TRV = \angle SRV$ and $\angle VTR + \angle RTS = \angle STV$. So, $\angle SRV \cong \angle STV$.

15. The points should be on the $\perp$ bisect. of the segment.

Section 5-5

Try This. . .

1.

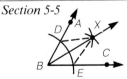

In bisecting $\angle ABC$, the fixed compass setting assures that $\overline{DB} \cong \overline{BE}$ and $\overline{DX} \cong \overline{XE}$. By SSS, $XDB \cong \triangle XEB$. Thus, $\angle DBX \cong \angle EBX$, which makes $\overrightarrow{BX}$ the bisector of $\angle ABC$.

Exercises

1.

In copying $\triangle ABC$, the compass assures that $\overline{A'B'}$ is a copy of $\overline{AB}$, $\overline{B'C'}$ is a copy of $\overline{BC}$, and $\overline{A'C'}$ is a copy of $\overline{AC}$. By SSS, $\triangle A'B'C'$ is a copy of $\triangle ABC$.

3.

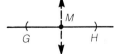

In constructing the $\perp$ to a line from a point M on the line, the compass assures that M becomes the midpoint of a segment $\overline{GH}$. By constructing the $\perp$ bisector of $\overline{GH}$ that uses Corollary 5.4, the desired line is obtained.

5.

1. With compass point on A, draw arc p above the segment. With the compass point on B (same setting), draw arc q below the segment.

2. Change the compass setting. At A, draw arc m below the segment. At B, draw arc n above the segment.

3. Label the points where the arcs meet: C above the segment, D below the segment.

4. Draw $\overleftrightarrow{CD}$. Label the point where $\overleftrightarrow{CD}$ meets $\overline{AB}$, M. $\overline{CD} \not\perp \overline{AB}$. M is the midpoint of $\overline{AB}$.

explanation: The compass settings assure that $\overline{AC} \cong \overline{BD}$ and $\overline{AD} \cong \overline{BC}$. Thus, because $\overline{CD} \cong \overline{CD}$, $\triangle ACD \cong \triangle BDC$ by SSS. This gives $\angle ACD \cong \angle BDC$. Likewise $\triangle ACB \cong \triangle BDA$, which gives $\angle CAB \cong \angle DBA$. Thus, by ASA, $\triangle CAM \cong \triangle DBM$. This gives $\overline{AM} \cong \overline{BM}$, making M the midpoint of $\overline{AB}$. If $\overleftrightarrow{CD}$ were $\perp$ to $\overline{AB}$, then the Perpendicular Bisector Th. would say $\overline{CA} \cong \overline{CB}$. But this would make the compass settings in steps 1 and 2 the same. Thus, $\overleftrightarrow{CD}$ is $\not\perp$ to $\overline{AB}$.

Chapter Review

1. We know P is the midpoint of $\overline{RS}$ and $\angle R \cong \angle S$. $\overline{SP} \cong \overline{RP}$ because P is the midpoint of $\overline{RS}$. $\angle TPR \cong \angle VPS$ by Vert. $\angle$ Th. By ASA, $\triangle SPV \cong \triangle RPT$. So, $\angle V \cong \angle T$, $\overline{PV} \cong \overline{TP}$, and $\overline{SV} \cong \overline{RT}$ as corr. parts of $\cong \triangle$.

3. $\triangle ADC$ and $\triangle BCD$, $\triangle ABD$ and $\triangle BAC$, $\triangle ABC$ and $\triangle DBC$, $\triangle ABD$ and $\triangle ADC$.

5. 8

7. We know $\overline{GK} \cong \overline{GN}$ and $\overline{KM} \cong \overline{NL}$. By the Isos. $\triangle$ Th., $\angle K \cong \angle N$. By SAS, $\triangle GKM \cong \triangle GNL$. As corr. parts are $\cong$, $\overline{GM} \cong \overline{GL}$.

9. 10

Skills Review

1. 50	3. 600	5. 3,250	7. 13,500	9. 500	11. 2,700
13. 89,900	15. 770,800	17. 6,000	19. 9,000	21. 43,000	23. 69,000
25. 8.7	27. 3.4	29. 499	31. 3.6	33. 3.01	35. 0.52
37. 16.4	39. 0.01	41. 6	43. 25	45. 308	47. 15

CHAPTER 6

Section 6-1

Try This. . .

1. $<$

3. $\angle C$ and $\angle CDB$ for $\angle ABC$, $\angle C$ and $\angle CBD$ for $\angle CDE$

Exercises

1. $<$

3. $>$

5. $\angle A$ and $\angle ACB$ for $\angle ABE$, $\angle A$ and $\angle ABC$ for $\angle ACD$

7. $\angle QRT$ and $\angle RTQ$ for $\angle MQT$, $\angle RQT$ and $\angle QRT$ for $\angle RTV$, $\angle RQT$ and $\angle RTQ$ for $\angle SRT$

9. $m\angle AFC > m\angle D$

11. $m\angle K < m\angle KSH$

13. $>$

15. $>$

17. The exterior $\angle$ that forms a linear pair with an obtuse $\angle$ must be acute. By Th. 6.3, the remote interior $\angle$s must also be acute.

19. No, by Th. 6.4, a $\triangle$ cannot have two right $\angle$s. If one $\angle$ is a right $\angle$, the other two $\angle$s are acute.

Section 6-2

Try This. . .

1. $m\angle T > m\angle S$

3. $\overline{NM}, \overline{LN}, \overline{LM}$

Exercises

1. $m\angle K > m\angle H$

3. $\angle T, \angle A, \angle F$

5. $\overline{XY}, \overline{WX}, \overline{WY}$

7. Th. 6.6: In any $\triangle ABC$, if CA is greater than CB, then the measure of $\angle B$ is greater than the measure of $\angle A$. Th. 6.7: In any $\triangle ABC$, if the measure of $\angle C$ is greater than the measure of $\angle B$, then AB is greater than AC.

9. Yes, any equiangular $\triangle$ is equilateral. If the $\angle$s of a $\triangle$ are equal, then the sides opposite those $\angle$s must be equal.

11. By Th. 6.3, $m\angle KMN > m\angle G$. Because $m\angle G > m\angle N$, then $m\angle KMN > \angle N$. By Th. 6.7, $NK > MK$.

13. By Th. 6.2, $m \angle DEF > m \angle BEF$. By Th. 6.2, $m \angle SFE > m \angle DFE$. Because $\overline{DE} \cong \overline{DF}$, $\angle DEF \cong \angle DFE$ by Isos. $\triangle$ Th. Thus, $m \angle SFE > m \angle DEF$, and $m \angle SFE > m \angle BEF$. By Th. 6.7, $ES > FS$.

Section 6-3

Try This...
1. $GK + KH > GH$, $GH + HK > GK$, $HG + GK > HK$

3. No

Exercises
1. $RS + ST > RT$, $RS + RT > ST$, $RT + TS > RS$

3. $MQ + QN > MN$, $MQ + MN > NQ$, $QN + MN > QM$

5. Yes

7. Yes

9. Yes

11. Yes

13. Yes

15. The difference of the lengths of two sides is less than the third side's length.

17. By Th. 6.10, $PQ + QR > PR$ and $QR + RS > QS$. Because $PQRS$ is a $\square$, $QR = PS$. By substituting PS for QR, $PS + RS > QS$. Thus, $PQ + QR + PS + RS > QS + PR$.

Section 6-4

Try This...
1. $EF < ST$

3. $m \angle P < m \angle T$

Exercises
1. $HK < EF$

3. $TS < RK$

5. The circle formed by the compass with the larger $\angle$ is the larger circle.

7. $<$

9. $<$

11. $>$

Section 6-5

Try This...
1. Pair b

3. We know $\angle GAL \cong \angle KAL$ because $\overline{AL}$ is the bisect. of $\angle GAK$. We know $\angle G \cong \angle K$. We know $\overline{LA} \cong \overline{LA}$. By SAA, $\triangle GAL \cong \triangle KAL$. Thus, $\overline{GL} \cong \overline{KL}$.

Exercises
1. $\not\cong$ by SAA

3. $\cong$ by SAA

5. $\cong$ by HL

7. $\not\cong$ by HL

9. We know $PQ \cong TS$. We know $\angle Q \cong \angle S$. $\angle PRQ \cong \angle TRS$ by Vert. $\angle$ Th.

11. Because $\overline{BA} \perp \overline{AE}$, $\triangle BAC$ is a right $\triangle$. Because $\overline{DE} \perp \overline{AE}$, $\triangle DEC$ is a right $\triangle$. We know $\overline{BC} \cong \overline{DC}$. Because C is the midpoint of $\overline{AE}$, $\overline{AC} \cong \overline{EC}$. Thus, by HL, $\triangle BAC \cong \triangle DEC$.

13. Because Y is the midpoint of $\overline{RS}$, $\overline{RY} \cong \overline{SY}$. We know $\angle T \cong \angle Q$. $\angle TYS \cong \angle QYR$ by Vert. $\angle$ Th. By SAA, $\triangle TYS \cong \triangle QYR$. Thus, $\overline{TS} \cong \overline{QR}$ as corr. parts of $\cong \triangle$.

15. We know $\overline{JT} \cong \overline{RT}$. We know $\overline{TK} \cong \overline{TS}$. Because $\overline{TK} \perp \overline{DJ}$, $\triangle TKJ$ is a right $\triangle$. Because $\overline{TS} \perp \overline{DR}$, $\triangle TSR$ is a right $\triangle$. By HL, $\triangle TKJ \cong \triangle TSR$. By corr. parts of $\cong \triangle$, $\angle J \cong \angle R$. By Isos. $\triangle$ Th., $\overline{DR} \cong \overline{DJ}$. Thus, $\triangle DJR$ is isos.

Section 6-6

Try This...
1. $x = 2$, $MR = MS = 14$

Exercises
1. $x = 6$, $MQ = MG = 39$

3. $x = -12$, $MG = MQ = 66$

5. $x = -\frac{1}{2}$ or -0.5, $MQ = MG = 11.75$

7. The answer should be a figure something like the figure for Example 2.

9. The answer should be like this figure.

11. We know $\angle ABD \cong \angle CBD$ because $\overrightarrow{BD}$ is an $\angle$ bisect. of $\angle ABC$. We know $\angle DAB$ and $\angle DCB$ are right $\angle$s because they are formed from $\perp$ segments. We know $\overline{BD} \cong \overline{BD}$. By SAA, $\triangle ABD \cong \triangle CBD$. $\overline{AD} \cong \overline{CD}$ as corr. parts of $\cong \triangle$. Thus, D is equidistant from $\overrightarrow{BA}$ and $\overrightarrow{BC}$.

13. Consider any equilateral $\triangle ABC$ with $\overline{BD}$ bisect. $\angle ABC$. We know $\overline{BD} \cong \overline{BD}$. We know $\overline{BA} \cong \overline{BC}$ because sides of an equilateral $\triangle$ are $\cong$. $\angle ABD \cong \angle CBD$ because $\overline{BD}$ is the $\angle$ bisect. of $\angle ABC$. By SAS, $\triangle ABD \cong \triangle CBD$. $\overline{AD} \cong \overline{CD}$ as corr. parts of $\cong \triangle$. Thus, $\overline{BD}$ is also a median of $\triangle ABC$.

15. No. The intersection of two different planes is always a line.

Chapter Review

1. $<$

3. $\angle GRT$ and $\angle GTR$ for $\angle PGT$, $\angle RGT$ and $\angle GTR$ for $\angle SRT$, $\angle RGT$ and $\angle GRT$ for $\angle RTQ$

5. $\angle S$, $\angle M$, $\angle E$

7. $LJ < JK + KL$, $JK < KL + LJ$, $KL < LJ + JK$

9. No

11. $m \angle P > m \angle V$

13. We know $\angle Y \cong \angle W$. $\overline{AZ} \cong \overline{KZ}$ because Z is the midpoint of $\overline{AK}$. $\angle AZY \cong \angle KZW$ by Vert. $\angle$ Th. By SAA, $\triangle AZY \cong \triangle KZW$. $\overline{AY} \cong \overline{KW}$ as corr. parts of $\cong \triangle$.

Skills Review

1.	80	3.	9,400	5.	16	7.	25	9.	$10	11.	$61
13.	60	15.	7,800	17.	3	19.	1	21.	$5	23.	$26
25.	560	27.	1,000	29.	20	31.	150	33.	$600	35.	$2,800
37.	60	39.	600	41.	8	43.	9	45.	$4	47.	$6

CHAPTER 7

Section 7-1

Try This...

1. They are many. Three are $\overleftrightarrow{AD}$ and $\overleftrightarrow{GF}$, $\overleftrightarrow{HG}$ and $\overleftrightarrow{EF}$, and $\overleftrightarrow{CG}$ and $\overleftrightarrow{BF}$.

3.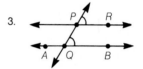

Exercises

1. $\overline{SR}$, $\overline{LK}$, $\overline{JH}$

3. $\overleftrightarrow{QR}$, $\overleftrightarrow{JK}$, $\overleftrightarrow{HL}$

5. $\overleftrightarrow{QJ}$, $\overleftrightarrow{RK}$, $\overleftrightarrow{JH}$, $\overleftrightarrow{LK}$

7. $\overleftrightarrow{PH}$, $\overleftrightarrow{SL}$, $\overleftrightarrow{PQ}$, $\overleftrightarrow{SR}$

9. Skew

11. Parallel

13.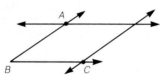

15.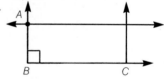

Section 7-2

Try This...

1. Alt. int.

3. Corr.

5. $\angle A \cong \angle ACB$ and $\angle D \cong \angle DBC$ by Isos. $\triangle$ Thm. $\angle A \cong \angle D$, so $\angle ACB \cong \angle CBD$. We know $\overline{BC} \cong \overline{BC}$. By SAA, $\triangle ABC \cong \triangle DCB$. $\angle ABC \cong \angle BCD$ as corr. parts of $\cong \triangle$. Because $\angle ABC \cong \angle BCD$, $AB \parallel CD$ by Th. 7.1. Because $\angle ACB \cong \angle CBD$, $AC \parallel BD$ by Th. 7.1.

Exercises

1. Corr.

3. Int.

5. Corr.

7. $\angle BCA$ and $\angle CAD$

9. $\overrightarrow{SP}$

11. $\overrightarrow{SQ}$

13. $\overrightarrow{SP}$

15. $n \parallel q$ by Th. 7.1. $m \parallel r$ by Cor. 7.2 and Cor. 7.4.

17. Cor. 7.2

19. Th. 7.1

21. $m \angle 1 + m \angle 2 = 180°$ and $m \angle 1 + m \angle 3 = 180°$. Thus, $m \angle 2 = m \angle 3$. By Th. 7.1, $\overleftrightarrow{AB} \parallel \overleftrightarrow{CD}$.

Section 7-3

Try This...

1. $\angle AEH \cong \angle BEF \cong \angle CFE \cong \angle GFD$. All measure 70°.

3. $\angle BAD \cong \angle ADC$

Exercises

1. $\angle AEH \cong \angle BEF \cong \angle CFE \cong \angle GFD$. All measure 45°. $\angle HEB \cong \angle AEF \cong \angle EFD \cong \angle CFG$. All measure 135°. $\angle AEF$ and $\angle CFE$, $\angle BEF$, and $\angle EFD$ are supp.

3. $\angle ABC \cong \angle BCD$. They measure 95°. $\angle DAB \cong \angle ADC$. $\angle AEB \cong \angle CED$.

5. $\angle AEC \cong \angle ECD$. They measure $50°$. $\angle BED$ $\cong \angle EDC$. They measure $41°$.

7. $\angle BAE \cong \angle CDE$; $\angle ABE \cong \angle ECD$; $\angle AEB \cong \angle CED$.

9. Suppose $\angle A$, $\angle B$, and $\angle C$ are right $\angle$s. By Cor. 7.3 $\overline{AD} \parallel \overline{BC}$. Because $\overline{AD} \parallel \overline{BC}$ and $\angle C$ and $\angle D$ are supp. (they are int. $\angle$s.), $m \angle C + m \angle D = 180°$. As $m \angle C = 90°$, $m \angle D = 90°$. Thus, $\angle D$ is a right $\angle$.

11. By the Vert. $\angle$ Th., $\angle 1 \cong \angle 3$. By Th. 7.5, $\angle 3 \cong \angle 4$. Because $\ell \parallel m$, by Cor. 7.6, $\angle 4 \cong \angle 2$, $\angle 1 \cong \angle 2$.

Section 7-4

Try This. . .

1. $130°$

3. $m \angle 3 = 95°$, $m \angle 4 = 85°$

5. $m \angle BCD = 55°$, $m \angle B = 70°$, $m \angle CDA = 125°$, $m \angle DCA = 35°$, $m \angle A = 20°$

Exercises

1. $25°$

3. $70°$

5. $86°$

7. $m \angle E = 100°$, $m \angle F = 32°$

9. $m \angle B = 48°$, $m \angle C = 88°$

11. $m \angle 1 = m \angle 2 = 52.5°$, $m \angle 3 = 82.5°$, $m \angle 4 = 97.5°$

13. $m \angle P = m \angle 2 = 57°$, $m \angle 1 = 33°$

15. $m \angle F = 109°$

17. $m \angle B = 23°$, $m \angle ACD = 39°$, $m \angle ACB = 141°$

19. By the Angle Sum Th., $m \angle 1 + m \angle EDA + m \angle A = 180°$ and $m \angle 2 + m \angle FDC + m \angle C = 180°$. Thus, $m \angle 1 + m \angle EDA + m \angle A = m \angle 2 + m \angle FDC + m \angle C$. We know that $\angle 1 \cong \angle 2$. By the Vert. $\angle$ Th., $\angle EDA \cong \angle FDC$. Thus, $m \angle 1 = m \angle 2$ and $m \angle EDA = m \angle FDC$. $m \angle 1 + m \angle EDA + m \angle A = m \angle 1 + m \angle EDA + m \angle C$. Hence, $\angle A \cong \angle C$.

Chapter Review

1. $\overline{BC}$, $\overline{AD}$, $\overline{EH}$

3.

5. $\angle CBF$ and $\angle BFG$, $\angle BGC$ and $\angle GCF$ are possible answers.

7. $\overleftrightarrow{BG} \parallel \overleftrightarrow{CF}$

9. $m \angle BED = m \angle EDC = 40°$, $m \angle AEC = m \angle ECD = 65°$, $m \angle CED = 75°$, supp. $\angle$s: $\angle BEC$ and $\angle C$, $\angle DEA$ and $\angle D$

11. $m \angle EFG = 65°$, $m \angle E = 25°$, $m \angle EFD = 115°$

Skills Review

1. 3,000	3. 0.7	5. 0.62	7. 3.521	9. 99	11. 0.034
13. 1,390	15. 0.52	17. 4.528	19. 0.004	21. 2,500	23. 0.63
25. 13	27. 10	29. 0.5	31. 4.792	33. 1.428	35. 4,000
37. 8.42	39. 3,300	41. 0.013	43. 6	45. 0.001	

CHAPTER 8

Section 8-1

Try This. . .

1. $\overline{DF}$ and $\overline{GE}$; opposite sides: $\overline{DE}$ and $\overline{GF}$, $\overline{DG}$ and $\overline{EF}$; opposite $\angle$s: $\angle D$ and $\angle F$, $\angle G$ and $\angle E$

3. $70°$

5. Parallelogram

Exercises

1. $\overline{AB}$ and $\overline{CD}$, $\overline{BC}$ and $\overline{AD}$; $\angle B$ and $\angle D$, $\angle A$ and $\angle C$

3. $\overline{JK}$ and $\overline{LM}$, $\overline{JM}$ and $\overline{KL}$; $\angle J$ and $\angle L$, $\angle M$ and $\angle K$

5. $\overline{DE}$ and $\overline{EF}$, $\overline{EF}$ and $\overline{FG}$, $\overline{FG}$ and $\overline{DG}$, $\overline{GD}$ and $\overline{DE}$; $\angle E$ and $\angle F$, $\angle F$ and $\angle G$, $\angle G$ and $\angle D$, $\angle D$ and $\angle E$

7. $\overline{BD}$ and $\overline{AC}$; $\overline{EG}$ and $\overline{HF}$; $\overline{JL}$ and $\overline{MK}$

9. Kite

11. Quadrilateral

13. Rectangle   15. 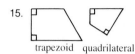   17. Impossible

trapezoid quadrilateral

19. Square   21. Impossible   23. The new quadrilateral is a ▱.

Section 8-2

Try This. . .

1. $m \angle B = 153°$, $m \angle C = 27°$, $m \angle D = 153°$ 3. $QR = 10$, $RS = 8$
5. 68°

Exercises

1. $m \angle A = 70°$, $m \angle B = m \angle D = 110°$ 3. $m \angle J = 71°$, $m \angle L = m \angle M = 109°$
5. $TU = 9$, $UN = 15$ 7. $JM = KL = 9$, $ML = JK = 23$
9. $m \angle B = m \angle D = 95°$ 11. $AC = 28$, $ED = 38$
13. By Cor. 8.6, $BE \cong DE$ and $AE \cong CE$.   15. Yes
    $\angle CEB \cong \angle AED$ and $\angle CED \cong \angle AEB$ by
    Vert. $\angle$ Th. By SAS, $\triangle AED \cong \triangle CEB$
    and $\triangle AEB \cong \triangle CED$. By Th. 8.2,
    $\triangle ADC \cong \triangle CBA$ and $\triangle ABD \cong \triangle CDB$.
17. We know $m \angle 1 = 90°$ because it is a right $\angle$.   19. By Th. 8.2, $\triangle BAD \cong \triangle DCB$. $\angle ADB \cong$
    By Cor. 8.3, $m \angle 1 = m \angle 3$. Thus, $m \angle 3 =$ $\angle CBD$ and $\angle ABD \cong \angle CDB$ as corr. parts
    90° and is a right $\angle$. By Th. 8.1, $m \angle 1 +$ of $\cong$ ▵. We know $\angle AED \cong \angle CFB$ because
    $m \angle 2 + m \angle 3 + m \angle 4 = 360°$. Because $m \angle 4 =$ both are right $\angle$s. $\angle AEB$ and $\angle CFD$ are
    $m \angle 2$, we have $90 + 90 + 2m \angle 4 = 360°$, $2m$ right $\angle$s because they form a linear pair with
    $\angle 4 = 180°$ or $m \angle 4 = 90°$. Thus, $m \angle 4 =$ $\angle AED$ and $\angle CFB$. $\angle AEB \cong \angle CFD$. $AD \cong$
    $m \angle 2 = 90°$ and both $\angle$s are right $\angle$s. It BC and $AB \cong DC$ by Cor. 8.4. By SAA,
    follows that if one $\angle$ of a ▱ is a right $\angle$, $\triangle CFD \cong \triangle AEB$ and $\triangle CFB \cong \triangle AED$.
    the other $\angle$s are also right $\angle$s.

Section 8-3

Try This. . .

1. ▱ by Th. 8.10

Exercises

1. ▱ by Th. 8.8   3. Not a ▱
5. Not a ▱   7. Not a ▱
9. Not a ▱   11. ▱ by Th. 8.10
13. We know $\triangle ZWX \cong \triangle YXW$. $\overline{WZ} \cong \overline{YX}$ 15. Both diagonals should *not* bisect each other.
    as corr. parts of $\cong$ ▵. $WXYZ$ is not
    necessarily a ▱ because there is only
    one pair of opposite sides that are $\cong$.
17. We know $ABCD$ is a ▱. $\overleftrightarrow{DA} \parallel \overleftrightarrow{BC}$ 19. $AFCE$ is a ▱. Suppose $ABCD$ is a ▱.
    because opposite sides of a ▱ are   Then $\angle A \cong \angle C$ by Cor. 8.3 and $AD \cong BC$
    parallel. We know E-D-A and F-B-C. Thus,   by Cor. 8.4. Because AE bisects $\angle A$ and
    $\overleftrightarrow{EA} \parallel \overleftrightarrow{FC}$. We know $\overline{AD} \cong \overline{DE}$ and $\overline{BC} \cong$ CF bisects $\angle C$, $\angle DAE \cong \angle BCF$.
    $\overline{BF}$. $\overline{AD} \cong \overline{BC}$ by Cor. 8.4. $\overline{BC} \cong \overline{DE}$ and   Because $AD \parallel BC$, $\angle ADE \cong \angle FBC$. Then
    $\overline{AD} \cong \overline{BF}$ by substitution. Thus, $\overline{AE} \cong \overline{FC}$. $\triangle ADE \cong \triangle CBF$ and $AE \cong FC$ as corr.
    By Th. 8.11, $AFCE$ is a ▱.   parts. Because $AB \cong DC$, $\angle ABD \cong$
    $\angle BDC$. $AB \cong DC$ by Cor. 8.3 and $\angle EAB$
    $\cong \angle FCD$ because both $\angle$s have measure
    $\frac{1}{2}$ that of $\angle A$ and $\angle C$. Thus, $\triangle AEB \cong$
    $\triangle CFD$ and $\angle AEB \cong \angle CFE$ as corr. parts.
    Now $\triangle AEF \cong \triangle CFE$ by SAS and $AF \cong$
    EC as corr. parts. Thus, by Th. 8.9, $AFCE$
    is a ▱.

Section 8-4

Try This. . .

1. 9 m   3. $ST = 7$, $QR = 14$

Exercises

1. 14 m   3. $BC = 13$, $DE = 26$
5. $BC = 4$, $DE = 8$ 7. $m \angle 1 = 73°$, $m \angle 2 = 54°$, $m \angle 3 = 53°$,
    $m \angle 4 = 54°$

9. $c = 6$

11. We know D, E, and F are midpoints of $\overline{AB}$, $\overline{AC}$, and $\overline{BC}$. By Th. 8.12, $\overline{DB} \parallel \overline{EF}$, $\overline{DE} \parallel \overline{BF}$, $\overline{DF} \parallel \overline{EC}$, $\overline{FE} \parallel \overline{AD}$, $\overline{DF} \parallel \overline{AE}$, and $\overline{DE} \parallel \overline{FC}$. Thus, $DECF$, $DEFB$, and $DFEA$ are all $\square$ s.

13. By Th. 8.12, $DE = \frac{1}{2} BC$, $DF = \frac{1}{2} AC$, $EF = \frac{1}{2} AB$. Thus, $DE + DF + EF = \frac{1}{2}(BC + AC + AB)$.

15. By Exercise 14, the midpoints of the sides of a quadrilateral form a $\square$. The midpoints of the opposite sides form the diagonals which bisect each other.

Section 8-5

Try This. . .
1. 6
3. $DE = EF = 16$
5. The method should be the same as that used in Example 5. Check the distance between columns for equality.

Exercises
1. 7
3. 6.5
5. 6
7. $DE = 11$, $EF = 11$
9. 15
11. Each segment should measure 1.6 cm.
13. Check the distances between lines for equality.

Section 8-6

Try This. . .
1. Rectangle
3. Parallelogram
5. $127°$
7. It's a $\square$.
9. 14

Exercises
1. Square
3. Rhombus
5. Rectangle
7. 6
9. 10
11. $\triangle CBA$
13. $90°$
15. 12
17. $\triangle QRS$, $\triangle QPS$, $\triangle PQR$
19. Isosceles
21. $90°$
23. Diagonals are $\cong$ and $\perp$. All sides are $\cong$. All $\angle$s are right $\angle$s.

25. All sides are $\cong$. The diagonals are $\perp$.

27. We know $ABCE$ is a $\square$ and $ACDE$ is a $\square$. $\overline{BC} \parallel \overline{AE}$ and $\overline{CD} \parallel \overline{AE}$ because opposite sides of a $\square$ are parallel. B, C, and D are collinear. $\angle BCE$ is a right $\angle$ because all $\angle$s of a $\square$ are right $\angle$s. $\angle BCE$ is supp. to $\angle ECD$. Thus, $\angle ECD$ is a right $\angle$. $\overline{BC} \cong \overline{CD}$ because they are both $\cong$ to $\overline{AE}$ by Cor. 8.4. $\triangle BCE \cong \triangle DCE$ by SAS. Thus, $\angle EBC \cong \angle D$. $\triangle EBD$ is isos. By Th. 8.16, $\overline{AC} \cong \overline{BE}$. By Cor. 8.6, $\overline{AC}$ bisects $\overline{BE}$. Thus, $\overline{AF} \cong \overline{FC} \cong \overline{EF} \cong \overline{FB}$. By Isos. $\triangle$ Th., $\triangle EFC$, $\triangle AFB$, $\triangle BFC$, $\triangle EFA$ are isos.

Section 8-7

Try This. . .
1. Bases: $\overline{AB}$ and $\overline{DC}$, legs: $\overline{AD}$ and $\overline{BC}$, median: $\overline{EF}$
3. Bases: $\overline{AD}$ and $\overline{BC}$, legs: $\overline{AB}$ and $\overline{DC}$, median: $\overline{EG}$
5. 14.5
7. $AB = RS = DC = 5$
9. $m \angle W = 125°$, $m \angle Y = 55°$, $m \angle ZXY = 95°$, $m \angle XZY = 30°$
11. $m \angle BAC = m \angle ABC = 43°$, $m \angle ACB = m \angle DCE = 94°$, $m \angle ACD = m \angle BCE = 86°$, $m \angle CBE = 76°$, $m \angle DAC = 76°$, $m \angle BDE = m \angle AED = 43°$, $m \angle ADB = 18°$

Exercises
1. Bases: $\overline{AC}$ and $\overline{GE}$, legs: $\overline{AG}$ and $\overline{CE}$, median: $\overline{HD}$
3. Bases: $\overline{LM}$ and $\overline{KN}$, legs: $\overline{LK}$ and $\overline{MN}$, median: $\overline{PR}$
5. $\overline{RS} = 7.8$
9. $m \angle C = 82°$, $m \angle A = m \angle B = 98°$
7. Bases: 3.5 and 9.5, median: 6.5
11. $m \angle Y = 80°$, $m \angle W = m \angle X = 100°$
13. $m \angle BEC = 62°$, $m \angle AED = 62°$, $m \angle AEB = 118°$, $m \angle BDC = m \angle ACD = 31°$, $m \angle BAC = m \angle ABD = 31°$, $m \angle DAC = 80°$, $m \angle ADB = m \angle BCA = 38°$, $\triangle DAB \cong \triangle CBA$, $\triangle AED \cong \triangle BEC$, $\triangle DAC \cong \triangle CBD$

15. Attach the brace so that the distance from the floor to the top of the brace on the left equals the corr. distance on the right.

17. In trapezoid $ABCD$, $\overline{AB} \parallel \overline{DC}$ by definition of a trapezoid. By Th. 8.17, $\overline{EG} \parallel \overline{DC}$ and $\overline{EG} \parallel \overline{AB}$. $\overline{AE} \cong \overline{ED}$ because the median of a trapezoid determines the midpoints of the legs. By Th. 8.13, $\overline{AF} \cong \overline{FC}$. Thus, median $\overline{EG}$ bisects diagonal $\overline{AC}$. The same reasoning holds true for $\overline{EG}$ and $\overline{BD}$. Thus, median $\overline{EG}$ bisects diagonal $\overline{BD}$.

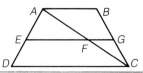

Chapter Review

1. ∠s: ∠K and ∠M or ∠L and ∠N; consecutive ∠s: ∠K and ∠L, ∠L and ∠M, ∠M and ∠N, or ∠N and ∠K

3. $LJ = 6.4$, $KM = 6$

5. The diagonals bisect each other (Th. 8.10).

7. 70°

9.
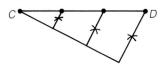

11. Rectangle

13. 9

15. △ JLM, △ LJK, △ MKL

17. $m \angle RQV = m \angle QRV = 25°$, $m \angle QVR = 130°$, $m \angle QVT = m \angle RVS = 50°$, $m \angle RTS = m \angle QST = 25°$, $m \angle QTV = m \angle RSV = 52°$, $m \angle TQV = 78°$

Skills Review

1. 48
3. 5,280
5. 16
7. 15
9. 32
11. 5

13. 13
15. $\frac{2}{3}$
17. $3\frac{1}{2}$
19. 24
21. 10
23. $1\frac{1}{2}$

25. 10,560
27. 64
29. 2,500
31. 18
33. 24
35. 3

37. 63,360
39. 20,000,000
41. 4
43. $2\frac{1}{2}$
45. 2

CHAPTER 9

Section 9-1

Try This...

1. $\frac{1}{3}$
3. $\frac{1}{2}$
5. False; $150 \neq 75$
7. 8 and 32 are proportional to 3 and 12.
9. 28

Exercises

1. $\frac{2}{9}$
3. $\frac{1}{5}$
5. $\frac{1}{6}$

7. $\frac{5}{28}$
9. 1
11. 36

13. 64
15. 10
17. $9\frac{1}{3}$

19. 42
21. 25
23. 39.05

25. $\approx 133.3\,\text{m}$
27. $\frac{8}{3}, \frac{5}{4}, \frac{y}{x}$
29. 80° and 100°

Section 9-2

Try This...

1. Pair a, pair b, pair d

3. $\angle J \cong \angle A$, $\angle K \cong \angle B$, and $\angle L \cong \angle C$.
$$\frac{JK}{AB} = \frac{KL}{BC} = \frac{JL}{AC}$$

5. $BT = 6\frac{3}{4}$, $CT = 9$

7. Span = 24 ft

Exercises

1. $\overline{RS} \leftrightarrow \overline{AB}$, $\overline{RT} \leftrightarrow \overline{AC}$, $\overline{ST} \leftrightarrow \overline{BC}$; $\angle R \leftrightarrow \angle A$, $\angle T \leftrightarrow \angle C$, $\angle S \leftrightarrow \angle B$

3. $\overline{BC} \leftrightarrow \overline{JW}$, $\overline{CS} \leftrightarrow \overline{WZ}$, $\overline{BS} \leftrightarrow \overline{JZ}$; $\angle C \leftrightarrow \angle W$, $\angle B \leftrightarrow \angle J$, $\angle S \leftrightarrow \angle Z$

5. $\overline{PQ} \leftrightarrow \overline{ST}$, $\overline{QR} \leftrightarrow \overline{TV}$, $\overline{PR} \leftrightarrow \overline{SV}$; $\angle P \leftrightarrow \angle S$, $\angle Q \leftrightarrow \angle T$, $\angle R \leftrightarrow \angle V$

7. $\overline{SM} \leftrightarrow \overline{WL}$, $\overline{MH} \leftrightarrow \overline{LK}$, $\overline{SH} \leftrightarrow \overline{WK}$; $\angle S \leftrightarrow \angle W$, $\angle M \leftrightarrow \angle L$, $\angle H \leftrightarrow \angle K$

9. $\frac{KG}{VU} = \frac{GH}{TU} = \frac{KH}{VT}$

11. $AM = 24$, $GT = 25$

13. $ED = 15$, $DF = 10$

15. $NP = 4$, $QV = 6$

17. 18 ft 8 in.

19. The $\triangle$'s vertices can be matched so that corr. $\angle$s are $\cong$ and the lengths of corr. sides are proportional.

Section 9-3

Try This. . .

1. Pair a, pair b

3. 18.75 m

Exercises

1. Not by AA Th.

3. Similar by AA. Th.

5. Not by AA Th.

7. $EM = 16.5$

9. $RC = 10$

11. About 18.67 cm

13. We know that $\overline{RK} \parallel \overline{ST}$. By Th. 7.5, $\angle STM \cong \angle RKM$. $\angle M \cong \angle M$. By AA Th., $\triangle STM \sim \triangle RKM$. Thus, $\frac{MR}{MK} = \frac{MS}{MT}$.

15. We know that $\overleftrightarrow{PQ} \parallel \overleftrightarrow{AB}$. By Th. 7.5, we have $\angle CPQ \cong \angle A$ and $\angle CQP \cong \angle B$. By the AA Th., $\triangle CPQ \cong \triangle CAB$.

17. Some possible theorems are: a) If two right $\triangle$ have one pair of acute $\angle$s $\cong$, then the $\triangle$ are similar. b) If two isosceles $\triangle$ have $\cong$ vertex $\angle$s, then the $\triangle$ are similar.

Section 9-4

Try This. . .

1. $RS = 9$

3. $EB = 7.5$

Exercises

1. 12

3. 8

5. 2.4

7. $3\frac{1}{3}$

9. 12

11. $\frac{8}{9} \sqrt{6}$

13. If $\overline{SW} \parallel \overline{TV}$ and $\overline{UW} \parallel \overline{RT}$, then $\frac{RS}{ST} = \frac{RW}{WV}$ and $\frac{RW}{WV} = \frac{TU}{UV}$ by Cor. 9.3. Thus, $\frac{RS}{ST} = \frac{TU}{UV}$.

15. We know that $\angle 1 \cong \angle 2$. Hence, $\overline{QT} \parallel \overline{RS}$ by Cor. 7.2. By Th. 9.2, $\frac{PQ}{QR} = \frac{PT}{TS}$.

Section 9-5

Try This. . .

1. a. Not by SAS or SSS; b. Similar by SSS; c. Similar by SAS.

3. We know that $\frac{AD}{AB} = \frac{AC}{AE}$. $\angle A \cong \angle A$. Thus, $\triangle ACD \sim \triangle AEB$ by SAS $\sim$ Th.

Exercises

1. Not by SAS

5. Not by SAS

3. $\sim$ by SAS

7. Pairs in Exercises 1, 5

9. We know that $\overline{AB} \parallel \overline{CT}$ and $\frac{AB}{CT} = \frac{BD}{CR}$. Because $\overline{AB} \parallel \overline{CT}$, by Cor. 7.6, $\angle B \cong \angle C$. Thus, $\triangle ABD \sim \triangle TCR$ by SAS $\sim$ Th. Thus, $\angle A \cong \angle T$, $\angle CRT \cong \angle ADB$ as corr. $\angle$s of $\sim$ $\triangle$ are $\cong$. $\overline{AD} \parallel \overline{RT}$ by Th. 7.1.

11. We know that $\frac{ME}{MS} = \frac{MC}{MG}$. $\angle M \cong \angle M$. $\triangle MEC \sim \triangle MSG$ by the SAS $\sim$ Th. Thus, $\frac{ME}{MS} = \frac{MC}{MG} = \frac{EC}{SG}$. Also, $\angle MEC \cong \angle MSG$ and $\angle MCE \cong \angle MGS$. Thus, $\overline{EC} \parallel \overline{SG}$ by Cor. 7.2.

13. We know that $\overline{AB} \parallel \overline{CT}$ and $\frac{AB}{CT} = \frac{BD}{CR}$. Because $\overline{AB} \parallel \overline{CT}$, $\angle B = \angle C$ by Cor. 7.6. $\triangle ABD \sim \triangle TCR$ by SAS $\sim$ Th.

15. We know that $\frac{ME}{MS} = \frac{MC}{MG}$. Also, $\angle M \cong \angle M$. Hence, $\triangle MEC \sim \triangle MSG$ by the SAS$\sim$ Th. Consequently, $\angle MEC \cong \angle MSG$ as corr. $\angle$s $\cong$. Thus, by Cor. 7.2, $\overline{EC} \parallel \overline{SG}$.

Chapter Review

1. I

3. $\frac{ER}{TG} = \frac{RS}{GF} = \frac{ES}{TF}$, $\angle E \cong \angle T$, $\angle R \cong \angle G$, $\angle S \cong \angle F$

5. $JA = 6.5$, $VY = 8\frac{2}{3}$ 7. $CB = 11\frac{2}{3}$ 9. We know that $\overline{AB} \parallel \overline{CT}$ and $\frac{AB}{CT} =$

$\frac{BD}{CR}$. Because $\overline{AB} \parallel \overline{CT}$, then $\angle B \cong \angle C$ by Th. 7.1. By the SAS Similarity Th., $\triangle BAD \sim \triangle CTR$. So, $\angle A \cong \angle T$ and $\angle ADB \cong$ $\angle CRT$. $\frac{AB}{CT} = \frac{BD}{CR} = \cdot \frac{AD}{RT}$.

Skills Review

1. 7	3. 10	5. -5	7. -20	9. 50	11. 90
13. -30	15. -80	17. ≈ 8.832	19. ≈ 6.782	21. ≈ 8.944	23. ≈ 7.416
25. ≈ 6.083	27. ≈ 5.657	29. ≈ 9.950	31. ≈ 2.828	33. 22	35. 47
37. 87	39. 92	41. 7	43. 44	45. 95	47. 57
49. 26	51. 5	53. 17	55. 100		

Skills Refresher (page 288)

1. $x = 5$ or $x = -5$ 3. $y = 2$ or $y = -2$ 5. $x = 8$ or $x = -8$
7. $n = 9$ or $n = -9$ 9. $x = \sqrt{5}$ or $x = -\sqrt{5}$ 11. $b = \sqrt{6}$ or $b = -\sqrt{6}$

CHAPTER 10

Section 10-1

Try This...
1. $\triangle PFS \sim \triangle PMF \sim \triangle FMS$ 3. $\sqrt{14}$
5. $2\sqrt{10}$

Exercises
1. $\triangle PMD \sim \triangle PHM \sim \triangle MHD$ 3. 10
5. 21   7. $\sqrt{0.036}$
9. 10   11. $3\sqrt{10}$
13. $\sqrt{57}$ 15. 10

17. 12.25 or $12\frac{1}{4}$ 19. $\frac{121}{23}$ or $5\frac{6}{23}$
21. $\sqrt{35}$

23. If y is the geometric mean of x and z, then $\frac{x}{y} = \frac{y}{z}$. Now, either $\frac{x}{y} < 1$, $\frac{x}{y} = 1$, or $\frac{x}{y} > 1$. If $\frac{x}{y} < 1$, then $x < y$. If $\frac{x}{y} < 1$, then $\frac{y}{z} < 1$ and $y < z$. So, $x < y < z$. If $\frac{x}{y} = 1$, then $x = y$. If $\frac{x}{y} = 1$, then $\frac{y}{z} = 1$ and $y = z$. So, $x = y = z$. Finally, if $\frac{x}{y} > 1$, then $x > y$. If $\frac{x}{y} > 1$, then $\frac{y}{z} > 1$ and $y > z$. So, $x > y > z$. Hence, $x \le y \le z$ or $x \ge y \ge z$.

Skills Refresher (page 291)

1. $4\sqrt{2}$ 3. $4\sqrt{10}$ 5. $6\sqrt{2}$ 7. $5\sqrt{3}$ 9. $2\sqrt{6}$ 11. $3\sqrt{6}$

Section 10-2

Try This...
1. 12   3. 40

Exercises
1. 30   3. 15   5. 39   7. $2\sqrt{14}$
9. $\sqrt{149}$ 11. $90\sqrt{2}$ ft or about 127 ft   13. About 55 m   15. 15
17. $\sqrt{97}$ 19. $6^2 + 8^2 = 10^2$; $9^2 + 12^2 = 15^2$; $12^2 + 16^2 = 20^2$; $15^2 + 20^2 = 25^2$; and $18^2 + 24^2 = 30^2$. These are a few possible answers.

21. Each triple of numbers is a Pythagorean triple.

Section 10-3

Try This... 1. A right $\triangle$

Exercises 1. No

3. No

5. No

7. Yes

9. Yes

11. Yes

13. The carpenter uses the converse of the Pythagorean Th. If $AB = 10$, then a right $\angle$ is formed, and the two pieces of wood are $\perp$.

15. $a = CB$, $b = CA$, and $c = AB$. By Th. 6.10, because $a + b > c$, $a^2 + b^2 > c^2$. Thus, in $\triangle ABC$ with $\angle C$ less than 90°, side c is less than the hypotenuse of right $\triangle A'B'C'$ with right $\angle C$, if $AC = A'C'$ and $BC = B'C'$.

Skills Refresher (page 299)

1. $\frac{5}{3}\sqrt{3}$ 3. $\frac{1}{5}\sqrt{5}$ 5. $\frac{3}{2}\sqrt{2}$ 7. $\frac{8}{7}\sqrt{7}$ 9. $\frac{6}{5}\sqrt{5}$

11. $\frac{1}{8}\sqrt{56}$ or $\frac{1}{4}\sqrt{14}$ 13. $\frac{1}{2}\sqrt{22}$ 15. $\frac{1}{2}\sqrt{14}$

Section 10-4

Try This... 1. $ON = 8$, $OR = 16$

3. $TS = 5$, $VT = 5\sqrt{3}$

5. $MF = 3$, $RF = 3\sqrt{2}$

7. $GK = \frac{15\sqrt{2}}{2}$

Exercises 1. $t = 5$, $r = 5\sqrt{3}$

3. $t = 13.5$, $r = 13.5\sqrt{3}$

5. $p = 10$, $r = 5\sqrt{3}$

7. $p = 48$, $r = 24\sqrt{3}$

9. $p = 12$, $t = 6$

11. $p = 38$, $t = 19$

13. $s = 2$, $m = 2\sqrt{2}$

15. $s = 4.5$, $m = 4.5\sqrt{2}$

17. $r = s = 14$

19. $r = s = 3.5$

21. 1.8 m, $0.9\sqrt{3}$ m

23. $1.8\sqrt{3}$ m

25. $\frac{10}{3}\sqrt{3}$

27. $h = \frac{s}{2}\sqrt{3}$

29. $\frac{BC}{AB} = \frac{\sqrt{2}}{1}$, $\frac{CD}{BD} = \frac{2}{\sqrt{2}} = \frac{2\sqrt{2}}{2}$; $= \sqrt{2}$, $\frac{DE}{CE} = \frac{2\sqrt{2}}{2} = \sqrt{2}$, $\frac{DF}{EF} = \frac{4}{2\sqrt{2}} = \frac{2\sqrt{2}}{2} = \sqrt{2}$

31. $6\sqrt{3}$ mm

Chapter Review

1. $\triangle TMK \sim \triangle TSM \sim \triangle MSK$

3. 8

5. 18

7. 25

9. No

11. $PQ = 8.5$, $QR = 8.5\sqrt{3}$

13. $MH = NH = 17$

15. $AR = 5$, $RD = 5\sqrt{2}$

Skills Review

1. $>$ 3. $<$ 5. $>$ 7. $>$ 9. $=$ 11. $<$

13. $\frac{1}{5}$ 15. $3\frac{4}{5}$ 17. $\frac{13}{100}$ 19. $1\frac{49}{100}$ 21. $1\frac{7}{1000}$ 23. $\frac{1}{10,000}$

25. $\frac{16}{3}$ 27. $\frac{35}{4}$ 29. $\frac{47}{8}$ 31. $\frac{9}{8}$ 33. $\frac{15}{4}$ 35. $\frac{27}{10}$

37. $1\frac{3}{4}$ 39. $1\frac{4}{5}$ 41. $2\frac{5}{6}$ 43. $8\frac{2}{7}$ 45. $2\frac{21}{100}$ 47. $4\frac{1}{12}$

49. 0.125   51. 1.4   53. 0.9   55. 2.36   57. 1.333   59. 7.182

CHAPTER 11

Section 11-1

Try This... 1. Not a polygon because line segments intersect at a point that is not a vertex

3. Not a polygon because endpoints A and E are not shared by exactly two sides

5. Heptagon

Exercises
1. Polygon

5. Polygon
9. Decagon
13. Concave
17. Concave

7. Concave
3. Not a polygon because line segments
    intersect at a point that is not a vertex
7. Octagon
11. Decagon
15. Concave
19. No

Section 11-2

Try This. . .
1. 170
5. 31 cm

Exercises
1. 90
5. 434
9. 4,850
13. $\dfrac{x^2 - 13x + 40}{2}$
17. $\dfrac{x^2 + x - 2}{2}$
21. 58.5 m
25. $79.65
29. $a + 1$ sides

3. $\dfrac{x^2 - 7x + 10}{2}$

3. 740
7. 2,345
11. $\dfrac{x^4 - 3x^2}{2}$
15. $\dfrac{a^2 - a - 2}{2}$
19. 20 mm
23. 41 dm
27. 3 sides

Section 11-3

Try This. . .
1. 12,240°
5. 94°

Exercises
1. 1,440°
5. 17,640°
9. 13
13. 91.5°

17. $x = 9$. The ext. ∠s measure: 18°, 27°, 36°,
     45°, 63°, 81°, 90°
21. Measure int. ∠ = 120°; measure ext. ∠ = 60°.

3. $180x - 900$
7. $x = 10$. The ext. ∠s measure: 50°, 60°, 70°,
    80°, 100°

3. 6,840°
7. $180x - 1,260$
11. 126°
15. $x = 24$. The ext. ∠s measure: 24°, 48°, 72°,
     96°, 120°
19. The ext. ∠s measure: 48°, 34°, 94°, 102°,
     54°, 28°, $x = 12$
23. Th. 11.3 does not hold for concave polygons
     because the proof of the th. demands that the
     polygon be convex so that $n - 2$ △ will
     always be formed. Th. 11.4 does not hold
     for concave polygons because its proof
     depends on Th. 11.3.

Section 11-4

Try This. . .
1. Follow steps shown in the Drawing Exercise.

Exercises
1. D is the circumcenter.

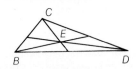

5. E is the centroid.

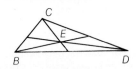

3. F is the circumcenter.

7. D is the centroid.

9. Acute △ have the circumcenter in the int. of the △. Obtuse △ have the circumcenter in the ext. of the △. Right △ have the circumcenter on the △.

13. The circumcenter, centroid, and orthocenter are the three points of concurrency that are collinear.

11. When the △ is equilateral.

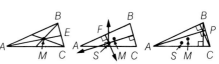

Section 11-5

Try This. . .   1. Similar

Exercises   1. Similar

5. $TV = 18$

9. $FG = 3\frac{1}{3}$, $RX = 11\frac{2}{3}$

3. $DE = \frac{14}{3}$ or $4\frac{2}{3}$; $GF = \frac{35}{3}$ or $11\frac{2}{3}$

3. Similar

7. $PQ = 10$, $DE = 15$

11. If two polygons do not have the same number of sides, they do not have the same number of vertices. Hence, a one-to-one correspondence between the vertices is impossible. Therefore, the polygons cannot be similar.

Section 11-6

Try This. . .   1. 135°

3.

Exercises   1. 120°

5. $128\frac{4}{7}°$

9. 176.4° or $176\frac{2}{5}°$

13. 120°

17. 18°

21.

23.

27. 8

31. The ∠ measure at each point of the star is 36°.
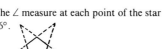

3. 60°

7. 162°

11. 60°

15. $51\frac{3}{7}°$

19. 3.6° or $3\frac{3}{5}°$

25.

29. The int. ∠ increases; the ext. ∠ decreases.

Chapter Review

1. Polygon

5. Heptagon

9. Concave

13. $x = 24$. The ∠ measures are: 24°, 48°, 48°, 48°, 72°, 120°.

3. Not a polygon because sides intersect at a point that is not a vertex

7. Dodecagon

11. 945

15. P is the centroid.

17. 168°

Skills Review

1. 8:10, $\frac{8}{10}$ 3. 6:5, $\frac{6}{5}$ 5. 3:100, $\frac{3}{100}$ 7. 2:13, 2 to 13 9. $\frac{1}{1000}$, 1 to 1,000 11. 2:3, 2 to 3
13. False 15. True 17. True 19. False 21. False 23. True

25. 10 27. 25 29. 14 31. 8 33. $3\frac{1}{2}$ 35. $1\frac{1}{2}$
37. 36 39. $10\frac{1}{2}$ 41. 10 43. 18

Chapter
12

Section 12-1

Try This. . .   1. This figure is one possible solution.

Exercises   1. One possible solution is this figure.

   5. 15

3. One possible solution is this figure.

7. 38

Section 12-2

Try This. . .   1. 87 cm²

3. Width = 6 cm; length = 18 cm. The unit is cm.

Exercises
1. 98 km²
5. 2.25 cm²
9. 13 km. The unit is km.
13. 64 cm²
17. 3 bundles
21. $\dfrac{A_1}{A_2} = \dfrac{\ell w_1}{\ell w_2} = \dfrac{w_1}{w_2}$

3. 10.5 cm²
7. $w = 13$ m. The unit is m.
11. 21 km. The unit is km.
15. 117 cm²
19. Halved; doubled; tripled

Section 12-3

Try This. . .
1. 65 m²
5. 108 cm²

3. 18.6 cm²

Exercises
1. 37.5 m²
5. 13.5 m²
9. 12 m
13. 6 m
17. $2\sqrt{66}$ m²
21. The altitude of the △ is twice the altitude of the ▱.
25. Suppose area △ one$= \frac{1}{2} b_1 h_1$ and area △ two $= \frac{1}{2} b_2 h_2$ and $b_1 = b_2$. Then

$$\frac{\text{area } \triangle \text{ one}}{\text{area } \triangle \text{ two}} = \frac{\frac{1}{2} b_1 h_1}{\frac{1}{2} b_1 h_2} = \frac{h_1}{h_2}.$$

3. 20 cm²
7. 15,732 m²
11. 12 cm
15. $36\sqrt{3}$ cm²
19. 36
23. The product of the base and altitude of the △ is twice the product of the sides of the □.

27. $\dfrac{\text{Area} \triangle \text{ one}}{\text{Area} \triangle \text{ two}} = \dfrac{\frac{1}{2}b_1 h_1}{\frac{1}{2}b_2 h_2} = \dfrac{b_1 h_1}{b_2 h_2} = \dfrac{b_1}{b_2} \cdot \dfrac{h_1}{h_2}$. Because the $\triangle$ are similar,

proportional sides imply proportional altitudes. Thus, $\dfrac{b_1}{b_2} = \dfrac{h_1}{h_2}$.

Hence, $\dfrac{\text{Area} \triangle \text{ one}}{\text{Area} \triangle \text{ two}} = \dfrac{h_1}{h_2} \cdot \dfrac{h_1}{h_2} = \left(\dfrac{h_1}{h_2}\right)^2$.

Section 12-4

Try This. . .
1. 36 mm²
5. 45 cm²

3. 12.8 m²

Exercises
1. 91 m²
5. 4,060 mm²
9. $15\sqrt{2}$ cm²
13. 1.5 m
17. 68 m²

3. 6 cm²
7. 8.75 km²
11. 14.7 cm²
15. 11.67 cm
19. 216 m²

Section 12-5

Try This. . .
1. 178.5 m²

3. 13 cm and 26 cm

Exercises
1. 10 m²
5. 126 cm²
9. 4 m
13. $72\sqrt{3}$ m²
17. $A = \left(\dfrac{a+b}{2}\right)(a+b)$ _or_ $\dfrac{2ab+c^2}{2}$.

3. 287 cm²
7. 3,125 cm²
11. 3.5 mm
15. 1 to 3
19. $m \angle AED = 90°$.

Section 12-6

Try This. . .
1. 76.8m²

Exercises
1. $384\sqrt{3}$ cm²
5. $36\sqrt{3}$ m²
9. $150\sqrt{3}$ cm²
11.

3. 10.8 cm²
7. 1,920 cm²

From similar $\triangle$, $\dfrac{a_1}{a_2} = \dfrac{s_1}{s_2}$. $\dfrac{\text{Area } P_1}{\text{Area } P_2} = \dfrac{\frac{1}{2}a_1 n s_1}{\frac{1}{2}a_2 n s_2} = \dfrac{a_1 s_1}{a_2 s_2} =$

$\dfrac{a_1}{a_2} \cdot \dfrac{s_1}{s_2} = \dfrac{s_1^2}{s_2^2}$.

Chapter Review

1. 78
5. 165
9. 27 mm²
13. 115.2 dm²
17. 28 dm²

3. 67 m²
7. $5\sqrt{299}$ mm²
11. 6.5 mm
15. $\sqrt{3}$ m

Skills Review

1. $\dfrac{1}{15}$ 3. $1\dfrac{7}{8}$ 5. $5\dfrac{1}{3}$ 7. $4\dfrac{1}{11}$ 9. $\dfrac{1}{6}$ 11. 6

13. 4   15. $\dfrac{9}{52}$ 17. $13\dfrac{1}{2}$ 19. 2   21. 1   23. $3\dfrac{3}{8}$

25. 2   27. 1   29. 72   31. $\dfrac{4}{81}$ 33. 4   35. $7\dfrac{1}{5}$

37. $\dfrac{3}{8}$ 39. $7\dfrac{4}{5}$ 41. $2\dfrac{8}{13}$ 43. 3   45. $1\dfrac{3}{5}$ 47. $\dfrac{7}{22}$

Try This. . .

1. Radii: $\overline{JK}, \overline{KH}, \overline{KG}, \overline{KL}$
   Chords: $\overline{GH}, \overline{GL}, \overline{JH}$
   Diameters: $\overline{JH}$ and $\overline{GL}$

3. 9.2

Exercises

1. Radii: $\overline{OR}, \overline{OP}, \overline{OG}, \overline{OT}$
   Chords: $\overline{HJ}, \overline{PT}, \overline{TS}$
   Diameters: $\overline{PT}$

3. 41.3

5. $2\frac{3}{8}$
9. 17.4
13. 3.8 cm

7. 0.1215
11. 0.16
15. By Th. 13.1 and 13.2, $\overline{AB}$ and $\overline{CD}$ are $\cong$ and bisect each other. By Th. 8.10 and 8.15, $ABCD$ is a ▱.

17. Consider a chord $\overline{AB}$ and a diameter $\overline{CD}$. By the Triangle Inequality Th. $AB < AO + OB$. But $AO + OB = CO + OD = CD$. Thus $AB < CD$ by substitution.

Section 13-2

Try This. . .

1. 16
5. Follow the directions in Example 5.

3. 4.5

Exercises

1. 24
5. 8
9. $\sqrt{5}$

3. 0.8 m
7. 20
11. The distance from the point you found and the circle should be constant.

13.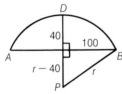

$100^2 + (r - 40)^2 = r^2$
$10,000 + r^2 - 80r + 1600 = r^2$
$11,600 = 80r$
$145 = r$
Radius is 145 m.

15. $\frac{\sqrt{3}}{2} r$

17. Because $\overleftrightarrow{OC} \perp \overleftrightarrow{AB}$ at D, $\overline{AD} \cong \overline{DB}$ by Th. 13.3. By SAS, $\triangle ADC \cong \triangle BDC$, and therefore $\overline{AC} \cong \overline{CB}$.

19. Consider three non-collinear points A, B, and C with the $\perp$ bisectors intersecting at a point D. If they did not intersect, they would be $\parallel$ and A, B, and C would be collinear. Because D is equidistant from A, B, and C by def. of a circle, A, B, and C are contained in a circle with center D and radii $\overline{AD}, \overline{BD},$ and $\overline{CD}$.

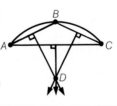

Section 13-3

Try This. . .

1. $CD = 9$

Exercises

1. $TW = 9$
5. $FB = 10, CB = KJ = JH = 8, FC = GJ = 6$

9. $AB = AC = BC = 9$; the distance from center $= 4$.
13. It is a circle whose center is the same as the given circle.

3. $OE = OF = 8$

3. $BD = 23.5$
7. $NQ = 10, LN = RS = ST = 24, PR = QM = 26$

11. 8

15. $\triangle ABC \cong \triangle DEF$ by SSS.

17.

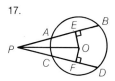

Because $\overline{AB} \cong \overline{CD}$, $\overline{OF} \cong \overline{OE}$ by Th. 13.6, and $\overline{OP} \cong \overline{OP}$. By the HL Th., $\triangle OEP \cong \triangle OFP$. So, $\overline{PE} \cong \overline{PF}$ by corr. parts. By Th. 13.3, E and F are midpoints of the $\cong$ chords. So, $\overline{EB} \cong \overline{FD}$. By segment addition, $\overline{PB} \cong \overline{PD}$.

Section 13-4

Try This...

1. Minor arcs: $\overset{\frown}{DF}$, $\overset{\frown}{FE}$, $\overset{\frown}{DG}$, $\overset{\frown}{GE}$, $\overset{\frown}{GF}$
   Major arcs: $\overset{\frown}{DGF}$, $\overset{\frown}{FDE}$, $\overset{\frown}{GED}$, $\overset{\frown}{EDG}$, $\overset{\frown}{GDF}$
   Semicircles: $\overset{\frown}{DFE}$, $\overset{\frown}{DGE}$

3. $197°$

5. $m\angle AOD = 24°$, $m\overset{\frown}{AD} = 24°$,
   $m\overset{\frown}{DB} = 156°$

Exercises

1. Minor arcs: $\overset{\frown}{XY}$, $\overset{\frown}{YZ}$, $\overset{\frown}{ZW}$, $\overset{\frown}{XW}$, $\overset{\frown}{YZW}$
   Major arcs: $\overset{\frown}{YXZ}$, $\overset{\frown}{XWY}$, $\overset{\frown}{XYW}$, $\overset{\frown}{WXZ}$
   Semicircles: $\overset{\frown}{XYZ}$, $\overset{\frown}{XWZ}$

3. $47°$

5. $224°$

7. $180°$

9. $m\overset{\frown}{ABC} = 177°$, $m\overset{\frown}{ADC} = 183°$

11. $m\angle ROU = 125°$, $m\overset{\frown}{RS} = 55°$, $m\overset{\frown}{TS} = 125°$

13. $30°$

15. $m\overset{\frown}{AE} = 60°$, $m\overset{\frown}{ED} = 30°$,
    $m\overset{\frown}{DAB} = 150°$, $BF = 0.5$

17. $2.5°$

19. $4,320°$

21. $8,280°$

Section 13-5

Try This...

1. $\overset{\frown}{DF} \cong \overset{\frown}{GK}$, $\overset{\frown}{FE} \cong \overset{\frown}{KJ}$, $\overset{\frown}{DCE} \cong \overset{\frown}{DFE} \cong \overset{\frown}{GHJ} \cong \overset{\frown}{GKJ}$, $\overset{\frown}{FDE} \cong \overset{\frown}{KGJ}$, $\overset{\frown}{DCF} \cong \overset{\frown}{GHK}$

3. $\overline{XZ} \cong \overline{TS}$, $\overline{ZY} \cong \overline{RT}$, $\overline{XY} \cong \overline{RS}$

Exercises

1. One possible answer is $\overline{RS} \cong \overline{ST}$, $\overset{\frown}{RU} \cong \overset{\frown}{UT}$
   $\overset{\frown}{RTU} \cong \overset{\frown}{URT}$, $\overset{\frown}{RSU} \cong \overset{\frown}{UST}$

3. One possible answer is $\overline{AB} \cong \overline{JK}$, $\overline{CD} \cong \overline{NM}$
   $\overset{\frown}{BEC} \cong \overset{\frown}{MLJ}$, $\overset{\frown}{CAD} \cong \overset{\frown}{NKM}$

5. $\overset{\frown}{AB} \cong \overset{\frown}{CD}$, $\overset{\frown}{CDB} \cong \overset{\frown}{ABD}$,
   $\overset{\frown}{CAB} \cong \overset{\frown}{ACD}$, $\overset{\frown}{CAD} \cong \overset{\frown}{ADB}$

7. $\overset{\frown}{MP} \cong \overset{\frown}{NQ}$, $\overset{\frown}{MN} \cong \overset{\frown}{PQ}$, $\overset{\frown}{MQN} \cong \overset{\frown}{PMQ}$,
   $\overset{\frown}{NMQ} \cong \overset{\frown}{MQP}$

9. $\overline{AB} \cong \overline{FG}$, $\overline{EA} \cong \overline{HJ}$, $\overline{BD} \cong \overline{FJ}$, $\overline{ED} \cong \overline{GH}$,
   $\overline{AD} \cong \overline{GJ}$ Diameter: $\overline{BE}$

11. Because $\overset{\frown}{AB} \cong \overset{\frown}{BC}$ and $\overset{\frown}{AD} \cong \overset{\frown}{CD}$, then by Th. 13.8, $\overline{AB} \cong \overline{BC}$ and $\overline{AD} \cong \overline{CD}$. Because $\overline{BD} \cong \overline{BD}$, $\triangle ABD \cong \triangle CBD$ by SSS.

Section 13-6

Try This...

1.

Exercises

1.

3.

5.

7. The right $\triangle$, the acute $\triangle$, the obtuse $\triangle$

Section 13-7

Try This...

1. 7.5π m

3. ≈ 24.2 cm

Exercises

1. 12π m

3. 0.5π km

5. 25π cm

7. 75π cm

9. 1.72π m

11. 13.4 cm

13. The circumference is halved.
17. ≈45,216 km

15. ≈18,840 cm
19. The radius is increased by 1.59 m. (about $5'2\frac{1}{2}''$.)

Section 13-8

Try This . . .
1. 64π cm^2
3. ≈ 24.6 km^2
5. ≈ 150.7 cm^2

Exercises
1. 196π m^2
3. 18π mm^2
5. 225π cm^2
7. ≈ 314 km^2
9. 144π cm^2
11. 0.36π m^2
13. $r \approx 11$ cm, $d \approx 22$ cm
15. $r \approx 1.5$ m, $d \approx 3$ m
17. 527 cm^2
19. ≈ 3.4 m^2
21. 8π m
23. 2.2π cm
25. 36π cm^2
27. $46.63

Chapter Review

1. Radii: $\overline{OF}, \overline{OA}, \overline{OB}, \overline{OD}$. Chords: $\overline{FD}, \overline{BE}, \overline{AD}$. Diameter: $\overline{AD}$.
3. 72
5. 5
7. $QR = ST = 10$, $OM = PN = 3$
9. 108°
11. 252°
13.

15. The diameter of the oak is 3.5 times the diameter of the sycamore.
17. ≈ 34.54 cm^2

CHAPTER 14

Section 14-1

Try This. . .
1. 13
3. 10

Exercises
1. 9
3. 1.2
5. 16
7. 120
9. 25
11. 145°
13. 9

15. By Th. 14.1, Th. 8.1, $m \angle BOA + m \angle APB = 180°$, and $\angle BOA$ and $\angle APB$ are supplementary.
17. $\triangle APB$ and $\triangle ABO$ are isos. $\triangle$.
19. From Exercise 16, we know $\triangle OAP \cong \triangle OBP$. By SAS, $\triangle BOQ \cong \triangle AOQ$.

Section 14-2

Try This . . .
1.

Exercises
1.
3.
5.
7.

9. 62
11. 48
13. We know that $\overline{AF} \cong \overline{AE}$, $\overline{BF} \cong \overline{BG}$, $\overline{CG} \cong \overline{CH}$, and $\overline{DH} \cong \overline{DE}$ by Cor. 14.2. $\overline{AB} \cong \overline{BC} \cong \overline{CD} \cong \overline{DA}$ because $ABCD$ is a square. $AF + FB = AB$. $BG + GC = BC$. $CH + HD = CD$. $DE + EA = DA$. By substitution, we get $AF = FB = BG = GC = CH = HD = DE = EA$. Thus, F, E, H, and G are midpoints.
15. Opposite ∠s of cyclic quadrilaterals are supp.
16. Yes

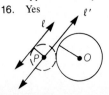

Section 14-3

Try This . . .   1. ∠*WOA* intercepts $\widehat{WA}$
∠*GEF* intercepts $\widehat{GF}$
∠*XWZ* intercepts $\widehat{XZ}$
∠*PQR* intercepts $\widehat{PR}$

3. $m\angle ADB = 30°$
$m\angle ADC = 60°$
$m\angle BEC = 30°$

5. 62°

Exercises   1. ∠*CAB* intercepts $\widehat{CB}$

3. ∠*XYW* intercepts $\widehat{XW}$
∠*XYZ* intercepts $\widehat{XWZ}$
∠*YZW* intercepts $\widehat{YXW}$
∠*YWZ* intercepts $\widehat{YZ}$
∠*WYZ* intercepts $\widehat{WZ}$

5. 68°
9. $m\angle MQP = 110°$
$m\angle QPN = 86°$
13. 120°
17. 39°
21. 20°
25. We know that $\overline{AB} \parallel \overline{CD}$. $\angle BAD \cong \angle CDA$ because alternate int. ∠s of $\parallel$ lines are $\cong$. So, $\widehat{AC} \cong \widehat{BD}$ by Cor. 14.6.

7. 45°
11. 36°
15. 138°
19. 121°
23. 360°
27. $m\angle AOC = 90°$. If we draw diameter $\overline{AD}$, we know that $\overline{DO} \cong \overline{AO}$. Radius $\overline{CO}$ bisects $\overline{AD}$ at *O*. By Th. 13.4, $\overline{CO}$ is $\perp$ $\overline{AD}$. So, $m\angle AOC = 90°$, because $\perp$ lines form right angles.

Section 14-4

Try This . . .   1. 39°

3. 50°

5. 195°

Exercises   1. 70°   3. 125.5°   5. $m\widehat{PQ} = 73°$ 7. 18°
$m\widehat{SR} = 73°$
9. 67°   11. $m\widehat{LJ} = 58°$ 13. $m\widehat{AB} = 71°$ 15. $m\angle C = 15°$
$m\widehat{MN} = 102°$ $m\widehat{DE} = 41°$ $m\angle AFB = 47°$
17. By Cor. 14.6, $\angle FAD \cong \angle BCF$. $\angle F \cong \angle F$. Therefore, $\triangle ADF \sim \triangle CBF$ by AA.

Section 14-5

Try This. . .   1. 42°

3. $m\widehat{AB} = 90°$
$m\widehat{BC} = 90°$

5. 30°

Exercises   1. 41°   3. 137.5°   5. 138°   7. 35°
9. 14°   11. $m\widehat{TM} = 108°$, $m\widehat{TR} = 52°$
13. 40°   15. 55°
17. $m\widehat{EFD} = m\widehat{EDF}$. Thus, $m\angle B = m\angle C$. By Isos. $\triangle$Th., $\triangle ABC$ is isos.

19. The distance from *D* to $\overleftrightarrow{AC}$ is equal to the distance from *D* to $\overleftrightarrow{AB}$.

Section 14-6

Try This. . .   1. 5   3. 24   5. $EA = 13.33$
$AB = 4\sqrt{5}$

Exercises   1. 14   3. 12
5. 4   7. 9
9. 22.5   11. $\sqrt{66}$
13. 28

Chapter Review

1. 12

3. This diagram is one possible answer.

5. $m\angle BCD = 25°$
$m\widehat{BC} = 130°$

7. 22°

9. 70°   11. 45°   13. 26   15. 5

CHAPTER 15

Section 15-1

Try This...   1. 3, 5, 7, 9.

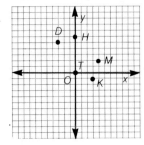

Exercises

11. $T(-3, 2)$; $Q(-6, -1)$; $R(0, 6)$;
$P(6, 3)$; $D(2, -6)$

13. $A(3, 1)$; $B(-4, 2)$; $C(-6, 0)$;
$D(-2, -4)$; $E(6, -6)$

15.

15-21. Any point on these lines satisfy the conditions.

17. 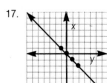   19. 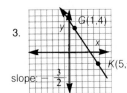   21.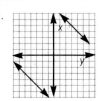

Section 15-2

Try This...   1. 8   3. $\sqrt{241}$

Exercises   1. 5   3. $3\sqrt{5}$ 5. $3\sqrt{2}$ 7. $\sqrt{26}$ 9. $\sqrt{197}$ 11. $\sqrt{97}$

13. $\sqrt{64 + y^2}$ 15. $2\sqrt{a^2 + b^2}$

17. $\sqrt{5} + \sqrt{34} + \sqrt{17}$ 19. The vertices in order are R, S, T, and V.
$RT = \sqrt{113}$, $SV = \sqrt{170}$

21. Consider quadrilateral $MNQP$. By the Distance Formula, $MN = QP = \sqrt{29}$ and $PM = QN = \sqrt{17}$. Because the opposite sides of the quadrilateral are $\cong$, quadrilateral $MNQP$ is a $\square$.

23. $y = 6 - 3\sqrt{11}$ or $6 + 3\sqrt{11}$

Section 15-3

Try This...   1. $\dfrac{2}{3}$,   3. 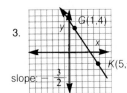   5. 0

slope: $-\dfrac{3}{2}$

Exercises   1. 9   3. 1   5. $\dfrac{3}{2}$ 7. $-\dfrac{1}{4}$ 9. $-\dfrac{1}{2}$ 11. -2

13. -1 15. 0   17. No slope   19. 0   21. No slope   23. 6

25. 13   27. The coordinates of (a,b) are (20,30).

Section 15-4

Try This...   1. $y = 3x - 3$ 3. slope $= -5$, y-intercept is 16

5. slope $= \dfrac{2}{3}$, y-intercept is $\dfrac{8}{3}$

Exercises   1. $y = 5x - 5$ 3. $y = 2x + 7$

5. $y = 7x + 11$ 7. $y = -2x$

9. $y = -3x - 9$ 11. $y = -x + 5$

13. $y = 6$ 15. $y = \dfrac{3}{4} x$

17. $y = -\dfrac{2}{3} x + \dfrac{28}{3}$ 19. slope is 8, y-intercept is 3

21. slope is −5, *y*-intercept is 4

23. slope is −6, *y*-intercept is −9

25. slope is $\frac{2}{3}$, *y*-intercept is 8

27. slope is $\frac{3}{4}$, *y*-intercept is $-\frac{7}{2}$

29. slope is $\frac{5}{8}$, *y*-intercept is $\frac{15}{8}$

31. slope is 0, *y*-intercept is 11

33. slope is 0, *y*-intercept is 0

35. $y = x + 4$

37. $y = \frac{3}{2} x$

39. $y = 18$

41. $y = 16$

Section 15-5

Try This. . .

1. yes

3. yes

Exercises

1. yes

3. no

5. no

7. yes

9. yes

11. yes

13. yes

15. no

Section 15-6

Try This. . .

1. (6,4)

3. $Q(-19, 6)$

Exercises

1. (4,4)

3. (1,5)

5. $(3, 2\frac{1}{2})$

7. $(1\frac{1}{2} , 3)$

9. $(-7 \frac{1}{2}, -5\frac{1}{2})$

11. $(-3, -4)$

13. $(3\frac{1}{2} s, 5t)$

15. $(-5, 2)$

17. $10\sqrt{2}, \sqrt{137}$

Chapter Review

1, 3.

5. $B(4, 0)$

7. $\sqrt{109}$

9. Slope = 0

11. $y = 2x - 2$

13. $y = 4x - 5$

15. $(5, 1\frac{1}{2})$

CHAPTER 16

Section 16-1

Try This. . .

1.

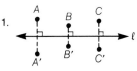

This diagram is one possible answer.

5. The ▱ s are not reflections of one another.

3. The answer should show one copy of the curve on the other side of the fold. Lines connecting corr. points should be ⊥ to the fold.

Exercises

1.

3. *G, J, K, M*, and *E*, respectively

5.

7.

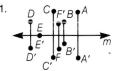

9.

11.

13.

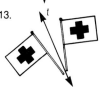

Section 16-2

Try This. . .
1. $\overline{AB} \cong \overline{A'B'}$, $\overline{AC} \cong \overline{A'C'}$, $\overline{BC} \cong \overline{B'C'}$,
$\angle A \cong \angle A'$, $\angle B \cong \angle B'$, $\angle C \cong \angle C'$.
$\overline{CE} \cong \overline{C'E}$, $\overline{B'D} \cong \overline{BD}$, $\overline{DC'} \cong$
$\overline{DC}$, $\overline{A'E} \cong \overline{AE}$, $\angle A'EC \cong \angle AEC'$,
$\angle CDB' \cong \angle C'DB$

3. Same

Exercises
1. Th. 16.1
3. Cor. 16.3
5. Post. 19
7. Th. 16.2 (Def. of reflection)
9. Same
11. Reverse
13. Draw $\overset{\leftrightarrow}{BC} \perp p$. Draw $\overset{\rightarrow}{BA}$ intersecting p at D.
Draw $\overset{\rightarrow}{DA'}$. B' is where $\overset{\leftrightarrow}{BC}$ meets $\overset{\rightarrow}{DA'}$.

Section 16-3

Try This. . .
1.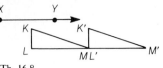

3. Ths. 16.6 and 16.7

5. Th. 16.8

Exercises
1.

3.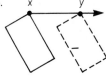

5.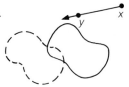

7. Yes

9. No
11. across ℓ then n
13. across ℓ, then m, then ℓ
15. Th. 16.6
17. Th. 16.7
19. The distance translated is twice the distance between the ∥ reflection lines.

Section 16-4

Try This. . .
1.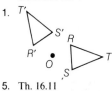

3. Th. 16.11

5. Th. 16.11

Exercises
1.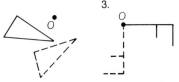
3.
5.
7. Th. 16.12
9. Th. 16.10
11.

13. The point between the two keys

Section 16-5

Try This. . .
1. line symmetry (see figure at right)

3. The line through the center
5. Neither point nor rotational symmetry

Exercises
1. No symmetry
3.
5. Both point and rotational symmetry
7. No symmetry

11.

This is one possible answer.

9. Point symmetry: *H, I, N, O, S, X, Z*
Line symmetry: *A, B, C, D, E, H, I, M, O, T, U, V, W, X, Y*
Rotational symmetry: *H, I, N, O, S, X, Z*

13. A quadrilateral is a ▱ whenever it has point symmetry.

17. These are possible answers.

15. If it has two lines of symmetry, then it is equilateral and must have a third line of symmetry.

19. There are none.

21. This is one possible answer.

Chapter Review

1.   *m*

3.

5. Th. 16.2

7. Reverse

9.
x   *y*

11. By Ths. 16.6 and 16.7

13.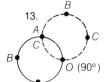
B
A
C
C
B
O (90°)
A

15. $\overline{A'P} \cong \overline{AP}$ by Th. 16.11

17.

19. This figure has rotational symmetry of 60°, 120°, 180°, 240°, and 300°; has point symmetry at center of gear.

Skills Review

1.   3.   5.   7.   9.   11.

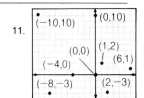
(−10,10)   (0,10)
(0,0)   (1,2)
(−4,0)   (6,1)
(−8,−3)   (2,−3)

13.   15.   17. (7,7)   19. (7,9)   21. (4,4)   23. (−3,−7)
25. (−2,−2)   27. (5,4)   29. (0,9)   31. (8,−10)   33. (4,−4)   35. (−3,7)

CHAPTER
17

Section 17-1

Try This. . .

1. Faces: *ABCDE, GHJKF, ABHG, BCJH, CDKJ, DKFE, EFGA*
Edges: $\overline{AB}, \overline{BC}, \overline{CD}, \overline{DH}, \overline{HA}, \overline{GH}, \overline{HJ}, \overline{JK},$
$\overline{KF}, \overline{FG}, \overline{AG}, \overline{BH}, \overline{CJ}, \overline{DK}, \overline{EF}$
Vertices: *A, B, C, D, E, G, H, J, K, F*

5. This figure is one possible answer.

3. Right hexagonal prism
Bases: *ABCDEF, GHJKLM*
Lateral faces: *ABHG, BCJH, CDKJ, EDKL, FELM, AFMG*
Lateral edges: $\overline{AG}, \overline{BH}, \overline{CJ}, \overline{DK}, \overline{EL}, \overline{FM}$

Exercises

1. Faces: *ABCD*, △*BCF*, △*ADE*, *ABFE*, *DCFE*
   Edges: $\overline{AD}$, $\overline{AB}$, $\overline{BC}$, $\overline{CD}$, $\overline{BF}$, $\overline{CF}$, $\overline{DE}$, $\overline{AE}$, $\overline{EF}$
   Vertices: *A*, *B*, *C*, *D*, *E*, *F*

3. Faces: △*SXW*, △*SWP*, △*SPZ*, △*SZY*, △*SYX*, *XYZPW*
   Edges: $\overline{SX}$, $\overline{SW}$, $\overline{SP}$, $\overline{SZ}$, $\overline{SY}$, $\overline{XW}$, $\overline{WP}$, $\overline{PZ}$, $\overline{ZY}$, $\overline{YX}$, Vertices: *S*, *X*, *W*, *P*, *Z*, *Y*

5. Right triangular prism
   Bases: △*ABC*, △*DEF*
   Lateral faces: *ABED*, *BCFE*, *ACFD*
   Lateral edges: $\overline{AD}$, $\overline{BE}$, $\overline{CF}$

7. Oblique quadrangular prism
   Bases: *MNPQ*, *URST*
   Lateral faces: *MNRU*, *NPSR*, *QPST*, *MQTU*
   Lateral edges: $\overline{MU}$, $\overline{NR}$, $\overline{PS}$, $\overline{QT}$

9. Right hexagonal prism
   Bases: *WXYZTS*, *BCDEFA*
   Lateral faces: *WXCB*, *XYDC*, *YZED*, *TZEF*, *STFA*, *WSAB*
   Lateral edges: $\overline{WB}$, $\overline{XC}$, $\overline{YD}$, $\overline{ZE}$, $\overline{TF}$, $\overline{SA}$

11.

13.   15. 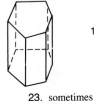   17.

Type of prism	Faces	Lateral Faces	Edges	Lateral Edges	Vertices
Triangular	5	3	9	3	6
Quadrangular	6	4	12	4	8
Pentagonal	7	5	15	5	10
Hexagonal	8	6	18	6	12
Octagonal	10	8	24	8	16

19. always   21. sometimes   23. sometimes   25. always

Section 17-2

Try This. . .   1. 1,020 cm³

Exercises   1. 42 m³   3. 4,500 m³   5. 3.6 m³   7. 288π m³   9. 135π m³
11. 57,700 liters   13. 9.3 cm   15. When the diameter is doubled, the volume is 4 times larger. When the diameter is halved, the volume is $\frac{1}{4}$ as large.   17. $\frac{\pi}{4}$

Section 17-3

Try This. . .   1. 64 cm²   3. 312 m²   5. 122.5π dm²

Exercises
1. Lateral area: 132 mm²
   Total area: 188 mm²
3. Lateral area: 468 cm²
   Total area: 655 cm²
5. Lateral area: 120 cm²
   Total area: 132 cm²
7. 4 *l*
9. Lateral area: 42π cm²
   Total area: 60π cm²
11. Lateral area: 1,512π cm²
   Total area: 2,160π cm²
13. Lateral area: 35π m²
   Total area: 59.5π m²
15. 336π cm²

Section 17-4

Try This. . .   1. 93.3 m³

Exercises   1. 24.75 cm³   3. 462 m³   5. 2,311,875 m³   7. 212.3π m³   9. 166.7 cm³

Section 17-5

Try This. . .   1. $(60 + 4\sqrt{3})$ cm²   3. 76π dm²

Exercises   1. $(48 + 4\sqrt{3})$ cm²   3. 35,280 m²   5. 79,772 m²   7. 120π dm²   9. $0.18

Section 17-6

Try This. . .   1. 36π cm³   3. 256πdm²

Exercises
1. Volume: 85.3π cm³
   Area: 64π cm²
3. Volume: 4.5π m³
   Area: 9π m²
5. Volume: 457.3π cm³
   Area: 196π cm²
7 Volume: 12.35 π cm³
   Area: 17.64 π cm²
9. Volume: 57.16 π cm³
   Area: 49 π cm²
11. Volume: 5.5π × 10⁹ km³
   Area: 10,240,000π km²
13. The radius of the larger sphere is $\sqrt[3]{2}$ times the radius of the smaller sphere.
15. $\frac{1}{6} \pi d^3$

17. When you multiply the radius by a number n, the volume is n^3 times the old volume.

19. The area of a sphere is equal to the area of 4 great circles.

Chapter Review

1. Right triangular prism   Bases: $\triangle ABC$, $\triangle FED$
Lateral faces: $FABD$, $FACE$, $DBCE$
Lateral edges: $\overline{FA}$, $\overline{EC}$, $\overline{DB}$

3. 900 dm^3

5. 243.6 m^3

7. $18{,}750\pi$ m^3

9. 141 cm^2

11. 808 cm^2

13. 75 cm^3

15. $1{,}536\pi$ m^3

17. 132.75 cm^2

19. Volume: $10{,}666.7\pi$ cm^3
Area: $1{,}600\pi$ cm^2

CHAPTER 18

Section 18-1

Try This...

1. $\triangle ABC \sim \triangle TSU$
$\triangle KLM \sim \triangle RQP$

3. $\frac{21}{20}$, $\frac{21}{29}$, $\frac{20}{21}$, $\frac{20}{29}$, $\frac{29}{20}$, $\frac{29}{21}$

Exercises

1. $P = 30$

3. $f = 16$

5. $\frac{12}{15}$, $\frac{12}{9}$, $\frac{9}{15}$, $\frac{9}{12}$, $\frac{15}{9}$, $\frac{15}{12}$

7. $\frac{7}{4}$, $\frac{7}{\sqrt{33}}$, $\frac{4}{7}$, $\frac{4}{\sqrt{33}}$, $\frac{\sqrt{33}}{4}$, $\frac{\sqrt{33}}{7}$

9. 18 and 24

11. $r = \frac{5\sqrt{6}}{\sqrt{2}} = 5\sqrt{3}$

13. false   true   false

15. $DC = 64$

Section 18-2

Try This...

1. $\sin R = \frac{9}{41}$; $\sin P = \frac{40}{41}$

3. 0.9231

Exercises

1. $\sin D = \frac{1}{2}$; $\sin F = \frac{\sqrt{3}}{2}$

3. $\sin A = \frac{4}{5}$; $\sin B = \frac{3}{5}$

5. $\sin R = \frac{8}{10}$; $\sin T = \frac{6}{10}$

7. $\sin D = 0.5$; $\sin F = 0.8660$

9. $\sin A = 0.8$; $\sin B = 0.6$

11. $\sin R = 0.8$; $\sin T = 0.6$

13. $\sin A = 0.9144$; $\sin B = 0.4048$

15. $AD = 36$, $DC = 64$

Section 18-3

Try This...

1. $\cos R = \frac{40}{41}$; $\cos P = \frac{9}{41}$

3. $\cos D = 0.3846$

5. $\tan \angle ABC = \frac{AC}{BC}$; $\tan \angle ADE = \frac{AE}{DE}$; $\tan \angle AFG = \frac{AG}{FG}$; $\frac{AC}{BC} = \frac{AE}{DE} = \frac{AG}{FG}$

Exercises

1. $\cos T = \frac{33}{55}$; $\cos S = \frac{44}{55}$

3. $\cos D = \frac{48}{52}$; $\cos F = \frac{20}{52}$

5. $\cos S = \frac{36}{39}$; $\cos E = \frac{15}{39}$

7. $\cos T = 0.6$; $\cos S = 0.8$

9. $\cos D = 0.9231$; $\cos F = 0.3846$

11. $\cos S = 0.9231$; $\cos E = 0.3846$

13. $\tan T = \frac{42}{40}$; $\tan R = \frac{40}{42}$

15. $\tan P = \frac{60}{11}$; $\tan R = \frac{11}{60}$

17. $\tan R = \frac{60}{32}$; $\tan P = \frac{32}{60}$

19. $\tan T = 1.05$; $\tan R = 0.9524$

21. $\tan P = 5.4545$; $\tan R = 0.1833$

23. $\tan R = 1.875$; $\tan P = 0.5333$

25. $\cos R = 0.2925$

27. Isosceles right triangle

29. $(\sin S)^2 = 0.36$; $(\cos S)^2 = 0.64$; $(\sin S)^2 + (\cos S)^2 = 1$

Section 18-4

Try This...

1. 0.8480

3. 1.6643

5. 58°

7. $\approx 57°$

Exercises

1. 0.6157

3. 1.4826

5. 0.9877

7. 0.8660

9. 1.0000

11. 0.9998

13. 0.9455

15. 0.2588

17. 70°

19. 81°

21. 66°

23. 11°

25. 50°

27. 5°

29. $\approx 61°$

31. $\approx 38°$

33. $\approx 65°$

35. $\approx 70°$

37. $\sin 37° \ 10' \approx 0.6041$;
$\sin 37° \ 20' \approx 0.6064$;
$\sin 37° \ 50' \approx 0.6134$

Section 18-5

Try This. . .	1. $a \approx 6.947$	3. ≈ 152.6 m		
Exercises	1. $b \approx 22.8$ cm	3. $e \approx 54$ cm	5. $\approx 35°$	7. ≈ 3.3 km
	9. ≈ 338.6 m	11. 5.3 m	13. ≈ 3.9 km	15. $\approx 8,159.6$ ft
	17. 36.8	19. 33.7		

Chapter Review

1. $f = 16$	3. $\sin Z = 0.3846$	5. $\tan Z = 0.4167$	7. 0.4226
9. 44°	11. 45°	13. 27.6 cm	15. 186.5 m

Photo Acknowledgments

x: (c) Charles Harbutt/Archive Pictures 1 bottom: (c) Frank Siteman/Stock, Boston 2: (c) Robert Barclay/Grant Heilman 6: (c) Michal Heron/Woodfin Camp 10: (c) Bohdan Hrynewych/Stock, Boston 15: (c) George Malave/Stock, Boston 21 top: (c) Ira Kirschenbaum/Stock, Boston 21 bottom: (c) Peter Southwick/Stock, Boston 30: (c) Mike Clemmer & Roy Zalesky/Black Star 40: (c) Hal Harrison/Grant Heilman 45: Tennessee Valley Authority 47 left: Peabody Museum of Salem, photo by M.W. Sexton 47 center: Peabody Museum of Salem, photo by M.W. Sexton 47 right: (c) Robert Burroughs/Black Star 55: (c) Frank Siteman/Stock, Boston 60: (c) Arthur C. Parsons/Black Star 72: (c) Charles Harbutt/Archive Pictures 74: (c) Hal Harrison/Grant Heilman 79: (c) Sepp Seitz/Woodfin Camp 86: (c) Dennis Brack/Black Star 94: (c) Ellis Herwig/Stock, Boston 105: (c) David Burnett/Contact 110: (c) Dan Budnik/Woodfin Camp 112: Tennessee Valley Authority 128: (c) David Strick/Black Star 140 top: (c) Jim Anderson/Woodfin Camp 140 bottom left: (c) Jeff Albertson/Stock, Boston 140 bottom right: (c) Dennis Brack/Black Star 149: (c) Irene Vandermolen/Leonard Rue Enterprises/Monkmeyer 158: (c) Peter Vandermark/Stock, Boston 161: (c) Owen Franken/Stock, Boston 165 top: (c) Peter Simon/Stock, Boston 165 bottom: Mount Wilson and Las Campanas Observatories, Carnegie Institution of Washington 168: U.S. Navy 188: (c) Timothy Eagan/Woodfin Camp 190: (c) George Hall/Woodfin Camp 192 top left: (c) Robert Eckert/EKM-Nepenthe 192: top right: (c) Mike Mazzaschi/Stock, Boston 192 bottom left: (c) Burk Uzzle/Woodfin Camp 192 bottom right: (c) W.B. Finch/Stock, Boston 196: (c) John Colwell/Grant Heilman 197: (c) Owen Franken/Stock, Boston 201: (c) W.B. Finch/Stock, Boston 214: (c) Hazel Hankin/Stock, Boston 219 top: (c) Peter Southwick/Stock, Boston 219 bottom: (c) Anestis Kiakopoulos/Stock, Boston 224 left: (c) Vicki Lawrence/Stock, Boston 224 right: (c) Joe Schuyler/Stock, Boston 227: (c) Owen Franken/Stock, Boston 258: (c) Bohdan Hrynewych/Stock, Boston 286: (c) Joel Gordon/Design Photographers International 294 top: (c) W.B. Finch/Stock, Boston 294 bottom: (c) Peter Menzel/Stock, Boston 304 bottom: (c) Cliff Garboden/Stock, Boston 310: (c) Tim Carlson/Stock, Boston 318 left: (c) Sylvia Johnson/Woodfin Camp 318 right: (c) Carl Zeiss/Monkmeyer 340: (c) Elliott Erwitt/Magnum 352 left: The Bettmann Archive 352 right: (c) John Blaustein/Woodfin Camp 360: (c) Susan S. Perry/Woodfin Camp 374: (c) Peter Southwick/Stock, Boston 381 top: (c) Sepp Seitz/Woodfin Camp 401 left: (c) Fredrik D. Bodin/Stock, Boston 401 center: The New York Historical Society 412: (c) Bill Ross/Woodfin Camp 446: (c) Mike Mazzaschi/Stock, Boston 474: (c) K. Rosenthal/Stock, Boston 487 top left: (c) Sepp Seitz/Woodfin Camp 487 bottom left: (c) Robert Eckert/EKM-Nepenthe 489: (c) Fredrik D. Bodin/Stock, Boston 493 top left: (c) Cary Wolinsky/Stock, Boston 498 top right: (c) Runk, Schoenberger/Grant Heilman 498 bottom right: (c) Carl Zeiss/Monkmeyer 502 right: (c) Barry L. Runk/Grant Heilman 504: (c) Allan Weitz/Black Star 506: (c) Joan Liftin/Archive Pictures 515 top left: (c) W.B. Finch/Stock, Boston 520 center: (c) Propix/Monkmeyer 520 right: (c) Charles Harbutt/Archive Pictures 526: (c) Runk, Schoenberger/Grant Heilman 531 bottom center: Mount Wilson and Las Campanas Observatories, Carnegie Institution of Washington 531 bottom right: NASA 538: (c) Thomas Hopker/Woodfin Camp.

Photographs provided expressly for the publisher: George B. Fry III: 416, 496, 498 top left, 515 top right, 531 top left Wayland Lee/Addison-Wesley Publishing Company: 1 top, 16, 17, 21 center, 44, 46, 50, 51, 58, 59, 73, 78, 80, 81, 106, 111, 131, 163, 166, 170, 173, 218, 225, 230, 244, 246, 248, 249, 250, 259, 274, 304 top and center, 312, 314, 364, 376, 381 center and bottom, 387, 391, 392, 399, 401 right, 481, 482, 483, 487 top right and bottom right, 488, 493 top center, top right and bottom, 497, 502 left, 514, 515 bottom left and bottom right, 516, 519, 520 left, 531 top center, top right and bottom left.